# Instructor's Guide with Solutions
for David Moore's

# **The Basic Practice of Statistics**
Fourth Edition

Darryl K. Nester
Bluffton University

W. H. Freeman and Company
New York

ISBN-13: 978-0-7167-7727-4
ISBN-10: 0-7167-7727-4



Printed in the United States of America

First printing

W. H. Freeman and Company
41 Madison Avenue
New York, NY 10010
Houndmills, Basingstoke RG21 6XS England

www.whfreeman.com

# CONTENTS

# Preface

This Instructor's Guide was written to make it easier to teach from the fourth edition of *The Basic Practice of Statistics* (*BPS*). The most helpful material is, without a doubt, the full solutions of all exercises, prepared by Darryl Nester, which make up the second part of the Guide. The first part of the Guide was written by David Moore and Darryl Nester, and updated by Matthew Bates. It contains some teaching aids: additional examples and data sets for class use, Internet resources, sample examinations, and suggestions for using the *Against All Odds* and *Decisions through Data* videos. It also contains brief discussions of the *BPS* approach for each chapter. These comments are one side of a many-sided conversation. Your position in this conversation will no doubt differ at some points. We hope we have at least made clear the reasons for our choices.

We welcome comments, suggestions for improvement of *BPS*, and reports of errors that escaped detection and can be fixed in new printings. Please send comments about the text to David Moore, and comments about this Guide—especially the solutions—to Darryl Nester. You can contact us using the following information:

David S. Moore
Department of Statistics
Purdue University
West Lafayette, IN 47907-1399
Telephone: (765) 494-6050
Fax: (765) 494-0558
E-mail: `dsmoore@stat.purdue.edu`

Darryl K. Nester
Department of Mathematics
Bluffton University
Bluffton, OH 45817-1196
(419) 358-3483
(419) 358-3704
`nesterd@bluffton.edu`
`www.bluffton.edu/~nesterd`

# 1 TO THE INSTRUCTOR

## Introduction

*The Basic Practice of Statistics* (*BPS*) is an introductory text that presents statistical ideas and methods for students with limited mathematical background. The preface in the text attempts to explain and in part to justify the approach taken, and we will not repeat that material here. Do note that *BPS* tries to avoid a formula-driven approach while remaining accessible to nonquantitative beginners. Many students view statistics (indeed, all of the mathematical sciences) as a collection of formulas that give correct results if the computations are performed accurately. This view was never accurate and is now hopelessly outdated. Because computations and graphics are now automated—more than 90% of white-collar workers have access to computers, and most of these carry at least Excel—what is not automated becomes more important. Even if the available technology is limited in the learning environment, students must prepare to read and use statistical arguments with understanding. Our focus as teachers should be to help students use statistical tools and reason effectively by providing conceptual understanding and practical strategies along with some basic recipes.

The preface describes the current consensus on the nature of a first course among statisticians concerned with teaching. For a longer discussion with responses by several leading statisticians, see Moore (1997). *BPS* tries to express that consensus. As a reminder, here are important ways in which *BPS* differs from more traditional texts:

- There is more attention to data analysis. Chapters 1 to 6 give quite full coverage with a review in Chapter 7. It is now becoming common to emphasize data in a first course, but many texts still begin with a too-brief treatment of "descriptive statistics."
- There is more attention to designing data production. It is surprising to a practicing statistician how little attention these ideas, among the most influential aspects of statistics, receive in many first courses. Chapters 8 and 9 discuss sampling and experimental design, with attention to some of the practical issues involved.
- Formal probability gets less attention. The preface explains why. Chapters 10 and 11 avoid emphasis on the laws of general probability and instead stress *distributions.* The presentation is arranged to motivate the study of probability distributions from distributions of data and from the variability of the results of random sampling. Chapters 10 and 11 briefly present all that is needed to read the rest of the book. The optional Chapters 12 and 13 allow a fuller treatment.
- There is more discussion of the ideas of inference. Chapters 14 and 15 (with the introduction to sampling distributions in Chapter 11) provide the core of the presentation of inference. The ideas are not easy but are the key to an understanding that is more than mechanical.

- The presentation of significance tests emphasizes $P$-values rather than probabilities of Type I and Type II errors and tests with fixed $\alpha$. This reflects common practice and helps students understand the output of statistical software. The alternative approach appears in an optional section at the end of Chapter 16.
- There is more attention to statistics in practice. Realism may be too much to claim in a book that is genuinely elementary. Nonetheless, Chapters 8 and 9 describe the practical difficulties of producing good data, and the exposition and examples in Chapters 18 to 23 raise many issues that arise in applying inference methods to real problems.

Upon completion of a course based on *BPS*, students should be able to think critically about data, to select and use graphical and numerical summaries, to apply standard statistical inference procedures, and to draw conclusions from such analyses. They are ready for more specialized statistics courses (such as applied regression or quality control), for "research methods" courses in many fields of study, and for projects, reports, or jobs that require basic data analysis.

## Calculators and computers

The practice of statistics requires a good deal of graphing and numerical calculation. Doing some graphing and calculating by hand may build understanding of methods. On the other hand, graphics and calculations are automated in statistical practice. Moreover, struggling with computational aspects of a procedure often interferes with a full understanding of the concepts. Students are easily frustrated by their inability to complete problems correctly. Automating the arithmetic greatly improves their ability to complete problems. We therefore favor automating calculations and graphics as much as your resources and setting allow.

**All students should have a calculator that does two-variable statistics**, that is, that calculates not only $\bar{x}$ and $s$ but the correlation $r$ and the least-squares regression line from keyed-in data. *BPS* is written so that a student with such a calculator will not often be frustrated by the required calculations. Even if you use computer software, students should have a calculator for use at home and on exams. Two-variable statistics calculators are inexpensive (generally available for less than $20). *BPS* does not present anachronistic computing formulas that presuppose a four-function calculator.

Graphing calculators now automate almost all procedures discussed in a first statistics course, including basic graphs. Calculators have the great advantage that students own them, carry them around, and take them home. If everyone in the classroom has a graphing calculator, class discussions can take on new dimensions: pose a problem and let everyone work on it. Students who took advanced math in high school are often familiar with graphing calculators when they arrive in our classes. If your circumstances favor using a specific type of graphing calculator, by all means use it.

Software retains some clear advantages in entering and editing data and in graphics not being constrained by the small window of a graphing calculator. Almost all students now have some familiarity with personal computers, so the learning curve for menu-driven software is short and steep. Use software, even a spreadsheet such as Excel, if you can. *BPS* does not presuppose use of software, let alone any specific package. A good deal of computer (Excel, Minitab, and CrunchIt!) and calculator (TI-83) output appears in *BPS*. Separate student guides keyed to *BPS* are available for most of these options. The output is deliberately varied because any statistics student should become accustomed to looking at computer output and should be able to recognize terms and results familiar from her study.

As a practical encouragement to software use, the CD-ROM packaged with the text includes all substantial data sets for examples and exercises in *BPS.* The data appear as plain text (ASCII) files and also in the special formats of several common software systems. The files are named by their locations in the book:

`eg01-06.dat` = Example 1.6
`ex01-05.dat` = Exercise 1.5
`ta01-01.dat` = Table 1.1

## Using video

One of the most effective ways to convince your students that statistics is useful is to show them real people (not professors) using statistics in a variety of settings. Video allows you to do this in the classroom. Two related video series that contain many short documentaries of statistics in use on location are

- *Against All Odds: Inside Statistics* (*AAO*). This telecourse, consisting of 26 half-hour programs, was prepared by COMAP for the Annenberg/Corporation for Public Broadcasting Project. It is available in the United States at a subsidized price. Call 1-800-LEARNER for information or to order a copy.
- *Statistics: Decisions through Data* (*DTD*). This set of 21 shorter modules (5 hours total) is intended for use as a classroom supplement in secondary schools. It was prepared by COMAP for the National Science Foundation and draws on the location segments of *AAO*. It is available from COMAP. Visit `www.comap.com` or call 1-800-77-COMAP for information.

If you are outside the United States, you can obtain information about both video series from

COMAP Inc.
Suite 210
57 Bedford Street
Lexington, MA 02173 USA
Fax: (617) 863-1202

Because David Moore was the content developer for these video series, they fit the style and sequence of *BPS* well. In several cases, data from the videos appear in the text. We do not recommend showing complete programs from *AAO* in the classroom. The shorter modules from *DTD* are more suitable for classroom use. Video is a poor medium for exposition, and it leaves viewers passive. It is therefore generally not a good substitute for a live teacher. We suggest regular showing of selected on-location stories from *AAO* or *DTD* in most classrooms, rather than full programs. If you have a large lecture (several hundred students), however, full *DTD* video modules along with computer demonstrations will help hold an audience too large for personal interaction.

Video has several strengths that make short segments an ideal supplement to your own teaching. Television can bring real users of statistics and their settings into the classroom. And psychologists find that television communicates emotionally rather than rationally, so it is a vehicle for changing attitudes. One of our goals in teaching basic statistics is to change students' attitudes about the subject. Because video helps do this, consider showing video segments regularly even if you do not think they help students learn the specific topic of that class period. You can find more discussion of the uses of video, and references, in Moore (1993).

Here are some specific suggestions for excerpts from *AAO* and *DTD* that work effectively in class. The parenthetical comments in each case state what section of *BPS* the video illustrates.

- The 14-minute video *What Is Statistics?* is a good way to start a course. This collage of examples from *AAO* forms part of the first unit of *AAO* and is the first module of *DTD*. It is available separately (and inexpensively) from

  The American Statistical Association
  1429 Duke Street
  Alexandria, VA 22314 USA
  (703) 684-1221 or `www.amstat.org`

- *Lightning research* from Program 2 of *AAO*, Module 3 of *DTD*. A study of lightning in Colorado discovers interesting facts from a histogram. (Chapter 1)
- *Calories in hot dogs* from Program 3 of *AAO*, Module 5 of *DTD*. The five-number summary and box plots compare beef, meat, and poultry hot dogs. (Chapter 2)
- *The Boston Beanstalk Club* from Program 4 of *AAO*, Module 7 of *DTD*. This social club for tall people leads to discussion of the 68–95–99.7 rule for Normal distributions. (Chapter 3)
- *Saving the manatees* from Program 8 of *AAO*, Module 11 of *DTD*. There is a strong linear relation between the number of powerboats registered in Florida and the number of manatees killed by boats. (The manatees can illustrate any of Chapter 4 [scatterplots and correlation], Chapter 5 [regression], or Chapter 24 [regression inference] in *BPS*.)

- *Obesity and metabolism* from Program 8 of *AAO*, Module 12 of *DTD*, looks at the linear relationship between lean body mass and metabolic rate in the context of a study of obesity. (Chapters 4 and 5)

- *Sampling at Frito-Lay* from Program 13 of *AAO*, Module 17 of *DTD*, illustrates the many uses of sampling in the context of making and selling potato chips. (Chapter 8) A student favorite.

- *The Physicians' Health Study* from Program 12 of *AAO*, Module 15 in *DTD*, is a major clinical trial (aspirin and heart attacks) that introduces design of experiments. (Chapter 9)

- *Sampling distributions* are perhaps the single most important idea for student understanding of inference. Module 19 of *DTD* presents the general idea, the basic facts about the sampling distribution of the sample mean $\bar{x}$, and the application of these ideas to an $\bar{x}$ control chart. The setting is a highly automated AT&T electronics factory. (Chapters 11 and 27 [supplement or CD-ROM])

- *Battery lifetimes* from Program 19 of *AAO* leads to an animated graphic that illustrates the behavior of confidence intervals in repeated sampling. Module 20 in *DTD* is a presentation of the reasoning of confidence intervals using the same setting that can be shown in its entirety. (Chapter 14)

- *Taste testing of colas* is the setting for an exposition of the reasoning of significance tests in Module 21 of *DTD*. This treatment is preferable to that in *AAO*. (Chapter 15 refers to this in Example 15.2 and Exercises 15.8 and 15.12.)

- *Welfare reform* in Baltimore, from Program 22 of *AAO*, is a comparative study of new and existing welfare systems that leads to a two-sample comparison of means. (Chapter 19)

- *The Salem witchcraft trials,* revisited in Program 23 of *AAO*, shows social and economic differences between accused and accusers via comparison of proportions. (Chapter 21)

- *Medical practice:* Does the treatment women receive from doctors vary with age? This story in Program 24 of *AAO* produces a two-way table of counts. (Chapter 23)

- *The Hubble constant* relates velocity to distance among extragalactic objects and is a key to assessing the age of the expanding universe. A story in Program 25 of *AAO* uses the attempt to estimate the Hubble constant to introduce inference about the slope of a regression line. (Chapter 24. Figure 5.4 is a scatterplot of Hubble's data, which is used to illustrate some descriptive facts about regression and correlation.)

Here is a complete list of the documentary segments in *AAO*, with timings for use if your VCR measures real time, along with ratings from one to four stars. This handy guide was prepared by Professor Edward R. Mansfield of the University of Alabama. We are grateful to him for permission to reproduce it here. Start your VCR timer when the first signal on the tape appears. Remember that *AAO* programs are packaged two to a tape; the timings for the even-numbered programs may need some adjustment because the gap between programs seems to vary a bit.

Program 1: What Is Statistics?

4:48 Domino's Pizza ***
13:15 The "What is statistics?" collage of later examples

Program 2: Picturing Distributions (timings/ratings not available)

—:— When does lightning strike?
—:— TV programming and demographics
—:— Diagnostic-related groups

Program 3: Describing Distributions

5:55 Comparable worth in Colorado Springs *
16:07 Calories in hot dogs **
21:00 Musical analysis of urine data **

Program 4: Normal Distributions

33:50 Age distributions and Social Security *
46:07 Boston Beanstalk social club for tall people *
50:38 Why don't baseball players hit .400 anymore? ***

Program 5: Normal Calculations

7:07 Auto emissions at GM Proving Ground *
14:10 Cholesterol values **
19:50 Sizes of military uniforms **

Program 6: Time Series

34:50 The body's internal clock *
43:48 Psychology: reaction time study *

Program 7: Models for Growth

3:00 Children's growth rates and hormone treatment ***
14:00 Gypsy moth infestations **

Program 8: Describing Relationships

32:25 Manatees versus motorboats in Florida ***
37:55 Cavities versus fluoride levels
39:31 1970 draft lottery ***
44:04 Obesity: metabolic rate versus lean body mass *

Program 9: Correlation

5:42 Identical twins raised apart ***
16:22 Baseball players' salaries **
20:53 The Coleman Report (education in the 1960s) *

Program 10: Multidimensional Data Analysis

32:28 Chesapeake Bay pollution **
47:42 Bellcore graphics **

Program 11: The Question of Causation

5:42 Simpson's paradox ****
12:47 Smoking and cancer (historical survey) ***

Program 12: Experimental Design

32:46 Observational study of lobster behavior *
36:14 Physicians' Health Study: aspirin and heart attacks ****
43:39 Is Ribavirin too good to be true? ***
47:22 Police response to domestic violence *

Program 13: Blocking and Sampling

4:45 Strawberry field research *
13:28 Undercounting in the Census ***
20:48 Sampling potato chips at Frito-Lay ****

Program 14: Samples and Surveys

41:21 National Opinion Research Center ****

Program 15: What Is Probability?

10:50 Persi Diaconis on randomness *
17:49 Traffic control in New York (simulation model) **

Program 16: Random Variables

33:36 Cheating on AP calculus *
34:33 Space shuttle *Challenger* disaster ****
43:02 Points in a professional basketball game
49:10 Earthquakes in California *

Program 17: Binomial Distributions

3:46 The "hot hand": free throws in basketball ***
9:45 A finance class experiment **
17:22 Sickle cell anemia *
24:25 Quincunx: falling balls **

Program 18: The Sample Mean and Control Charts

33:45 Roulette
35:04 Interviews with gamblers **
40:44 The casino always wins ****
47:03 Control charts at Frito-Lay ***
53:41 W. Edwards Deming ****

Program 19: Confidence Intervals

11:35 Duracell batteries **
18.25 Rhesus monkeys in medical studies *
21:21 Feeding behavior of marmosets

Program 20: Significance Tests

34:18 Is this poem by Shakespeare? **
49:06 Discrimination within the FBI ***

Program 21: Inference for One Mean

5:55 National Institute of Standards and Technology **
13:30 Taste testing of cola ***
21:08 Autism *

Program 22: Comparing Two Means

33:32 Welfare programs in Baltimore **
45:05 Product development at Union Carbide ***
51:00 SAT exams: Can coaching help?

Program 23: Inference for Proportions

3:03 Measuring unemployment (Bureau of Labor Statistics) *
11:58 Safety of drinking water ***
20:15 The Salem witch trials

Program 24: Inference for Two-Way Tables

34:11 Ancient humans (markings on teeth) **
43:30 Does breast cancer treatment vary by age? **
52:02 Mendel's peas **

Program 25: Inference for Relationships

3:32 How fast is the universe expanding (Edwin Hubble)? ****

Program 26: Case Study

35:49 How AZT for treatment of AIDS was tested ***

## Resources on the Internet

The World Wide Web has made great amounts of information—of varying degrees of usefulness—easily available. Here are some worthwhile sites with resources for use in conjunction with *BPS;* all of these (and several others) can be reached from

`www.bluffton.edu/~nesterd/statres.html.`

Some of these sites have links to other interesting locations. The fluid nature of the Internet means that addresses may change, and other resources may show up from time to time; Web searches for phrases such as "statistics tutor" or "statistics applets" will almost certainly yield some useful results.

First, some general collections:

- Carnegie-Mellon University maintains *StatLib*, an electronic repository of things of statistical interest, including data sets. To get started, visit `lib.stat.cmu.edu`. Note in particular the "Data and Story Library," an online source related to the EESEE collection of case studies that is included on the *BPS* CD-ROM.

- The *Journal of Statistics Education*, an electronic journal of the American Statistical Association, contains much of interest to teachers of statistics. For more information, visit `www.amstat.org/publications/jse`.

- The Chance Web site, hosted by Dartmouth College, provides timely "current events" material to supplement a statistics course. Find it at `www.dartmouth.edu/~chance`.

- If you want to find some examples of "bad statistics," visit `www.junkscience.com`.

It is useful for students to visit "real statistics" sites to get a glimpse of the richness of the subject:

- Ask students to locate facts about their home counties at the U.S. Census Bureau, `www.census.gov`, or read the latest press release about employment and unemployment from the Bureau of Labor Statistics at `stats.bls.gov`. Look under "Economic News Releases" and then under "Employment & Unemployment" for releases with the title "Employment Situation." Also, the unified gateway to federal statistical agencies at `www.fedstats.gov` is comprehensive but a bit overwhelming.

- Find current Gallup poll press releases and Gallup's explanations of how sample surveys work at `www.gallup.com`. The National Council on Public Polls (`www.ncpp.org`) has statements on "Principles of Disclosure" and "20 Questions a Journalist Should Ask about a Poll" that make interesting reading.

- The abstracts of current medical research in the *New England Journal of Medicine* (`www.nejm.org`) demonstrate that you must know some statistics to read medical literature. Choose a clinical trial and an observational study from the available abstracts, then ask students to search for them by subject and to write a description of the design, the explanatory and response variables, and the conclusions.

Applets deserve separate mention. You can find a large number of attractive interactive animated simulations that demonstrate important facts about probability and statistics. We recommend these for class demonstrations as well as for student work, particularly if you are not using software in your course. Most are at university locations, and their URLs change often.

- First, we must mention the StatsPortal applets at `www.whfreeman.com/bps4e`, the *BPS* companion Web site. Some exercises in the text refer to these applets.
- David Lane of Rice University has an excellent collection of Java applets and links to other similar sites: `www.ruf.rice.edu/~lane/stat_sim`.
- James Hardin of Texas A & M University also has a wide selection of Java applets: `www.stat.tamu.edu/~jhardin/applets` and `www.stat.tamu.edu/~jhardin/StatConcepts.html`.
- Also, look at the collection by Todd Ogden of Columbia and R. Webster West at the University of South Carolina: `www.stat.sc.edu/rsrch/gasp`.
- Another nice applet collection, from the University of Newcastle in Australia, is `www.anu.edu.au/nceph/surfstat/surfstat-home/surfstat.html`. This URL seems to change often, so you may need to search for "surfstat."
- A collection emphasizing probability, by Charles Stanton of California State University at San Bernardino:

  `www.math.csusb.edu/faculty/stanton/m262/probstat.html`.

  Another that is especially strong in probability (look at the poker hand applet) is by Kyle Siegrist of the University of Alabama at Huntsville: `www.math.uah.edu/stat`.
- Want to select an SRS or do experimental randomization, even for large samples, and bypass the table of random digits? Visit the Research Randomizer at `www.randomizer.org`.

# 2 PLANNING A COURSE

## Introduction

In preparing to teach from *BPS*, look carefully at each **Chapter Summary.** There you will find a detailed list of the essential skills that students should gain from study of each chapter. Additionally, each larger group of chapters (Part I, consisting of Chapters 1 to 6, etc.) concludes with a **Part Summary Chapter,** listing the skills and knowledge covered in that set of chapters. These learning objectives are given at the end of the chapters and parts because they would make little sense to students in advance. However, you can use them for advance planning as you decide what to emphasize and how much time to devote to each topic.

Also, look at the **APPLY YOUR KNOWLEDGE** exercises, short sets of exercises that cover the specific content of the preceding exposition. Their location tells students, "You should be able to do this right now." They also show the instructor what students can be expected to do at each step. The longer sets of **Chapter Exercises** at the end of each chapter ask students to integrate their knowledge, if only because their location does not give as clear a hint to the skills required. The **Review Exercises** in the last chapter of each part add another level of integration. You can help students by judicious selection of exercises from all three locations.

One of the emphases of the movement to reform teaching in the math sciences is that we should make our classrooms as interactive as possible by involving students in discussion, reaction, problem solving, and the like. Those who try this find that course outlines cover a bit less material, but that the students master more of it. The outlines below reflect this; your success may vary. Mature students who have learned how to learn can create their own interaction with text and lecture, and so progress much faster. Reformers tend to undervalue lectures for mature students. I assign the entire content of *BPS* (except Chapters 12 and 13) in a course for graduate students in education, and introduce SAS as well. These students, while not quantitatively strong, are mature (many are over 30 years old) and hardworking. The outlines below are intended for more typical undergraduate students.

## Course outlines

The sample outlines for courses using *BPS* are aids for instructors, not strict rules. You should adapt the pace and extent of your course to your students.

**OUTLINE I** is a semester course for students with relatively low quantitative skills. I am always tempted to go faster than this outline suggests, and always find that when I do the students do not keep up with me. In particular, I find that each exam, viewed as an opportunity to solidify learning, uses a week. I spend one class on active review. I often distribute a sample exam in class and ask the students to work on the first problem for about five minutes, long enough to determine whether they know how to approach it. We then discuss that problem together. Continue through the sample exam in this manner. Starting work under conditions similar to an exam concentrates the mind. The exam itself occupies a second class period, and returning and discussing it fills most of a third. This is not lost time; exams are learning tools. I recommend omitting all starred subsections for this audience, but use your judgment.

OUTLINE I

| Week | Assignment |
|---|---|
| 1 | Course introduction; Chapter 1 |
| 2 | Chapter 2 |
| 3 | Chapter 3 |
| 4 | Chapter 4 |
| 5 | Chapter 5 |
| 6 | Chapter 7, EXAM I |
| 7 | Chapters 8 and 9 |
| 8 | Chapter 10 |
| 9 | Chapters 11 and 14 |
| 10 | Chapters 15 and 16 |
| 11 | Review of inference ideas (Chapter 17), EXAM II |
| 12 | Chapter 18 |
| 13 | Chapter 19 |
| 14 | Chapters 20 and 21 |
| 15 | Course review and extended examples |
| Comprehensive Final Exam | |

**OUTLINE II** is a semester course for somewhat better-prepared but still nonquantitative students. *BPS* offers many choices of material here. This outline ends with inference for regression (Chapter 24); you may prefer to substitute Chapters 23 or 25. In addition to one chapter from Part IV, this course adds Chapters 6 (two-way tables) and 12 (general probability) to the material of OUTLINE I. You may prefer to substitute the optional material from Chapter 16 (Type I and Type II errors) or to omit all of these and assign either Chapter 23 or Chapter 25.

OUTLINE II

| Week | Assignment |
|---|---|
| 1 | Course introduction; Chapters 1 and 2 |
| 2 | Chapter 3 |
| 3 | Chapters 4 and 5 |
| 4 | Chapters 5 and 6 |
| 5 | Chapters 8 and 9 |
| 6 | Review of Chapters 1 to 9, EXAM I |
| 7 | Chapters 10 and 11 |
| 8 | Chapter 12 |
| 9 | Chapters 14 and 15 |
| 10 | Chapters 15 and 16 |
| 11 | Review of Chapters 10 to 16, EXAM II |
| 12 | Chapters 18 and 19 |
| 13 | Chapters 20 and 21 |
| 14 | Chapter 23 |
| 15 | Course review and extended examples |
| Comprehensive Final Exam | |

**OUTLINE III** describes a one-quarter course. It covers the essentials, ending with the *t* procedures (and the introduction to inference in practice) in Chapters 18 and 19. This provides a good foundation for any of a number of more specialized courses in statistics or related areas. This outline is quite tentative; the number of class meetings per week varies in institutions using the quarter system, and I have not taught in such institutions. You may be able to assign more than is shown (e.g., Chapter 20). The main point of this outline is the goal of completing Chapter 19 in even the briefest introduction. Note that in my opinion a full treatment of data analysis for one and two variables is essential in even a brief course.

OUTLINE III

| Week | Assignment |
|---|---|
| 1 | Chapters 1 and 2 |
| 2 | Chapters 2 and 3 |
| 3 | Chapters 4 and 5 |
| 4 | Chapter 5; review data analysis |
| 5 | Chapters 8 and 9 |
| 6 | Chapters 10 and 11 |
| 7 | Chapters 14 and 15 |
| 8 | Chapters 15 and 16 |
| 9 | Chapters 18 and 19 |
| 10 | Course review or selected topics |
| Comprehensive Final Exam | |

# 3 CHAPTER COMMENTS

The comments below contain brief discussions of philosophy, teaching suggestions, and additional data and examples for use in teaching.

## Part I: Exploring Data

One of the most noteworthy changes in statistics instruction in the past decade is the renewed focus on helping students learn to work with data. The change in instruction follows a change in research emphases. Statistics research has pulled back a bit from mathematics (though, as the wise saying goes, you can never be too rich or too thin or know too much mathematics) in favor of renewed attention to data analysis and the problems of scientific inference. It is no longer thought proper to devote a week to descriptive statistics (means, medians, and histograms) before plunging into probability and probability-based inference. Contemporary introductions to statistics include a substantial dose of data analysis. In addition to reflecting statisticians' consensus view of the nature of their subject, working with data has clear pedagogical advantages. Students who may be a bit anxious about the study of statistics can begin by learning concrete skills and exercising judgment that amounts to enlightened common sense.

Students taking a first course in statistics often do not know what to expect. Some may view statistics as a field in which the major task is to tabulate large collections of numbers accurately. Others have heard that statistics is more like mathematics with a lot of complicated formulas that are difficult to use. Few are expecting a course in which they need to use their common sense and to think.

Your presentation of the material in the first chapters sets the tone for the entire course. We would like students to see that they can succeed and to become accustomed to making judgments and discussing findings rather than just solving problems. Try to use selected examples or exercises as a basis for class discussion. Presenting new data of special interest to your students is useful. Do not speed through the descriptive material because it seems simple; students do not always find the mechanics simple, and are not accustomed to "reading" graphics. And they certainly are not used to talking about what the data show.

Chapters 1 to 6 present the principles and some of the tools of data analysis. For teachers whose training is primarily mathematical, effective teaching of data analysis requires some reorientation. Here are four principles.

**1. Emphasize the strategy, not just the skills.** It is easy to treat data analysis as a longer stretch of descriptive statistics. Now we present stemplots, boxplots, and the five-number summary, in addition to means, medians, and histograms. There is a larger strategy for looking at data, which these tools help implement. The chapter summaries and the figures and summary in the Part I Review stress some elements of this strategy, such as the following.

- Begin with a graph, then move to numerical descriptions of specific aspects of the data and (sometimes) to a compact mathematical model. *Which* graphs, numerical summaries, and mathematical models are helpful depends on the setting.

- Look for an overall pattern and for striking deviations from that pattern. Deviations such as outliers may influence the choice of descriptive summaries, and the presence and clarity of the overall pattern suggest what mathematical models may be useful.

**2. Do not import inferential ideas too soon.** The point of view of data analysis is to let the data speak, to examine the peculiarities of the data in hand without at first asking whether they represent some wider universe or answer some broader question. The distinction between sample and population, which is central to inference, is deliberately ignored in data analysis. John Tukey of Bell Labs and Princeton, who shaped the subject, refers to "bunches" of data. *BPS* does not go that far, but does delay the sample–population distinction until Chapter 8, where it is essential to the discussion of designs for producing data. One aspect of successful teaching is to resist the temptation to tell students everything at once. Let them grasp the strategy and tools of basic data analysis first. These will be under control and helpful when we come to inference.

**3. Use real data.** Remember the mantra: Data are not just numbers; they are numbers with a context. The context enables students to communicate conclusions in words and to judge whether their conclusions are sensible. Data come with at least a bit of background, though for beginning instruction that background may not fully reflect the complexities of the real world. I am willing to oversimplify for the sake of clarity, but not to ask for empty operations with mere numbers.

*BPS* provides small and moderate-size data sets in more than adequate number for basic instruction. You should want more. Here are some suggestions.

- Start with the data and stories in the EESEE collection on the *BPS* CD-ROM. These are indexed by statistical topic and area of application and contain questions as well as data with background. The Instructor's CD also contains solutions. These are helpful but not always up to a high standard.

- Two general compilations are *A Handbook of Small Data Sets* (Hand et al., 1994) and *A Casebook for a First Course in Statistics and Data Analysis* (Chatterjee et al., 1995). Both contain data with background and are accompanied by data disks. Specialized texts now often contain more data disks. For example, Thiébaux (1994) and McBean and Rovers (1998) have data on the subjects of their titles.

- Mine the electronic terrain. Many data sets and other resources are available on the World Wide Web and through other electronic means. Check the Internet sites listed earlier in this Guide for some good sources.

- Amass your own collection of data. Data about the states, with $n = 50$ or $n = 51$, are of a convenient size for simple data analyses. The *Statistical Abstract of the*

*United States* is a good place to start. The *Information Please Environmental Almanac,* which includes the provinces of Canada as well as the states, has much data of interest to students. Consider the percent of solid waste output that is recycled (Minnesota is an outlier), toxic chemical releases (Louisiana and Texas are outliers), or per capita energy use in Canada (Alberta is an outlier). The "Almanac" issue of the *Chronicle of Higher Education,* published each year around September 1, contains much data on students and education.

- The students themselves are another source of data. You should consider starting the term with a survey asking a variety of questions. Assure students that responses are anonymous. Try to get both quantitative and categorical data, and ask students' gender to allow two-sample comparisons. You can use these data for in-class illustrations throughout the course. For example, you might ask some of these items:
  - Are you male or female?
  - To the nearest inch, how tall are you?
  - On a typical school day, how much time do you spend watching television? (Answer in minutes. For example, 2 hours is 120 minutes or $1\frac{1}{2}$ hours is 90 minutes.)
  - On a typical school day, how much time do you spend outside of class studying and doing homework? (Answer in minutes.)
  - How much money in coins are you carrying right now? (Do not count any paper money, just coins.)
  - How old [tall, heavy] do you think Dr. X is?
  - How many siblings do you have?
  - How large was your high school graduating class?
  - What is your favorite type of cheese?
  - How many credit cards do you have? How high is your balance?
- Encourage students to look carefully at the data they encounter *outside* of class. You might ask students to collect examples of statistics used poorly or in a misleading way, and to comment on the context of the data they find. If they gain nothing else from this course, they at least should become more intelligent consumers of data. Far too many people give only slight attention to the numbers they read or hear. For example,
  - A home security company, hoping to sell its services, placed an ad in a Sunday newspaper stating, "When you go on vacation, burglars go to work. . . . According to FBI statistics, over 26% of home burglaries take place between Memorial Day and Labor Day." Is that a convincing reason to install a security system?

- Shortly before O.J. Simpson was found not guilty in his criminal murder trial, a poll in the Los Angeles area found that 27% of whites and 73% of blacks believed he was innocent. Asked their impressions of this result, quite a few students observed only that the two percents add to 100%. This is true, but completely coincidental (they are percents of two separate groups!). An informed citizen should find much more interesting issues to consider here.

**4. Communicating results is important.** If we could offer just one piece of advice to teachers using *BPS*, it would be this: *A number or a graph, or a magic phrase such as "Reject $H_0$," is not an adequate answer to a statistical problem.* Insist that students state a brief conclusion in the context of the specific problem setting. We are dealing with data, not just with numbers. In particular, remind them that the answers to the odd-numbered exercises in the back of the text are by no means complete; they merely serve as a way for students to check their work.

## Chapter 1: Picturing Distributions with Graphs

Be flexible in assessing student graphs and interpretations: It is not always clear whether to split stems in a stemplot or how to choose the classes for a histogram. Try by your flexibility to help students not to get hung up on minor details of graphing. Similarly, how symmetric a histogram or stemplot must be to warrant calling the distribution symmetric is a matter for judgment. So is singling out outliers. Be flexible, but discourage students from, for example, calling the largest observation an outlier regardless of whether it is isolated from the remaining observations. Flexibility may also help students live with software. In making stemplots, for example, some software packages truncate long numbers and others round; some put the larger stems on top and others put the smaller stems there. These variations have little effect on our picture of the distribution.

## Chapter 2: Describing Distributions with Numbers

The common descriptive measures summarize things we can see graphically, but they summarize only part of what we can see. The graphical presentation is primary for data analysis.

Students should have a calculator that gives them $\bar{x}$ and $s$ from keyed-in data. Do warn them that many calculators offer a choice between dividing by $n$ and dividing by $n - 1$ in finding the standard deviation $s$. We want $n - 1$. (What is worse, many calculators label their choices as $\sigma_n$ and $\sigma_{n-1}$. We have not met $\sigma$ yet, but we want to use $s$ to denote the standard deviation of a set of data.) Ask students to do (for example) Exercise 2.9 to check their calculator skills. Because students should use calculators, *BPS* gives only the defining formula for $s$. This formula shows (at least to those who can read algebra) what $s$ is. The computing formula based on sums of squares is an anachronism and does not appear.

If you use software, you may find versions of a boxplot and rules for calculating quartiles that differ slightly from those in *BPS*. Encourage students to ignore this and to work with what the software reports. Remember that no single numerical summary is appropriate for all sets of data and that any numerical summary may miss important features, such as gaps or multiple peaks. Exercise 2.10 is instructive.

**Example.** Table 1 gives the weights of the players on an NCAA Division III team, along with their positions. (These are the weights for the 2002 team at Bluffton College.) We can explore how much football players weigh and how weights vary among positions and within a position. Here are Minitab's descriptive statistics for these data:

```
        POS       N     Mean   Median   TrMean    StDev   SEMean
WT      WR       11   181.27   181.00   181.67    11.88     3.58
        OB       14   182.43   182.50   182.42    20.67     5.52
        OL       17   252.76   258.00   250.80    34.98     8.48
        DB       15   172.27   174.00   172.46    10.81     2.79
        LB       10   194.40   192.00   191.37    21.31     6.74
        DL       18   231.67   229.00   231.75    22.03     5.19

        POS     Min      Max       Q1       Q3
WT      WR   164.00   195.00   171.00   195.00
        OB   147.00   218.00   168.50   199.25
        OL   204.00   331.00   222.00   271.00
        DB   150.00   192.00   168.00   179.00
        LB   172.00   241.00   176.00   203.75
        DL   193.00   269.00   215.75   245.25
```

The side-by-side boxplots (right) show the expected effects of position and of two heavy offensive lineman. It may be interesting to have students compare these boxplots to those in the Instructor's Guide for the second edition of *BPS* (for the 1994 Purdue University team). Both data sets can be found at `www.bluffton.edu/~nesterd/bps`. See also Exercise 2.33 and its solution on page 76 of this guide.

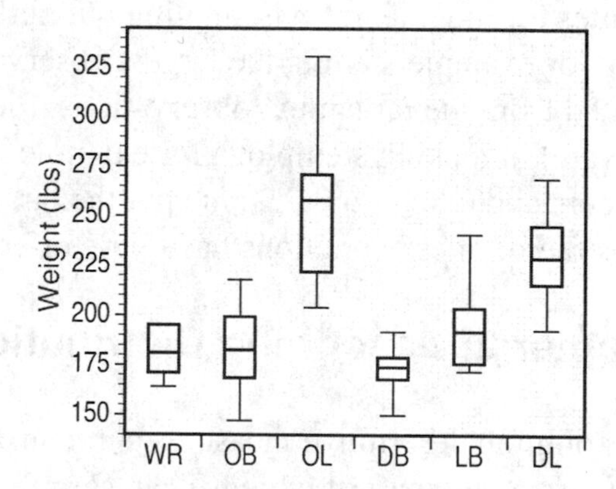


## Chapter 3: The Normal Distributions

Note that Normal distributions are introduced here as models for the overall pattern of some sets of data, not in the context of probability theory. Although this ordering of material is unusual, it has several advantages. The Normal distributions appear naturally in the description of large amounts of data, so that the later assumption for inference that the population has a Normal distribution becomes clearer. Moreover, mastering Normal calculations at this point reduces the barrier posed by the material on probability and sampling distributions (Chapters 10 and 11). If the students already know how to compute

**Table 1.** Player weights (pounds) and positions for a football team

| Wt. | Pos. | Wt. | Pos. | Wt. | Pos. | Wt. | Pos. | Wt. | Pos. | Wt. | Pos. |
|---|---|---|---|---|---|---|---|---|---|---|---|
| 164 | WR | 181 | OB | 224 | OL | 155 | DB | 172 | LB | 219 | DL |
| 165 | WR | 182 | OB | 230 | OL | 159 | DB | 173 | LB | 224 | DL |
| 171 | WR | 182 | OB | 236 | OL | 168 | DB | 177 | LB | 225 | DL |
| 172 | WR | 183 | OB | 239 | OL | 171 | DB | 182 | LB | 226 | DL |
| 180 | WR | 183 | OB | 258 | OL | 173 | DB | 192 | LB | 226 | DL |
| 181 | WR | 184 | OB | 260 | OL | 174 | DB | 192 | LB | 232 | DL |
| 188 | WR | 199 | OB | 262 | OL | 174 | DB | 200 | LB | 237 | DL |
| 188 | WR | 200 | OB | 263 | OL | 175 | DB | 200 | LB | 238 | DL |
| 195 | WR | 212 | OB | 270 | OL | 175 | DB | 215 | LB | 239 | DL |
| 195 | WR | 218 | OB | 272 | OL | 176 | DB | 241 | LB | 245 | DL |
| 195 | WR | 204 | OL | 280 | OL | 179 | DB | 193 | DL | 246 | DL |
| 147 | OB | 215 | OL | 315 | OL | 180 | DB | 205 | DL | 266 | DL |
| 153 | OB | 218 | OL | 331 | OL | 183 | DB | 206 | DL | 268 | DL |
| 158 | OB | 220 | OL | 150 | DB | 192 | DB | 206 | DL | 269 | DL |
| 172 | OB | | | | | | | | | | |

*Position key*: WR = wide receiver, OB = offensive back, OL = offensive lineman, DB = defensive back, LB = linebacker, DL = defensive lineman

Normal probabilities and have some understanding of the relative frequency interpretation from this section, the transition to ideas about probability is easier. It is also true that meeting Normal distributions early explains the otherwise mysterious affection statisticians have for the standard deviation.

The organizing idea is that we can sometimes use a mathematical model as an approximation to the overall pattern of data. Normal distributions are one example; a linear regression line (next chapter) is another. The 68–95–99.7 rule is a useful device for interpreting $\mu$ and $\sigma$ (or $\bar{x}$ and $s$) for Normal distributions. It also makes it possible to think about Normal distributions without a table. Many distributions are nonnormal, so do not make this into the so-called empirical rule for distributions in general.

## Relationships (Chapters 4 to 6)

Having dealt with methods for describing a single variable, we turn to relationships among several variables. At the elementary level of *BPS*, that means mostly relationships between two variables. That a relationship between two variables can be strongly affected by other ("lurking") variables is, however, a theme that runs throughout Chapters 4 to 6. Note the new vocabulary (explanatory and response variables) on the opening page of Chapter 4, as well as the reiteration of basic strategies for data analysis.

Correlation and regression are traditionally messy subjects based on opaque computing formulas based on sums of squares. *BPS* asks that students have a two-variable statistics calculator that will give them the correlation and the slope and intercept of the least-squares regression line from keyed-in data. This liberates instructors; we can give reasonably realistic problems and concentrate on intelligent use rather than awful arithmetic. The computing formulas are anachronistic and do not appear in the text. Remember that data input and editing can be frustrating on a calculator, so reserve large problems for computer software.

The descriptive methods in this chapter, like those in Chapters 1 to 3, correspond to formal inference procedures presented later in the text. Many texts delay the descriptive treatment of correlation and regression until inference in these settings can also be presented. There are, we think, good reasons not to do this. By carefully describing data first, we emphasize the separate status and greater generality of data analysis. There are many data sets for which inference procedures do not apply (data for the 50 states, for example). Fitting a least-squares line is a general procedure, while using such a line to give a 95% prediction interval requires additional assumptions that are not always valid. In addition, students become accustomed to examining data *before* proceeding to formal inference, an important principle of good statistical practice. Finally, correlation and regression are so important that they should certainly appear in a first course even if you choose not to discuss formal inference in these settings.

Because elementary data analysis for relationships between categorical variables consists mainly of calculating and comparing percents, you can choose to delay the descriptive material of Chapter 6 to accompany the inference methods (the chi-square test) in Chapter 23. If you do not plan to discuss the chi-square test, you can omit Chapter 6 altogether.

## Chapter 4: Scatterplots and Correlation

Using graphs should be comfortable by now. Constructing scatterplots is a relatively easy task (but tedious without software for all but small data sets). Interpreting the plots takes some practice. In the classroom, build instruction on examples and stress that common sense and some understanding of the data are necessary to do a good job of description. Computers can make the plots, but people are needed to describe them. Again, the general rule is to look for overall patterns and deviations from them. Patterns such as clusters and positive and negative association are useful in many cases but can lead to distorted descriptions when imposed in situations where they do not apply.

**Example.** Table 2 gives data that can be used to illustrate scatterplots, correlation, and regression. The data come from a study of students' self-concept by Darlene Gordon. The table records the grade point average (GPA) of 78 seventh-grade students from a rural Midwestern school along with one component of self-concept (SC), that concerning their school status. We might expect GPA and SC to be positively correlated.

First, you may be interested in the distributions of the two variables. Here is S-PLUS output that describes them:

**Table 2.** Grade point average and self-concept about school status for seventh-grade students

| GPA | SC | GPA | SC | GPA | SC | GPA | SC | GPA | SC |
|---|---|---|---|---|---|---|---|---|---|
| 7.940 | 17 | 8.292 | 12 | 4.643 | 10 | 7.470 | 15 | 8.882 | 15 |
| 7.585 | 11 | 7.650 | 17 | 2.412 | 12 | 6.000 | 9 | 8.883 | 16 |
| 7.470 | 5 | 5.528 | 8 | 7.167 | 14 | 7.571 | 12 | 4.700 | 13 |
| 8.167 | 15 | 7.822 | 11 | 7.598 | 16 | 4.000 | 5 | 6.231 | 15 |
| 7.643 | 12 | 1.760 | 2 | 6.419 | 13 | 9.648 | 14 | 10.700 | 17 |
| 10.580 | 16 | 9.429 | 17 | 8.000 | 13 | 9.585 | 14 | 9.571 | 15 |
| 8.998 | 13 | 8.333 | 11 | 8.175 | 17 | 8.000 | 14 | 9.333 | 13 |
| 9.500 | 17 | 9.167 | 16 | 10.140 | 15 | 9.999 | 13 | 10.760 | 16 |
| 9.763 | 7 | 9.410 | 16 | 9.167 | 16 | 9.348 | 17 | 8.167 | 10 |
| 3.647 | 10 | 3.408 | 10 | 3.936 | 11 | 7.167 | 17 | 7.647 | 13 |
| 0.530 | 10 | 6.173 | 16 | 7.295 | 14 | 7.295 | 8 | 8.938 | 16 |
| 7.882 | 14 | 8.353 | 17 | 5.062 | 7 | 8.175 | 13 | 8.235 | 14 |
| 7.588 | 11 | 7.647 | 8 | 5.237 | 8 | 7.825 | 11 | 7.333 | 16 |
| 9.167 | 15 | 7.996 | 15 | 8.714 | 11 | 7.833 | 15 | 4.885 | 8 |
| 7.998 | 15 | 3.820 | 2 | 5.936 | 4 | 9.000 | 13 | 9.500 | 17 |
| 6.057 | 12 | 6.057 | 3 | 6.938 | 12 | | | | |

```
GPA:
Mean    =    7.447
Standard deviation    =    2.1
N = 78    Median = 7.829
Quartiles = 6.231, 8.998

Decimal point is at the colon

Low:   0.53

    1 : 8
    2 : 4
    3 : 4689
    4 : 0679
    5 : 1259
    6 : 0112249
    7 : 22333556666666688899
    8 : 0000222223347999
    9 : 002223344556668
   10 : 01678
```

```
SC:
Mean    =    12.54
Standard deviation    =    3.82
N = 78    Median = 13
Quartiles = 11, 16

Decimal point is at the colon

    2 : 00
    3 : 0
    4 : 0
    5 : 00
    6 :
    7 : 00
    8 : 00000
    9 : 0
   10 : 00000
   11 : 0000000
   12 : 000000
   13 : 000000000
   14 : 0000000
   15 : 0000000000
   16 : 0000000000
   17 : 0000000000
```

S-PLUS (using the 1.5 × *IQR* criterion discussed in Chapter 2) identifies one suspected low outlier in GPA. The GPA of 0.53 is printed above the stemplot, marked "Low." Notice that both variables have left-skewed distributions.

The scatterplot of SC versus GPA is shown at right. There is a weak linear pattern with modest positive association. The scatter is great enough that none of the points are clear outliers.

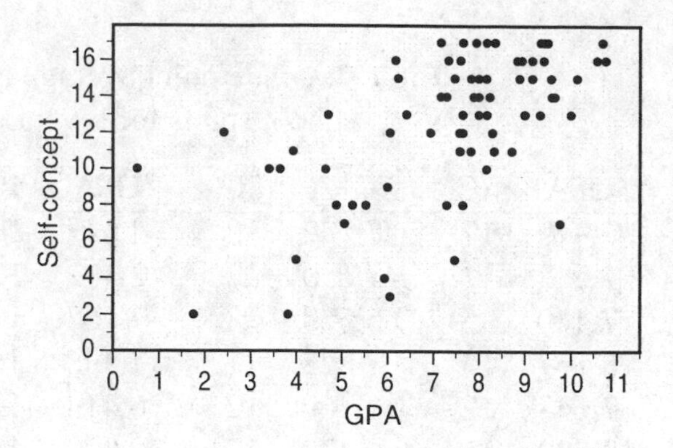


Correlation is presented before regression in part because it does not require the explanatory-response distinction. This also allows us to give a meaningful formula for the regression slope, using the correlation. Each student should have a calculator that gives $r$ from keyed-in data. You can therefore use the somewhat messy formula for $r$ as a basis for explaining how correlation behaves (fit this to your students' ability to read algebra), but avoid using it for computation.

**Example.** Return to the data on GPA and SC in Table 2. The correlation is $r = 0.6008$, reflecting the moderate positive linear association seen in the scatterplot. This is a good example to illustrate the point that correlation is not causation. We might imagine that students who do well in school feel good about their school status (GPA influences SC). We might also imagine that students who feel good about school are more likely to do well (SC influences GPA). Despite the fact that we put GPA on the $x$-axis of the plot, there is no clear choice for explanatory variable. Linear association with GPA predicts about 36% of the observed variation in SC for these students.

## Chapter 5: Regression

The background to regression is not always clear to students, so do not skip over it. We would like to draw the *best* line through the points on our scatterplot; to do this, we need an explicit statement of what we mean by "best." The least-squares idea gives such a statement, one that assumes we want to use the line to predict $y$ from $x$. Least-squares is not terribly natural. At this point, just say that it is the most common way to fit a line. (Least-squares is easily influenced by extreme observations, but it has many nice properties that have kept it the standard method even though computers have reduced its ease-of-computation advantage.)

Using a calculator for the arithmetic allows us to skip the usual opaque formulas for the least-squares line in favor of the wonderful expression

$$b = r\,\frac{s_y}{s_x}$$

for the slope. This formula tells the algebra-literate a lot, but assess your students before expounding on it. The concepts of "outlier" and "influential observation" are important. An observation is influential if removing it would move the regression line. This is clearly a matter of degree. More advanced statistical methods include numerical measures of influence. I have defined "outlier" broadly to keep things simple for students; they only have to look for isolated extreme points in any direction. That is a matter of degree also. Outliers in $y$ have large residuals; outliers in $x$ are often influential.

**Example.** The least-squares line for predicting SC from GPA for the data in Table 2 is $\widehat{\text{SC}} = 4.400 + 1.093\ \text{GPA}$. The least-squares regression line of GPA on SC is a very different line: $\widehat{\text{GPA}} = 3.060 + 0.3302\ \text{SC}$. That is another reminder that regression requires that you choose the explanatory variable.

At right is a stemplot of the residuals from the least-squares regression of SC on GPA, rounded to one decimal place. The most negative is $-8.1$.

The stemplot shows a roughly symmetric pattern plus a cluster of large negative residuals. Looking back at the scatterplot, we see a group of students with quite low SC scores at the bottom of the plot. The researcher might ask what characterizes these students.

```
−8 | 10
−7 | 6
−6 | 96
−5 |
−4 | 843
−3 | 83
−2 | 99543100
−1 | 97776522
−0 | 99875321
 0 | 0012566999
 1 | 003666667889999
 2 | 0223344
 3 | 3556789
 4 | 289
 5 | 00
```

**Example.** The Boston Marathon is one of the world's best-known foot races. The winning time in the Boston Marathon has decreased as runners get faster. Table 3 shows time of the winning man, in minutes, for the years from 1959 to 1980. (The winning time for men has not improved much in more recent years, so we do not give those data. Women's data appear in Table 1.5 of *BPS*.) You can use these data for a variety of class examples or student work. The scatterplot below shows a rough linear pattern with quite a bit of year-to-year variation. Nonetheless, $r^2 = 0.5993$. Ask students to suggest some factors that help explain the variation about the line. (Weather is one.) The least-squares regression line is

$$\widehat{\text{Time}} = 1221.05 - 0.5505\ \text{Year}.$$

This line appears in the scatterplot. By how much on average did the winning time improve per year during this period? Use the line to predict the winning time in 1990, a decade later. Is this prediction trustworthy? (Beware of extrapolation. The actual 1990 winning time was 128 minutes.)

**Table 3.** Winning time (minutes) for the Boston Marathon, 1959 to 1980

| Year | Time | Year | Time |
|---|---|---|---|
| 1959 | 143 | 1970 | 131 |
| 1960 | 141 | 1971 | 139 |
| 1961 | 144 | 1972 | 136 |
| 1962 | 144 | 1973 | 136 |
| 1963 | 139 | 1974 | 134 |
| 1964 | 140 | 1975 | 130 |
| 1965 | 137 | 1976 | 140 |
| 1966 | 137 | 1977 | 135 |
| 1967 | 136 | 1978 | 130 |
| 1968 | 142 | 1979 | 129 |
| 1969 | 134 | 1980 | 132 |

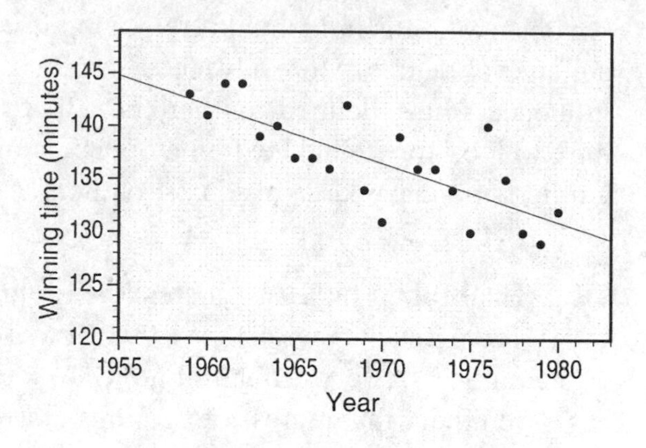


For now at least, computers can do little with the process of interpreting regression or assessing its appropriateness. As calculations are automated, interpretive ideas become a more important part of even basic instruction.

## Chapter 6: Two-Way Tables

This is applied arithmetic, but students do not find it trivial. There is no recipe (I do give guidelines) for deciding what percents to calculate and compare in describing a relationship between two categorical variables. I usually do not assign this section to weaker groups of students. If you will do Chapter 23, you may wish to delay this section and assign both description and inference together.

## Chapter 7: Exploring Data: Part I Review

As has often been said, people often fail to see the forest for the trees. Likewise many students get caught up trying to learn the different techniques of describing data with univariate and bivariate summaries, stemplots, scatterplots, etc., and tend to fail to see the big picture, or how these different techniques are related and when to use them properly. Chapter 7 is geared to help strengthen the overall connection of the material covered up to this point, as well as help train students to distinguish when to use a specific summary or graph. This chapter can be easily skipped over, provided that the students have a firm grasp of Chapters 1–6.

### Part II: From Exploration to Inference

Chapters 8 and 9 are both relatively short, with a lot of ideas and little numerical work. Students find the essentials quite easy, but they are important. These chapters are not mathematics, but are core content for statistics. Weaknesses in data production account for most erroneous conclusions in statistical studies. The message is that production of good data requires careful planning. Random digits (Table B) are used to select simple random samples and to assign units to treatments in an experiment. There are numerous examples that can serve as the basis for classroom discussion.

Chapters 8 and 9 also have a secondary purpose: the use of chance in random sampling and randomized comparative experiments motivates the study of chance behavior in Chapter 9. I have tried to motivate probability by its use in statistics, and to concentrate on the probabilistic ideas most directly associated with basic statistics. These chapters start that process.

## Chapter 8: Producing Data: Sampling

The deliberate use of chance to select a sample is the central idea. Many of the inference procedures in later chapters assume that the data are a simple random sample. Others require several independent SRSs or another simple model. In this section, we learn what an SRS is and also get a glimpse of the practical difficulties that can damage a sample to the point that formal inference is of little value.

> **Example.** Do the people of Scotland want to break up the United Kingdom by gaining independence from England? A 1998 opinion poll asked whether they would vote for "independence" in a referendum: 51% said yes. Another poll at the same time asked about becoming "an independent Scotland separate from the United Kingdom." Result: 34% said yes. It seems that "independence" is an attractive word but "separate" is not. Such is the power of question wording.

## Chapter 9: Producing Data: Experiments

The randomized comparative experiment may be the single greatest contribution of statistics to the advance of knowledge. Since Fisher introduced randomization in the 1920s, these ideas have revolutionized the conduct of studies in fields from agriculture to medicine. No student should leave a first statistics course without understanding the distinction between experiments and observational studies and understanding why properly designed experiments are the gold standard for evidence of causation. When experiments cannot be done, causation is a slippery subject, and statistical methods that claim to give evidence for causation are not for beginners and often are debated by experts. Good experiments allow relatively clean conclusions.

> **Example.** You can find current medical trials on the Web site of the *New England Journal of Medicine*, `www.nejm.org`. Choose a topic comprehensible and perhaps interesting to students, such as quitting smoking. Here is part of the abstract of Douglas E. Jorenby et al., "A controlled trial of sustained-release bupropion, a nicotine patch, or both for smoking cessation," from the March 4, 1999, issue of the journal. The design of this experiment is

like that of *BPS* Figure 3.5, but with four arms. Remind your students that doctors are assumed to understand this much statistics.

*Use of nicotine-replacement therapies and the antidepressant bupropion helps people stop smoking. We conducted a double-blind, placebo-controlled comparison of sustained-release bupropion (244 subjects), a nicotine patch (244 subjects), bupropion and a nicotine patch (245 subjects), and a placebo (160 subjects) for smoking cessation. . . .*

*The abstinence rates at 12 months were 15.6 percent in the placebo group, as compared with 16.4 percent in the nicotine-patch group, 30.3 percent in the bupropion group ($P < 0.001$), and 35.5 percent in the group given bupropion and the nicotine patch ($P < 0.001$).*

**Example.** Here, in contrast, is a report on an observational study that leaves issues of causation unsettled. *The New York Times* (September 30, 1993) carried a report of a study appearing that day in the *New England Journal of Medicine*. The study followed a large probability sample of women forward over time. The researchers compared obese women (the top 5% on an index relating weight to height) with other women. Here are excerpts from *The New York Times* article.

*Women who are fat suffer enormous social and economic consequences, a new study has shown. They are much less likely to marry than women of normal weight and are more likely to be poor and to earn far less. . . .*

*The findings are from an eight-year study of 10,039 randomly selected people who were 16 to 24 years old when the research began. . . .*

*Fat women were disproportionately found in lower socioeconomic classes, and some researchers say this is because poor women are more likely to eat fat-laden food and junk foods and to get less exercise than richer women. But Dr. Gortmaker and his colleagues wrote, "Our data suggest that at least some of this relation may be a socioeconomic consequence of being overweight." . . .*

*The fat women were 20 percent less likely to marry, had household incomes that were an average of $6,710 lower, and were 10 percent more likely to be living in poverty.*

## Commentary: Data Ethics

How data is obtained is as important as how it is analyzed. Data that is collected in an unethical way either will have very misleading conclusions, or will generate a distrust for statistics in general. Furthermore, data collected in unethical fashion can have costs far higher then the monetary value of a study. There are many examples in the past where people have been embarrassed, injured, or even killed in the name of science to produce valid statistical conclusions. In order to prevent such costs, federal guidelines and rules have been for developed for experimenters to abide by.

An unethical experiment may have the ability to suggest a strong inference, but the cost of bad ethics is generally not worth it. Obviously the most effective way to show that smoking causes cancer would be to do an experiment by randomly choosing individuals either to smoke or not. In the process of assigning the treatment of smoking, many subjects more than likely would be damaging their health by smoking—probably against their will. The cost of conducting such an unethical experiment would be deemed by most to be too high for the results. Therefore when designing an experiment, one must clearly take into account the ethics that are involved.

## Probability (Chapters 10 to 13)

The reasoning of classical statistical inference is built on asking, "What would happen if I used this method many times?" Confidence limits, $P$-values, and error probabilities answer that question in varied settings. All of these answers use the *sampling distribution* of a statistic (Chapter 11), which addresses the underlying question by displaying the distribution of the statistic in repeated samples or experiments carried out under the same circumstances. Sampling distributions are a tough idea to convey to students, but they are central to inference and cannot be avoided without loss of conceptual mastery.

General probability, on the other hand, is a tough subject that we can largely avoid. In basic statistics, our use of probability laws such as the complements rule is limited to noting that the area in the upper tail of a density curve is 1 minus the remaining area. *Distributions* are the big idea of probability for understanding the reasoning of basic statistical inference. The goal of Chapter 10 is to convey efficiently the probability ideas needed to understand inference, in particular sampling distributions as described in Chapter 10. The optional Chapters 12 and 13 contain additional material on probability, which is not needed to read the remainder of the text.

Chapters 14 to 16 are the most difficult in the book (apart from the optional Chapters 12 and 13). There is no hiding the fact that the reasoning behind confidence intervals and (even more so) significance tests is not easy. But if all the calculations are done by software, as is now the case in practical applications of statistics, students must carry away this reasoning if our presentation of inference is to have much lasting value.

Students have a limited capacity for hard topics in a course. We recommend applying that capacity to sampling distributions and the reasoning of inference rather than using much of it on general probability. Unless your students are quite well prepared, we suggest skipping Chapters 12 and 13. In effect, the traditional first course is being modified to place more emphasis on data (Chapters 1 to 9) and concepts (Chapters 14 to 16). This is exactly the direction recommended by the ASA/MAA joint curriculum committee. Try it. You may like it.

## Chapter 10: Introducing Probability

Much evidence shows that even students who can do formal probability exercises have little conceptual understanding of random behavior. We therefore start very informally. Do take the time to do some of the simulation exercises in this section.

If you have the capability to automate simulations, use it here. Most statistical software packages and many graphing calculators will simulate the Bernoulli and binomial distributions, for example. That allows you to have students actually do simulations. Perhaps they will see that coin tossing, Shaq's free throws, and the results of a "Yes/No" opinion poll question are instances of the same thing. We think that is a more profound mathematical insight than learning the binomial formula.

The latter part of Chapter 10 introduces the simplest facts about probability—all we need to use the language of probability to discuss statistical inference. A probability model is a set of possible outcomes plus a way of assigning probabilities that satisfies some basic rules. There are two common ways to assign probabilities: assign a number to each of a finite set of outcomes, or assign a number as the area under a density curve. That is it. If you find it necessary to do more, you can jump to Chapter 12, but do not do that out of mere habit. Probability is a high barrier to students, and this is a statistics course.

Yes, we know that discrete distributions can take infinitely many values. That is not very helpful to students without a math background that includes infinite series. Recall the saying of the physicist Richard Feynman: "The real problem in speech is not precise language. The problem is clear language." He was talking about mathematics textbooks when he said that. We need not tell students everything we know.

## Chapter 11: Sampling Distributions

Chapter 10 gave us a language to use. Now we continue the main track, following up on the discussion of sampling in Chapter 8. Sampling distributions are of course one of the big ideas of statistics. We also get in context some important probability facts, the law of large numbers, and the central limit theorem. Draw pictures similar to Figure 11.2 constantly to reinforce the "do it many times" reasoning, which will recur with similar figures in Chapter 14.

Do more simulations here, following up on those you did for Chapter 10. If you did mostly success/failure trials there, it is fine to do that here even though we eventually want to learn about $\bar{x}$. Here are examples that do look at $\bar{x}$.

> **Example: Law of Large Numbers.** The mean result of betting $1 on red in roulette is −$0.053, a loss of 5.3 cents. (The dollar bet wins another dollar if the ball falls into a red slot. There are 18 red slots among the 38 slots of the roulette wheel, so the bettor wins $1 with probability 18/38 and loses $1 with probability 20/38. The mean follows from the idea that proportions approach probabilities, even though we do not make this formal.) Ask your students

what the law of large numbers says about the result of making many $1 bets. In particular, the average loss is small. So if I make many bets, I am nearly certain not to lose much, right?

Wrong. My *mean* loss will be close to 5.3 cents, but the *total* loss keeps growing. In 1000 bets I expect to lose about $53, and in 10,000 bets I expect a loss of about $530. Here is a fine point: notice, for example, that when the mean is between 5.2 and 5.4 cents per bet, the amount lost is between $520 and $540. Saying that the mean is close to 5.3 cents still allows the total loss to vary by a larger amount when you make more bets. It is important to talk in terms of the mean of many outcomes when applying the law of large numbers.

**Example: Sampling Distribution.** Prepare a population of 100 identical small pieces of stiff paper. Write numbers on the slips as shown in the table on the right.

Of course, you could program this simulation on a calculator or computer. Before doing so, ask yourself whether your students really understand simulation. There are advantages to starting with actual physical simulations before moving to the computer, which beginning students often regard as a "magic box."

| Write each of these numbers | On this many slips |
|---|---|
| 50 | 10 |
| 49, 51 | 9 |
| 48, 52 | 9 |
| 47, 53 | 8 |
| 46, 54 | 6 |
| 45, 55 | 5 |
| 44, 56 | 3 |
| 43, 57 | 2 |
| 42, 58 | 1 |
| 41, 59 | 1 |
| 40, 60 | 1 |

The 100 slips form a population. The distribution of measurements (the numbers on the slips) in this population is roughly normal with mean $\mu = 50$ and standard deviation $\sigma = 4$. Make a histogram or stemplot of the 100 population values and find their mean (it is exactly $\mu = 50$ because of the symmetry). This is a population distribution, and its mean is a parameter.

Next put the slips in a box and have a student take a random sample of size $n = 9$ by drawing nine slips blindly and recording the numbers on them. Calculate the mean $\bar{x}$ of the nine observations. This is a statistic. Return these slips to the box and shuffle the slips in the box thoroughly. Draw another random sample of size nine, record the numbers, and find $\bar{x}$. Repeat this as many times as is convenient, preferably about 100 times. Make a histogram of the $\bar{x}$ values and find their mean and standard deviation. This is an approximation to the sampling distribution of $\bar{x}$.

**Example: Central Limit Theorem.** The previous simulation illustrates how $\bar{x}$ is less variable than individual observations. You can demonstrate the central limit theorem effect by a similar simulation. Make (or program the equivalent of) another set of 100 slips, 10 for each number from 1 to 10. This is a uniform distribution. Even though $n = 9$ is not a large sample size, the histogram of $\bar{x}$'s from many random samples of size 9 will look roughly Normal.

In addition to the big idea of a sampling distribution, students must understand the facts about $\bar{x}$, which will be used right away in Chapter 14. Qualitatively, they should know that

- Averages are less variable than individual observations.
- Averages are more Normal than individual observations.

Chapter 11 makes these statements more precise. It completes the discussion of Normal distributions begun in Chapter 3 and continued in Chapter 11 by showing the Normal distributions as sampling distributions.

## Chapter 12: General Rules of Probability

Chapter 14 on the reasoning of inference follows immediately on the treatment of sampling distributions in Chapter 11. Chapters 12 and 13 are optional, and none of the content of those chapters is needed to understand the reasoning of inference. If you must cover some or all of this chapter, consider doing so between Chapters 10 and 11. Chapter 12 presents more general probability, especially the multiplication rule for independent events, as well as conditional probability and related topics. Chapter 13, on the binomial distributions, applies the multiplication rule.

## Chapter 13: Binomial Distributions

The inference methods for proportions introduced in beginning statistics (including Chapters 20 and 21 of *BPS*) use the Normal approximation for the sampling distribution of a sample proportion. This is presented when needed in Chapter 20. The binomial distributions are therefore an unnecessary complication when our goal is to help students learn basic statistical ideas and methods. I recommend not covering this section unless your students' needs or your course description forces the binomial upon you. All the basic facts about the binomial distributions are here, with emphasis on recognizing the binomial setting. The derivation of the formula for binomial probabilities of course uses the multiplication rule; if you are willing to omit the derivation, you could discuss binomial distributions without the general probability of Chapter 12.

### Inference (Chapters 14 to 16)

These chapters contain many fundamental ideas. We introduce confidence intervals and tests along with some cautions concerning the use and abuse of tests. Throughout, the setting is inference about the mean $\mu$ of a Normal population with known standard deviation $\sigma$. As a consequence, the $z$ procedures presented are not applicable to most real sets of data. They introduce ideas in a setting where students can do familiar Normal calculations, and they pave the way for the more useful $t$ procedures presented in later chapters.

Experience shows that many students will not master this material upon seeing it for the first time. Fortunately, they will meet the key ideas again. By the time they have completed Chapters 18 and 19 and worked many exercises, they should have grasped the fundamentals. Be patient, and remember that understanding the reasoning of inference is more important than the number of procedures learned.

## Chapter 14: Confidence Intervals: The Basics

Figures 14.3 and 14.4 display the big idea: the recipe for a 95% confidence interval produces intervals that hit the true parameter in 95% of all possible samples. (In formal language, the recipe has probability 0.95 of producing an interval that catches the true parameter.) Simulation can help students understand this central idea.

> **Example.** You can use the same population prepared for the simulation activity for *BPS* Chapter 11. For random samples of size $n = 9$, the 95% confidence interval for the mean $\mu$ is
>
> $$\bar{x} \pm 1.96\frac{\sigma}{\sqrt{n}} = \bar{x} \pm 1.96\frac{4}{\sqrt{9}} \doteq \bar{x} \pm 2.61.$$
>
> Once again, it is a good idea to begin with several samples drawn by hand. A follow-up computer simulation would generate $n = 9$ observations from the Normal distribution with mean $\mu = 50$ and standard deviation $\sigma = 4$, find the sample mean $\bar{x}$ of these observations, and calculate $\bar{x} \pm 2.61$. Do this at least 100 times and observe how many of the intervals cover 50. A drawing similar to Figure 14.4, constructed sample by sample, is very instructive. Note that it is unlikely that exactly 95 of 100 samples cover the true $\mu$, even though 95% will cover in the long run.

## Chapter 15: Tests of Significance: The Basics

The reasoning of significance tests is conceptually the hardest point in a first course in statistics. Figure 15.1 is my best attempt to convey the core idea visually: if the true mean $\mu$ were 0, one $\bar{x}$ value is surprising, and the other value is not. If we got the surprising value, we would doubt that $\mu$ really is 0. Stripped of all jargon, this reasoning is fairly straightforward *if* the distinction between parameter and statistic is firmly in place.

> **Example.** The diastolic blood pressure for American women ages 18 to 44 has approximately the Normal distribution with mean $\mu = 75$ millimeters of mercury (mm Hg) and standard deviation $\sigma = 10$ mm Hg. We suspect that regular exercise will lower the blood pressure. A sample of 25 women who jog at least 5 miles per week gives sample mean blood pressure $\bar{x} = 71$ mm Hg. Is this good evidence that the mean blood diastolic blood pressure for the population of regular exercisers is lower than 75 mm Hg?

The alternative is one-sided because we suspect that exercisers have *lower* blood pressure: $H_0$: $\mu = 75$ versus $H_a$: $\mu < 75$. Assuming that joggers have the same $\sigma$ as the general population, the $z$ statistic is

$$z = \frac{\bar{x} - \mu_0}{\sigma/\sqrt{n}} = \frac{71 - 75}{10/\sqrt{25}} = -2.00.$$

Sketch a standard Normal curve. How surprising is a $z$ this small? The 68–95–99.7 rule says that it is quite surprising. More formally, the $P$-value is the probability that $z$ takes a value this small or smaller. This is $P(Z \leq -2.00)$. From Table A, $P = 0.0228$. This result *is* significant at the 5% level ($\alpha = 0.05$) but is *not* significant at the 1% level ($\alpha = 0.01$).

## Chapter 16: Inference in Practice

In discussing $z$ confidence intervals, *BPS* offers a "warning label" reminding users of conditions for proper use. That label applies to the $z$ tests also. However, tests are more difficult to interpret than are confidence intervals. Many statisticians feel that tests are overused, or at least overinterpreted. The discussions of choosing a level of significance and statistical significance and practical significance offer some cautions about the interpretation of statistical significance. "Statistical inference is not valid for all sets of data" and "beware of multiple analyses" apply to confidence intervals as well, but abuses seem more common in the setting of tests.

The (optional) latter part of Chapter 16 discusses error probabilities and power. Some instructors stress $P$-values in teaching beginners; others stress the two types of error and their associated error probabilities. We are in the former camp. Why begin with $P$-values? First, "assessing the strength of evidence" is a better description of practical inference than is "making decisions." Second, $P$-values are prominent in the output from statistical software, so users of statistics must understand them. The fact that there is an elegant mathematical theory (Neyman–Pearson) based on the fixed-$\alpha$ approach should not be allowed to sway practical instruction for beginners.

That said, $P$-values are not sufficient for a full account of statistical tests. The idea of *power*—how likely this test is to detect an alternative you really want to detect if it is true—is important in practice. To compute a power, we start with a fixed $\alpha$ even if in practice we plan to report a $P$-value. So we must ask, given the actual state of our students, how far should we go on from $P$-values? But we rarely cover this material with undergraduates.

Your choice may differ. Be aware that the ideas are sophisticated and that the proper approach to inference is still hotly debated. Some statisticians, for example, deny that $P$-values assess the strength of evidence against $H_0$ at all. They do this because they are Bayesians who (we think) import elements that are not in fact present in a majority of real statistical problems and judge $P$-values based on these imports. *BPS* organizes the material in the order of its importance in current statistical practice. That is why $P$-values are up front and the two types of error are in an optional section.

## Part II: Inference about Variables

The one- and two-sample $t$ procedures are among the most-used methods of inference. One-sample $t$ confidence intervals and significance tests are a short step from the $z$ procedures of Chapter 15. The two-sample procedures present a complication: the textbook standard method assumes equal variances in the population, an assumption that is hard to verify and often not justified. *BPS* ignores that method in favor of two alternatives that work even if the population variances differ: a reasonably good conservative approximation for hand use, and a very accurate approximation that is implemented in almost all statistical software packages (page 474). Another deviation from the textbook standard occurs in the optional latter part of Chapter 19, where the basic recommendation concerning inference about population spread is "Do not do it without expert advice." This choice is also well justified by literature citations.

The exposition in these chapters pays at least some attention to the problems of applying statistical inference to real data. For examples, see the discussions following Examples 18.1, 18.3, 19.2, and 19.4, and the sections on the robustness of one- and two-sample $t$ procedures.

### Chapter 17: From Exploration to Inference: Part II Review

As with Chapter 7, this part can be skipped if necessary. Because these problems draw on topics from all of the chapters in Part II, they require students to think about which procedures are appropriate.

### Chapter 18: Inference about a Population Mean

If you want to do inference about $\mu$ but do not know $\sigma$, just replace the unknown $\sigma$ by its sample estimate $s$ in the $z$ procedures. That is the driving idea. It leads to the $t$ distributions and to the use of all of Table C. Because the mechanics are so similar to those of Chapter 16, you can replay the reasoning of inference and pay more attention to interpreting the results. The section calls attention to the use of one-sample methods for matched-pairs data and to the conditions needed to use the methods in practice.

**Example.** A milk processor monitors the number of bacteria per milliliter in raw milk received for processing. A random sample of 10 one-milliliter specimens from milk supplied by one producer gives the following data:

$$5370, 4890, 5100, 4500, 5260, 5150, 4900, 4760, 4700, 4870$$

Entering these data into a calculator gives $\bar{x} = 4950$ and $s = 268.45$. So a 90% confidence interval for the mean bacteria count per milliliter in this producer's milk is

$$\bar{x} \pm t^* \frac{s}{\sqrt{n}} = 4950 \pm 1.833 \frac{268.45}{\sqrt{10}} = 4950 \pm 155.6.$$

This interval uses the critical value from the $t(9)$ distribution for $C = 90\%$, found in Table C. Next, ask your students what assumptions this calculation requires and how they would verify the assumptions. We must be confident that the data are an SRS from the producer's milk and that the distribution of bacteria counts in the population of milk is approximately normally distributed. We must learn how the sample was chosen to see whether it can be regarded as an SRS. The data show no outliers and no strong skewness; it is hard to assess Normality more closely from only nine observations. In practice, we would probably rely on the fact that past measurements of this type have been roughly Normal.

**Example.** The amount of wax deposited on the outside surface of waxed-paper bags during production may differ from the amount deposited on the inside surface. Select a sample of 25 bags, determine the wax concentration in pounds per square foot on the inside and outside, and calculate the difference (outside minus inside) for each bag. The mean and standard deviation of these 25 differences are

$$\bar{x} = 0.093 \qquad \text{and} \qquad s = 0.723.$$

Is there good evidence that the mean concentrations on the two surfaces are not equal?

This is a matched-pairs situation. The inner and outer surface of the same bag are paired with each other. We want to test the hypothesis of "no difference," or $H_0$: $\mu = 0$ versus $H_a$: $\mu \neq 0$, where $\mu$ is the mean of the difference in wax concentrations on the two surfaces. The one-sample $t$ statistic is

$$t = \frac{\bar{x} - \mu_0}{s/\sqrt{n}} = \frac{0.093 - 0}{0.723/\sqrt{25}} = 0.643.$$

Compare this value with critical points of the $t(24)$ distribution. Table C shows that $t = 0.643$ is less than the $p = 0.25$ critical value, which is $t^* = 0.685$. Because the test is two-sided, we double the $p$ from the table to get the $P$-value. So $P$ is greater than 0.5. There is no evidence that the wax concentrations on the two surfaces differ.

## Chapter 19: Two-Sample Problems

Students now need to distinguish one-sample, matched-pairs, and two-sample settings. That is how this section opens. For inference about the difference $\mu_1 - \mu_2$ of two population means, we start with the natural sample estimator $\bar{x}_1 - \bar{x}_2$ and its sampling distribution. The distribution is (at least approximately) normal, so standardize the estimator and replace the unknown $\sigma_i$ by the sample standard deviations $s_i$. You may not wish to emphasize this intuitive derivation, depending on your students' capacities for generalization, but it repeats the logic of earlier settings. We then come to the actual two-sample $t$ procedures: just use the smaller of $n_1 - 1$ and $n_2 - 1$ as the degrees of freedom ("option 2" on page 464). If you are using software, you will want students to be familiar with the more accurate option 1, and you may want to refer them to the optional section headed "Details of the $t$ approximation" (page 473).

**Example.** In an experiment to study the effect of the spectrum of the ambient light on the growth of plants, researchers assigned tobacco seedlings at random to two groups of eight plants each. The plants were grown in a greenhouse under identical conditions except for lighting. The experimental group was grown under blue light, the control group under natural light. Here are the data on stem growth in millimeters:

| Control | | | | Experimental | | | |
|---|---|---|---|---|---|---|---|
| 4.3 | 4.2 | 3.9 | 4.1 | 3.1 | 2.9 | 3.2 | 3.2 |
| 4.1 | 4.2 | 3.8 | 4.1 | 2.7 | 2.9 | 3.0 | 3.1 |

This is a two-sample situation. Call plants grown under natural light Population 1 and plants grown under blue light Population 2. We will give a 90% confidence interval for the amount by which blue light reduces stem growth during this period. A calculator gives

| Population | Sample Size | Sample Mean | Sample Variance |
|---|---|---|---|
| 1 | $n_1 = 8$ | $\bar{x}_1 = 4.0875$ | $s_1^2 = 0.0270$ |
| 2 | $n_2 = 8$ | $\bar{x}_2 = 3.0125$ | $s_2^2 = 0.0298$ |

The 90% confidence interval for the difference $\mu_1 - \mu_2$ between the population means is

$$(\bar{x}_1 - \bar{x}_2) \pm t^* \sqrt{\frac{s_1^2}{n_1} + \frac{s_2^2}{n_2}} = (4.0875 - 3.0125) \pm 1.895 \sqrt{\frac{0.0270}{8} + \frac{0.0298}{8}}$$
$$= 1.075 \pm 0.160 = (0.915,\ 1.235).$$

The degrees of freedom are 7 because both $n_1 - 1$ and $n_2 - 1$ are 7. The confidence interval uses the $C = 90\%$ critical value of the $t(7)$ distribution, which Table C gives as $t^* = 1.895$.

**Example.** A study of the effect of eating sweetened cereals on tooth decay in children compared 73 children (Group 1) who ate such cereals regularly with 302 children (Group 2) who did not. After three years the number of new cavities was measured for each child. The summary statistics are

| Group | $n$ | $\bar{x}$ | $s$ |
|---|---|---|---|
| 1 | 73 | 3.41 | 3.62 |
| 2 | 302 | 2.20 | 2.67 |

The researchers suspected that sweetened cereals increase the mean number of cavities. Do the data support this suspicion?

This is another two-sample situation. We wish to test the hypotheses $H_0$: $\mu_1 = \mu_2$ versus $H_a$: $\mu_1 > \mu_2$. The two-sample $t$ test statistic is

$$t = \frac{\bar{x}_1 - \bar{x}_2}{\sqrt{\dfrac{s_1^2}{n_1} + \dfrac{s_2^2}{n_2}}} = \frac{3.41 - 2.20}{\sqrt{\dfrac{3.62^2}{73} + \dfrac{2.67^2}{302}}} = 2.68.$$

To assess the significance of the one-sided test, compare $t = 2.68$ with the upper critical values of the $t(72)$ distribution. The degrees of freedom are the smaller of $n_1 - 1 = 72$ and $n_2 - 1 = 301$. Using the df = 60 line in Table C, we see that $P < 0.005$. In particular, the result is significant at the 1% level. There is strong evidence that the sweetened cereal group has more cavities on the average.

Normality of the cavity counts is not important to the validity of the test because of the large samples. We do need to know how the samples were chosen. We cannot conclude from this study that eating sweetened cereal *causes* more cavities. The children who eat such cereal may differ in many ways from those who do not.

An optional section on inference for population spread ends Chapter 19. The contrast in the practical usefulness of the $t$ procedures for means and the chi-square and $F$ procedures for standard deviations is a good argument for not allowing theoretical statistics to set the agenda for a first course in statistical methods. These tests are all (at least approximately) likelihood ratio tests for Normal distributions. They therefore share a widely accepted general principle and some large-sample optimality properties. But they are vastly different in their actual usefulness. The $t$ tests (and their extension to ANOVA for comparing many means) are little affected by deviations from Normality. Tests for standard deviations, on the other hand, are so sensitive to deviations from Normality that I do not believe that they should be used in practice. I recommend starting with the paper "Relation between the shape of population distribution and the robustness of four simple test statistics," Pearson and Please, *Biometrika* 62 (1975). Their graphs effectively display the contrast between tests on means and tests on standard deviations and add several fine points to the brief discussion in *BPS*.

What then should we do about the standard tests for standard deviations in the context of a first statistics course? *BPS* allows three choices. You can ignore the issue altogether; this section is optional. You can discuss the issue and also present the most common of the questionable procedures, the $F$ test for comparing two standard deviations. Or you can discuss the section of Chapter 19 bluntly titled "Avoid inference about standard deviations," and omit the actual $F$ test on the grounds that we have explained why it is not of much value. I usually take the third approach.

## Inference for Proportions (Chapters 20 to 21)

These chapters present the $z$ procedures for one-sample and two-sample inference about population proportions. The procedures are approximate, based on the large-sample Normal approximation. Note that we avoid a common source of confusion by giving only the Normal approximation for $\hat{p}$ rather than starting with the Normal approximation for binomial counts. "Do no more probability than you need" is a key to success in teaching statistics to less prepared students. By now the students should be comfortable with the general framework for confidence intervals and significance tests. Those who have not yet mastered these concepts get an additional opportunity to learn these important ideas.

## Chapter 20: Inference about a Population Proportion

Here are confidence intervals and significance tests for a single proportion. There is a slight additional complication concerning the standard deviation of $\hat{p}$. For confidence intervals, we use the standard error $\sqrt{\hat{p}(1-\hat{p})/n}$, whereas for tests we use $\sqrt{p_0(1-p_0)/n}$. Students will just follow the recipes given, but you may want to point out why the basic idea is reasonable. We use all of the information available in a problem for inference. For the confidence interval, $p$ is unknown and the standard error therefore must be estimated using the value of $\hat{p}$ obtained from the data. On the other hand, when testing $H_0 : p = p_0$, our calculations are based on the supposition that $H_0$ is true and we therefore use the value $p_0$ in the calculations. Note that these choices destroy the exact correspondence between confidence intervals and two-sided tests (reject if the hypothesized parameter value is outside of the confidence interval).

With growing evidence that the "plus four" method should be the standard for confidence intervals in practice, consider using this procedure (described in the optional section beginning on page 499).

## Chapter 21: Comparing Two Proportions

This chapter presents confidence intervals and significance tests for comparing two population proportions. Students should be able to distinguish two-sample from one-sample settings from their work in Chapters 18 and 19. As in the previous chapter, we use different standard errors for confidence intervals and tests. Pooling the two samples in the test statistic, while making the test inconsistent with the confidence interval, keeps the two-sample test consistent with the $2 \times 2$ case of the chi-square test for two-way tables in Chapter 23.

If you covered the optional "plus four" method in Chapter 20, you will likely want to include the corresponding optional section from Chapter 21, which begins on page 517.

There are "exact" inference procedures for proportions based on the binomial distributions. The discreteness of the binomial makes these procedures a bit awkward. You can find details in Myles Hollander and Douglas Wolfe, *Nonparametric Statistical Methods,* 2nd ed., New York: Wiley, 1999.

## Chapter 22: Inference about Variables: Part III Review

Chapter 22 is recommended to help train students to distinguish between proportions and means. The flowcharts are helpful in grasping not only the difference in the meaning of a sample mean and sample proportion, but also whether or not a problem is a one-sample or two-sample scenario, and whether or not a test should be constructed as one-sided or two-sided. This chapter can be skipped if necessary without hindrance to material covered in the remaining chapters.

### Part IV: Inference about Relationships

The concluding chapters of *BPS* present independent accounts of inference in three more advanced settings: two-way tables of count data (Chapter 23), simple linear regression (Chapter 24), one-way analysis of variance (Chapter 25), and (on the CD-ROM or optional printed supplement) nonparametric tests (Chapter 26), quality control (Chapter 27), multiple regression (Chapter 28), and two-way analysis of variance (Chapter 29). The last four chapters are not discussed here.

Each of these settings introduces a distinctive new idea. The issue of multiple comparisons arises in Chapter 21 (comparing many proportions) and in Chapter 19 (comparing many means). In fact, the sections headed "The problem of multiple comparisons" are identical in both chapters except that one mentions proportions and the other mentions means. Chapter 24 must face the fact that the data are no longer one or several simple random samples. The section headed "The regression model" presents the model of random variation about a nonrandom relationship of known form (a line) but unknown parameters. In all of these chapters, however, I have refrained from introducing new types of inference methods such as formal multiple comparisons procedures or confidence bands for the entire true regression line. These chapters are a capstone for a first course and perhaps an introduction to further study. The methods are still the confidence intervals and tests whose logic is the heart of a basic introduction to statistical inference.

## Chapter 23: Two Categorical Variables: The Chi-Square Test

The Pearson chi-square test is one of the most common inference procedures and, because it tests the existence of a relationship between two categorical variables under several sampling models, one of the most versatile. Do note the stress that the overall test ("Yes, these variables are related") is not a full analysis of the data. The descriptive analysis of the nature of the relationship is essential.

**Example.** The type of medical care that a patient receives sometimes varies with the age of the patient. For example, women should receive a mammogram and biopsy of a suspicious lump in the breast. Here are data from a study that asked whether women received these diagnostic tests when a lump in the breast was discovered.

| | Tests done? | |
|---|---|---|
| Age | No | Yes |
| 45–64 | 61 | 158 |
| 65–74 | 40 | 103 |
| 75–90 | 53 | 77 |

In this study, a single sample was classified two ways: by age and by whether or not the tests were done.

The chi-square test for this table gives $X^2 = 7.3668$, $\text{df} = 2$, $P = 0.0251$. There is quite good evidence that the proportion of women in the population for whom the tests were done differs among the three age groups. We see that the sample proportions are 72% for women ages 45 to 64 years, 72% again for women ages 65 to 74 years, and 59% for women over 75 years. The data do not show the reason for the observed difference. It may be that doctors judge that surgery or other intervention is too risky for older women in poor health and so do not do the diagnostic tests on such women.

The chi-square test, like the tests in Chapters 20 and 21, is an approximate test whose accuracy improves as the cell counts increase. There is an "exact" test for two-way tables, called the Fisher exact test. This test treats *both sets of marginal totals* as fixed in advance. Some statisticians always prefer to do inference "conditional" on the observed marginal totals, as Fisher's test does. This is a debate that you do not want to reveal to your students! You can find a description of the Fisher test in Agresti (1990) and a more advanced survey in Agresti (1992).

*BPS* presents as optional the chi-square goodness-of-fit test that assesses, for example, whether the six sides of a die really are equiprobable. This test is more common in texts than in practice. Once we escape dice and coins, the test-of-fit problem usually concerns not fit to a fully specified model but fit to a *family* of models. "Do these data come from a Normal population?" is an example. Unfortunately, adapting the chi-square test of fit to such settings is a bit complicated (and often is done incorrectly in texts). In an earlier incarnation, David Moore did considerable research on variations of chi-square tests of fit. You can find the facts in his survey paper cited in this guide's references (page 43).

## Chapter 24: Inference for Regression

There are many interesting problems in which the relationship between two variables can be summarized graphically and numerically with a least-squares line. Not all of these can be analyzed using the methods presented in this chapter. Inference for linear regression is based on a statistical model that expresses the assumptions underlying the inference procedures. The section headed "Conditions for Regression Inference" (page 583) therefore is essential to understanding regression inference. The section that follows it introduces $s$, the standard error about the line, as the key measure of sample variability in the regression setting. You will sometimes find $s$ called "residual standard error" or "root MSE" in computer output or other texts.

The calculations required for regression inference, even after the least-squares line is in hand, are quite unpleasant without software. Most exercises in this chapter therefore give the output from a regression program. If your students are using software, you can ask them to produce the equivalent output from the data. Many exercises are not feasible without software. If your students lack software access, you can give them the results of key calculations (see the exercise solutions).

**Example.** A study of the force $y$ (in pounds) required to draw a plow at tractor speed $x$ (miles per hour) gave the following data.

| $x$ | 0.9 | 1.3 | 2.0 | 2.7 | 3.4 | 3.4 | 4.1 | 5.2 | 5.5 | 6.0 |
|---|---|---|---|---|---|---|---|---|---|---|
| $y$ | 425 | 420 | 480 | 495 | 540 | 530 | 590 | 610 | 690 | 680 |

The scatterplot with the least-squares line is shown at right, and the regression output is below.

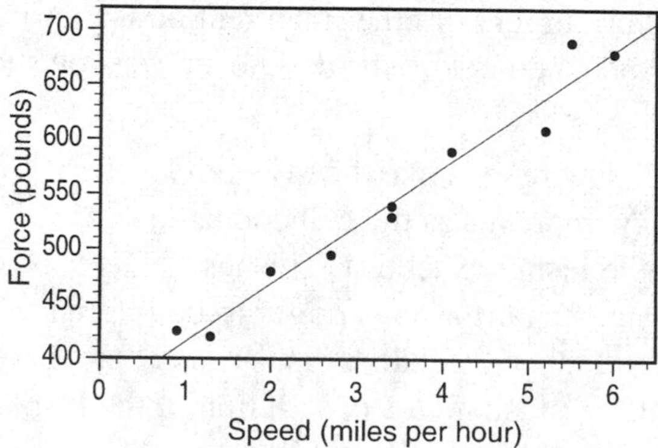


```
Residual Standard Error = 19.1869,  Multiple R-Square = 0.9643
N = 10,  F-statistic = 216.0738 on 1 and 8 df, p-value = 0

               coef   std.err    t.stat  p.value
Intercept  362.0657   13.9064   26.0358        0
        X   53.3143    3.6270   14.6994        0
```

The linear relationship is both very strong ($r^2 = 0.9643$) and highly significant (test for $H_0$: $\beta = 0$ has $t = 14.7$ and $P < 0.0001$). The slope $\beta$ of the true regression line is the rate at which the force required to pull the plow increases with speed. The 95% confidence interval for $\beta$ is

$$b \pm t^* \mathrm{SE}_b = 53.3143 \pm (2.306)(3.6270) = 53.31 \pm 8.37.$$

# Chapter 25: One-Way Analysis of Variance: Comparing Several Means

This chapter presents the one-way ANOVA $F$ test, with the descriptive analysis needed to suggest *what differences* among the observed means account for significance of the overall test. Although *BPS* does not do formal multiple comparisons, this chapter (like Chapter 23) points to the problem and avoids suggesting that the ANOVA test is all there is to comparing several means.

You should now assign the part of Chapter 19 (beginning on page 477) that introduces the $F$ distributions, if you did not do so earlier.

The algebra of ANOVA is a bit formidable for beginning students and does not help most students see how the analysis works. I therefore try to explain the nature of the ANOVA test in the section headed "The idea of analysis of variance" (page 630). This being a more advanced chapter, the algebraic details do appear in the optional section called "Some details of ANOVA" (page 639). Even here, however, formulas intended for calculation with a basic calculator do not appear. I would not make students do ANOVA calculations without software. If you wish to present this chapter to students who lack computer access, I suggest modifying the exercises by giving the sums of squares (see the solutions to the exercises). Students can then find degrees of freedom, mean squares, and the $F$ statistic, and use Table D to assess significance.

**Example.** In the discussion of Part I, we recommended the *Handbook of Small Data Sets* by D. J. Hand et al. One of their data sets (page 7) records the weight gains (in grams) of 10 rats fed each of four diets. The data come from G. W. Snedecor and G. C. Cochran, *Statistical Methods,* 6th ed., Iowa State University Press, 1967, page 347, so you can find the data in either source.

Boxplots of the four sets of weight gains are shown at right. The spreads appear similar and there are no outliers according to the $1.5 \times IQR$ criterion (this can be judged easily from the boxplots because the length of the box is the $IQR$). Diet B appears to give somewhat higher weight gains than the other three diets.

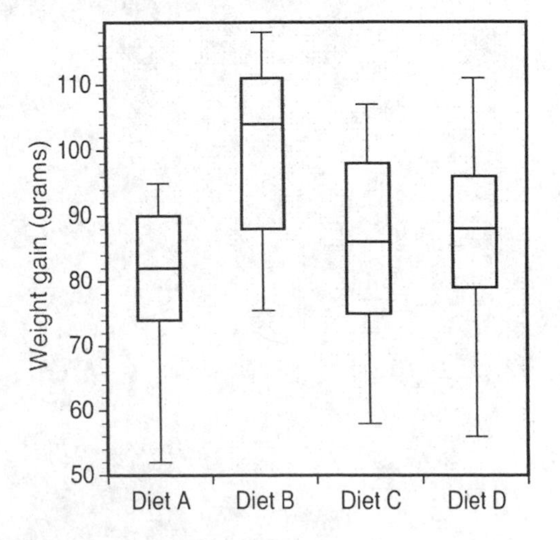


The basic descriptive statistics are

| | Diet A | Diet B | Diet C | Diet D |
|---|---|---|---|---|
| $n_i$ | 10 | 10 | 10 | 10 |
| $\bar{x}_i$ | 79.2 | 100.0 | 83.9 | 85.9 |
| $s_i$ | 13.89 | 15.14 | 15.71 | 15.02 |

and output from an ANOVA is

|  | df | Sum of Sq | Mean Sq | F Value | P value |
|---|---|---|---|---|---|
| diet | 3 | 2404.1 | 801.367 | 3.58402 | 0.0229666 |
| error | 36 | 8049.4 | 223.594 |  |  |

The degrees of freedom are $I - 1 = 4 - 1 = 3$ in the numerator and $N - I = 40 - 4 = 36$ in the denominator. The $P$-value 0.023 indicates good evidence of some differences among the population mean weight gains.

# 4 REFERENCES


1. Agresti, A. *Categorical Data Analysis*. New York: Wiley, 1990.

2. Agresti, A. "A survey of exact inference for contingency tables," *Statistical Science* 7 (1992):131–177.

3. Chatterjee, S., Handcock, M. S., and Simonoff, J. S. *A Casebook for a First Course in Statistics and Data Analysis*. New York: Wiley, 1995.

4. Hand, D. J., Daly, F., Lunn, A. D., McConway, K. J., and Ostrowski, E. *A Handbook of Small Data Sets*. London: Chapman and Hall, 1994.

5. McBean, E. A., and Rovers, F. A. *Statistical Procedures for Analysis of Environmental Monitoring Data and Risk Assessment*. Upper Saddle River, New Jersey: Prentice Hall, 1998.

6. Moore, D. S. "Tests of chi-squared type," in *Goodness-of-Fit Techniques,* R. B. D'Agostino and M. A. Stephens, eds. New York: Marcel Dekker, 1986.

7. Moore, D. S. "The place of video in new styles of teaching and learning statistics," *The American Statistician* 47 (1993):172–176.

8. Moore, D. S., and discussants. "New pedagogy and new content: The case of statistics," *International Statistical Review* 65 (1997):123–165.

9. Thiébaux, H. J. *Statistical Data Analysis for Ocean and Atmospheric Sciences*. San Diego, California: Academic Press, 1994.

# 5 SAMPLE EXAMINATIONS

These sample examinations illustrate typical questions, most of them quite straightforward.

- Sample Examination I covers material from Chapters 1 to 9 of *BPS*. Most students grasp this content well. Warn them not to become complacent, because later chapters contain more difficult material.

- Examination II covers Chapters 10, 11, and 14 to 16. I generally avoid exam questions on probability in the abstract.

- The third examination is comprehensive, but emphasizes Chapters 16 to 19 and 21. (I find that my students can realistically master only one of Chapters 20, 21, and 22.)

You can use these questions as examination items or as class examples. As mentioned earlier, I often use a sample exam distributed in class as review before a scheduled exam.

## Sample examination I

(25) 1. A study examined how long aircraft air-conditioning units operated after being repaired. Here are the operating times (in hours) for one unit:

| | | | | | | | | |
|---|---|---|---|---|---|---|---|---|
| 97 | 51 | 11 | 4 | 141 | 18 | 142 | 68 | 77 |
| 80 | 1 | 16 | 106 | 206 | 82 | 54 | 31 | 216 |
| 46 | 111 | 39 | 63 | 18 | 191 | 18 | 163 | 24 |

(a) Make a histogram of these data, using 40-hour classes, starting with

$$0 \le \text{time} < 40, \quad 40 \le \text{time} < 80, \quad \ldots.$$

(b) Describe the overall shape of the distribution. Is it roughly symmetric, skewed to the right, or skewed to the left? Are there any outliers?

(c) Is the five-number summary or the mean and standard deviation a better brief summary for this distribution? Explain your choice. Calculate the one of these summaries that you choose.

(20) 2. Biologists and ecologists record the distributions of measurements made on animal species to help study the distribution and evolution of the animals. The African finch *Pyrenestes ostrinus* is interesting because the distribution of its bill size has two peaks even though other body measurements follow normal distributions. For example, a study in Cameroon found that the wing length of male finches varies according to a Normal distribution with mean 61.2 mm and standard deviation 1.8 mm.

(a) What proportion of male finches have wings longer than 65 mm?

(b) What is the wing length that only 2% of male finches exceed?

(20) 3. The drug AZT was the first effective treatment for AIDS. An important medical experiment demonstrated that regular doses of AZT delay the onset of symptoms in people in whom HIV is present. The researchers who carried out this experiment wanted to know the following:

- Does taking either 500 mg of AZT or 1500 mg of AZT per day delay the development of AIDS?
- Is there any difference between the effects of these two doses?

The subjects were 1200 volunteers already infected with HIV but with no symptoms of AIDS when the study started.

(a) Outline the design of the experiment.

(b) Describe briefly how you would use a table of random digits to do the randomization required by your design. Then use Table B beginning at line 110 to choose *the first five* subjects for one of your groups.

(35) 4. A long-term study of changing environmental conditions in Chesapeake Bay found the following annual average salinity readings in one location in the bay:

| Year | 1971 | 1972 | 1973 | 1974 | 1975 | 1976 | 1977 |
|---|---|---|---|---|---|---|---|
| Salinity (%) | 13.2 | 9.3 | 14.9 | 13.9 | 14.8 | 13.3 | 15.0 |

| Year | 1978 | 1979 | 1980 | 1981 | 1982 | 1983 | 1984 |
|---|---|---|---|---|---|---|---|
| Salinity (%) | 15.3 | 15.1 | 13.1 | 17.0 | 19.3 | 15.6 | 15.3 |

(a) Make a plot of salinity against time. Was salinity generally increasing or decreasing over these years? Is there an overall straight-line trend over time?

(b) What is the correlation between salinity and year? What percent of the observed variation in salinity is accounted for by straight-line change over time?

(c) Find the least-squares regression line for predicting salinity from year. Explain in simple language what the slope of this line tells you about Chesapeake Bay.

(d) If the trend in these past data had continued, what would be the average salinity at this point in the bay in 1988?

## Sample examination I solutions

1. (a) Here is the histogram.

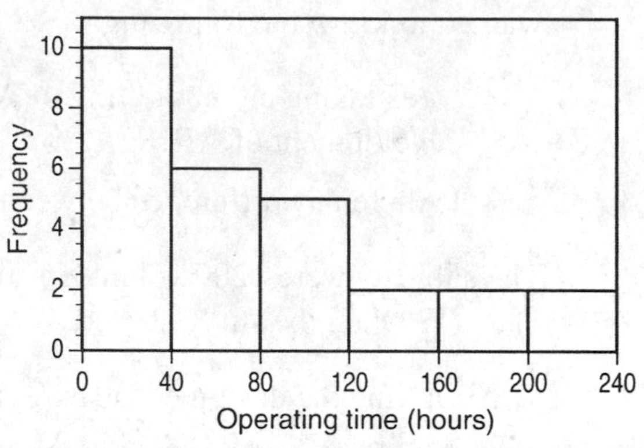


(b) The distribution of operating times is strongly skewed to the right. There are no outliers.

(c) The five-number summary is preferable for this strongly skewed distribution. First, arrange the observations in increasing order:

| | | | | | | | | | | | | | |
|---|---|---|---|---|---|---|---|---|---|---|---|---|---|
| 1 | 4 | 11 | 16 | 18 | 18 | 18 | 24 | 31 | 39 | 46 | 51 | 54 | 63 |
| 68 | 77 | 80 | 82 | 97 | 106 | 111 | 141 | 142 | 163 | 191 | 206 | 216 | |

The five-number summary of these $n = 27$ observations is

1 18 63 111 216

2. (a) Wing length $x$ has the $N(61.2, 1.8)$ distribution. So we want the area under a Normal curve such that

$$x > 65$$

$$\frac{x - 61.2}{1.8} > \frac{65 - 61.2}{1.8}$$

$$z > 2.11$$

Table A gives this area as $1 - 0.9826 = 0.0174$. About 17.4% of male finches have wing lengths exceeding 64.9 mm.

(b) We want the $x$ with area 0.02 to its right, or area 0.98 to its left. In the body of Table A, find $z = 2.06$ as the entry with left tail area closest to 0.98. So

$$x = 61.2 + (1.8)(2.06) = 64.9 \text{ mm}.$$

3. (a) The goals of the experiment require *three* treatment groups, one of which receives a placebo. (Because AZT was the first AIDS drug, it was considered ethical to give a placebo to test its effectiveness. Later drugs were tested against AZT.) Here is the design:

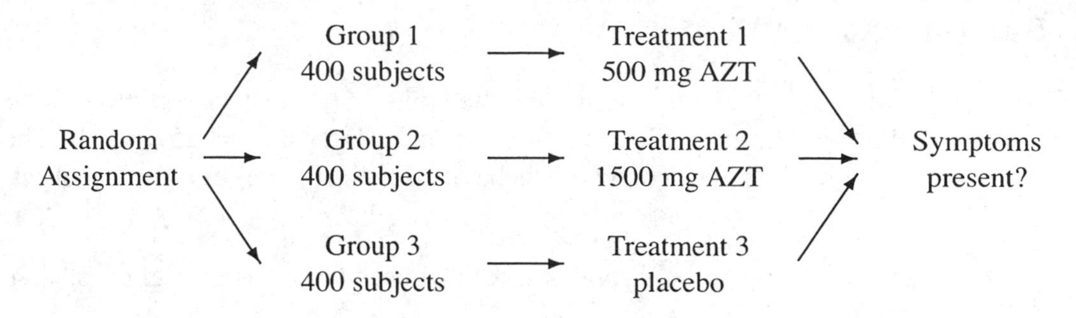


(b) First, assign labels. We use labels 0001 to 1200. Next, read four-digit groups from line 110, continuing to the following lines. The first five subjects chosen are

0676 0041 0404 1197 0640

4. (a) The plot (right) shows an increasing linear trend over time.

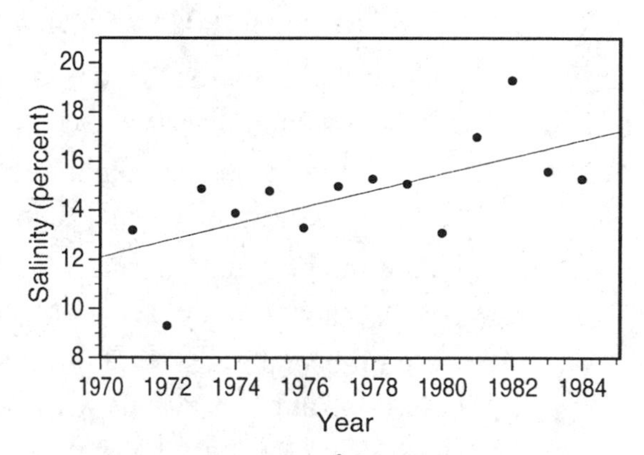


(b) The correlation (use a calculator) is $r = 0.6386$. Because $r^2 = 0.4079$, linear change over time explains about 41% of the observed variation in salinity over this period.

(c) The least-squares line (use a calculator) is

$$\hat{y} = -659.4385 + 0.340879x.$$

That is, salinity is increasing by 0.34% per year on the average. This line is drawn on the scatterplot above.

(d) The prediction for $x = 1988$ is

$$\hat{y} = -659.4385 + (0.3409)(1988) = 18.23\%.$$

## Sample examination II

(20) 1. The weights of newborn children in the United States vary according to the normal distribution with mean 7.5 pounds and standard deviation 1.25 pounds. The government classifies a newborn as having low birth weight if the weight is less than 5.5 pounds.

(a) What is the probability that a baby chosen at random weighs less than 5.5 pounds at birth?

(b) You choose three babies at random. What is the probability that their average birth weight is less than 5.5 pounds?

(20) 2. Answer each of the following short questions.

(a) Give the upper 0.025 critical value for the standard Normal distribution.

(b) An animal scientist is studying factors that affect the level of milk production in dairy cows. He wonders,

> Is the mean production different for cows who are given forage spread on the ground than for cows whose forage is in bunks?

State the null and alternative hypotheses that you would use in a statistical test of this question. (We cannot test these hypotheses yet.)

(c) An opinion poll asks 1500 randomly chosen United States residents their opinions about relations with the nations of Europe. The announced margin of error for 95% confidence is $\pm 3$ points. But some people were not on the list from which respondents were chosen, some could not be contacted, and some refused to answer. Does the announced margin of error include errors from these causes?

(d) A student organization plans to ask of 100 randomly selected students how much they spent on textbooks last semester. You argue for a sample of 900 students instead of 100. You know that the standard deviation of the sample mean $\bar{x}$ of the amounts spent will be __ times as large with the larger sample. Should the blank "__" be nine, one-ninth, three, or one-third? Explain your answer.

(e) You read in a journal a report of a study that found a statistically significant result at the 5% significance level. What can you say about the significance of this result at the 1% level? Is it certainly significant, at the 1% level, certainly not significant at the 1% level, or maybe significant and maybe not significant?

(40) 3. A friend who hears that you are taking a statistics course asks for help with a chemistry lab report. She has made four independent measurements of the specific gravity of a compound. The results are

3.82,  3.93,  3.67,  and  3.78.

You are willing to assume that the measurements are not biased. This means that the mean $\mu$ of the distribution of measurements is the true specific gravity.

(a) The lab manual asks for a 95% confidence interval for the true specific gravity. Your friend does not know how to do this. Do it for her.

(b) Explain to your friend in simple language what "95% confidence" means.

(c) What must be true about your friend's measurements for your result in part (a) to be correct?

(d) You now notice that the lab manual says that repeated measurements will vary according to a Normal distribution with standard deviation $\sigma = 0.15$. Redo the confidence interval of part (a) using this additional information. Explain in nontechnical language why we expect the new interval to be shorter.

(e) What critical value from the Normal table would you use if you wanted 80% confidence in part (d) rather than 95% confidence? Would the 80% confidence interval be wider or narrower than your 95% confidence from (a)? (Do *not* actually compute the 80% confidence interval.)

(20) 4. Your friend needs yet more help with her lab report.

(a) The lab manual also asks whether the data show convincingly that the true specific gravity is less than 3.9. State the null and alternative hypotheses used to answer this question. Then calculate the test statistic and find its $P$-value. Use the lab manual's value $\sigma = 0.15$ and calculate the $P$-value in detail.

(b) Explain to your friend in one or two sentences what the specific $P$-value you found in (a) means.

## Sample examination II solutions

1. (a) The weight $x$ of a single child has the $N(7.5, 1.25)$ distribution. So

$$P(x < 5.5) = P\left(\frac{x - 7.5}{1.25} < \frac{5.5 - 7.5}{1.25}\right) = P(Z < -1.60) = 0.0548.$$

(b) The mean birth weight $\bar{x}$ of a sample of three children still has mean 7.5 pounds, but its standard deviation is

$$\frac{\sigma}{\sqrt{3}} = \frac{1.25}{\sqrt{3}} = 0.7217 \text{ pound.}$$

Therefore, the probability we want is

$$P(\bar{x} < 5.5) = P\left(\frac{\bar{x} - 7.5}{0.7217} < \frac{5.5 - 7.5}{0.7217}\right) = P(Z < -2.77) = 0.0028.$$

2. (a) Use Table C to see that the upper 0.025 critical value is $z^* = 1.960$.

   (b) The key words are "is different," indicating that the alternative hypothesis is two-sided—$H_0$: $\mu_G = \mu_B$ versus $H_a$: $\mu_G \neq \mu_B$. Here $\mu_G$ and $\mu_B$ are the mean milk production for all cows of this breed with forage spread on the ground and in bunks, respectively.

   (c) No. The margin of error in a confidence interval covers only the random sampling error due to chance variation in random sampling.

   (d) The standard deviation goes down as the sample size $n$ goes up, at the rate $\sqrt{n}$. (The standard deviation of a sample mean $\bar{x}$ is $\sigma/\sqrt{n}$, where $\sigma$ is the population standard deviation.) So a sample nine times larger has a standard deviation *one-third* as large.

   (e) A result significant at the 5% level is in the extreme 5% of the sampling distribution; so it *may or may not* also be in the extreme 1%.

3. (a) Enter the data into a calculator to find that $\bar{x} = 3.80$ and $s = 0.1074$. With $n = 4$, we use the $t$ distribution with $n - 1 = 3$ degrees of freedom. The 95% confidence interval is

$$\bar{x} \pm t^* \frac{s}{\sqrt{n}} = 3.80 \pm 3.182 \frac{0.1074}{\sqrt{4}} = 3.80 \pm 0.1708.$$

   (b) "95% confidence" means that we got this interval by using a method that in 95% of all samples will produce an interval that covers the true specific gravity.

   (c) The $n = 4$ measurements are treated as an SRS from the population of all measurements your friend would get if she kept working forever. The sample is small, so we are also assuming that the distribution of the repeated measurements is normal or close to normal.

   (d) If we assume that we know the population standard deviation $\sigma$, we need not estimate it from the data. The interval then uses $z$ rather than $t$. The 95% confidence interval is

$$\bar{x} \pm z^* \frac{\sigma}{\sqrt{n}} = 3.80 \pm 1.960 \frac{0.15}{\sqrt{4}} = 3.80 \pm 0.147.$$

   Knowing $\sigma$ exactly means that we do not need to estimate it from the data. This removes one source of variation from the confidence interval. The margin of error can be smaller because it need not cover this added variation.

   (e) For 80% confidence, $z^* = 1.282$. The 80% confidence interval is narrower than the 95% confidence interval because the critical value required is smaller.

4. (a) We test $H_0$: $\mu = 3.9$ versus $H_a$: $\mu < 3.9$. The $z$ test statistic is

$$z = \frac{\bar{x} - \mu_0}{\sigma/\sqrt{n}} = \frac{3.8 - 3.9}{0.15/\sqrt{4}} = -1.33,$$

   and its $P$-value (one-sided on the low side) is $P(Z \leq -1.33) = 0.0918$.

(b) There is probability 0.0918 that the mean of four readings would be as small as 3.8 if the true specific gravity were 3.9. That is, we observed a value in the smallest 9.2% of all results we could get if 3.9 were correct. This is only weak evidence that the specific gravity is less than 3.9 because a value this small would come up more than 9% of the time just by chance.

## Sample final examination

(15) 1. A historian examining British colonial records for the Gold Coast in Africa suspects that the death rate was higher among African miners than among European miners. In the year 1936, there were 223 deaths among 33,809 African miners and 7 deaths among 1541 European miners in the Gold Coast. (Data courtesy of Raymond Dumett, Department of History, Purdue University.)

Consider this year as a sample from the prewar era in Africa. Is there good evidence that the proportion of African miners who died during a year was higher than the proportion of European miners who died? (State hypotheses, calculate a test statistic, give a $P$-value as exact as the tables in the text allow, and state your conclusion in words.)

(25) 2. An agricultural researcher reasons as follows. A heavy application of potassium fertilizer to grasslands in the spring seems to cause lush early growth but depletes the potassium before the growing season ends. So spreading the same amount of potassium over the growing season might increase yields. He therefore compares two treatments: 100 pounds per acre of potassium in the spring (Treatment 1) and 50, 25, and 25 pounds per acre applied in the spring, early summer, and late summer, respectively (Treatment 2). The experiment is continued over several years because growing conditions may vary from year to year.

The table below gives the yields, in pounds of dry matter per acre. It is known from long experience that yields vary roughly Normally. (Data from R. R. Robinson, C. L. Rhykerd, and C. F. Gross, "Potassium uptake by orchardgrass as affected by time, frequency, and rate of potassium fertilization," *Agronomy Journal* 54[1962] 351–353.)

| Treatment | Year 1 | Year 2 | Year 3 | Year 4 | Year 5 |
|---|---|---|---|---|---|
| 1 | 3902 | 4281 | 5135 | 5350 | 5746 |
| 2 | 3970 | 4271 | 5440 | 5490 | 6028 |

(a) Do the data give good evidence that Treatment 2 leads to higher average yields? (State hypotheses, carry out a test, give a $P$-value as exact as the tables in the text allow, and state your conclusions in words.)

(b) Give a 98% confidence interval for the mean increase in yield from spreading potassium applications over the growing season.

(15) 3. Before an intensive TV advertising campaign, the manufacturers of Nike athletic shoes find that 29 of a random sample of 200 upper-income adults are aware of their new leisure shoe line. A second random sample of 300 such adults is taken after the campaign. Now 96 of the persons sampled can identify the new line.

Give a 99% confidence interval for the increase in the proportion of upper-income adults showing brand awareness.

(30) 4. Here are data on the years of schooling completed $x$, and annual income $y$ (in thousands of dollars), for a sample of 18 40-year-old men.

| Years | 10 | 16 | 12 | 6 | 12 | 12 | 16 | 16 | 18 |
|---|---|---|---|---|---|---|---|---|---|
| Income | 48 | 58 | 36 | 33 | 45 | 50 | 55 | 47 | 48 |

| Years | 12 | 10 | 12 | 16 | 14 | 11 | 12 | 19 | 16 |
|---|---|---|---|---|---|---|---|---|---|
| Income | 48 | 46 | 41 | 54 | 50 | 41 | 47 | 49 | 44 |

A scatterplot (do not do it) shows a generally linear relation, but with considerable scatter about the line of best fit. A computer least-squares regression program gives the output below. (The "Coef" column gives the slope $a$ and intercept $b$; the "Std Err" column gives the standard errors of these statistics. The "Residual Standard Error" is the observed standard deviation $s$ about the regression line.)

```
                Coef      Std Err     t Value
Intercept   30.84249    5.103363    2.124577
years        1.18681    0.372311    3.187693

Residual Standard Error = 5.02275      R-Square = 0.3884116
N = 18          F Value = 10.16139 on 1, 16 df
```

(a) What percent of the observed variation in income is explained by the straight-line relation between income and education?

(b) Is there strong evidence that there is a straight-line relation between education and income? (State hypotheses, carry out a test, use a table to find values between which the $P$-value falls, and state your conclusion.)

(c) Consider 40-year-old men who have 16 years of education. (These are men with 4 years of college but no further education.) Give a 95% interval for their average income.

(15) 5. Answer each of the following questions. (No explanation is needed—just a short answer.)

(a) You are reading an article in your field that reports several statistical analyses. The article says that the $P$-value for a significance test is 0.045. Is this result significant at the 5% significance level?

(b) Is the result with $P$-value 0.045 significant at the 1% significance level?

(c) For another significance test, the article says only that the result was significant at the 1% level. Are such results always, sometimes, or never significant at the 5% level?

(d) Reaction times of a subject to a stimulus are often strongly skewed to the right because of a few slow reaction times. You wish to test

$$H_0\colon \mu_1 = \mu_2$$

where $\mu_1$ is the mean reaction time for Stimulus 1, and $\mu_2$ for Stimulus 2. You have two independent samples, 8 observations for Stimulus 1 and 10 for Stimulus 2. Which, if any, of the tests that you have studied can be used to test this?

(e) The article contains a 95% confidence interval. Would the margin of error in a 99% confidence interval computed from the same data be less, the same, or greater?

## Sample final examination solutions

1. This is a two-sample setting, with

Population 1 = African miners and Population 2 = European miners.

We want to test $H_0\colon p_1 = p_2$ versus $H_a\colon p_1 > p_2$. The two sample proportions are

$$\hat{p}_1 = \frac{223}{33{,}809} = 0.006596 \quad \text{and} \quad \hat{p}_2 = \frac{7}{1541} = 0.004543.$$

The pooled sample proportion is therefore

$$\hat{p} = \frac{\text{total count of deaths in both samples}}{\text{total count of miners in both samples}} = \frac{223 + 7}{33{,}809 + 1541} = \frac{230}{35{,}350} = 0.006506$$

and the $z$ test statistic is

$$z = \frac{\hat{p}_1 - \hat{p}_2}{\sqrt{\hat{p}(1-\hat{p})\left(\frac{1}{n_1} + \frac{1}{n_2}\right)}}$$

$$= \frac{0.006596 - 0.004543}{\sqrt{(0.006506)(0.993494)\left(\frac{1}{33{,}809} + \frac{1}{1541}\right)}} = \frac{0.002053}{0.0020943} = 0.980.$$

Table A gives the $P$-value as $1 - 0.8365 = 0.1635$. There is, surprisingly, no significant evidence that the African death rate is higher.

2. This is a *matched pairs* setting because the observations are paired by years.

(a) The hypotheses, expressed in terms of the mean differences (Treatment 2 – Treatment 1), are $H_0\colon \mu = 0$ and $H_a\colon \mu > 0$. The differences are

$$68 \quad -10 \quad 305 \quad 140 \quad 282$$

with

$$\bar{x} = 157 \quad \text{and} \quad s = 135.672.$$

Apply the one-sample $t$ test to these differences. The test statistic is

$$t = \frac{\bar{x} - 0}{s/\sqrt{n}} = \frac{157}{135.672/\sqrt{5}} = 2.588.$$

The $P$-value based on the $t$ distribution with $n - 1 = 4$ degrees of freedom falls between 0.025 and 0.05 (using Table C). This is moderately strong evidence that Treatment 2 produces a higher mean yield.

(b) For 98% confidence and df = 4, use $t^* = 3.747$. The confidence interval is

$$\bar{x} \pm t^* \frac{s}{\sqrt{n}} = 157 \pm 3.747 \frac{135.672}{\sqrt{5}} = 157 \pm 227.3 = (-70.3, 384.3).$$

3. There are two independent samples. We want a confidence interval for a difference between two population proportions. The sample proportions are

$$\hat{p}_1 = \frac{29}{200} = 0.145 \quad \text{and} \quad \hat{p}_2 = \frac{96}{300} = 0.320.$$

We can use procedures based on the normal approximation because the population is large and all counts are more than 5:

$$n\hat{p}_1 = 29 \qquad n(1 - \hat{p}_1) = 191 \qquad n\hat{p}_2 = 96 \qquad n(1 - \hat{p}_2) = 204.$$

The standard error for $\hat{p}_2 - \hat{p}_1$ is

$$\text{SE} = \sqrt{\frac{\hat{p}_1(1 - \hat{p}_1)}{n_1} + \frac{\hat{p}_2(1 - \hat{p}_2)}{n_2}}$$

$$= \sqrt{\frac{(0.145)(0.855)}{200} + \frac{(0.320)(0.680)}{300}} = \sqrt{0.0013452} = 0.03668.$$

The 99% confidence interval for $p_2 - p_1$ is

$$(\hat{p}_2 - \hat{p}_1) \pm z^*\text{SE} = (0.320 - 0.145) \pm (2.576)(0.03668)$$
$$= 0.175 \pm 0.0945 = (0.0805, 0.2695).$$

We are 99% confident that between 8% and 27% of upper-income adults are aware of the new shoe line.

4. (a) The output says `R-Square = 0.3884116`, so the linear relationship explains 38.8% of the observed variation in income.

(b) The null hypothesis of "no relation" says that the slope of the true regression line is 0. We test $H_0$: $\beta = 0$ versus $H_a$: $\beta \neq 0$. The computer output shows that the $t$ statistic for the test is $t = 3.187693$. The degrees of freedom are $n - 2 = 16$. From Table C we see that $t$ falls between the 0.0025 and 0.005 upper critical values of $t(16)$. Doubling these values (because $H_a$ is two-sided) gives $0.005 < P < 0.01$. There is strong evidence that a linear relationship exists.

(c) The predicted mean income for $x = 16$ is

$$\hat{y} = 30.84249 + (1.186813)(16) = 49.831$$

or \$49,831. The rest of this is a bit tedious by hand, so consider your options. Here goes. Using a calculator gives $\bar{x} = 13.33$ and $s_x = 3.27198$, so

$$\sum(x - \bar{x})^2 = (n-1)s_x^2 = (17)(3.27198)^2 = 182.$$

The proper standard error for estimating the mean income is

$$\begin{aligned} \mathrm{SE}_{\hat{\mu}} &= s\sqrt{\frac{1}{n} + \frac{(x^* - \bar{x})^2}{\sum(x - \bar{x})^2}} \\ &= 5.02275\sqrt{\frac{1}{18} + \frac{(16 - 13.33)^6}{182}} = 5.02275\sqrt{0.0946275} = 1.5451. \end{aligned}$$

The 90% confidence interval is therefore

$$\hat{y} \pm t^*\mathrm{SE}_{\hat{\mu}} = 49.831 \pm (2.120)(1.5451) = 49.831 \pm 3.276$$

or \$46,555 to \$53,107.

5. (a) Yes. The $P$-value is less than 0.05.
   (b) No. The $P$-value is greater than 0.01.
   (c) A result significant at the 1% level lies in the extreme 1% of a sampling distribution. This is certainly in the extreme 5%, so the result is always significant at the 5% level.
   (d) The samples are small and the distributions are strongly skewed. It would be unwise to use the $t$ test in this setting. None of the tests that we have studied is appropriate.
   (e) The margin of error would be greater. Higher confidence is paid for with a greater margin of error.

# 6 APPLICATIONS

*BPS* presents a wide variety of applications from diverse disciplines. The list below indicates the number of exercises and examples that relate to various fields:

| Field | Number of examples | Number of exercises |
|---|---|---|
| Agriculture | 8 | 56 |
| Biological and environmental sciences | 25 | 128 |
| Business and economics | 10 | 145 |
| Education | 29 | 162 |
| Entertainment | 5 | 33 |
| People and places | 20 | 168 |
| Physical sciences | 5 | 23 |
| Political science and public policy | 3 | 37 |
| Psychology and behavioral sciences | 6 | 22 |
| Public health and medicine | 33 | 189 |
| Sports | 7 | 36 |
| Technology | 16 | 37 |
| Transportation and automobiles | 14 | 65 |

For a complete index of applications of examples and exercises, please see the Annotated Instructor's Edition or the Web site, `www.whfreeman.com/bps`.

# 7 CONVERSION GUIDE

The chapters in the fourth edition of *BPS* correspond closely to those of the third edition, except that review chapters are now numbered in sequence with the other chapters. The table below shows the relationships between chapter numbers in the two editions.

| *BPS* 3e | *BPS* 4e |
|---|---|
| PART I: EXPLORING DATA | PART I: EXPLORING DATA |
| Exploring Data: Variables and Distributions | Exploring Data: Variables and Distributions |
| 1. Picturing Distributions with Graphs | 1. Picturing Distributions with Graphs |
| 2. Describing Distributions with Numbers | 2. Describing Distributions with Numbers |
| 3. Normal Distributions | 3. The Normal Distributions |
| Exploring Data: Relationships | Exploring Data: Relationships |
| 4. Scatterplots and Correlation | 4. Scatterplots and Correlation |
| 5. Regression | 5. Regression |
| 6. Two-Way Tables (optional) | 6. Two-Way Tables (optional) |
| Exploring Data Review Chapter | 7. Part I Review |
| PART II: FROM EXPLORATION TO INFERENCE | PART II: FROM EXPLORATION TO INFERENCE |
| Producing Data | Producing Data |
| 7. Producing Data: Sampling | 8. Producing Data: Sampling |
| 8. Producing Data: Experiments | 9. Producing Data: Experiments |
| | NEW: Commentary on Data Ethics |
| Probability and Sampling Distributions | Probability and Sampling Distributions |
| 9. Introducing Probability | 10. Introducing Probability |
| 10. Sampling Distributions | 11. Sampling Distributions |
| 11. General Rules of Probability (optional) | 12. General Rules of Probability (optional) |
| 12. Binomial Distributions (optional) | 13. Binomial Distributions |
| Introducing Inference | Introducing Inference |
| 13. Confidence Intervals: The Basics | 14. Confidence Intervals: The Basics |
| 14. Tests of Significance: The Basics | 15. Tests of Significance: The Basics |
| 15. Inference in Practice | 16. Inference in Practice |
| Exploration to Inference Review Chapter | 17. Part II Review |
| PART III: INFERENCE ABOUT VARIABLES | PART III: INFERENCE ABOUT VARIABLES |
| Quantitative Response Variable | Quantitative Response Variable |
| 16. Inference about Population Mean | 18. Inference about a Population Mean |
| 17. Two-Sample Problems | 19. Two-Sample Problems |
| Categorical Response Variable | Categorical Response Variable |
| 18. Inference about Population Proportion | 20. Inference about a Population Proportion |
| 19. Comparing Two Proportions | 21. Comparing Two Proportions |
| Inference about Variables Review Chapter | 22. Part III Review |
| PART IV: INFERENCE ABOUT RELATIONSHIPS | PART IV: INFERENCE ABOUT RELATIONSHIPS |
| 20. Two Categorical Variables: The Chi-Square Test | 23. Two Categorical Variables: The Chi-Square Test |
| 21. Inference for Regression | 24. Inference for Regression |
| 22. One-Way Analysis of Variance: Comparing Several Means | 25. One-Way Analysis of Variance: Comparing Several Means |

| PART V: COMPLEMENTARY CHAPTERS | PART V: COMPLEMENTARY CHAPTERS |
|---|---|
| 23. Nonparametric Tests | 26. Nonparametric Tests |
| 24. Statistical Process Control | 27. Statistical Process Control |
| | NEW: 28. Multiple Regression |
| | NEW: 29. Two-Way Analysis of Variance |

# 8 SOLUTIONS TO EXERCISES

## About these solutions

The solutions that follow were prepared by Darryl Nester. In some cases, solutions were based on those prepared for earlier editions of *BPS* (and other texts); I hope that I did not miss any subtle changes in an exercise that should have resulted in a change in the solution. Should you discover any errors or have any comments about these solutions (or the odd-numbered answers, in the back of the text), please report them to me:

Darryl K. Nester
Department of Mathematics
Bluffton University
Bluffton, OH 45817-1196
E-mail: `nesterd@bluffton.edu`
`www.bluffton.edu/~nesterd`

Thanks to Jackie Miller (Ohio State University), who checked these solutions for accuracy. I should also note the software used to prepare these solutions:

- For typesetting: TEX (Textures, from Blue Sky Software).
- For the graphs: DeltaGraph (from Red Rock Software) and Adobe Illustrator.
- For statistical analysis: primarily Minitab (Version 10 for Macintosh) and Excel. Additionally, I used the TI-83 calculator from Texas Instruments.

**Note:** The solutions given to the applet exercises, and the sample output screens, were based on the current versions of the applets at the time the solutions were written. As revisions are made to these applets, the appearance of the output screens (and in some cases, the answers) may change. Additionally, output screens look somewhat different on different computers. (These screenshots were taken on a computer running Mac OS X.)

## Using the table of random digits

Grading SRSs chosen from Table B is complicated by the fact that students can find some creative ways to (mis)use the table. Some approaches are not mistakes, but may lead to different students having different "right" answers. Correct answers will vary based on

- The line in the table on which students begin (you may want to specify one if the text does not).
- Whether they start with, e.g., 00 or 01.
- Whether they assign multiple labels to each unit.
- Whether they assign labels across the rows or down the columns (nearly all lists in the text are alphabetized down the columns).

Some approaches can potentially lead to wrong answers. Mistakes to watch out for include the following:

- Students may forget that all labels must be the same length (e.g., assigning labels such as 0, 1, 2, ..., 9, 10, ... rather than 00, 01, 02, ...).
- In assigning multiple labels, they may not give the same number of labels to all units. For example, if there are 30 units, they may try to use up all the two-digit numbers, thus assigning four labels to the first 10 units and only three to the remaining 20.

As an alternative to using the random digits in Table B, students can pick a random sample by generating (pseudo-)random numbers. With many, if not all, calculators, the sequence of random numbers produced is determined by a "seed value" (which can be specified by the user). Rather than pointing students to a particular line of Table B, you could specify a seed value for generating random numbers, so that all students would obtain the same results (if all are using the same model of calculator).

On a TI-83, for example, after executing the command `0→rand`, the `rand` command will produce the sequence (rounded to four decimals) 0.9436, 0.9083, 0.1467, ... , while `1→rand` initiates the sequence 0.7456, 0.8559, 0.2254, ... . So to choose, say, an SRS of size 10 from 30 subjects, use the command `0→rand` to set the seed, and then type `1+30*rand`, and press ENTER repeatedly. Ignoring the decimal portion of the resulting numbers, this produces the sample

29, 28, 5, 15, 13, 23, 2, 11, 30, 7

(Generally, to generate random numbers from 1 to $n$, use the command `1+n*rand` and ignore the decimal portion of the result.)

## Using statistical software

The use of computer software or a calculator is a must for all but the most cursory treatment of the material in this text. Be aware of the following considerations:

- *Standard deviations:* Students may be confused by software that gives both the so-called "sample standard deviation" (the one used in the text) and the "population standard deviation" (dividing by $n$ rather than by $n-1$). Symbolically, the former is usually given as $s$ and the latter as $\sigma$ (sigma), but the distinction is not always clear. For example, many computer spreadsheets have a command such as "`STDEV(...)`" to compute standard deviations, but you may need to check the manual to find out which kind it is.

  As a quick check: for the numbers $1, 2, 3$, $s = 1$, while $\sigma \doteq 0.8165$. In general, if two values are given, the larger one is $s$ and the smaller is $\sigma$. If only one value is given, and it is the wrong one, use the relationship $s = \sigma\sqrt{\frac{n}{n-1}}$.

- *Stemplots:* The various choices one can make in creating a stemplot (e.g., rounding or truncating the data) have already been mentioned. Minitab opts for truncation over rounding, so all of the solutions in this guide show truncated-data stemplots (except for exercises that instructed students to round). This usually makes little difference in the overall appearance of the stemplot.

  I have come to prefer truncation over rounding for two reasons. First, there is less chance of making a mistake using truncation (if doing the task by hand). More important, truncating keeps the shape of the stemplot similar to the shape of a histogram of the same data. For example, if our data set ranges from 20 to 99, then using the tens digits 2 through 9 as stems, the number 59.6 would be represented as either a 0 on stem 6 (with rounding) or a 9 on stem 5 (using truncation). If we made a histogram of the same data, with intervals 20 to 29.9, 30 to 39.9, etc. (a fairly natural choice), the number 59.6 would fall in the 50s interval, so the truncated stemplot is the best match for the histogram.

- *Significant digits in these solutions:* Most numerical answers in these solutions (and in the odd-numbered answers in the back of the text) are reported to four significant figures. In many cases, that is an absurd overrepresentation of the accuracy of those numbers, but those digits are provided to give students a better "check" on their answers.

  This extra accuracy is a double-edged sword, however, because a student might have a correct answer that does not agree with all the digits in the printed answer. This might occur (rarely, I hope) because my answer is wrong, but it also might occur because of rounding, differences in software accuracy, or use of an approximation. For example, in reporting binomial probabilities for exercises in Chapter 13, I have listed four or five answers for some problems: exact answers and Normal approximations (with or without the continuity correction, and computed with software or using Table A). In the answers at the back of the text, only one answer is given, so that students may have to be satisfied with being close.

- *Quartiles and five-number summaries:* Methods of computing quartiles vary between different packages. Some use the approach given in the text (that is, $Q_1$ is the median of all the numbers below the location of the overall median, etc.), while others use a more complicated approach. For the numbers $1, 2, 3, 4$, for example, we would have $Q_1 = 1.5$ and $Q_3 = 2.5$, but Minitab reports these as 1.25 and 2.75, respectively.

  In these solutions (and the odd-numbered answers in the back of the text), I opted to report five-number summaries as they would be found using the text's method. Because I used Minitab for most of the analysis in these solutions, I wrote a Minitab macro to compute quartiles the *BPS* way. This and other macros are available on my Web site.

- *Boxplots:* Some programs that draw boxplots use the convention that the "whiskers" extend to the lower and upper deciles (the 10th and 90th percentiles) rather than to the minimum and maximum. While the decile method is merely *different* from that given in the text, some methods are (in my opinion) just plain *wrong*. Some early graphing calculators drew "box charts," which have a center line at the mean (not the median), and a box extending from $\bar{x} - \sigma$ to $\bar{x} + \sigma$! I know of no statistics text that uses that method, and I hope that such graphing calculators are no longer manufactured (or used).

# Chapter 1 Solutions

**1.1.** **(a)** The individuals are vehicles (or "cars"). **(b)** The variables are make/model (categorical), vehicle type (categorical), transmission type (categorical), number of cylinders (quantitative), city mpg (quantitative), and highway mpg (quantitative).

**1.2.** Possible categorical variables: year in school, gender, major. Possible quantitative variables: age (years), time watching TV (hours), time in class (hours), time sleeping (hours), time studying (hours—or perhaps minutes).

**1.3.** **(a)** The given percentages add up to 90%, so 10% must be some other color. **(b)** The bar graph shown does not include the "other" category, although it certainly could be included. With the "other" category, a pie chart could be used because these percentages show parts of a whole (if we assume, as we did in part (a), that a car can be only one color).

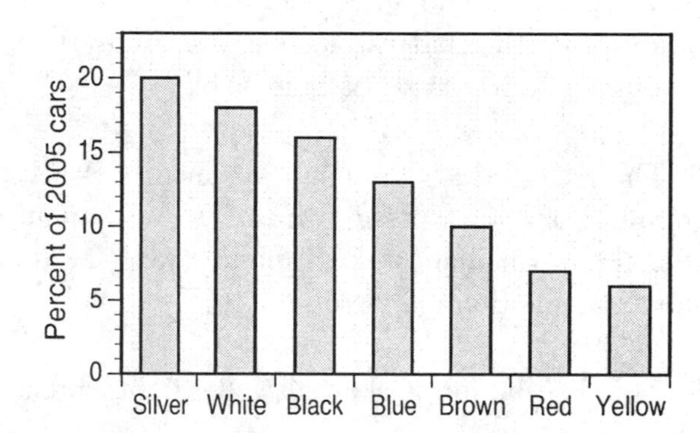


**1.4.** A pie graph could also be made, but the relative heights of the bars are easier to compare than the relative sizes of the "slices" of the pie.

The most likely explanation for the lower weekend numbers is that, when a birth is "planned" (either by inducement or cesarean section), it is usually scheduled for a weekday—perhaps more due to the preferences of the physician or midwife.

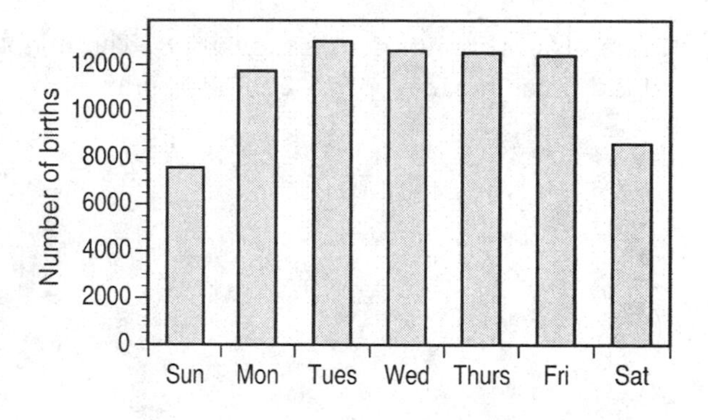


**1.5.** In order to know what percent of owners of portable MP3 players are 18 to 24 years old, we would need to know two things: the number of people who own MP3 players, and the number of those owners in that age group. The Arbitron data tells us neither of those things.

**1.6.** With the intervals 15–16.9, 17–18.9, etc., the histogram should look like the one on the right. When asked to make intervals that are 2 minutes wide, some students might use 15–17, 17–19, etc., which causes confusion about where to place the three states (Illinois, Oregon, and South Carolina) that fall on an interval boundary. If a student's histogram looks different from this one, that may be the reason.

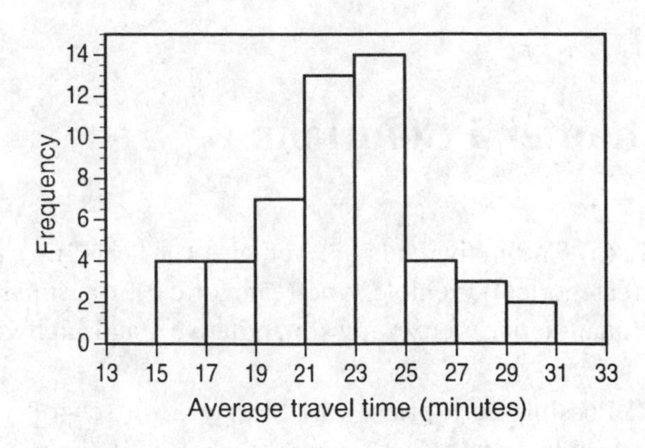


**1.7.** **(a)** The applet creates a histogram with 23 classes. **(b)** It is possible to get to one class ranging from 17 to 44.30 (not a very useful histogram). **(c)** The most classes the applet will allow is 46; the largest classes have 5 observations. **(d)** Choices will vary; anything from about 10 to 30 classes is reasonable.

**1.8.** The distribution is roughly symmetric. Based on the histogram, the center is near 23 minutes, and the spread is from 15 to 31 minutes. If we look at the actual data, we find that the center (median) is 22.7 minutes, and the times range from 15.2 to 30.4 minutes. See also the solution to Exercise 1.10.

**1.9.** The distribution is skewed to the right, spread from 0% to 30%. The midpoint lies in the 5%–10% class.

**1.10.** See also the solution to Exercise 1.8. The midpoint is 22.7 minutes, and the times range from 15.2 to 30.4 minutes.

| Stem | Leaves |
|---|---|
| 15 | 24 |
| 16 | 59 |
| 17 | 55 |
| 18 | 19 |
| 19 | 14579 |
| 20 | 34 |
| 21 | 026788 |
| 22 | 1156779 |
| 23 | 023344678 |
| 24 | 56788 |
| 25 | 8 |
| 26 | 015 |
| 27 | 0 |
| 28 | 45 |
| 29 | |
| 30 | 24 |

**1.11.** Shown are two versions of this stemplot. For the first, we have (as the text suggests) rounded to the nearest 10; for the second, we have trimmed numbers (dropped the last digit). 359 mg/dl appears to be an outlier. The stemplot seems to be slightly right-skewed (even if we ignore the outlier). Overall, glucose levels are not under control: Only 4 of the 18 had levels in the desired range.

| Stem | Leaves |
|---|---|
| 0 | 8 |
| 1 | 000134 |
| 1 | 5555677 |
| 2 | 0 |
| 2 | 67 |
| 3 | |
| 3 | 6 |

| Stem | Leaves |
|---|---|
| 0 | 799 |
| 1 | 0134444 |
| 1 | 5577 |
| 2 | 0 |
| 2 | 57 |
| 3 | |
| 3 | 5 |

**1.12.** **(a)** On the right. **(b)** After adjusting for inflation, tuition and fees have increased fairly steadily, apart from a slight dip in the late 1970s. **(c)** There are no outliers in the plot. As noted in (b), charges decreased at the beginning of this time period. Since the year 2000, the rate of increase seems to have risen.

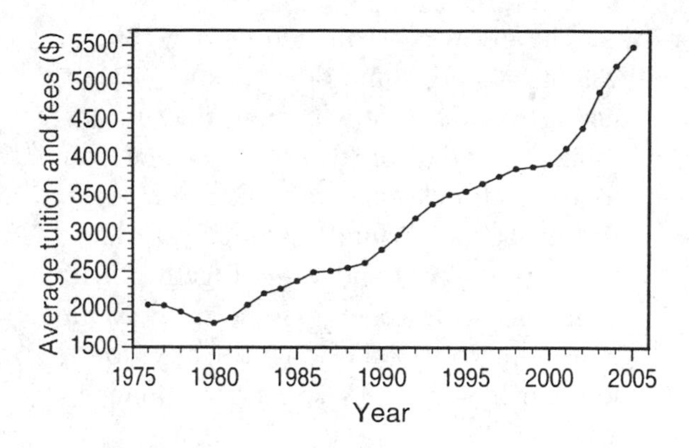


**1.13.** (a) The individuals are the students.

**1.14.** (c) Either a pie chart or a bar graph would be appropriate.

**1.15.** (c) Sex is a categorical variable, and college debt is a quantitative variable.

**1.16.** (c) There are 7 colleges in the leftmost (lowest-cost) class.

**1.17.** (b) The leftmost class is for costs from about $4000 to $7000.

**1.18.** (b) The stems should be the first two digits.

**1.19.** (b) The highest percent is 17.6% (a stem of 17, with leaf 0.6).

**1.20.** (c) The distribution is slightly left-skewed.

**1.21.** (a) The 25th and 26th percents are 12.7% and 12.8%.

**1.22.** (c) These housing prices are (fairly sharply) right-skewed.

**1.23.** **(a)** Type of wood is categorical. **(b)** Type of water repellent is categorical. **(c)** Paint thickness is quantitative. **(d)** Paint color is categorical. **(e)** Weathering time is quantitative.

**1.24.** **(a)** The individuals are baseball players. **(b)** There are six variables: team, position, age, height, weight, salary. The first two are categorical, and the last four of these are quantitative. **(c)** Age is given in years, height in feet and inches, weight in pounds, and salary in dollars per year.

**1.25.** The given percents add up to 93%, so 7% of cars are some other color. (Actually, taking rounding into account, the true percent might be higher or lower—anywhere from 4% to 10%.) Black appears to be more popular in Europe, and white less popular (although if we group gray and white together, that difference is lessened). Some fairly common colors in North America (brown, yellow, red) are considerably less common in Europe.

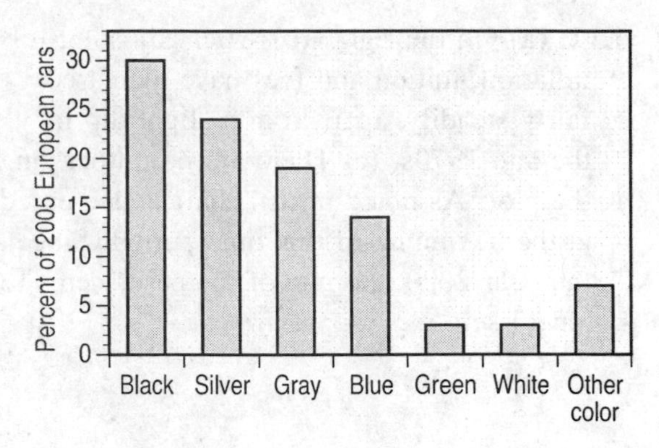


**1.26.** **(a)** Shown on the right. **(b)** In order to make a pie chart, we would need to know the total number of deaths in this age group (so that we could compute the number of deaths due to other causes).

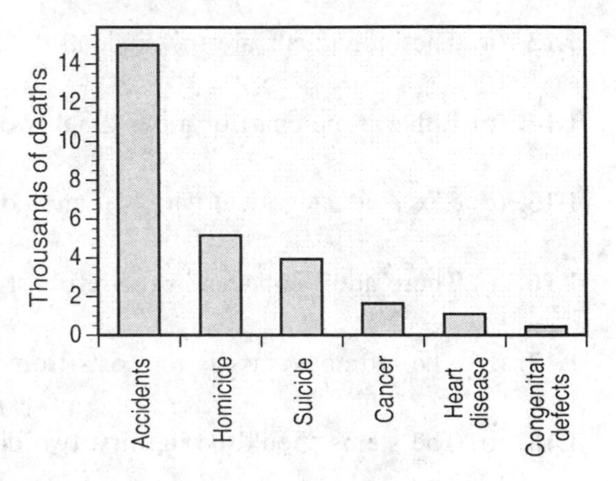


**1.27.** Approximately 60% Mexican and 10% Puerto Rican. (Of course, student answers may vary, but because this is an odd-numbered exercise, most will likely give this answer from the back of the textbook. Enterprising students might go to the Census Bureau website to discover the actual reported numbers, which were 58% and 9.6%, respectively.)

**1.28.** **(a)** Movie attendance decreases steadily with age. **(b)** No: For a pie chart, we would need to know what fraction of all moviegoers were in each age range, rather than what fraction of each age range goes to the movies. **(c)** In order to know what percent of the movie audience is 18 to 24 years old, we would need to know two things: the number of people who go to the movies, and the number of moviegoers in that age group. We know neither of these things.

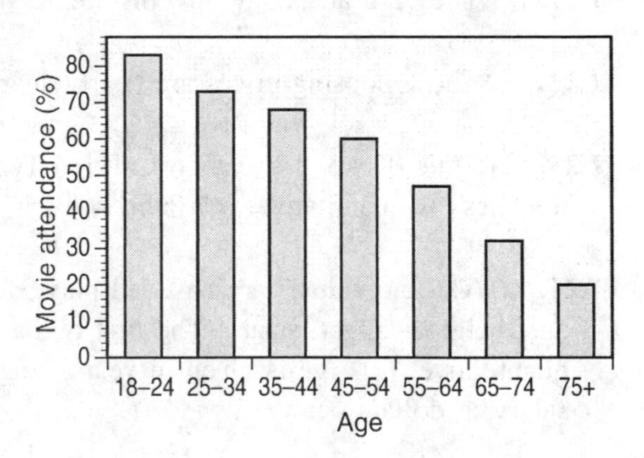

**1.29.** The two bar graphs are shown below.

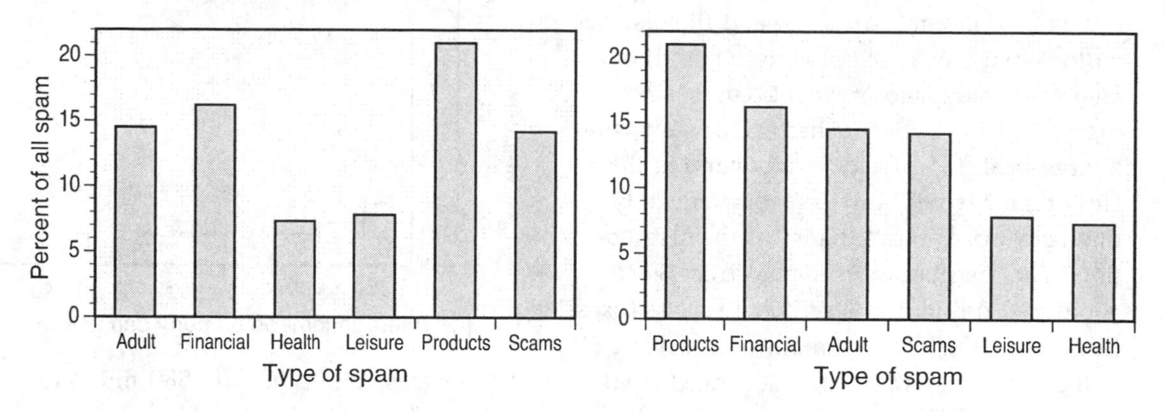


**1.30.** The distribution is skewed to the right, spread from 0 to 8 servings, and the center is about 2 or 3 servings of fruit. (The median number of servings is 2, but student judgments of the "center" may vary from the median.) About 35% (26 out of 74) ate 0 or 1 ("fewer than 2") servings of fruit.

**1.31.** **(a)** The distribution is slightly skewed to the left, although not strikingly so if one ignores the low outlier. **(b)** The center is between 0% and 2%; student estimates will vary. **(c)** The lowest return (ignoring the outlier) was between −16% and −14%, and the highest was between 12% and 14%. **(d)** About 37% of these months (91 out of 243) had negative returns. Student estimates of the count may vary, but the percentage should be roughly 35–40% in every case.

**Note:** *By examining the raw data, we find that the median return was 1.23%, the minimum return (apart from the outlier) was −15.99%, and the largest return was 12.5%. This data is in the first column of the file "Fama/French Benchmark Factors(Monthly)" found at*

`http://mba.tuck.dartmouth.edu/pages/faculty/ken.french/data_library.html`

**1.32.** **(a)** is variable 4. Minutes spent studying would likely be skewed to the right (many study for a short time, a few study longer).

**(b)** is variable 2, and **(c)** is variable 1—unless this was a particularly unusual class! We would expect that male/female counts should be somewhat close, while right-handed students should outnumber lefties substantially. (Roughly 10% to 15% of the population as a whole is left-handed.)

**(d)** is variable 3. One would expect a fair amount of variation in student heights, but no particular skewness to such a distribution.

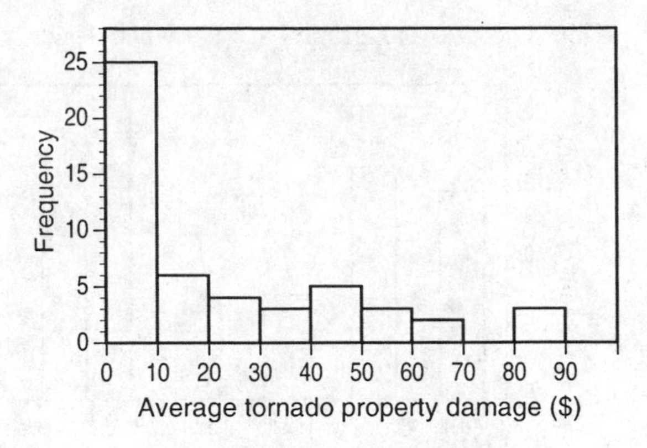


**1.33. (a)** The top five states are Texas, Minnesota, Oklahoma, Missouri, and Illinois. The bottom five are Alaska, Puerto Rico, Rhode Island, Nevada, and Vermont. **(b)** The histogram (right) shows a sharp right skew, with a large peak (25 of the 51 numbers) in the "less than $10 million" category; arguably, that category is the "center" of the distribution. The distribution is spread from $0 to about $90 million; the top three states (Texas, Minnesota, Oklahoma) might be considered outliers, because that bar is separated from the rest (no states fell in the $70–$80 million category). **(c)** The default histogram will vary with the software used.

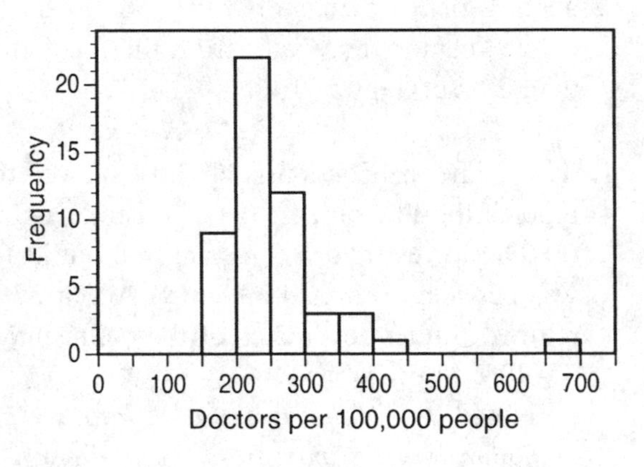


**1.34. (a)** In a state with many people, more doctors are needed to serve the larger population. For example, having 1000 doctors in Rhode Island would be very different from having 1000 doctors in California. **(b)** The distribution is clearly skewed to the right, with the District of Columbia a high outlier. The states all have numbers between 161 and 427; D.C. is different from the states in that it includes very little area that would be considered "rural," where we would expect the density of doctors would drop off considerably. (Observe that the states with large cities tend to have high numbers; D.C. is an extreme case, because it consists mainly of a large city.)

**1.35. (a)** Totals emissions would almost certainly be higher for very large countries; for example, we would expect that even with great attempts to control emissions, China (with over 1 billion people) would have higher total emissions than the smallest countries in the data set. **(b)** We see a strong right skew with a peak from 0 to 0.2 metric tons per person, and a smaller peak from 0.8 to 1. The three highest countries (the United States, Canada, and Australia) appear to be outliers; apart from those countries, the distribution is spread from 0 to 11 metric tons per person.

| Stem | Leaves |
|---|---|
| 0 | 000000000000000011111 |
| 0 | 222233333 |
| 0 | 445 |
| 0 | 6677 |
| 0 | 888999 |
| 1 | 001 |
| 1 | |
| 1 | |
| 1 | 67 |
| 1 | 9 |

**1.36.** Shown are two versions of this stemplot. For the first, we have (as the text suggests) rounded to the nearest 100; for the second, we have trimmed the numbers (dropped the last two digits). The distribution is clearly skewed to the right, with a high outlier (4700 million sole, from 1987). The center is around 700 million, and the spread is from 173 million to 4700 million (2809 million, if we omit the outlier).

| | | | |
|---|---|---|---|
| 0 | 22233444 | 0 | 12233344 |
| 0 | 5556677 | 0 | 55556679 |
| 1 | 001344 | 1 | 01244 |
| 1 | 788 | 1 | 777 |
| 2 | 24 | 2 | 24 |
| 2 | 8 | 2 | 8 |
| 3 | | 3 | |
| 3 | | 3 | |
| 4 | | 4 | |
| 4 | 7 | 4 | 7 |

**1.37.** **(a)** Not only are most responses multiples of 10; many are multiples of 30 and 60. Most people will round their answers when asked to give an estimate like this; in fact, the most striking answers are ones such as 115, 170, or 230. The students who claimed 360 minutes (6 hours) and 300 minutes (5 hours) may have been exaggerating. (Some students might also "consider suspicious" the student who claimed to study 0 minutes per night. As a teacher, I can easily believe that such students exist.) **(b)** The stemplots suggest that women (claim to) study more than men. The approximate centers are 175 minutes for women and 120 minutes for men.

| Women | | Men |
|---:|:---:|:---|
| | 0 | 033334 |
| 96 | 0 | 66679999 |
| 22222221 | 1 | 2222222 |
| 888888888875555 | 1 | 558 |
| 4440 | 2 | 00344 |
| | 2 | |
| | 3 | 0 |
| 6 | 3 | |

**1.38.** The time plot shows that the number of recruits peaked in the mid-1980s, and in recent years has fallen back to levels similar to those in the 1970s.

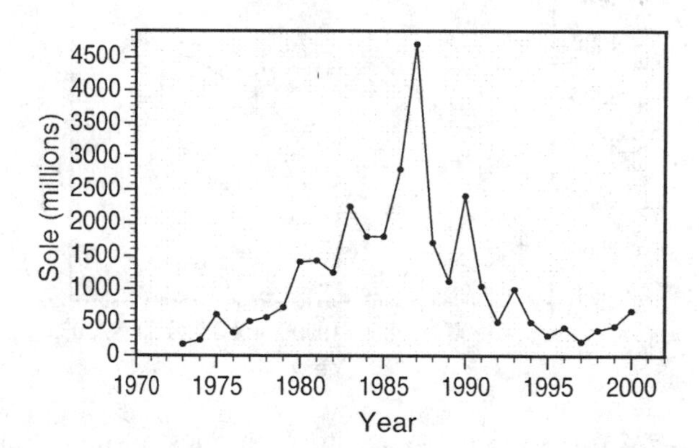


**1.39.** **(a)** If the four groups were roughly equal in size, then it would be valid to compare accident counts. However, because those who never used marijuana (or at least denied using it) accounted for about half of the group, we would expect the number of accidents for that group to be larger—and it is the largest of the four. By computing accidents per driver (e.g., $\frac{59}{452} \doteq 13\%$), we can compare the relative risks for the four unequal-sized groups. **(b)** Increasing marijuana usage is associated with increasing accident rates. (Students will not necessarily use the technical language of association or correlation, but should somehow acknowledge that when one number is high, the other is, too.)

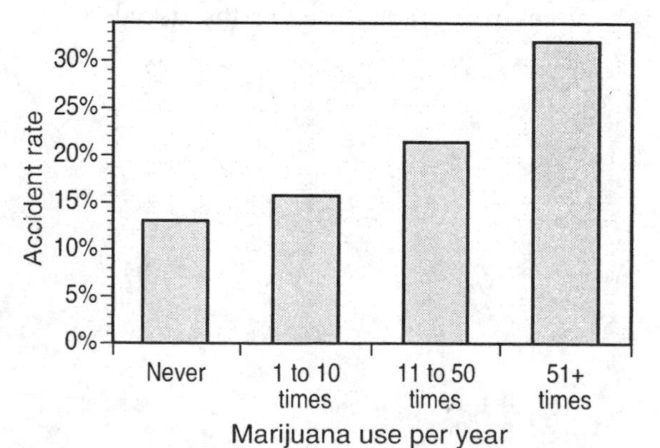

**1.40.** Sketches will vary. The distribution of coin years would be left-skewed because newer coins are more common than older coins.

**1.41.** The time plots show that both manufacturers have generally improved over this period, with one slight jump in problems in 2003. Toyota vehicles typically have fewer problems, but GM appears to have closed the gap slightly.

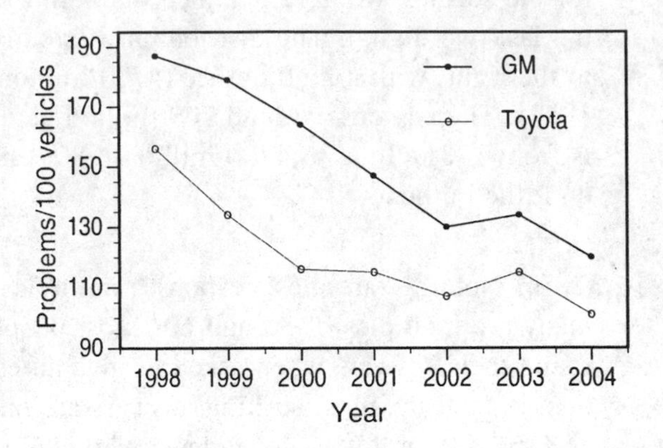


**1.42.** Here are examples that do the trick. With most software that can create such plots, it is very easy to achieve the desired effects by using the mouse to resize the plot.

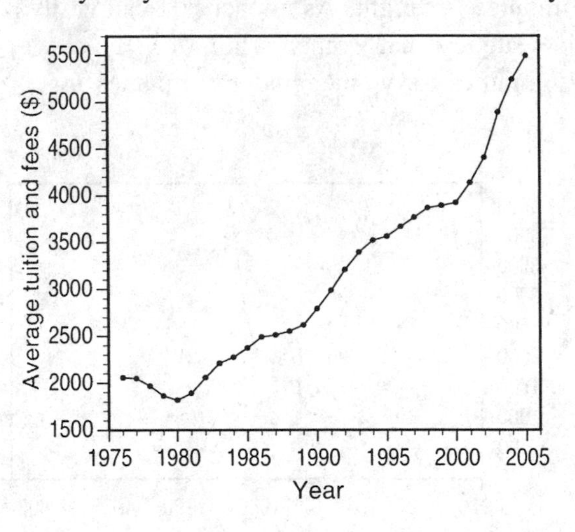


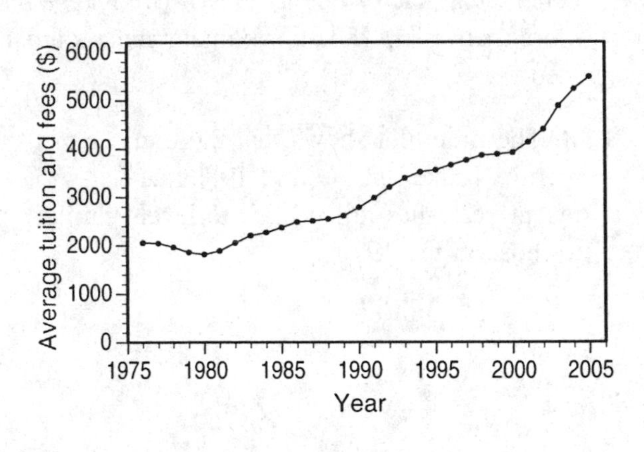


**1.43.** **(a)** Prices appear to be highest in the summer and lowest in the winter. **(b)** Overall, prices rise gradually over the decade.

**1.44.** **(a)** The histogram shows a slight skew to the right. (The exact appearance of the histogram will vary with the choice of interval width.) The middle number of attacks is 9 per year. **(b)** The time plot shows a lot of fluctuation, but clearly reveals that attacks have been generally higher in recent years. The typical number of attacks over the entire period is probably not a good indication of what to expect in the future; at least, it appears that we should exclude data from years before 1985.

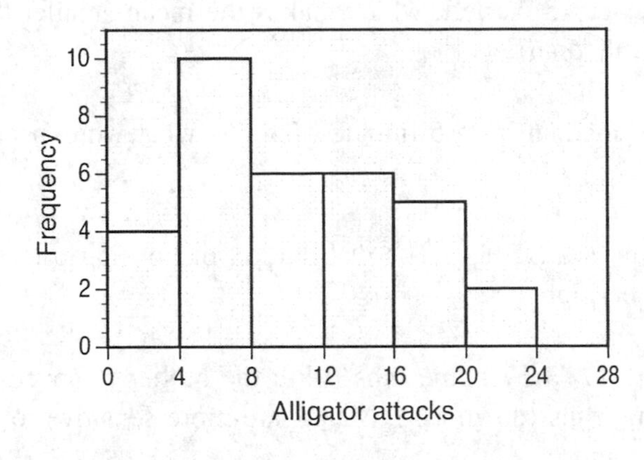


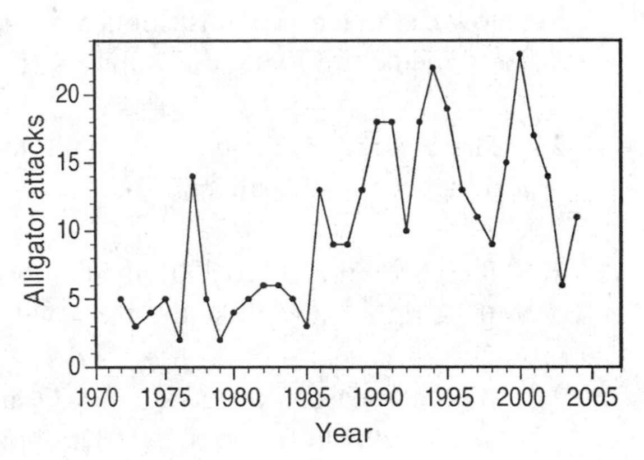


**1.45.** Both stemplots are shown below. Student preferences will vary.

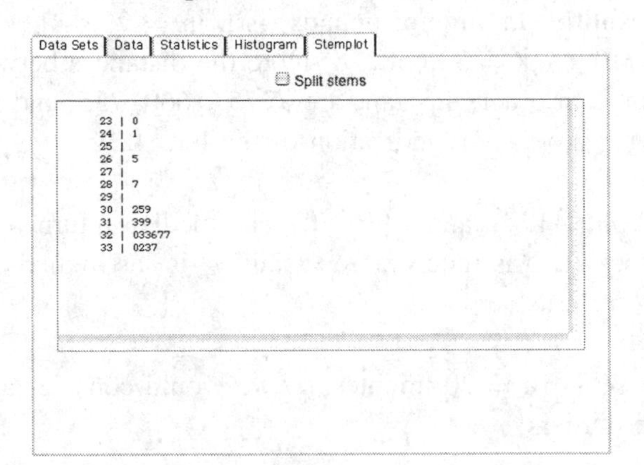


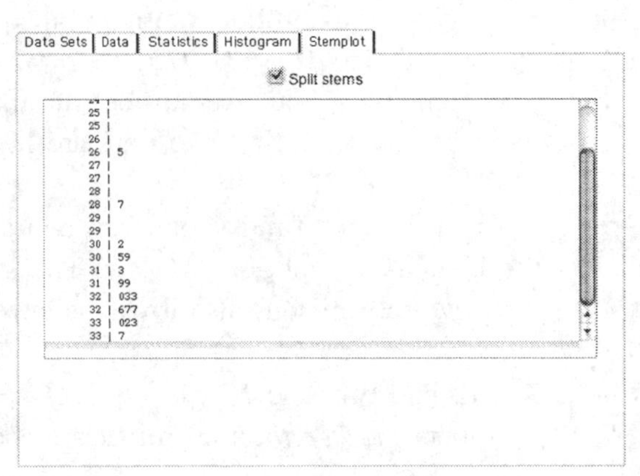

# Chapter 2 Solutions

**2.1.** The mean is $\bar{x} = 30{,}841$ pounds. Only 6 of the 20 pieces of wood had breaking strengths below the mean. The distribution is skewed to the left, which makes the mean smaller than the "middle" of the set of numbers (the median).

**2.2.** The mean is 31.25 minutes, while the median is 22.5 minutes. This is what we expect for a right-skewed distribution like this one.

**2.3.** The median is $216,200, and the mean is $265,000. The distribution of housing prices will be right-skewed, so the mean will be higher.

**2.4.** With all seasons included, $\bar{x} = 37$ and $M = 37$ home runs. With the outlier removed, $\bar{x}^* = 35$ (down 2) and $M^* = 35.5$ home runs (down 1.5). Means are more sensitive to outliers, while medians are resistant to them.

**2.5.** **(a)** The five-number summary (all quantities in units of pounds) is Min = 23,040, $Q_1 = 30{,}315$, $M = 31{,}975$, $Q_3 = 32{,}710$, Max = 33,650. **(b)** Note the distances between the numbers in the five-number summary: In order, the gaps are 7275, 1660, 735, and 940 pounds. That the first two gaps are larger gives some indication of the left skew.

**2.6.** **(a)** The stock fund varied between about −1.7% and 1.9%. **(b)** The median return for both funds was about 0.1%. **(c)** The stock fund is much more variable—it has higher positive returns, but also lower negative returns.

**2.7.** No (barely): The *IQR* is $Q_3 - Q_1 = 30 - 10 = 20$ minutes, so we would consider any numbers *greater than* 60 minutes to be outliers.

**2.8.** **(a)** The five-number summary is Min = 5.7%, $Q_1 = 11.7\%$, $M = 12.75\%$, $Q_3 = 13.5\%$, Max = 17.6%. **(b)** Yes: The *IQR* is $Q_3 - Q_1 = 13.5\% - 11.7\% = 1.8\%$, so we would consider to be outliers any numbers below $11.7\% - 2.7\% = 9\%$ or above $13.5\% + 2.7\% = 16.2\%$. Along with Florida and Alaska, Utah is an outlier (8.5% older residents).

**2.9.** **(a)** $\bar{x} = \frac{32.4}{6} = 5.4$ mg of phosphate per deciliter of blood. **(b)** The details of the computation are shown on the right. The standard deviation is $s = \sqrt{\frac{2.06}{5}} \doteq 0.6419$ mg/dl.

| $x_i$ | $x_i - \bar{x}$ | $(x_i - \bar{x})^2$ |
|---|---|---|
| 5.6 | 0.2 | 0.04 |
| 5.2 | −0.2 | 0.04 |
| 4.6 | −0.8 | 0.64 |
| 4.9 | −0.5 | 0.25 |
| 5.7 | 0.3 | 0.09 |
| 6.4 | 1 | 1 |
| 32.4 | 0 | 2.06 |

**2.10.** The means and standard deviations are basically the same: For set A, $\bar{x}_A \doteq 7.501$ and $s_A \doteq 2.032$, while for set B, $\bar{x}_B \doteq 7.501$ and $s_B \doteq 2.031$. Set A is left-skewed, while set B has a high outlier.

Set A

| Stem | Leaves |
|---|---|
| 3 | 1 |
| 4 | 7 |
| 5 | |
| 6 | 1 |
| 7 | 2 |
| 8 | 1177 |
| 9 | 112 |

Set B

| Stem | Leaves |
|---|---|
| 5 | 257 |
| 6 | 58 |
| 7 | 079 |
| 8 | 48 |
| 9 | |
| 10 | |
| 11 | |
| 12 | 5 |

**2.11.** **(a)** Not appropriate: The distribution of percents of college graduates has a high outlier. (If we can justify removing the outlier, the distribution is reasonably symmetric, so $\bar{x}$ and $s$ would be fine for the remaining data.) **(b)** $\bar{x}$ and $s$ are fine: The Iowa Test score distribution is quite symmetric and has no outliers. **(c)** Not appropriate: The wood breaking-strength distribution is strongly skewed.

**2.12. State:** How does logging affect tree count?
**Formulate:** We need to compare the distributions, including appropriate measures of center and spread.
**Solve:** Stemplots are shown below. Based on these, $\bar{x}$ and $s$ are reasonable choices; the means and standard deviations (in units of trees) are given in the table (below, right).
**Conclude:** The means and the stemplots appear to suggest that logging reduces the number of trees per plot and that recovery is slow (the 1-year-after and 8-years-after means and stemplots are similar).

Never logged

| Stem | Leaves |
|---|---|
| 0 | |
| 0 | |
| 1 | |
| 1 | 699 |
| 2 | 0124 |
| 2 | 7789 |
| 3 | 3 |

1 year earlier

| Stem | Leaves |
|---|---|
| 0 | 2 |
| 0 | 9 |
| 1 | 2244 |
| 1 | 57789 |
| 2 | 0 |
| 2 | |
| 3 | |

8 years earlier

| Stem | Leaves |
|---|---|
| 0 | 4 |
| 0 | |
| 1 | 22 |
| 1 | 5889 |
| 2 | 22 |
| 2 | |
| 3 | |

| Group | $\bar{x}$ | $s$ |
|---|---|---|
| 1 | 23.7500 | 5.06548 |
| 2 | 14.0833 | 4.98102 |
| 3 | 15.7778 | 5.76146 |

**2.13.** (a) The mean is $\bar{x} = 122.9$.

**2.14.** (b) The median is 123.5.

**2.15.** (c) The five-number summary is 96, 118, 123.5, 130, 145.

**2.16.** (c) The mean is pulled in the direction of the skew.

**2.17.** (b) Half the observations lie between the quartiles.

**2.18.** (c) A boxplot is a picture of the five-number summary.

**2.19.** (b) The standard deviation is $s \doteq 13.95$.

**2.20.** (a) Standard deviations can be any nonnegative number.

**2.21.** (b) $s$ is measured in the same units as the data.

**2.22.** (a) The median is resistant to outliers.

**2.23.** The median is \$42,087 and the mean is \$53,581: Income distributions will be skewed to the right, so the mean will be larger.

**2.24.** The distribution of household net worth would almost surely be strongly skewed to the right, perhaps more so for young households: A few would have earned (or inherited) substantial assets, but most have not had time to accumulate very much wealth. This strong skew pulls the mean to be higher than the median.

**2.25.** **(a)** The mean will be greater than the median because of the right skew. We find that $\bar{x} = 251.9$ and $M = 236$ doctors per 100,000 people. **(b)** Outliers have a greater effect on the mean, so removing D.C. should change $\bar{x}$ more than $M$. Indeed, we find that $\bar{x}^* = 243.26$ and $M^* = 234.5$ doctors per 100,000 people—$\bar{x}$ decreased by about 8.6 while the median changed by 1.5.

**2.26.** **(a)** The mean (green arrow) moves along with the moving point (in fact, it moves in the same direction as the moving point, at one-third the speed). At the same time, as long as the moving point remains to the right of the other two, the median (red arrow) points to the middle point (the rightmost nonmoving point). **(b)** The mean follows the moving point as before. When the moving point passes the rightmost fixed point, the median slides along with it until the moving point passes the leftmost fixed point, then the median stays there.

**2.27.** The five-number summaries (all in millimeters) are

| | Min | $Q_1$ | $M$ | $Q_3$ | Max |
|---|---|---|---|---|---|
| *bihai* | 46.34 | 46.71 | 47.12 | 48.245 | 50.26 |
| red | 37.40 | 38.07 | 39.16 | 41.69 | 43.09 |
| yellow | 34.57 | 35.45 | 36.11 | 36.82 | 38.13 |

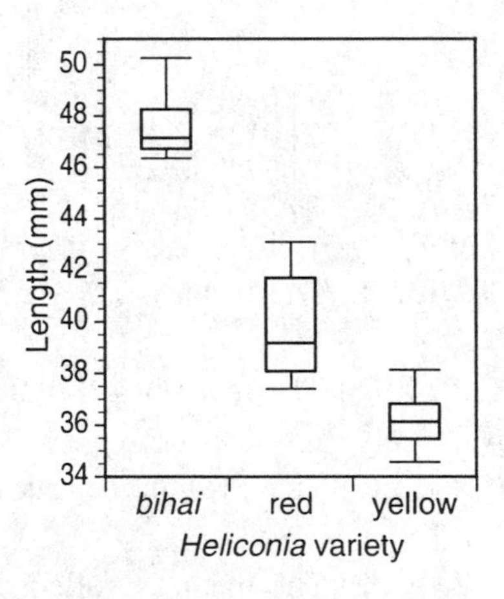


Although we lose the detail of the individual measurements visible in the stemplots, we can draw essentially the same conclusions: *H. bihai* is clearly the tallest variety—the shortest *bihai* was more than 3 mm taller than the tallest red. Red is generally taller than yellow, with a few exceptions. Another noteworthy fact: The red variety is more variable than either of the other varieties.

**2.28.** The median is at position $\frac{741+1}{2} = 371$, $Q_1$ is at position $\frac{370+1}{2} = 185.5$ (the average of the 185th and 186th values), and $Q_3$ is at position $371 + 185.5 = 556.5$ (the average of the 556th and 557th values).

**2.29.** $M = 2$, $Q_1 = 1$, and $Q_3 = 4$ servings: We can use the frequencies shown in the histogram to reconstruct the (sorted) data list; it begins with 15 zeros, then 11 ones, etc. The median is halfway between the 37th and 38th numbers in this list; because the 27th through 41st numbers in the list are all "2," that is the median. The first quartile is the 19th number in the list, and $Q_3$ is the 56th number.

**2.30.** **(a)** The total number of births in a year will vary greatly from one country to another; it would be difficult to compare counts for a small country with those of a large country. **(b)** There were 4,018,734 total births recorded in the table; divide each count by this number to compute the percents. **(c)** The positions and weight classes are given in the table below.

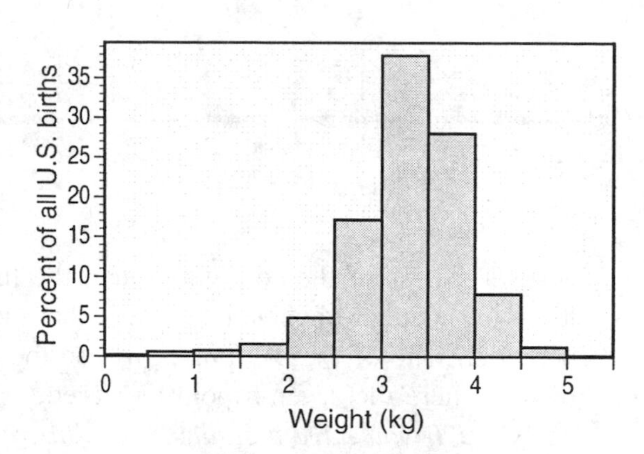


| Measurement | Position | Weight class |
|---|---|---|
| Median | $\frac{4{,}018{,}734 + 1}{2} = 2{,}009{,}362.5$ | 3,000 to 3,499 grams |
| $Q_1$ | $\frac{2{,}009{,}362 + 1}{2} = 1{,}004{,}681.5$ | 3,000 to 3,499 grams |
| $Q_3$ | $2{,}009{,}362 + 1{,}004{,}681.5 = 3{,}014{,}043.5$ | 3,500 to 3,999 grams |

**2.31.** **(a)** $\bar{x}$ and $s$ are appropriate for symmetric distributions with no outliers. **(b)** The table on the right shows the effect of removing these outliers.

| | Women | | Men | |
|---|---|---|---|---|
| | $\bar{x}$ | $s$ | $\bar{x}$ | $s$ |
| Before | 165.2 | 56.5 | 117.2 | 74.2 |
| After | 158.4 | 43.7 | 110.9 | 66.9 |

**2.32.** **(a)** There are several different answers, depending on the configuration of the first five points. *Most students* will likely assume that the first five points should be distinct (no repeats), in which case the sixth point *must* be placed at the median. This is because the median of 5 (sorted) points is the third, while the median of 6 points is the average of the third and fourth. If these are to be the same, the third and fourth points of the set of 6 must both equal the third point of the set of 5.

The diagram below illustrates all of the possibilities; in each case, the arrow shows the location of the median of the initial five points, and the shaded region (or dot) on the line indicates where the sixth point can be placed without changing the median. Notice that there are four cases where the median does not change regardless of the location of the sixth point. (The points need not be equally spaced; these diagrams were drawn that way for convenience.)

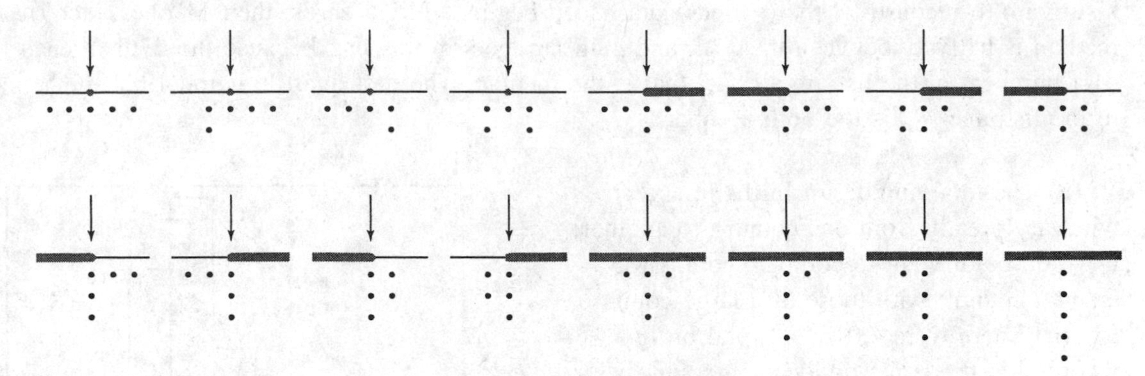

**(b)** Regardless of the configuration of the first 5 points, if the sixth point is added so as to leave the median unchanged, then in that (sorted) set of 6, the third and fourth points must be equal. One of these 2 points will be the middle (fourth) point of the (sorted) set of 7, no matter where the seventh point is placed.

**Note:** *If you have a student who illustrates all possible cases above, then it is likely that the student (1) obtained a copy of this solutions manual, (2) should consider a career in writing solutions manuals, (3) has too much time on his or her hands, or (4) both 2 and 3 (and perhaps 1) are true.*

**2.33. (a)** The five-number summaries (all measured in pounds) for the six groups are:

| | Min | $Q_1$ | $M$ | $Q_3$ | Max; |
|---|---|---|---|---|---|
| RB | 185 | 199.5 | 215.5 | 221 | 235 |
| WR | 154 | 168 | 183 | 199 | 215 |
| OL | 254 | 283.5 | 291 | 317.5 | 337 |
| DL | 230 | 240 | 264 | 285.5 | 301 |
| LB | 199 | 214 | 221 | 233.5 | 237 |
| DB | 177 | 184 | 188 | 195 | 201 |

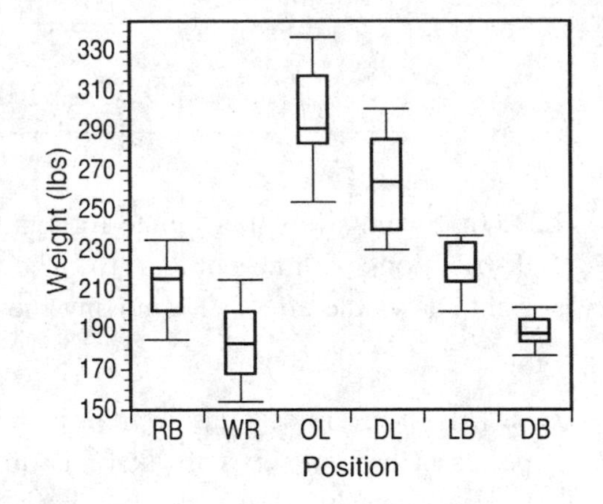


**(b)** Not surprisingly, offensive linemen are generally the heaviest, followed by defensive linemen. Running backs and linebackers are similar in center (though not as much in spread), as are wide receivers and defensive backs. The latter two groups are typically the lightest players.
**(c)** There are no striking outliers (none qualify using the $1.5 \times IQR$ criterion).

**2.34.** **(a)** A stemplot is shown; a histogram would also be appropriate. The expected right skew is clearly evident; the split stems emphasize the skewness by showing the gaps. The main peak occurs from 50 to 150 days—the guinea pigs that lived more than 500 days seem to be outliers. **(b)** Because of the skew, choose the five-number summary:

43  82.5  102.5  151.5  598

(all measured in days). The difference between $Q_3$ and the maximum is relatively much larger than the other differences between successive numbers. This indicates a large spread among the high observations—that is, it shows that the data are skewed to the right.

| Stem | Leaves |
|---|---|
| 0 | 44 |
| 0 | 5555566777888888888889999999 |
| 1 | 00000000000111222223333444 |
| 1 | 56777899 |
| 2 | 1144 |
| 2 | |
| 3 | 2 |
| 3 | 8 |
| 4 | 0 |
| 4 | |
| 5 | 12 |
| 5 | 9 |

**2.35.** Student observations will vary. Clearly, Saturday and Sunday are quite similar and considerably lower than other days. Among weekdays, Monday births are least likely, and Tuesday and Friday are also very similar. One might also note that the *total* number of births on a given day (over the course of the year) would be the sum of the 52 or so numbers that went into each boxplot. We could use this fact to come up with a rough estimate of the totals for each day, and observe that, like the U.S. figures (from Exercise 1.4), Monday appears to have the smallest number of births (after Saturday and Sunday).

**2.36.** **State:** Is bone mineral loss greater among the breast-feeding women?
**Formulate:** We need to compare the distributions, including appropriate measures of center and spread.
**Solve:** Shown are two stemplots; it would also be appropriate to produce two histograms, a back-to-back stemplot (see the solution to Exercise 1.37), or two boxplots (five-number summaries are given below). Note that for negative stems, the leaves appear to be in "reverse" order, so that they increase from left to right like the leaves on the positive stems. Students who create stemplots by hand might not consider this issue.

| BF women | | Other women | |
|---|---|---|---|
| −8 | 3 | −8 | |
| −7 | 80 | −7 | |
| −6 | 88552 | −6 | |
| −5 | 97633221 | −5 | |
| −4 | 9977430 | −4 | |
| −3 | 86310 | −3 | |
| −2 | 755322110 | −2 | 2 |
| −1 | 800 | −1 | 65 |
| −0 | 83 | −0 | 64442111 |
| 0 | 234 | 0 | 0379 |
| 1 | 7 | 1 | 0127 |
| 2 | 2 | 2 | 249 |

Here are numerical summaries; students may give all or just some of these in response to this question.

| | $\bar{x}$ | Min | $Q_1$ | $M$ | $Q_3$ | Max |
|---|---|---|---|---|---|---|
| BF women | −3.59% | −8.3% | −5.3% | −3.8% | −2.1% | 2.2% |
| Other women | 0.31% | −2.2% | −0.4% | −0.05% | 1.1% | 2.9% |

**Conclude:** Both the graphs and the numerical summaries suggest that breast-feeding women lose calcium.

**2.37. State:** How does increasing compression affect soil penetrability?
**Formulate:** We need to compare the distributions, including appropriate measures of center and spread.
**Solve:** Shown are three stemplots; it would also be appropriate to produce histograms or boxplots (five-number summaries are given below).

```
Compressed        Intermediate      Loose
2 | 67777         2 |               2 |
2 | 8888899999    2 | 99            2 |
3 | 00011         3 | 0111111       3 |
                  3 | 2333          3 |
                  3 | 4445          3 |
                  3 | 6             3 |
                  3 | 8             3 | 9999
                  4 |               4 | 0011111
                  4 | 2             4 | 22233
                                    4 | 44
                                    4 |
                                    4 | 89
```

Here are numerical summaries; students may give all or just some of these in response to this question. The slight skew evident in the "Intermediate" stemplot makes the five-number summary preferable, but note that the mean and median for that group are nearly identical.

| | $\bar{x}$ | Min | $Q_1$ | $M$ | $Q_3$ | Max |
|---|---|---|---|---|---|---|
| Compressed | 2.9075 | 2.68 | 2.795 | 2.880 | 2.99 | 3.18 |
| Intermediate | 3.3360 | 2.92 | 3.130 | 3.310 | 3.45 | 4.26 |
| Loose | 4.2315 | 3.94 | 4.015 | 4.175 | 4.32 | 4.91 |

**Conclude:** Both the graphs and the numerical summaries suggest that soil penetrability is greatest for loose soil and least for compressed soil.

**2.38.** A stemplot is shown; a histogram would also be appropriate. Because the distribution is clearly skewed to the right and has possible outliers, we should report the five-number summary rather than $\bar{x}$ and $s$:

$316,000 $1,500,000 $3,250,000 $7,500,000 $19,806,820.

While they are poor choices for this distribution, some students might compute the mean and standard deviation: $\bar{x} = \$4,632,344$ and $s = \$4,589,390$. Note that by the 1.5 × *IQR* criterion, Ramirez's salary is an outlier, but Schilling's is not. (The question of outliers is also asked in Exercise 2.46.)

```
0 | 000000111
0 | 222333
0 | 445
0 | 677
0 | 888
1 |
1 |
1 | 4
1 |
1 | 9
```

**2.39. State:** How have real returns on stocks behaved over the years?
**Formulate:** We should examine the distribution through graphs and numerical summaries. Because this is a variable that changes over time, we should also look at a time plot.
**Solve:** A stemplot and time plot are shown below. Because the stemplot appears to be somewhat skewed to the left, the five-number summary is preferred, but some students may compute the mean and standard deviation:

| $\bar{x}$ | $s$ | Min | $Q_1$ | $M$ | $Q_3$ | Max |
|---|---|---|---|---|---|---|
| 7.92% | 17.76% | −34.54% | −5.4715% | 11.677% | 22.4145% | 34.167% |

**Conclude:** The time plot shows no particular pattern. From the stemplot and the summary statistics, we see that returns have typically been positive (in 23 of the 33 years listed), but the wide fluctuations are an indication of the risk involved for short-term investing.

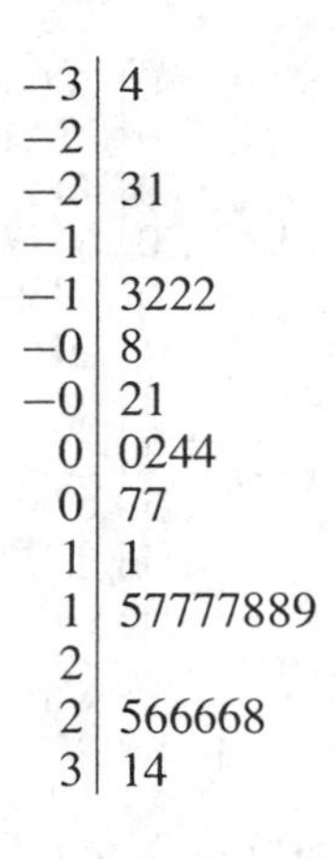


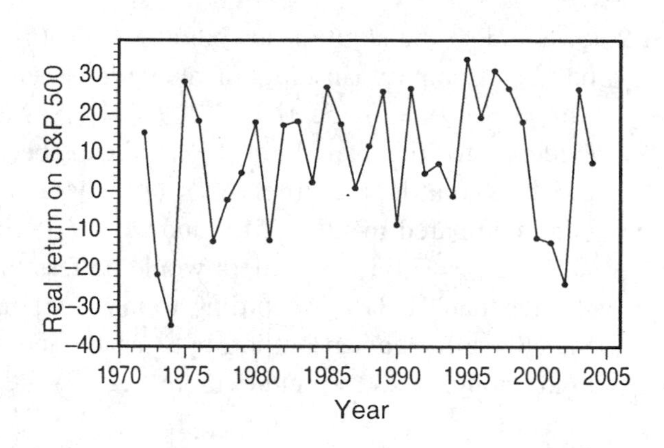


**2.40.** **(a)** One possible answer is 1, 1, 1, 1. **(b)** 0, 0, 10, 10. **(c)** For (a), any set of four identical numbers will have $s = 0$. For (b), the answer is unique; here is a rough description of why. We want to maximize the "spread-out-ness" of the numbers (which is what standard deviation measures), so 0 and 10 seem to be reasonable choices based on that idea. We also want to make each individual squared deviation—$(x_1 - \bar{x})^2$, $(x_2 - \bar{x})^2$, $(x_3 - \bar{x})^2$, and $(x_4 - \bar{x})^2$—as large as possible. If we choose 0, 10, 10, 10—or 10, 0, 0, 0—we make the first squared deviation $7.5^2$, but the other three are only $2.5^2$. Our best choice is two at each extreme, which makes all four squared deviations equal to $5^2$.

**2.41.** Answers will vary. Typical calculators will carry only about 12 to 15 digits; for example, a TI-83 fails (gives $s = 0$) for 13-digit numbers. *Excel* (at least the version I checked) gives $s = 0$ for nine-digit numbers. The (old) version of Minitab used to prepare these answers fails at 100,000,001 (nine digits).

**2.42.** Because the mean is to be 7, the five numbers must add to 35. Also, the third number (in order from smallest to largest) must be 10 because that is the median. Beyond that, there is some freedom in how the numbers are chosen.

**Note:** *It is likely that most students will interpret "positive numbers" as meaning positive integers only, which leads to eight possible solutions, shown below.*

| | | | |
|---|---|---|---|
| 1 1 10 10 13 | 1 1 10 11 12 | 1 2 10 10 12 | 1 2 10 11 11 |
| 1 3 10 10 11 | 1 4 10 10 10 | 2 2 10 10 11 | 2 3 10 10 10 |

**2.43.** The simplest approach is to take (at least) 6 numbers; call them (in increasing order) $a, b, c, d, e, f$. For this set, $Q_3 = e$; we can cause the mean to be larger than $e$ simply by choosing $f$ to be *much* larger than $e$. For example, if all numbers are nonnegative, $f > 5e$ would accomplish the goal because then $\bar{x} = (a + b + c + d + e + f)/6 > (e + f)/6 > (e + 5e)/6 = e$.

**2.44.** **(a)** The five-number summary (in 1999 dollars) is Min = 0, $Q_1 = 2.14$, $M = 10.64$, $Q_3 = 40.96$, Max = 88.6. The evidence for the skew is in the large gaps between the higher numbers; that is, the differences $Q_3 - M$ and Max $- Q_3$ are large compared to $Q_1$ − Min and $M - Q_1$. **(b)** $IQR = Q_3 - Q_1 = 38.82$, so outliers would be less than −56.09 or greater than 99.19. **(c)** The mean is 21.95 (1999 dollars), much greater than the median 10.64. The mean is pulled in the direction of the skew—in this case, to the right, making it larger.

**2.45.** See also the solution to Exercise 1.35. **(a)** The five-number summary (in units of metric tons per person) is Min = 0, $Q_1 = 0.75$, $M = 3.2$, $Q_3 = 7.8$, Max = 19.9. The evidence for the skew is in the large gaps between the higher numbers; that is, the differences $Q_3 - M$ and Max $- Q_3$ are large compared to $Q_1$ − Min and $M - Q_1$. **(b)** The *IQR* is $Q_3 - Q_1 = 7.05$, so outliers would be less than −9.825 or greater than 18.375. According to this rule, only the United States qualifies as an outlier, but Canada and Australia seem high enough also to include them.

| | |
|---|---|
| 0 | 0000000000000011111 |
| 0 | 222233333 |
| 0 | 445 |
| 0 | 6677 |
| 0 | 888999 |
| 1 | 001 |
| 1 | |
| 1 | |
| 1 | 67 |
| 1 | 9 |

**2.46.** See also the solution to Exercise 2.38. We find $Q_1$ = \$1,500,000 and $Q_3$ = \$7,500,000, so *IQR* = \$6 million, and outliers are those salaries above \$16,500,000. Based on that rule, only Ramirez's salary is an outlier.

**2.47.** See also the solution to Exercise 2.39. We find $Q_1 = -5.4715\%$ and $Q_3 = 22.4145\%$, so $IQR = 27.886\%$ and $1.5 \times IQR = 41.829\%$. None of the returns would be considered outliers by this rule, because all of them fall in the range $Q_1 - 1.5 \times IQR = -47.3005\%$ to $Q_3 + 1.5 \times IQR = 64.2435\%$.

# Chapter 3 Solutions

**3.1.** Sketches will vary. Use them to confirm that students understand the meaning of (a) symmetric and (b) skewed to the left.

**3.2.** **(a)** The density curve forms a $1 \times 1$ square, which has area 1. **(b)** 20% (the region is a rectangle with height 1 and base width 0.2; hence the area is 0.2). **(c)** 60% (a $1 \times 0.6$ rectangle). **(d)** 50% (a $1 \times 0.5$ rectangle).

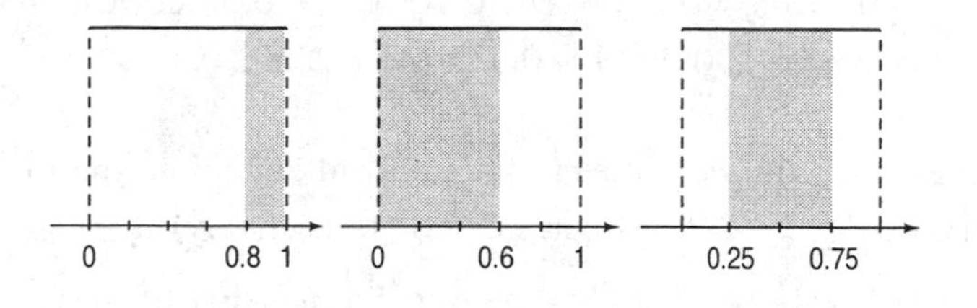


**3.3.** $\mu = 0.5$—the obvious balance point of the square. The median is also 0.5 because the distribution is symmetric (so that median = mean) and because half of the area lies to the left and half to the right of 0.5.

**3.4.** **(a)** Mean is C, median is B (the right skew pulls the mean to the right). **(b)** Mean B, median B (this distribution is symmetric). **(c)** Mean A, median B (the left skew pulls the mean to the left).

**3.5.** Students may at first make mistakes such as drawing a half-circle instead of the correct "bell-shaped" curve, or being careless about locating the change-of-curvature (inflection) point.

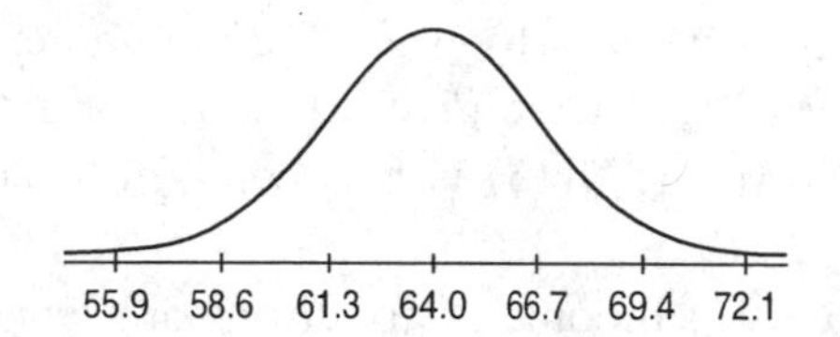


**3.6.** Refer to the sketch in the solution to the previous exercise. **(a)** $64 \pm 2(2.7) = 58.6$ to 69.4 inches. **(b)** 84% (50% plus half of 68%).

**3.7.** **(a)** Within 3 standard deviations of the mean: $266 \pm 3(16)$, or 218 to 314 days. **(b)** Shorter than 234 days (more than 2 standard deviations below the mean).

**Note:** *This exercise did not ask for a sketch of the Normal curve, but students should be encouraged to make such sketches anyway.*

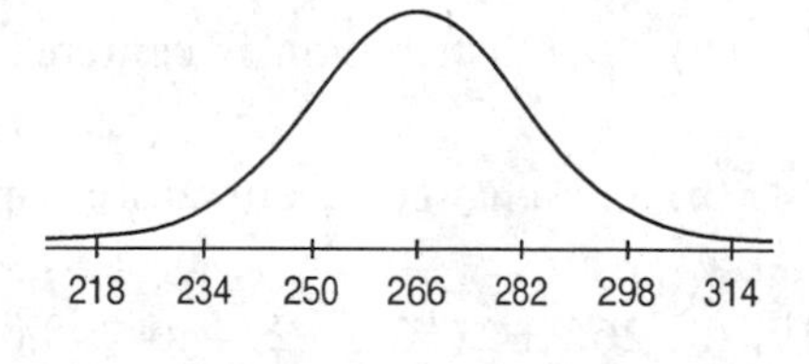


**3.8.** Eleanor's standardized score is $z = \frac{680-518}{114} \doteq 1.42$, and Gerald's standardized score is $z = \frac{27-20.7}{5.0} = 1.26$. Eleanor's score is higher.

**3.9.** The $z$-scores are $z_w = \frac{72-64}{2.7} \doteq 2.96$ for women and $z_m = \frac{72-69.3}{2.8} \doteq 0.96$ for men. The $z$-scores tell us that 6 feet is quite tall for a woman, but not at all extraordinary for a man.

**3.10.** **(a)** 0.9978. **(b)** 0.0022. **(c)** 0.9515. **(d)** $0.9515 - 0.0022 = 0.9493$.

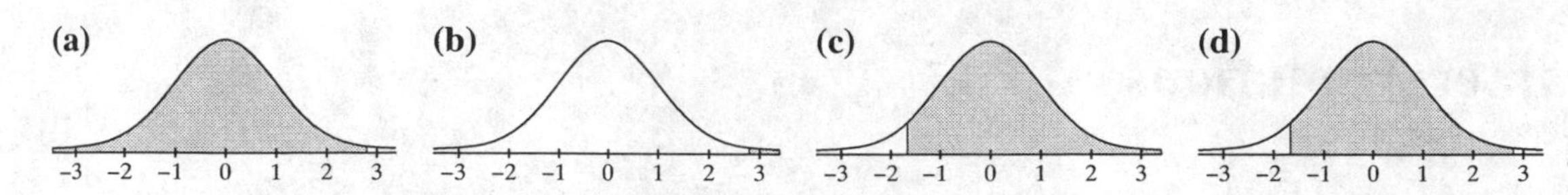


**3.11.** **(a)** $x > 0.40$ corresponds to $z > \frac{0.40-0.37}{0.04} = 0.75$, for which Table A gives $1 - 0.7734 = 0.2266$. **(b)** $0.40 < x < 0.50$ corresponds to $0.75 < z < \frac{0.50-0.37}{0.04} = 3.25$; this proportion is $0.9994 - 0.7734 = 0.2260$.

**3.12.** With the new mean and standard deviation, the inequalities $x > 0.40$ and $0.40 < x < 0.50$ correspond (respectively) to $z > \frac{0.40-0.41}{0.02} = -0.5$ and $-0.5 < z < \frac{0.50-0.41}{0.02} = 4.5$. For the first of these, Table A gives proportion $1 - 0.3085 = 0.6915$; the second is essentially 0.6915 as well.

**3.13.** **(a)** Search Table A for 0.25: $z \doteq -0.67$ (software gives $-0.6745$).
**(b)** Search Table A for 0.60: $z \doteq 0.25$ (software: 0.2533).

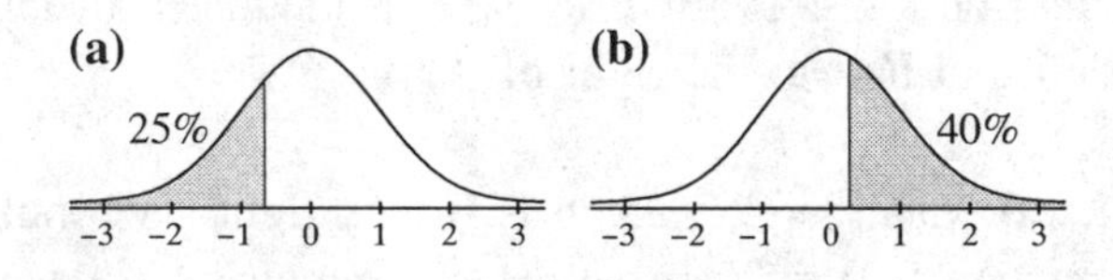


**3.14.** **(a)** IQs below about 90: Searching Table A for 0.25 leads to $z < -0.67$, which corresponds to $x < 100 - 0.67(15) \doteq 90$. (Using the software value $z < -0.6745$ gives $x < 89.9$.) **(b)** About 125 or more: Searching Table A for 0.95 leads to $z > 1.64$ or 1.65; software gives 1.6449. For any value of $z^*$ between 1.64 and 1.65, we find that $100 + (z^*)(15)$ is between 124.6 and 124.75.

**3.15.** (a) Income distributions are typically skewed.

**3.16.** (a) Mean and standard deviation tell you center and spread, which is all you need for a Normal distribution.

**3.17.** (b) This distribution is centered at 2.

**3.18.** (b) The change of curvature happens over 5 and $-1$.

**3.19.** (b) $266 \pm 2(16) = 234$ to 298 days.

**3.20.** (c) 130 is two standard deviations above the mean, so 2.5% of adults have IQs of 130 or more.

**3.21.** (a) $z = \frac{118-100}{15} = 1.2$.

**3.22.** (c) Table A shows an area of 0.8749 for $z = 1.15$.

**3.23.** (b) Table A shows an area of 0.2266 for $z = -0.75$ (or 0.7734 for $z = 0.75$).

**3.24.** (b) Corinne's standard score is $z = \frac{118-100}{15} = 1.2$, for which Table A gives 0.8849.

**3.25.** Sketches will vary, but should be some variation on the one shown here: The peak at 0 should be "tall and skinny," while near 1, the curve should be "short and fat."

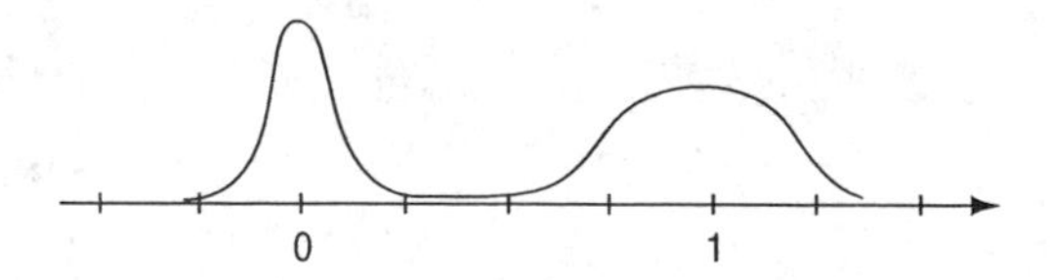


**3.26.** See also the solution to Exercise 2.37. Both stemplots suggest that the distributions may be slightly skewed to the right, rather than perfectly symmetric (as a Normal distribution would be).

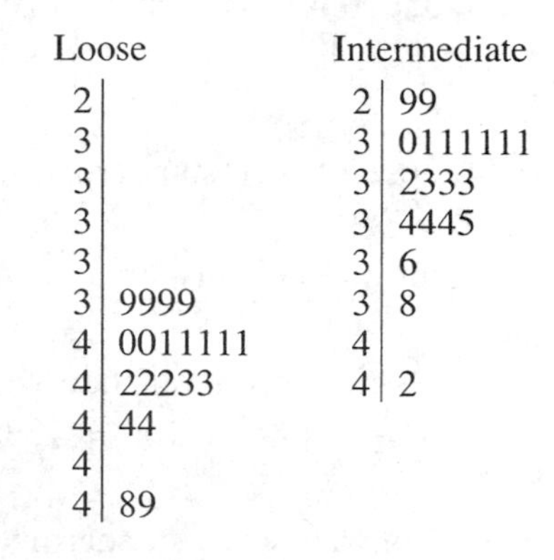

| Loose | |
|---|---|
| 2 | |
| 3 | |
| 3 | |
| 3 | |
| 3 | |
| 3 | 9999 |
| 4 | 0011111 |
| 4 | 22233 |
| 4 | 44 |
| 4 | |
| 4 | 89 |

| Intermediate | |
|---|---|
| 2 | 99 |
| 3 | 0111111 |
| 3 | 2333 |
| 3 | 4445 |
| 3 | 6 |
| 3 | 8 |
| 4 | |
| 4 | 2 |

**3.27.** The Normal curve at right is shown for reference. Students should be encouraged to draw these even if the instructions do not call for them. **(a)** 50%. **(b)** 0.15% (half of the outer 0.3%). **(c)** 16% (half of the outer 32%).

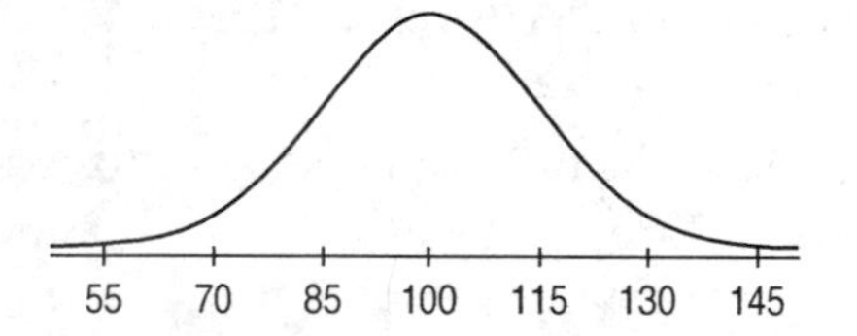


**3.28.** See the density curve drawn in the solution to Exercise 3.27. 70 is two standard deviations below the mean (that is, it has standard score $z = -2$), so about 2.5% (half of the outer 5%) of adults would have WAIS scores below 70.

**3.29.** **(a)** There are two somewhat low IQs—72 qualifies as an outlier by the $1.5 \times IQR$ rule, while 74 is on the boundary. However, for a small sample, this stemplot looks reasonably Normal. **(b)** We compute $\bar{x} \doteq 105.84$ and $s \doteq 14.27$ and find:

$\frac{23}{31} \doteq 74.2\%$ of the scores in the range $\bar{x} \pm 1s \doteq 91.6$ to 120.1, and

$\frac{29}{31} \doteq 93.5\%$ of the scores in the range $\bar{x} \pm 2s \doteq 77.3$ to 134.4.

For an exactly Normal distribution, we would expect these proportions to be 68% and 95%.

| Stem | Leaves |
|---|---|
| 7 | 24 |
| 7 | |
| 8 | |
| 8 | 69 |
| 9 | 13 |
| 9 | 68 |
| 10 | 023334 |
| 10 | 578 |
| 11 | 11222444 |
| 11 | 89 |
| 12 | 0 |
| 12 | 8 |
| 13 | 02 |

**3.30.** **(a)** 0.0122. **(b)** $1 - 0.0122 = 0.9878$. **(c)** $1 - 0.9616 = 0.0384$. **(d)** $0.9616 - 0.0122 = 0.9494$.

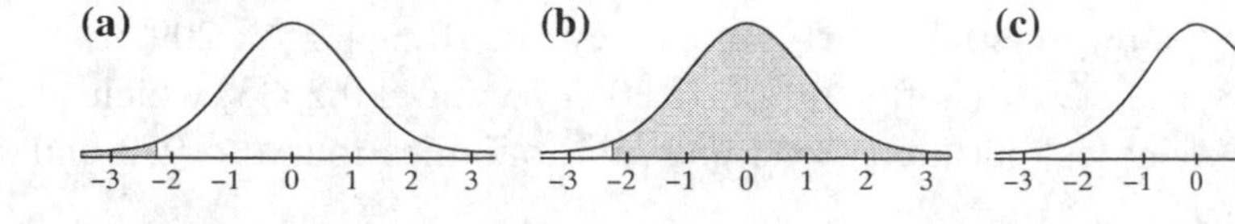


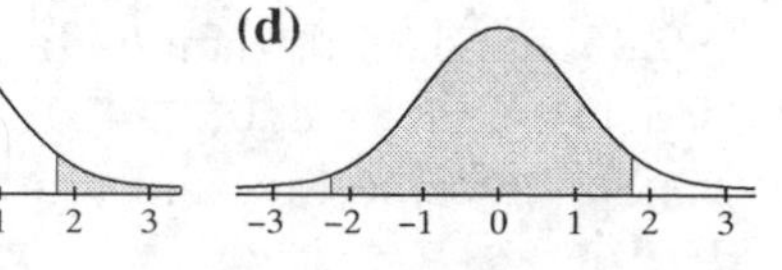

**3.31.** **(a)** Search Table A for 0.80: $z \doteq 0.84$ (software: 0.8416). **(b)** Search Table A for 0.65: $z \doteq 0.39$ (software: 0.3853).

**3.32.** Tonya's score standardizes to $z = \frac{1318-1026}{209} \doteq 1.40$, while Jermaine's score corresponds to $z = \frac{27-20.9}{4.8} \doteq 1.27$. Tonya's score is higher.

**3.33.** Jacob's score standardizes to $z = \frac{16-20.9}{4.8} \doteq -1.02$, while Emily's score corresponds to $z = \frac{670-1026}{209} \doteq -1.70$. Jacob's score is higher.

**3.34.** José's score standardizes to $z = \frac{1287-1026}{209} \doteq 1.2488$, so an equivalent ACT score is $20.9 + 1.2488 \times 4.8 \doteq 26.9$. (Of course, ACT scores are reported as whole numbers, so this would presumably be a score of 27.)

**3.35.** Maria's score standardizes to $z = \frac{28-20.9}{4.8} \doteq 1.4792$, so an equivalent SAT score is $1026 + 1.4792 \times 209 \doteq 1335.1$ (presumably reported as 1330 or 1340.)

**3.36.** Tonya's score standardizes to $z = \frac{1318-1026}{209} \doteq 1.40$; this is about the 92nd percentile (Table A gives 0.9192).

**3.37.** Jacob's score standardizes to $z = \frac{16-20.9}{4.8} \doteq -1.02$; this is about the 15th percentile (Table A gives 0.1539).

**3.38.** A score of 1600 standardizes to $z = \frac{1600-1026}{209} \doteq 2.75$. 99.7% of standard scores are below this level, so about 0.3% are above this level (and are therefore reported as 1600).

**3.39.** A score of 36 standardizes to $z = \frac{36-20.9}{4.8} \doteq 3.15$. About 99.9% of standard scores are below this level, so about 0.1% are above this level (and are therefore reported as 36).

**3.40.** The top 10% corresponds to a standard score of $z = 1.28$, which in turn corresponds to a score of $1026 + 1.28 \times 209 \doteq 1294$ on the SAT. (Software gives $z = 1.2816$, which yields the same SAT score after rounding.)

**3.41.** The top 20% corresponds to a standard score of $z = 0.84$, which in turn corresponds to a score of $20.9 + 0.84 \times 4.8 \doteq 24.9$ (or 25) on the ACT. (Software gives $z = 0.8416$, which yields the same ACT score after rounding.)

**3.42.** From Table A, we estimate that the quartiles of a Normal distribution are $\pm 0.675$ standard deviations from the mean, so for ACT scores they are $20.9 \pm 0.675 \times 4.8 = 17.7$ to 24.1. (Software gives $\pm 0.6745$, which yields the same ACT scores after rounding.)

**3.43.** From Table A, we estimate that the quintiles of a Normal distribution are $\pm 0.84$ and $\pm 0.25$ standard deviations from the mean, so for SAT scores they are $1026 + z^* \times 209$, which rounds to 850, 974, 1078, and 1202. (Software gives $\pm 0.8416$ and $\pm 0.2533$, which yields the same first and fourth quintiles, but the second and third quintiles round to 973 and 1079.)

**3.44.** About 2.5% of young women are taller than the mean height of young men, because 69.3 inches corresponds to a standard score (on the women's scale) of $z = \frac{69.3-64}{2.7} \doteq 1.96$, which yields 0.0250 in Table A (or round to $z = 2$ and use the 68–95–99.7 rule to get the same result).

**3.45.** About 2.9% of young men are shorter than the mean height of young women: A height of 64 inches corresponds to a standard score (on the men's scale) of $z = \frac{64-69.3}{2.8} \doteq -1.89$, which yields 0.0294 in Table A.

**3.46. (a)** Among men, a score of 750 corresponds to standard score $z = \frac{750-537}{116} \doteq 1.84$, so about 3.29% score 750 or more. **(b)** Among women, a score of 750 corresponds to standard score $z = \frac{750-501}{110} \doteq 2.26$, so about 1.19% score 750 or more.

**3.47.** If the distribution is Normal, it must be symmetric about its mean—and in particular, the 10th and 90th percentiles must be equal distances below and above the mean—so the mean is 250 points. If 225 points below (above) the mean is the 10th (90th) percentile, this is 1.28 standard deviations below (above) the mean, so the distribution's standard deviation is $\frac{225}{1.28} \doteq 175.8$ points.

**3.48. (a)** About 0.6% of healthy young adults have osteoporosis (the cumulative probability below a standard score of $-2.5$ is 0.0062). **(b)** About 31% of this population of older women has osteoporosis: The BMD level that is 2.5 standard deviations below the young adult mean would standardize to $-0.5$ for these older women, and the cumulative probability for this standard score is 0.3085.

**3.49.** A score of 27 corresponds to a standard score of $z = \frac{27-20.9}{4.8} \doteq 1.27$. From Table A, we find that 89.8% of scores in a Normal distribution would fall below this level; the actual fraction was $\frac{1,052,490}{1,171,460} \doteq 0.8984$. This is a good match, suggesting that the Normal distribution fits the actual data.

**3.50. (a)** The mean $\bar{x} = \$17,776$ is greater than the median $M = \$15,532$. Meanwhile, $M - Q_1 = \$5,632$ and $Q_3 - M = \$6,968$; the second difference is larger. Both of these observations are what we would expect for right-skewed distributions. **(b)** From Table A, we estimate that the third quartiles of a Normal distribution would be 0.675 standard deviations above the mean, which would be $\$17,776 + 0.675 \times \$12,034 \doteq \$25,899$. (Software gives 0.6745, which yields \$25,893.) As the exercise suggests, this is larger than the actual value of $Q_3$.

**3.51.** **(a)** The applet shows an area of 0.6826 between −1.000 and 1.000, while the 68–95–99.7 rule rounds this to 0.68. **(b)** Between −2.000 and 2.000, the applet reports 0.9544 (compared with the rounded 0.95 from the 68–95–99.7 rule). Between −3.000 and 3.000, the applet reports 0.9974 (compared with the rounded 0.997).

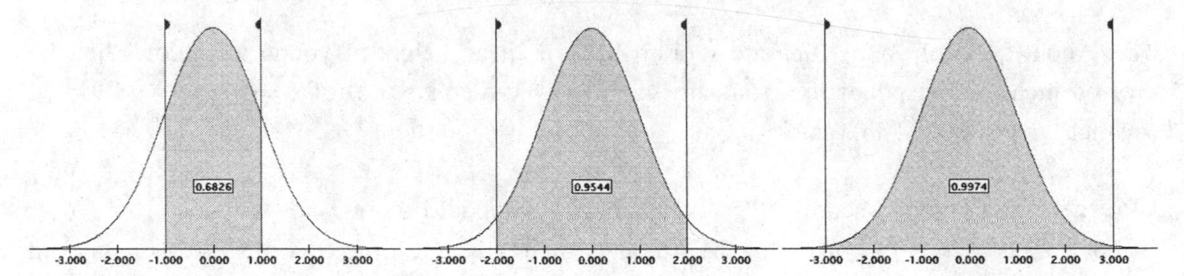


**3.52.** Because the quartiles of any distribution have 50% of observations between them, we seek to place the flags so that the reported area is 0.5. The closest the applet gets is an area of 0.5034, between −0.680 and 0.680. Thus the quartiles of any Normal distribution are about 0.68 standard deviations above and below the mean.

**Note:** *Table A places the quartiles at about ±0.67; other statistical software gives ±0.6745.*

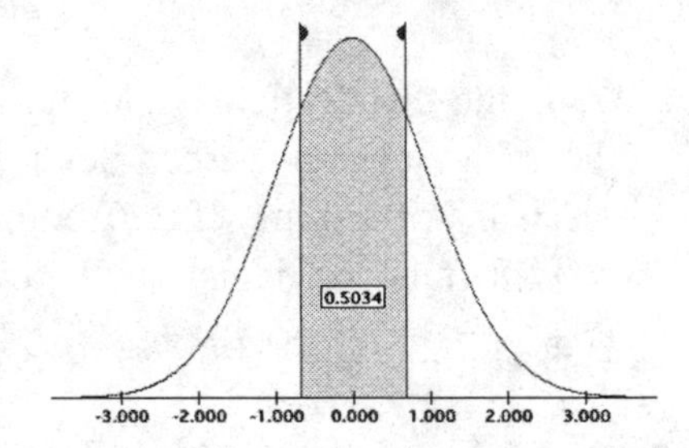


**3.53.** Placing the flags so that the area between them is as close as possible to 0.80, we find that the A/B cutoff is about 1.28 standard deviations above the mean, and the B/C cutoff is about 1.28 standard deviations below the mean.

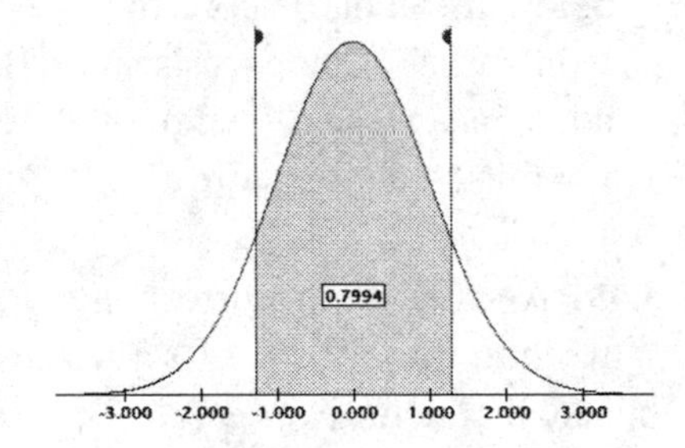

# Chapter 4 Solutions

**4.1.** **(a)** Time spent studying is explanatory; the grade is the response variable. **(b)** Explore the relationship; there is no reason to view one or the other as explanatory. **(c)** Time spent on extracurricular activities is explanatory, GPA is the response variable. **(d)** Explore the relationship.

**4.2.** Water temperature is explanatory, and weight change (growth) is the response variable. Both are quantitative.

**4.3.** For example: Weight, gender, other food eaten by the students, type of beer (light, imported, . . . ).

**4.4.** Check that students understand that the explanatory variable (returning birds) goes on the horizontal axis.

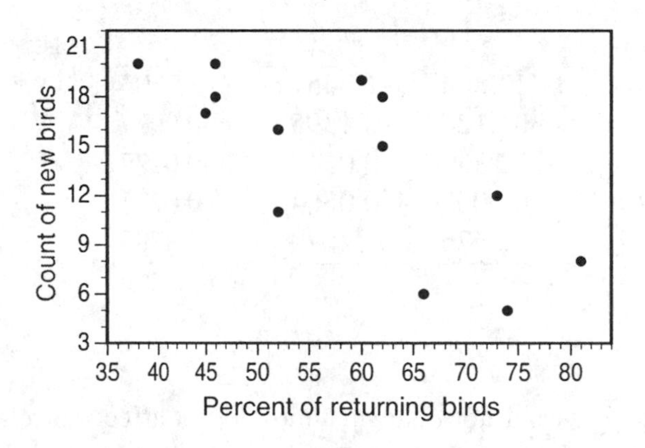


**4.5.** The scatterplot (see the previous exercise) shows a linear, negative, fairly weak relationship. (Note: form = linear, direction = negative, strength = weak.) Because this association is negative, we conclude that the sparrowhawk is a long-lived territorial species.

**4.6.** **(a)** At right; speed is explanatory. **(b)** The relationship is curved—low in the middle, higher at the extremes. Because low "mileage" is actually *good* (it means that we use less fuel to travel 100 km), this makes sense: moderate speeds yield the best performance. Note that 60 km/hr is about 37 mph. **(c)** Above-average (that is, bad) values of "fuel used" are found with both low and high values of "speed." **(d)** The relationship is very strong—there is little scatter around the curve, so the curve is very useful for prediction.

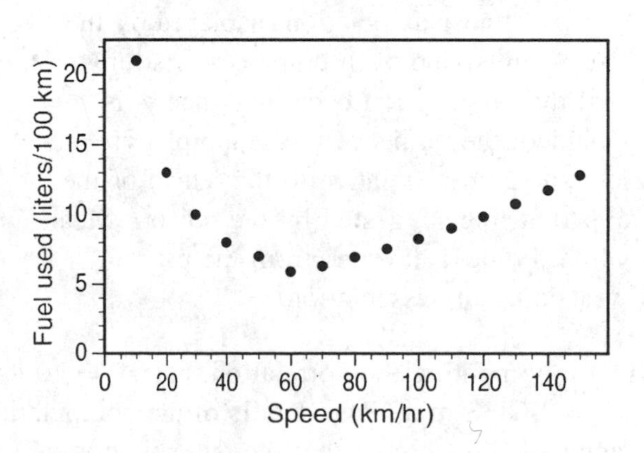

**4.7.** **(a)** In the scatterplot on the right, the open circles represent Run 8905, the higher flow rate. **(b)** Icicles seem to grow faster when the water runs more slowly. (Note that there is no guarantee that the pattern we observe with these two flow rates applies to rates much faster than 29.6 mg/s, or slower than 11.9 mg/s.)

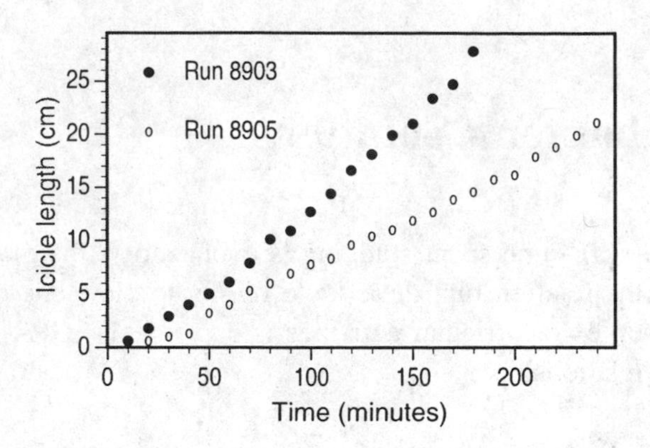


**4.8.** **(a)** Price is explanatory (and so is on the horizontal axis). The plot shows a positive linear association. **(b)** $\bar{x} = 50$ cents/lb and $s_x \doteq 16.3248$ cents/lb; $\bar{y} = 1.738\%$ and $s_y \doteq 0.9278\%$. The standardized values are below; the correlation is $r = 3.8206/4 = 0.955$. **(c)** Obviously, the calculator value should be the same.

| $z_x$ | $z_y$ | $z_x\, z_y$ |
|---|---|---|
| −1.2864 | −1.3451 | 1.7303 |
| −0.6126 | −0.1595 | 0.0977 |
| 0.2450 | −0.0517 | −0.0127 |
| 0.3063 | 0.0884 | 0.0271 |
| 1.3476 | 1.4679 | 1.9783 |
| | | 3.8206 |

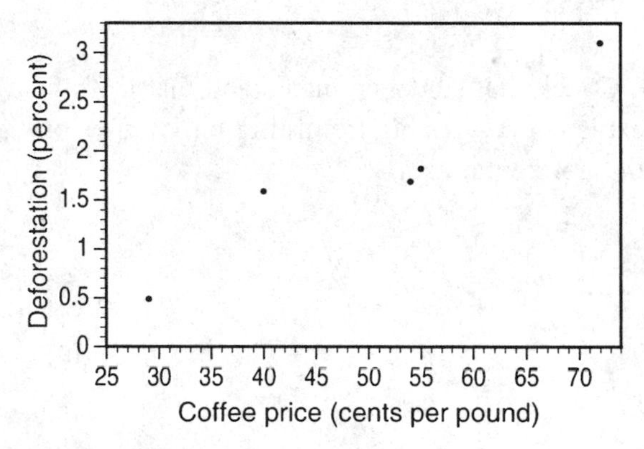


**4.9.** $r$ would not change; units do not affect correlation.

**4.10.** **(a)** $r \doteq -0.748$. **(b)** With Point A included, the correlation is −0.807; with Point B, it is −0.469. **(c)** Point A fits in with the negative linear association displayed by the other points, and even emphasizes (strengthens) that association because, when A is included, the points of the scatterplot are less spread out (relative to the length of the apparent line suggested by the points). Meanwhile, Point B deviates from the pattern, weakening the association.

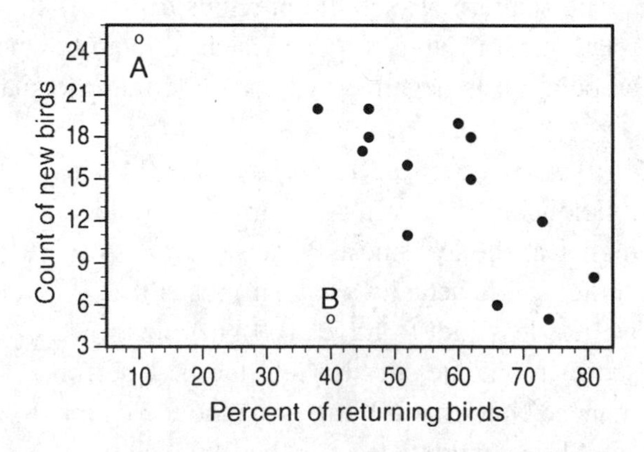


**4.11.** In computing the correlation, note $\bar{x} = 40$ and $s_x \doteq 15.8114$ mph, while $\bar{y} = 26.8$ and $s_y \doteq 2.6833$ mpg. The details of the computation are below; as an alternative to finding standard scores, note that the denominators are all the same ($s_x\, s_y$), and the sum of the numerators of the terms is

$$\sum(\bar{x} - x_i)(\bar{y} - y_i) = (-20)(-2.8) + (-10)(1.2) + (0)(3.2) + (10)(1.2) + (20)(-2.8)$$
$$= 56 - 12 + 0 + 12 - 56 = 0.$$

The correlation is 0 because these variables do not have a straight-line relationship; the association is neither positive nor negative.

| $z_x$ | $z_y$ | $z_x z_y$ |
|---|---|---|
| −1.2649 | −1.0435 | 1.3199 |
| −0.6325 | 0.4472 | −0.2828 |
| 0 | 1.1926 | 0 |
| 0.6325 | 0.4472 | 0.2828 |
| 1.2649 | −1.0435 | −1.3199 |
| | | 0 |

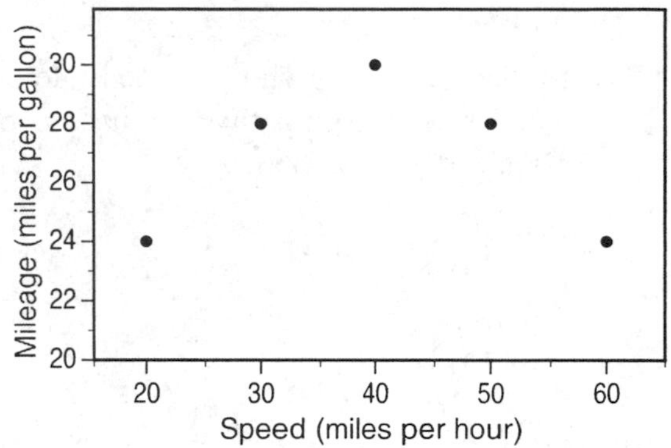


**4.12.** (a) We would expect that parents' income would have an effect on the education of their children.

**4.13.** (a) More affluent families can afford more education.

**4.14.** (c) The low point is for an IQ of about 124 and a reading score around 10.

**4.15.** (a) Without the outlier, the remaining points would be less scattered around the line.

**4.16.** (a) There is a positive association, but not so strong that the correlation would be 0.95.

**4.17.** (c) Correlations range from −1 to 1 inclusive.

**4.18.** (b) The correlation is negative because the slope of the line is negative.

**4.19.** (a) This would be a perfect linear relationship: If the husband's age is $y$ and the wife's age is $x$, the linear relationship $y = x + 2$ would hold, and hence $r = 1$ (because the slope is positive).

**4.20.** (b) Correlation is unaffected by units.

**4.21.** (a) Computation with calculator or software gives $r \doteq 0.8770$.

**4.22.** **(a)** From the scatterplot, we estimate 50% in 1954 and about −28% in 1974. (The data file `ex04-22.dat` gives the values 50.28% and −27.87%.) **(b)** The return on Treasury bills in 1981 was about 14.8%. (The data file gives the value 14.72%.) **(c)** The scatterplot shows no clear pattern. (The statement that "high treasury bill returns tend to go with low returns on stocks" implies a negative association; there may be *some* suggestion of such a pattern, but it is extremely weak.)

**4.23.** **(a)** The response variable (estimated level) can take only the values 1, 2, 3, 4, 5, so the points in the scatterplot must fall on one of those five levels. **(b)** The association is (weakly) positive. **(c)** The estimate is 4, which is an overestimate; that child had the lowest score on the test.

**4.24.** **(a)** The scatterplot shows a moderate positive association, so $r$ should be positive, but not close to 1. **(b)** The correlation is $r = 0.5653$.

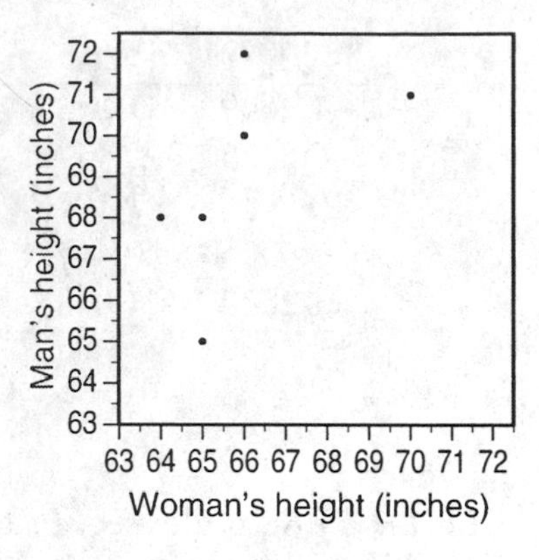


**4.25.** **(a)** Both men (filled circles) and women (open circles) show fairly steady improvement. Women have made more rapid progress, but their progress seems to have slowed, while men's records may be dropping more rapidly in recent years. **(b)** $r_{\text{men}} \doteq -0.9878$ and $r_{\text{women}} \doteq -0.9705$. These numbers are consistent with the strong negative linear associations visible in the scatterplot. **(c)** The data support the first claim, but do not seem to support the second.

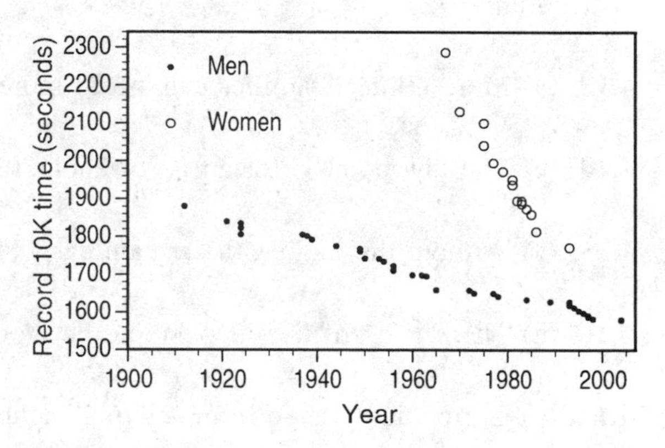


**4.26.** **(a)** $r$ would not change if all the men were six inches shorter. A positive correlation does not tell us that the men were generally taller than the women; instead it indicates that women who are taller (shorter) than the average woman tend to date men who are also taller (shorter) than the average man. **(b)** $r$ would not change, because it is unaffected by units. **(c)** $r$ would be 1, because the points of the scatterplot would fall on a positively sloped line.

**4.27.** The scatterplot is shown on the right; note that degree-days is explanatory, and so should be on the horizontal axis. It shows a strong, positive, linear association; because the pattern is linear, correlation is appropriate. We find that $r = 0.9953$.

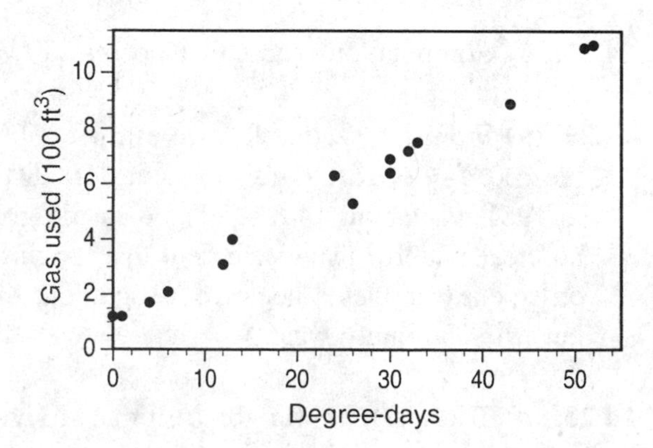

**4.28.** **(a)** Planting rate is explanatory. **(b)** At right. **(c)** As we would expect from the discussion, the pattern is curved—high in the middle and lower on the ends. The association is not linear, and is neither positive nor negative, so there is reason to compute the correlation. **(d)** The means are 131.025, 143.15, 146.225, 143.0$\overline{6}$, and 134.75 bushels/acre. The mean yields first increase with plant density, then decrease; the greatest yield occurs at or around 20,000 plants per acre.

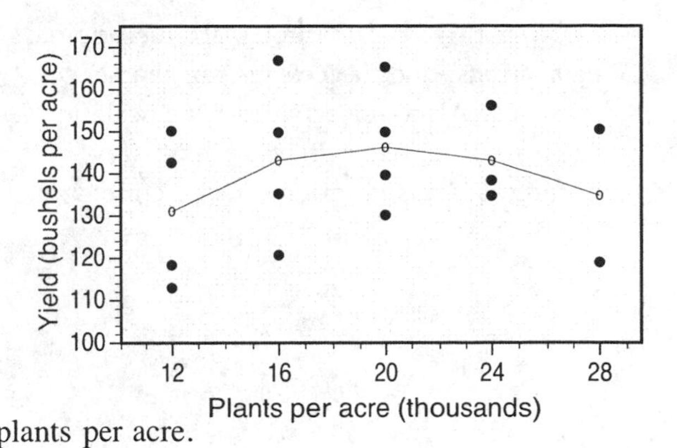


**4.29.** The new data in the scatterplot are plotted with open circles. The new points are generally slightly lower than the pre-solar-panel points, suggesting that gas usage has dropped slightly.

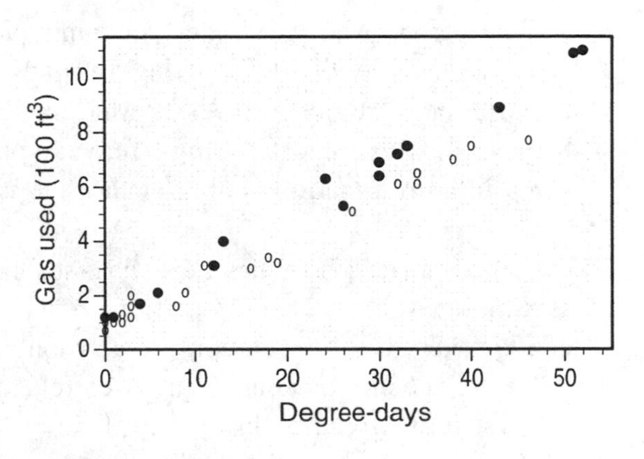


**4.30.** **(a)** Plot shown on the right. Means (plotted with crosses) are 30.96%, 32.76%, 23.32%, and 54.31%. (Note that the sectors on the horizontal axis are shown in alphabetical order, as in the text, but that is completely arbitrary.) **(b)** Technology had the highest average performance. **(c)** Referring to a positive or negative association makes sense only when both variables are quantitative. (There *is* an association here, but it cannot be called positive or negative.) The correlation is not useful for this situation.

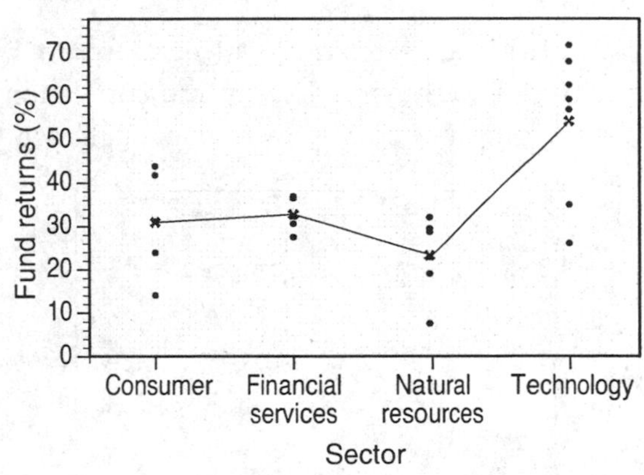


**4.31.** Explanations and sketches will vary, but should note that correlation measures the strength of the association, not the slope of the line. The hypothetical Funds A and B mentioned in the report, for example, might be related by a linear formula with slope 2 (or 1/2).

**4.32.** **(a)** Small-cap stocks have a lower correlation with municipal bonds, so the relationship is weaker. **(b)** She should look for a negative correlation (although this would also mean that this investment tends to *decrease* when bond prices rise).

**4.33.** **(a)** At right. The circles are the original data points, and the crosses are the new ones. **(b)** Although changing the scales (units) makes the scatterplot look very different, it has no effect on the correlation.

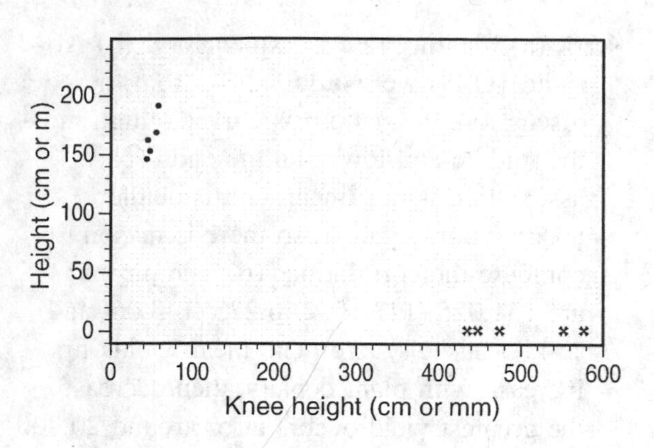


**4.34.** The person who wrote the article interpreted a correlation close to 0 as if it were a correlation close to $-1$ (implying a negative association between teaching ability and research productivity). Professor McDaniel's findings mean there is little linear association between research and teaching—for example, knowing that a professor is a good researcher gives little information about whether she is a good or bad teacher.

**4.35.** **(a)** Because gender has a nominal scale, we cannot compute the correlation between sex and anything. (There is a strong *association* between gender and income. Some writers and speakers use "correlation" as a synonym for "association." It is much better to retain the more specific meaning.) **(b)** A correlation $r = 1.09$ is impossible because $-1 \leq r \leq 1$ always. **(c)** Correlation has no units, so $r = 0.23$ *bushel* is incorrect.

**4.36.** **(a)** The correlation will be closer to 1. One possible answer is shown below, left. **(b)** Answers will vary, but the correlation will decrease, and can be made negative by dragging the point down far enough (see below, right).

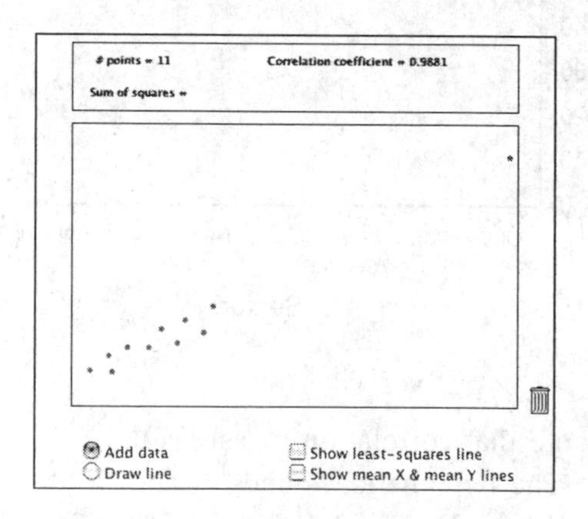


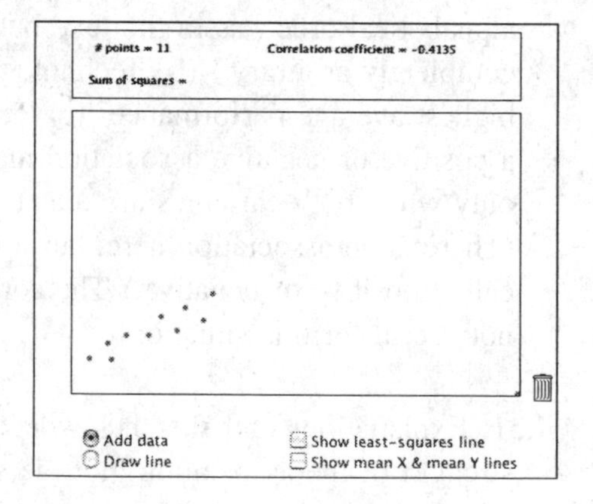

**4.37.** **(a)** Because two points determine a line, the correlation is always 1. **(b)** Sketches will vary; an example is shown on the right. Note that the scatterplot must be positively sloped, but $r$ is affected only by the scatter about the line, not by the steepness of the slope. **(c)** The first nine points cannot be spread from the top to the bottom of the graph because in such a case the correlation cannot exceed about 0.66 (based on empirical evidence—that is, from a reasonable amount of playing around with the applet). One possibility is shown below, left. **(d)** To have $r \doteq 0.7$, the curve must be higher at the right than at the left. One possibility is shown below, right.

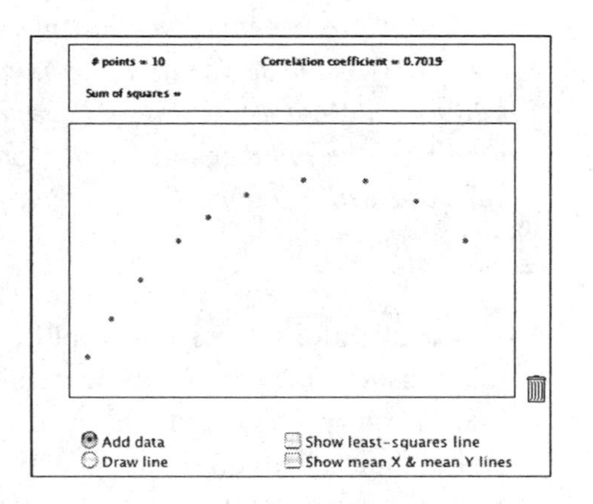


**4.38. Formulate:** To describe the change in solar radiation over time, we begin with a scatterplot (with time as the explanatory variable). If appropriate for the relationship, we compute the correlation coefficient to measure the strength of the association. **Solve:** The plot suggests that sunlight has brightened overall, but the increase has not been steady—from 1992 through 1999, there seems to be a curved relationship. Although it might not be the best summary of this (not entirely linear) relationship, the correlation is $r \doteq 0.773$. **Conclude:** Over time, sunlight has gotten brighter, but with quite a bit of fluctuation.

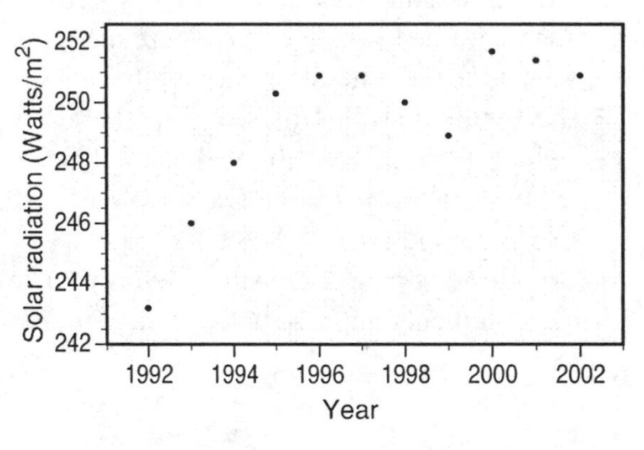

**4.39. Formulate:** We wish to observe the effect of the number breeding pairs on the survival rates (the percent of males returning). We begin with a scatterplot, and compute the correlation if appropriate.

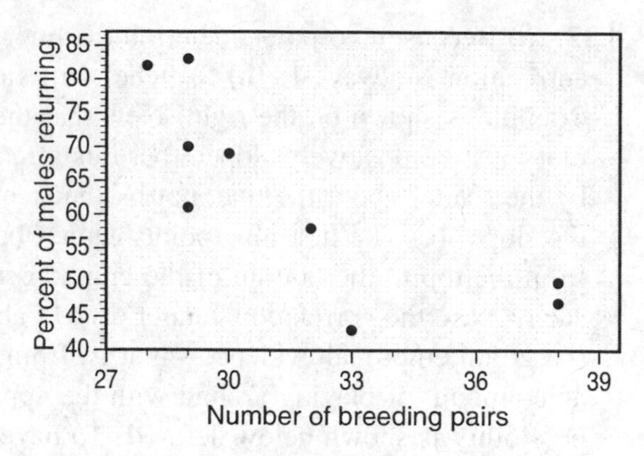


**Solve:** A scatterplot of the percent returning against the number of breeding pairs shows the expected negative association. Though slightly curved, it is reasonable to compute $r \doteq -0.7943$ as a measure of the strength of the association.

**Conclude:** This supports the theory: A smaller percent of birds survive following a successful breeding season.

**Note:** *We examine the* percent *returning, rather than the* number *returning, because with the latter response variable, we might not see the relationship: Areas with many breeding pairs would correspondingly have more males that might potentially return. (In the given numbers, the number of breeding pairs varies only from 28 to 38, but considering hypothetical data with 10 and 100 breeding pairs makes more apparent the reason for using percents rather than counts.)*

**4.40. Formulate:** We wish to explore the relationship between social distress and brain activity. We begin with a scatterplot, and compute the correlation if appropriate.

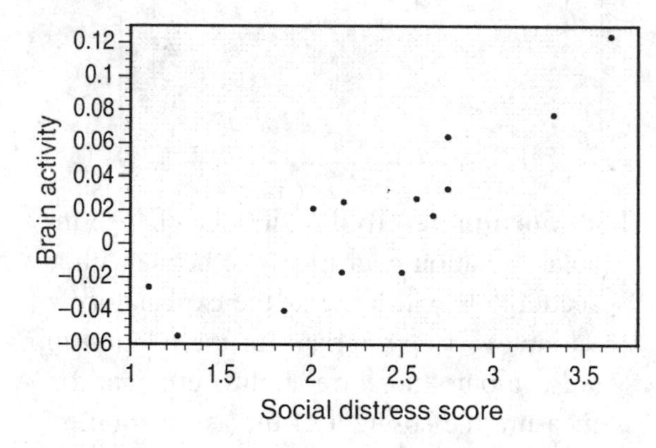


**Solve:** A scatterplot shows a fairly strong, positive, linear association. There are no particular outliers; each variable has low and high values, but those points do not deviate from the pattern of the rest. The relationship seems to be reasonably linear, so we compute $r \doteq 0.8782$.

**Conclude:** Social exclusion does appear to trigger a pain response: Higher social distress measurements are associated with increased activity in the pain-sensing area of the brain.

**4.41. Formulate:** For a side-by-side comparison, either boxplots or back-to-back stemplots are good. Another option is a plot of returns against market sector, as was created in the solution to Exercise 4.30. To explore the relationship among the returns, we can look at a scatterplot of 2003 returns against 2002 returns (treating the latter as explanatory), or examine the distribution of the difference between 2003 returns and 2002 returns.

| 2002 | | 2003 |
|---|---|---|
| 0 | −5 | |
| 279 | −4 | |
| 7 | −3 | |
| 136 | −2 | |
| 1112778 | −1 | |
| 0025679 | −0 | |
| | 0 | 7 |
| | 1 | 49 |
| | 2 | 236789 |
| | 3 | 0122566 |
| | 4 | 13 |
| | 5 | 79 |
| 4 | 6 | 28 |
| | 7 | 1 |

| 2003 − 2002 retu | |
|---|---|
| −0 | 3 |
| −0 | |
| 0 | 0 |
| 0 | 223333 |
| 0 | 444455555 |
| 0 | 6 |
| 0 | 9 |
| 1 | 001 |
| 1 | 2 |

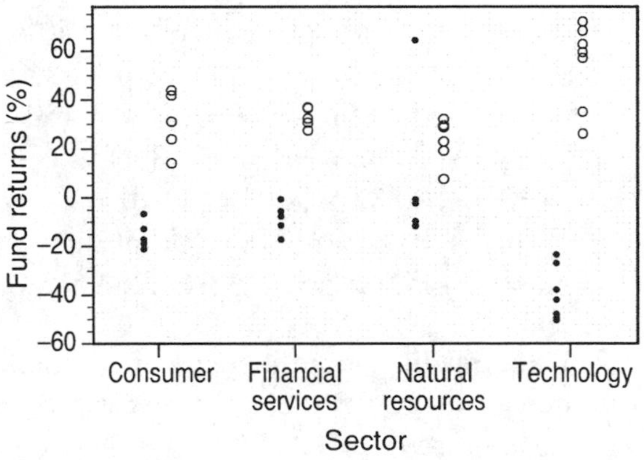

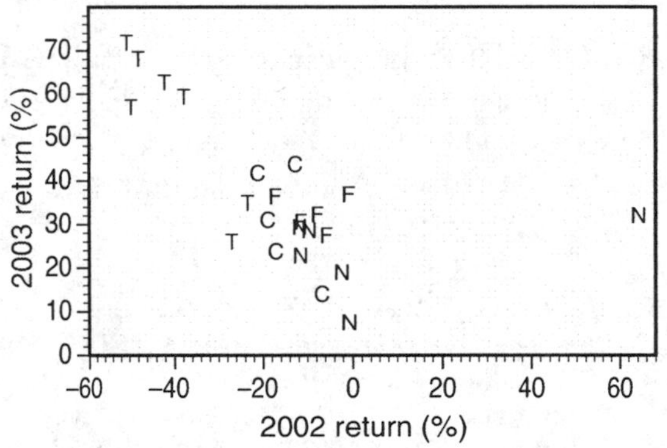

**Solve:** The back-to-back stemplots on the right clearly show that the main difference between 2002 and 2003 is that only one fund increased in 2002, while all increased in 2003. In the plot below it, for each sector, 2002 returns are shown as filled circles and 2003 returns are open circles; again, we see that nearly all 2002 returns were negative, and all the 2003 returns were positive.

The other stemplot shows the differences for each fund (that is, each fund's 2003 return minus its 2002 return). Only one fund return decreased; every other fund increased its return by between 8.3% and 122.4%. In the final scatterplot, the letters C, F, T, and N indicate the different fund types. The Fidelity Gold Fund stands out as a clear outlier; ignoring that point, the correlation is $r \doteq -0.8722$.

**Conclude:** The side-by-side comparison confirmed what was stated in the problem: 2002 was a bad year, and 2003 was a good year. The negative association in the second scatterplot makes more clear something that can also be observed in the other scatterplot: Generally, the worse a fund did in 2002, the better it did in 2003 (and vice versa).

# Chapter 5 Solutions

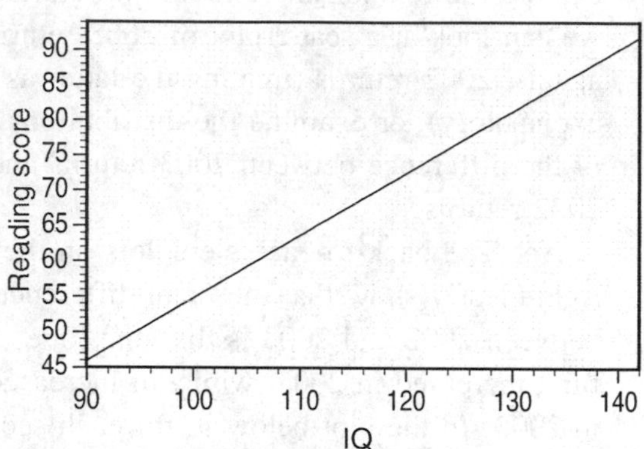


**5.1.** **(a)** The slope is 0.882; this means that, on the average, reading score increases by 0.882 for each one-point increase in IQ. **(b)** The intercept (−33.4) would correspond to the expected reading score for a child with an IQ of 0; neither that reading score nor that IQ has any meaningful interpretation. **(c)** The predicted scores for $x = 90$ and $x = 130$ are

$-33.4 + 0.882 \times 90 = 45.98$ and

$-33.4 + 0.882 \times 130 = 81.26$.

**(d)** This is most easily done by plotting the points (90, 45.98) and (130, 81.26), and then drawing the line connecting them.

**5.2.** If the reading score increases by 1 for each IQ point, the professor's line has slope 1. In order for an IQ of 100 to correspond to a reading score of 50, the equation must be

reading score = IQ − 50.

**5.3.** **(a)** Minitab output is below; regardless of the software or calculator used, the formula should agree with the one given in the text (except for differences due to rounding). **(b)** The means and standard deviations are $\bar{x} \doteq 324.75$ and $s_x \doteq 257.66$ calories, $\bar{y} \doteq 2.3875$ and $s_y \doteq 1.1389$ kg. The correlation is $r \doteq -0.7786$. This yields $b = r \cdot s_y/s_x \doteq -0.00344$ and $a = \bar{y} - b\bar{x} \doteq 3.505$.

**Minitab output**

```
The regression equation is fat = 3.51 - 0.00344 nea

Predictor        Coef       Stdev    t-ratio       p
Constant       3.5051      0.3036      11.54   0.000
nea        -0.0034415   0.0007414      -4.64   0.000

s = 0.7399        R-sq = 60.6%     R-sq(adj) = 57.8%
```

**5.4.** See also the solution to Exercise 4.4.

**(a)** The correlation is $r \doteq -0.7485$. **(b)** The regression equation is $\hat{y} = 31.9 - 0.304x$. **(c)** The slope (−0.304) tells us that, on the average, for every one-percent increase in returning birds, the number of new birds joining the colony decreases by 0.304. **(d)** When $x = 60$, we predict $\hat{y} \doteq 13.69$ new birds will join the colony.

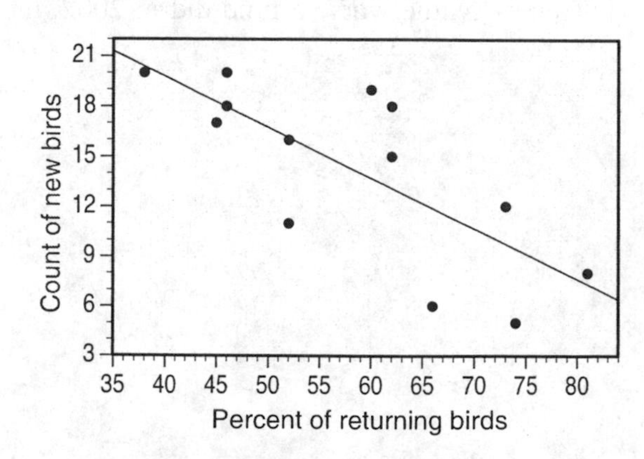

**Minitab output**

```
The regression equation is New = 31.9 - 0.304 PctRtn

Predictor        Coef       Stdev    t-ratio        p
Constant       31.934       4.838       6.60    0.000
PctRtn       -0.30402     0.08122      -3.74    0.003

s = 3.667        R-sq = 56.0%      R-sq(adj) = 52.0%
```

**5.5.** **(a)** Scatterplot at right. Regression gives $\hat{y} = 132.45 + 0.402x$ (Minitab output below). The plot suggests a curved pattern, so a linear formula is not appropriate for making predictions. **(b)** $r^2 = 0.0182$. This confirms what we see in the graph: This line does a poor job of summarizing the relationship. **(c)** The mean planting rate is $\bar{x} = 18.82$ thousand plants per acre, and the mean yield is $\bar{y} = 140.02$ bushels/acre, which is approximately equal to $132 + 0.402 \times 18.82$ (except for rounding error).

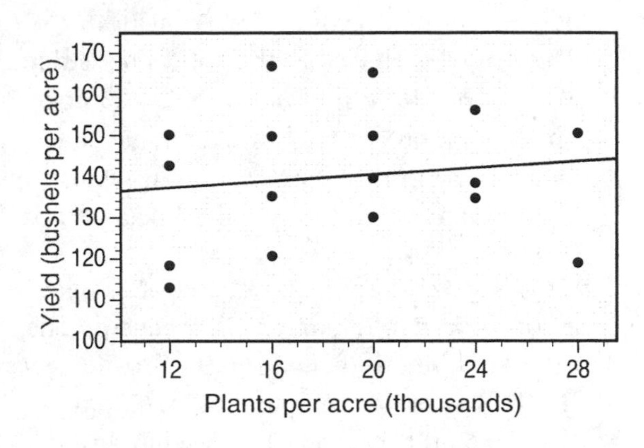


**Minitab output**

```
The regression equation is Yield = 132 + 0.402 Plants

Predictor        Coef       Stdev    t-ratio        p
Constant       132.45       14.91       8.89    0.000
Plants         0.4020      0.7625       0.53    0.606

s = 16.57        R-sq = 1.8%       R-sq(adj) = 0.0%
```

**5.6.** Correlations close to 1 or $-1$ mean that a line is a good match for the scatterplot, while correlations close to 0 mean that the scatterplot is spread widely about any line we attempt to use for prediction. Therefore, we expect that prediction of gas used will be quite accurate, while stock return predictions are much more uncertain.

**5.7.** **(a)** Below, left. **(b)** No; the pattern is curved, so a linear formula is not the appropriate choice for prediction. **(c)** For $x = 10$, we estimate $\hat{y} = 11.058 - 0.01466(10) \doteq 10.91$, so the residual is $21.00 - 10.91 = 10.09$. The sum of the residuals is $-0.01$. **(d)** The first two and last four residuals are positive, and those in the middle are negative. Plot below, right.

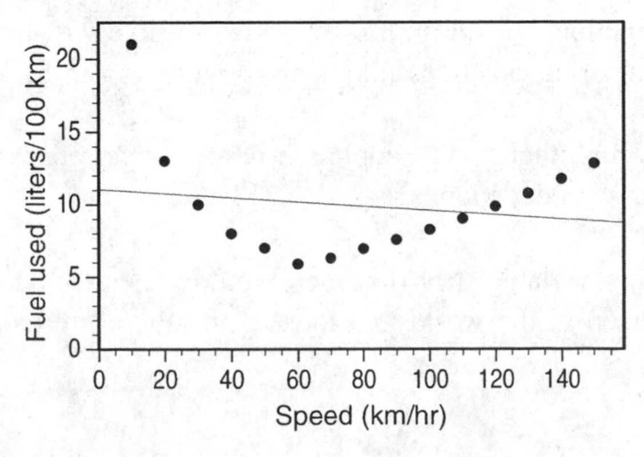


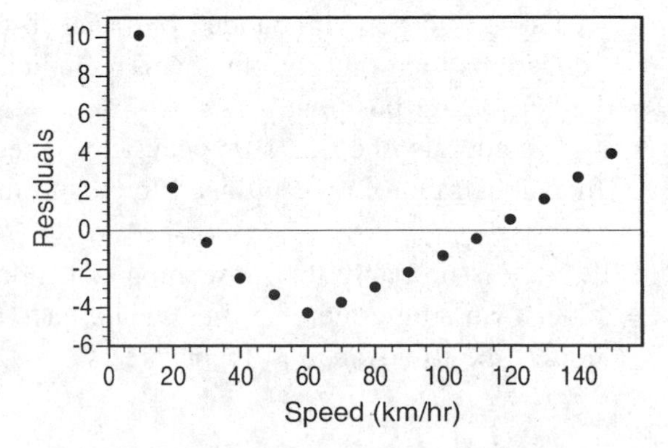

**5.8.** **(a)** Point A is a horizontal outlier; that is, it has a much smaller $x$-value than the others. Point B is a vertical outlier; it lies above the other points (i.e., it has a higher $y$ value).
**(b)** The three regression formulas are
$\hat{y} = 31.9 - 0.304x$ (the original data)
$\hat{y} = 22.8 - 0.156x$ (with Point A)
$\hat{y} = 32.3 - 0.293x$ (with Point B)
The original data gives the solid line. Adding Point B has little impact—it pulls the line up slightly, but would not change predicted values very much. Point A is influential; it pulls the line down, and changes how the line looks relative to the original 13 data points.

**5.9.** **(a)** The scatterplot shows a strong negative association with a straight-line pattern. The regression line is $\hat{y} = 1166.93 - 0.5868x$. **(b)** This is the slope—about 0.5868 million (586,800) per year during this period. Because $r \doteq -0.9885$, the regression line explains $r^2 \doteq 97.7\%$ of the variation in population. **(c)** Substituting $x = 2000$ gives $\hat{y} \doteq -6.65$, an impossible result because a population must be greater than or equal to 0. The rate of decrease in the farm population dropped in the 1980s. Beware extrapolation.

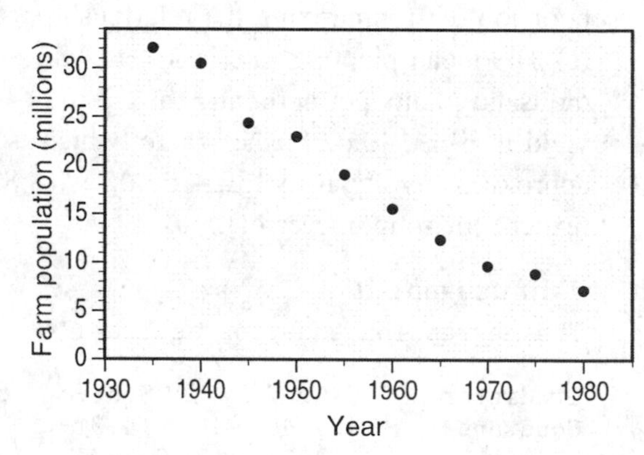


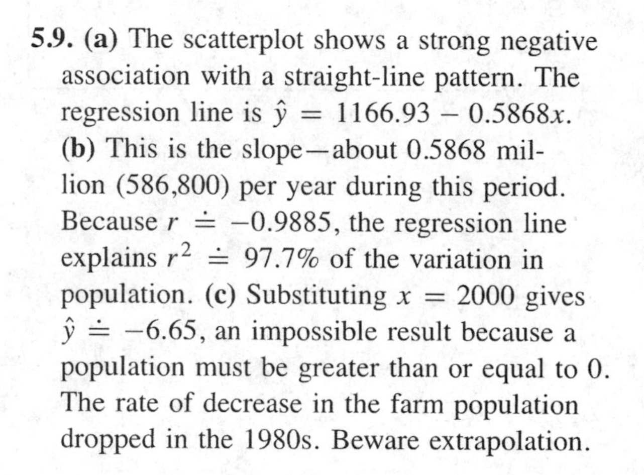

**5.10.** A student's intelligence may be a lurking variable: Stronger students (who are more likely to succeed when they get to college) are more likely to choose to take these math courses, while weaker students may avoid them. Other possible answers might be variations on this idea; for example, if we believe that success in college depends on a student's self-confidence, and perhaps confident students are more likely to choose math courses.

**5.11.** Social status is a possible lurking variable: Children from upper-class families can more easily afford higher education, and they would typically have had better preparation for college as well. They may also have some advantages when seeking employment, and have more money should they want to start their own businesses.

This could be compounded by racial distinctions: Some minority groups receive worse educations than other groups, and prejudicial hiring practices may keep minorities out of higher-paying positions.

It could also be that some causation goes the other way: People who are doing well in their jobs might be encouraged to pursue further education.

**5.12.** Age is probably the most important lurking variable: Married men would generally be older than single men, so they would have been in the workforce longer, and therefore had more time to advance in their careers.

**5.13.** Patients suffering from more serious illnesses are more likely to go to larger hospitals (which may have more or better facilities) for treatment. They are also likely to require more time to recuperate afterwards. So, the patient's condition is a lurking variable.

**5.14.** (b) The line passes through (or near) the point (110, 60).

**5.15.** (c) The line is clearly positively sloped. (In Exercise 5.1, we found the slope to be 0.882.)

**5.16.** (c) The slope is the coefficient of $x$.

**5.17.** (a) The slope is \$100/yr, and the intercept is \$500.

**5.18.** (b) The soap would get lighter as it is used up.

**5.19.** (a) The slope is 3 mm per gram.

**5.20.** (a) The predicted tail length is $20 + 3(18) = 54$ mm.

**5.21.** (a) The slope and the correlation always have the same sign.

**5.22.** (a) A slope of 3 mm/gram is equivalent to 0.3 cm/gram.

**5.23.** (b) One can also guess this by considering the slope between the first two points: $y$ changes by about $-40$ when $x$ changes by about $-10$. The only slope that is even close to that is 2.4. Alternatively, note that when $x = 50$ cm, the data suggests that $y$ should be about 160 cm, and only the second equation gives a result close to that.

**5.24. (a)** The slope is 0.0138 minutes per meter. On the average, if the depth of the dive is increased by one meter, it adds 0.0138 minutes (about 0.83 seconds) to the time spent underwater. **(b)** When D = 200, the regression formula estimates DD to be 5.45 minutes. **(c)** To plot the line, compute DD = 3.242 minutes when D = 40 meters, and DD = 6.83 minutes when D = 300 meters.

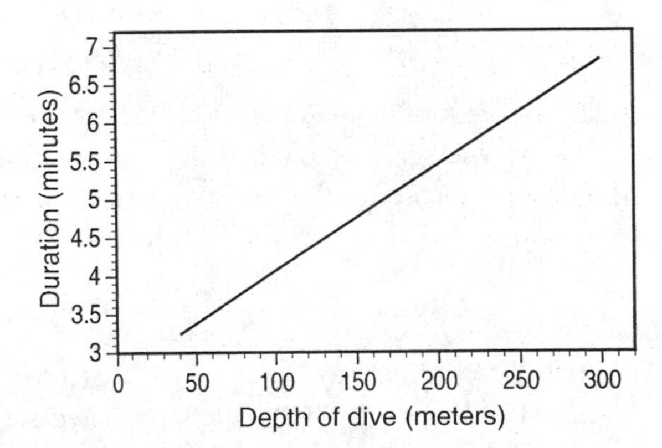


**5.25. (a)** The slope (1.507) says that, on the average, BOD rises (falls) by 1.507 mg/l for every 1 mg/l increase (decrease) in TOC. **(b)** When TOC = 0 mg/l, the predicted BOD level is $-55.43$ mg/l. This must arise from extrapolation; the data used to find this regression formula must not have included values of TOC near 0.

**5.26.** **(a)** The correlation is $r = 0.558$. **(b)** When $x = 70$ inches, we predict Tonya's height to be $\hat{y} = 64.5$ inches. Because of the relatively low correlation ($r^2 \doteq 0.311$) and the variation about the line in the scatterplot, we should not place too much confidence in this prediction.

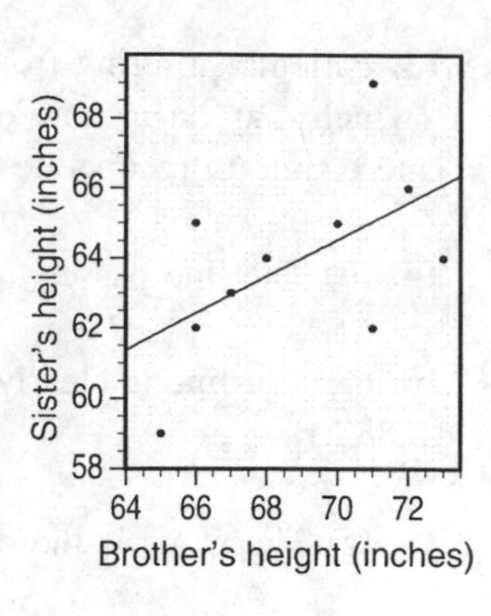


**5.27.** The regression formula is $\hat{y} = 1.0892 + 0.1890x$; when $x = 20$ degree-days per day, the predicted gas usage is about 4.87 hundred (i.e., 487) cubic feet. This should be a reasonably accurate prediction: The scatterplot showed very little scatter about the line, and the correlation is quite high ($r^2 \doteq 99.1\%$).

**5.28.** See also the solution to Exercise 4.40. **(a)** The regression equation is $\hat{y} = 0.06078x - 0.1261$. For $x = 2.0$, this formula gives $\hat{y} = -0.0045$. **(b)** The correlation is $r \doteq 0.8782$, so the line explains $r^2 = 77.1\%$ of the variation in brain activity.

**5.29.** See also the solution to Exercise 4.39. **(a)** The regression line is $\hat{y} = 157.7 - 2.993x$. Following a season with 30 breeding pairs, we predict that about 68% (67.88%) of males will return. **(b)** The linear relationship explains $r^2 \doteq 63.1\%$ of the variation in the percent of returning males.

**5.30.** Women's heights are the $x$ values; men's are the $y$ values. The slope and intercept are

$$b = r \cdot s_y/s_x = 0.5 \cdot 2.8/2.7 \doteq 0.5185$$

$$a = \bar{y} - b\bar{x} = 69.3 - (0.5185)(64) \doteq 36.115.$$

The regression equation is $\hat{y} = 36.115 + 0.5185x$. Ideally, the scales should be the same on both axes. For a 67-inch-tall wife, we predict the husband's height will be about 70.85 inches.

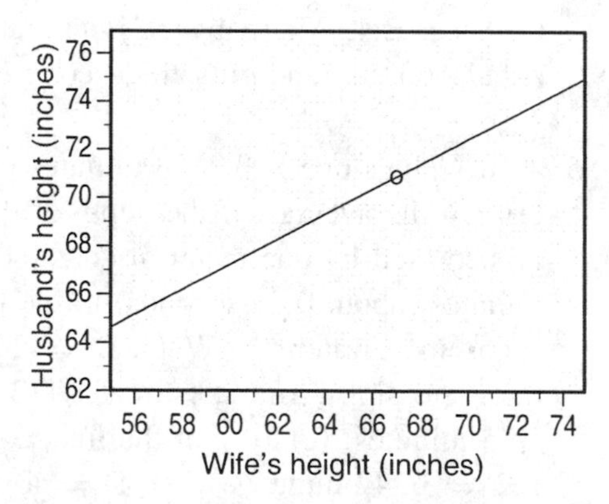


**5.31.** **(a)** The slope is $b = r \cdot s_y/s_x = (0.6)(8)/(30) = 0.16$, and the intercept is $a = \bar{y} - b\bar{x} = 30.2$. **(b)** Julie's predicted score is $\hat{y} = 78.2$. **(c)** $r^2 = 0.36$; only 36% of the variability in $y$ is accounted for by the regression, so the estimate $\hat{y} = 78.2$ could be quite different from the real score.

**5.32.** $r = \sqrt{0.16} = 0.40$ (high attendance goes with high grades, so the correlation must be positive).

**5.33.** **(a)** Plot at right; based on the discussion in part (b), absorbence is the explanatory variable, so it has been placed on the horizontal axis. The correlation is $r \doteq 0.9999$, so recalibration is not necessary. **(b)** The regression line is $\hat{y} = 8.825x - 14.52$; when $x = 40$, we predict $\hat{y} \doteq 338.5$ mg/l. **(c)** This prediction should be very accurate because the relationship is so strong.

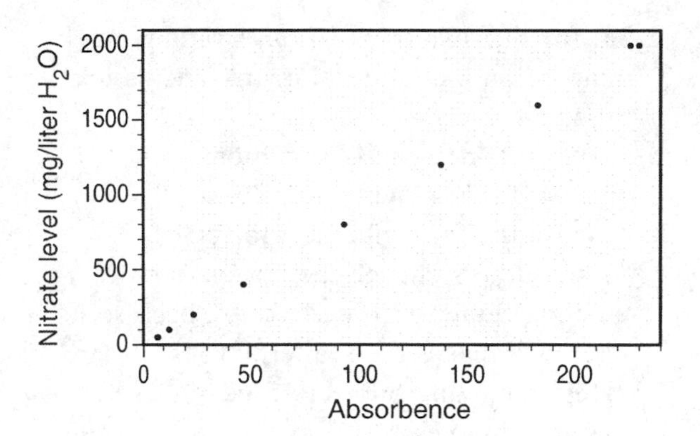


**5.34.** **(a)** To three decimal places, the correlations are all approximately 0.816 (for Set D, $r$ actually rounds to 0.817), and the regression lines are all approximately $\hat{y} = 3.000 + 0.500x$. For all four sets, we predict $\hat{y} \doteq 8$ when $x = 10$. **(b)** Below. **(c)** For Set A, the use of the regression line seems to be reasonable—the data do seem to have a moderate linear association (albeit with a fair amount of scatter). For Set B, there is an obvious *non*linear relationship; we should fit a parabola or other curve. For Set C, the point (13, 12.74) deviates from the (highly linear) pattern of the other points; if we can exclude it, the (new) regression formula would be very useful for prediction. For Set D, the data point with $x = 19$ is a very influential point—the other points alone give no indication of slope for the line. Seeing how widely scattered the $y$-coordinates of the other points are, we cannot place too much faith in the $y$-coordinate of the influential point; thus we cannot depend on the slope of the line, and so we cannot depend on the estimate when $x = 10$. (We also have no evidence as to whether or not a line is an appropriate model for this relationship.)

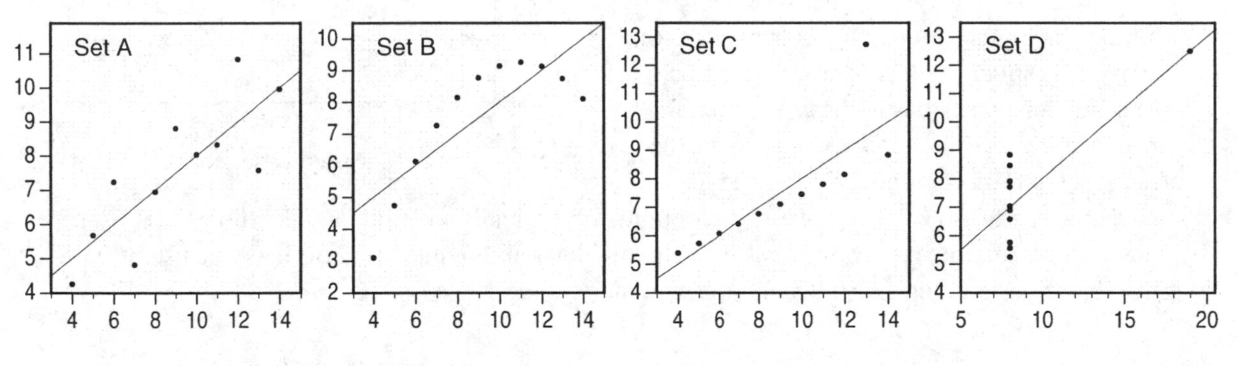


**5.35.** **(a)** The outlier (circled) is at the upper right of the scatterplot. Ignoring this point, the plot shows a moderately strong negative linear relationship. **(b)** The correlation for all 12 points is $r = -0.3387$. Omitting the outlier gives $r = -0.7866$. The outlier weakens the linear pattern and so moves $r$ away from $-1$.

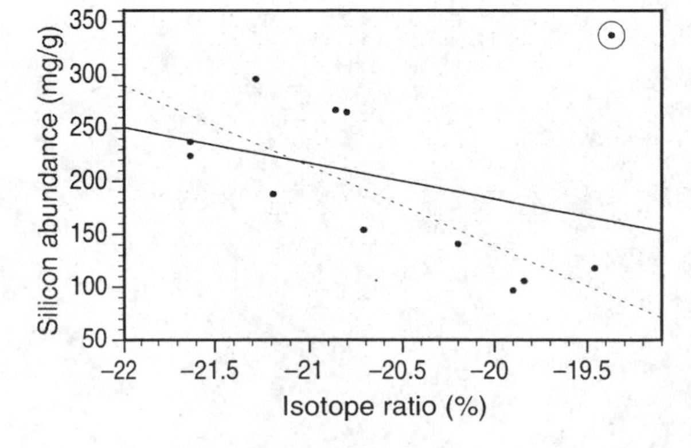

**5.36.** **(a)** The two unusual observations are marked on the scatterplot. **(b)** The correlations are

$r_1 \doteq 0.4819$ (all observations)
$r_2 \doteq 0.5684$ (without Subject 15)
$r_3 \doteq 0.3837$ (without Subject 18)

Both outliers change the correlation. Removing Subject 15 increases $r$, because its presence makes the scatterplot less linear, while removing Subject 18 decreases $r$, because its presence decreases the relative scatter about the linear pattern.

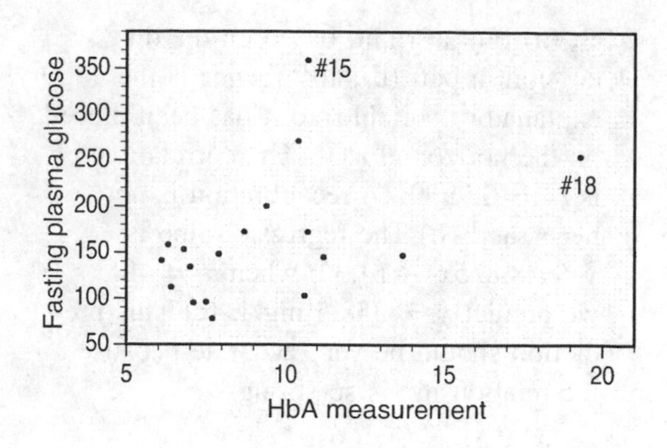


**5.37.** The least-squares line for all 12 points (the solid line in the plot shown in the solution to Exercise 5.35) is $\hat{y} = -492.6 - 33.79x$. Omitting the outlier, the line (dashed in the plot) becomes $\hat{y} = -1371.6 - 75.52x$. Adding the outlier—that is, moving from the dashed line to the solid line—pivots the least-squares line up toward the outlier to reduce the very large vertical deviation of this point from the line.

**5.38.** The scatterplot from Exercise 5.36 is reproduced here with the regression lines added. The equations are

$\hat{y} \doteq 66.4 + 10.4x$ (all observations)
$\hat{y} \doteq 69.5 + 8.92x$ (without #15)
$\hat{y} \doteq 52.3 + 12.1x$ (without #18)

While the equation changes in response to removing either subject, one could argue that neither one is particularly influential, because the line moves very little over the range of $x$ (HbA) values. Subject 15 is an outlier in terms of its $y$ value; such points are typically not influential. Subject 18 is an outlier in terms of its $x$ value, but is not particularly influential because it is consistent with the linear pattern suggested by the other points.

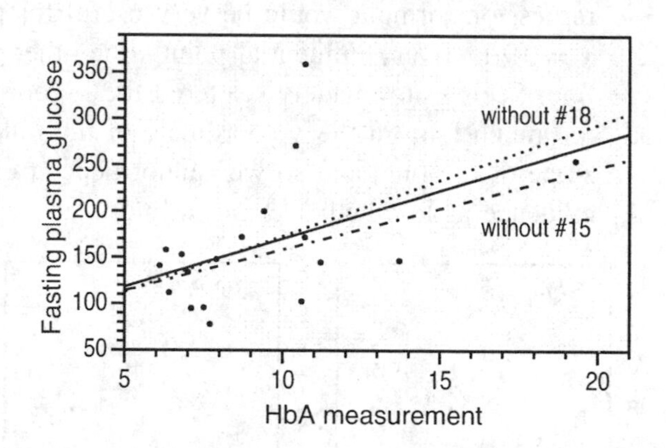

**5.39. (a)** Any point that falls exactly on the regression line will not increase the sum of squared vertical distances (which the regression line minimizes). Any other line—even if it passes through this new point—will necessarily have a higher total sum of squares. Thus the regression line does not change. Possible output is shown below, left. The correlation changes (increases) because the new point reduces the *relative* scatter about the regression line. (That is, the distance of the points above and below the line remains the same, but the spread of the $x$ values increases.) **(b)** Influential points are those whose $x$ coordinates are outliers; this point is on the right side, while all others are on the left. Possible output is shown below, right.

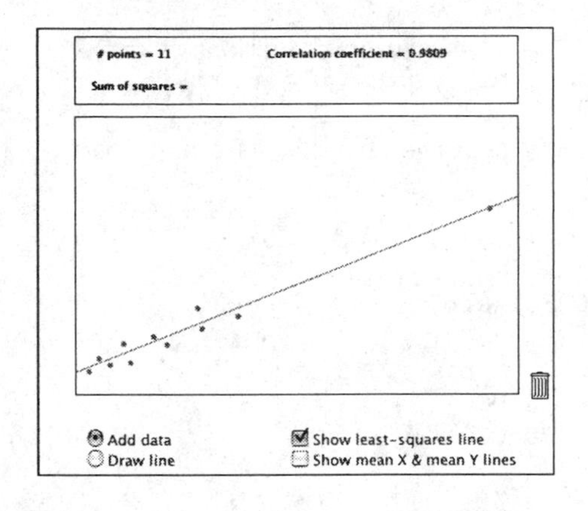


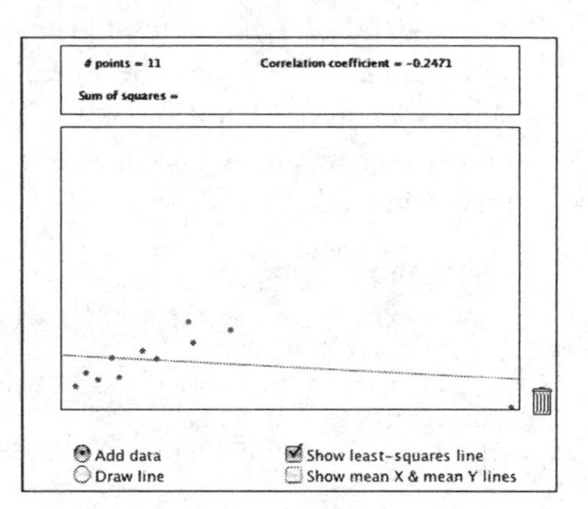


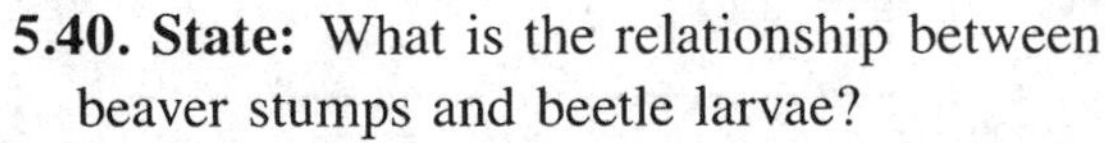

**5.40. State:** What is the relationship between beaver stumps and beetle larvae?
**Formulate:** We construct a scatterplot (with beaver stumps as the explanatory variable), and if appropriate, find the regression line and correlation.
**Solve:** The scatterplot shows a positive linear association. Regression seems to be an appropriate way to summarize the relationship; the regression line is $\hat{y} = -1.286 + 11.89x$. The straight-line relationship explains $r^2 \doteq 83.9\%$ of the variation in beetle larvae.
**Conclude:** The strong positive association supports the idea that beavers benefit beetles.

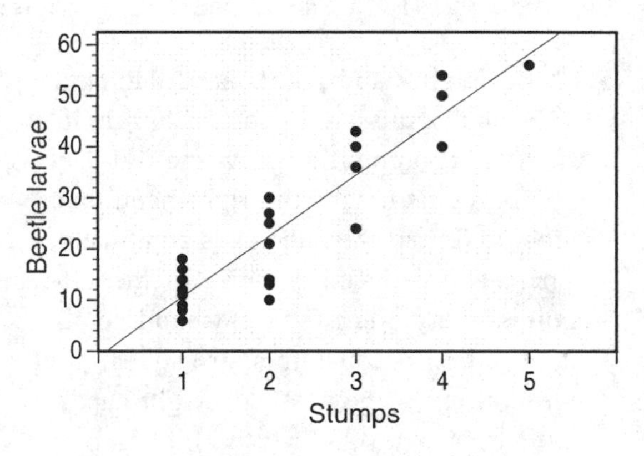


**Minitab output**

```
The regression equation is larvae = - 1.29 + 11.9 stumps

Predictor        Coef       Stdev    t-ratio       p
Constant       -1.286       2.853      -0.45   0.657
stumps         11.894       1.136      10.47   0.000

s = 6.419       R-sq = 83.9%     R-sq(adj) = 83.1%
```

**5.41. State:** What is the relationship between snow cover and wind stress?
**Formulate:** We examine a scatterplot of wind stress against snow cover—viewing the latter as explanatory—and (if appropriate) compute correlation and regression lines.
**Solve:** The scatterplot suggests a negative linear association, with correlation $r \doteq -0.9179$. The regression line is $\hat{y} = 0.212 - 0.00561x$; the linear relationship explains $r^2 \doteq 84.3\%$ of the variation in wind stress.

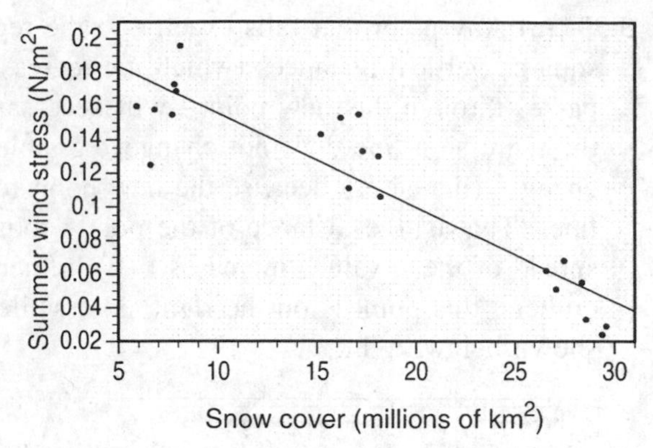


**Conclude:** We have good evidence that decreasing snow cover is strongly associated with increasing wind stress.

**Minitab output**

```
The regression equation is wind = 0.212 - 0.00561 snow

Predictor        Coef       Stdev    t-ratio       p
Constant      0.21172     0.01083      19.56   0.000
snow       -0.0056096   0.0005562     -10.09   0.000

s = 0.02191      R-sq = 84.3%      R-sq(adj) = 83.4%
```

**5.42. (a)** Right-hand points are filled circles; left-hand points are open circles. **(b)** The right-hand points lie below the left-hand points. (This means the right-hand times are shorter, so the subject is right-handed.) There is no striking pattern for the left-hand points; the pattern for right-hand points is obscured because they are squeezed at the bottom of the plot. **(c)** Right hand: $\hat{y} = 99.4 + 0.0283x$ ($r = 0.305$, $r^2 = 9.3\%$). Left hand: $\hat{y} = 172 + 0.262x$ ($r = 0.318$, $r^2 = 10.1\%$). The left-hand regression is slightly better, but neither is very good: distance accounts for only 9.3% (right) and 10.1% (left) of the variation in time.

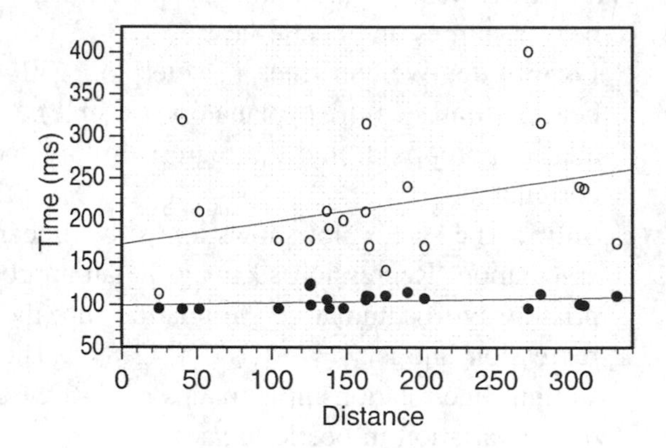


**5.43.** See also the solution to Exercise 5.41. The 21 points in the scatterplot are divided into three clusters of seven points each, suggesting that the points within each cluster are somehow related to one another. One reasonable explanation would be that the seven highest snow-cover data points were recorded early in the summer (May), and the lowest snow-cover data points were recorded after the snow has had more time to melt (July).

**5.44.** The two residual plots are shown below; neither shows a systematic pattern.

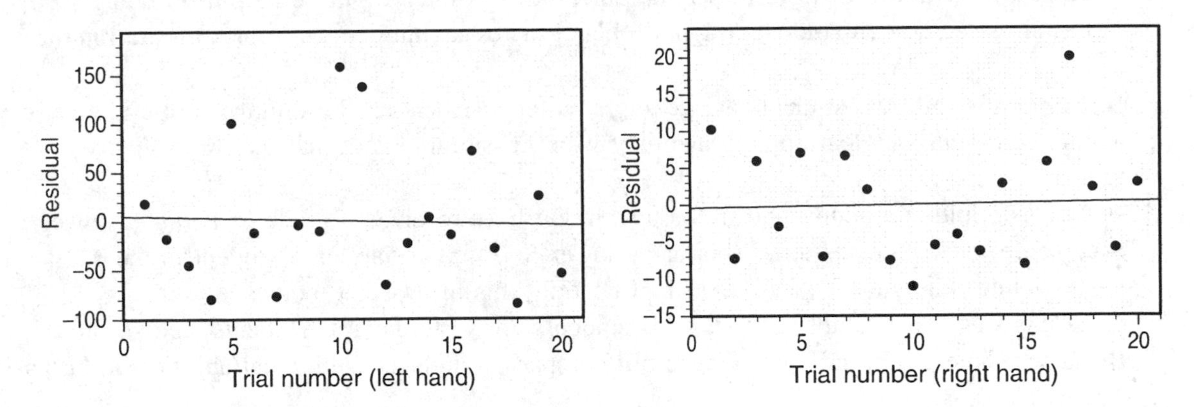


**5.45. (a)** The regression line is $\hat{y} = 157.68216 - 2.9934945x$ (using all of the digits displayed in Figure 5.11). The table on the right shows the fitted values ($\hat{y}$) for each $x$ value, and the residual $y - \hat{y}$. Student values may vary based on how many digits are used for the slope and intercept. **(b)** The correlation between the residuals and the explanatory variable $x$ (number of breeding pairs) is 0, except for rounding error.

| $x$ | $y$ | $\hat{y}$ | Residual |
|---|---|---|---|
| 28 | 82 | 73.86 | 8.14 |
| 29 | 83 | 70.87 | 12.13 |
| 29 | 70 | 70.87 | −0.87 |
| 29 | 61 | 70.87 | −9.87 |
| 30 | 69 | 67.88 | 1.12 |
| 32 | 58 | 61.89 | −3.89 |
| 33 | 43 | 58.90 | −15.90 |
| 38 | 50 | 43.93 | 6.07 |
| 38 | 47 | 43.93 | 3.07 |

**5.46. (a)** Without the two years with $x = 38$, the residuals appear to be decreasing with the number of breeding pairs. The $x = 38$ years break from this pattern, because they are both positive. **(b)** Scatterplot below (right). Without the two $x = 38$ years, the new regression line is $\hat{y} = 266 - 6.65x$; this is much steeper than with all nine years included.

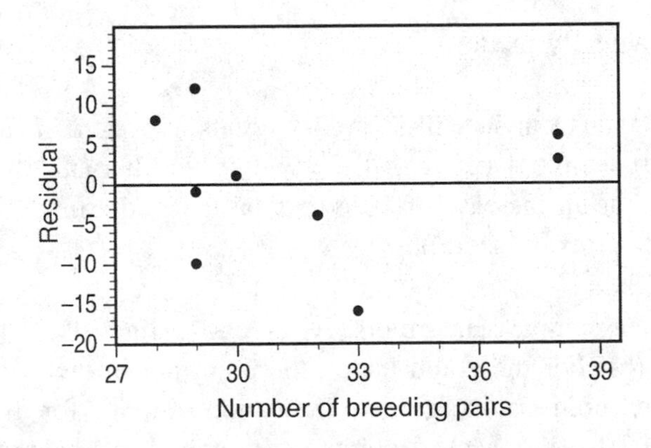


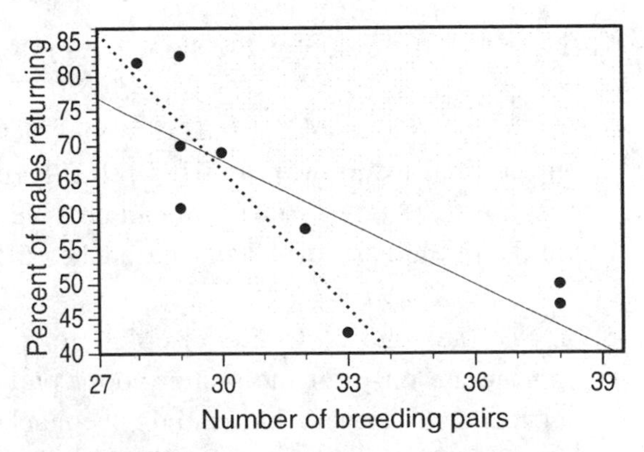


**5.47.** In this case, there may be a causative effect, but in the direction opposite to the one suggested: People who are overweight are more likely to be on diets, and so choose artificial sweeteners over sugar. (Also, heavier people are at a higher risk to develop Type 2 diabetes; if they do, they are likely to switch to artificial sweeteners.)

**5.48.** Responses will vary. For example, students who choose the online course might have more self-motivation, or have better computer skills (which might be helpful in doing well in the class; e.g., such students might do better at researching course topics on the Internet).

**5.49.** Some possibilities: students are getting smarter; teachers are becoming more effective; or technology improves learning. (I said they were possibilities, not that they were likely.)

**5.50.** For example, a student who in the past might have received a grade of B (and a lower SAT score) now receives an A (but has a lower SAT score than an A student in the past). While this is a bit of an oversimplification, this means that today's A students are yesterday's A and B students, today's B students are yesterday's C students, and so on. Because of the grade inflation, we are not comparing students with equal abilities in the past and today.

**5.51.** Here is a (relatively) simple example to show how this can happen: Suppose that most workers are currently 30 to 50 years old; of course, some are older or younger than that, but this age group dominates. Suppose further that each worker's current salary is his/her age (in thousands of dollars); for example, a 30-year-old worker is currently making $30,000.

Over the next 10 years, all workers age, and their salaries increase. Suppose every worker's salary increases by between $4000 and $8000. Then every worker will be making *more* money than he/she did 10 years before, but *less* money than a worker of that same age 10 years before.

During that time, a few workers will retire, and others will enter the workforce, but that large cluster that had been between the ages of 30 and 50 (now between 40 and 60) will bring up the overall median salary despite the changes in older and younger workers.

**5.52.** We have slope $b = r\, s_y/s_x$ and intercept $a = \bar{y} - b\bar{x}$, and $\hat{y} = a + bx$, so when $x = \bar{x}$,

$$\hat{y} = a + b\bar{x} = (\bar{y} - b\bar{x}) + b\bar{x} = \bar{y}.$$

(Note that the value of the slope does not actually matter.)

**5.53.** Note that $\bar{y} = 46.6 + 0.41\bar{x}$. We predict that Octavio will score 4.1 points above the mean on the final exam: $\hat{y} = 46.6 + 0.41(\bar{x} + 10) = 46.6 + 0.41\bar{x} + 4.1 = \bar{y} + 4.1$. (Alternatively, because the slope is 0.41, we can observe that an increase of 10 points on the midterm yields an increase of 4.1 on the predicted final exam score.)

**5.54.** See the solution to Exercise 4.37 for three sample scatterplots. A regression line is appropriate only for the scatterplot of part (b). For the graph in (c), the point not in the vertical stack is very influential—the stacked points alone give no indication of slope for the line (if indeed a line is an appropriate model). If the stacked points are scattered, we cannot place too much faith in the $y$-coordinate of the influential point; thus we cannot depend on the slope of the line, and so we cannot depend on predictions made with the regression line. The curved relationship exhibited by the scatterplot in (d) clearly indicates that predictions based on a straight line are not appropriate.

**5.55.** **(a)** Drawing the "best line" by eye is a very inaccurate process; few people choose the best line (although you can get better at it with practice). **(b)** Most people tend to overestimate the slope for a scatterplot with $r \doteq 0.7$; that is, most students will find that the least-squares line is less steep than the one they draw.

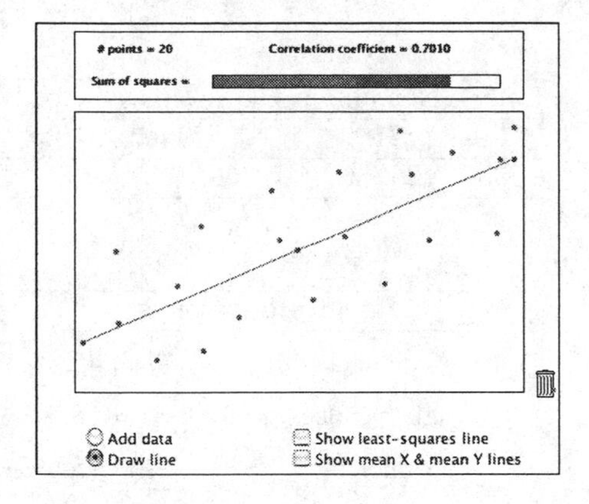


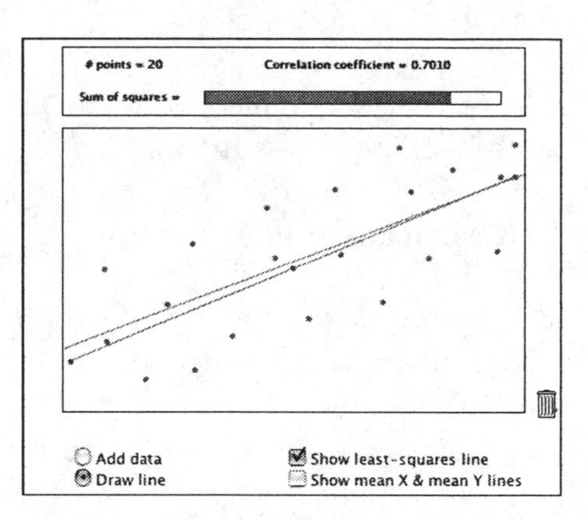

# Chapter 6 Solutions

**6.1.** **(a)** The six counts add up to 858 people. **(b)** Adding across the top row, we find that 43 people had arthritis. **(c)** The marginal distribution is summarized in the table on the right.

| Elite | Non-elite | Did not play | Total |
|---|---|---|---|
| 71 | 215 | 572 | 858 |
| 8.3% | 25.1% | 66.7% | |

**6.2.** Shown on the right are the top *four* causes for each age group; some students might not consider the "Other causes" group.

Accidents, other causes, and homicide account for about 79% of deaths among young people; few young people die from disease. Accidents and other causes make up nearly 53% of deaths among 25- to 44-year-olds, but cancer now accounts for 14.8% (and heart diseases are close behind). In middle age (45 to 64 years), almost 34% are due to other causes, and over 56% are due to cancer and heart diseases.

| 15 to 24 years | |
|---|---|
| Accidents | $\frac{14{,}966}{33{,}022} \doteq 45.3\%$ |
| Other causes | $\frac{6105}{33{,}022} \doteq 18.5\%$ |
| Homicide | $\frac{5148}{33{,}022} \doteq 15.6\%$ |
| Suicide | $\frac{3921}{33{,}022} \doteq 11.9\%$ |
| **25 to 44 years** | |
| Other causes | $\frac{40{,}259}{128{,}924} \doteq 31.2\%$ |
| Accidents | $\frac{27{,}844}{128{,}924} \doteq 21.6\%$ |
| Cancer | $\frac{19{,}041}{128{,}924} \doteq 14.8\%$ |
| Heart diseases | $\frac{16{,}283}{128{,}924} \doteq 12.6\%$ |
| **45 to 64 years** | |
| Other causes | $\frac{148{,}010}{437{,}058} \doteq 33.9\%$ |
| Cancer | $\frac{144{,}936}{437{,}058} \doteq 33.2\%$ |
| Heart diseases | $\frac{101{,}713}{437{,}058} \doteq 23.3\%$ |
| Accidents | $\frac{23{,}669}{437{,}058} \doteq 5.4\%$ |

**6.3.** For the conditional distribution of age among female college students, we use only the numbers from the first column of Table 6.1, dividing each age-group count by the total number of female college students.

| | |
|---|---|
| 15 to 17 years | $\frac{89}{9321} \doteq 1.0\%$ |
| 18 to 24 years | $\frac{5668}{9321} \doteq 60.8\%$ |
| 25 to 34 years | $\frac{1904}{9321} \doteq 20.4\%$ |
| 35 years or older | $\frac{1660}{9321} \doteq 17.8\%$ |

**6.4. (a)** Use column percents, e.g., $\frac{68}{225} \doteq 30.2\%$ of females are in accounting, etc. See the table and graph below. The biggest difference between women and men is in administration: A higher percentage of women chose this major. Meanwhile, a greater proportion of men chose other fields, especially finance. **(b)** There were 386 responses; $\frac{336}{722} \doteq 46.5\%$ did not respond.

| | Female | Male |
|---|---|---|
| Accounting | 30.2% | 34.8% |
| Administration | 40.4% | 24.8% |
| Economics | 2.2% | 3.7% |
| Finance | 27.1% | 36.6% |

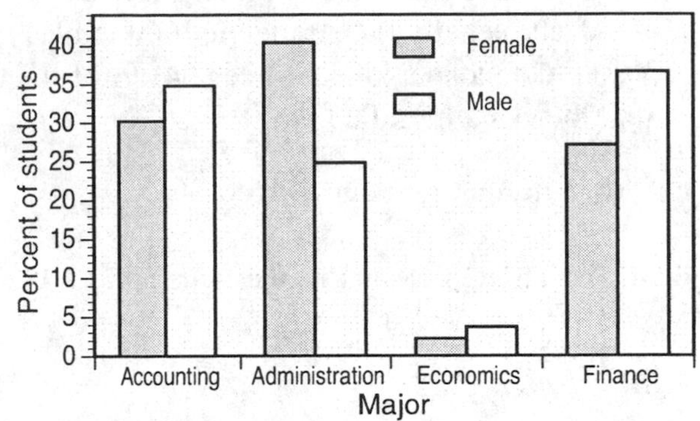


**6.5. State:** Are high-level soccer players are more likely to suffer from arthritis later in life?

| | Elite | Non-elite | None |
|---|---|---|---|
| Arthritis | 14.1% | 4.2% | 4.2% |
| No Arthritis | 85.9% | 95.8% | 95.8% |

**Formulate:** Calculate and compare the conditional distributions of occurrence of arthritis among the different soccer groups.
**Solve:** The conditional distributions are shown on the right. (A bar graph could also be constructed, but with so few percents, the comparison can be made without a graph.)
**Conclude:** There is no difference between the non-elite group and those who did not play at all, but the percentage of elite players with arthritis is noticeably higher.

**6.6.** Two examples are shown on the right. In general, choose $a$ to be any number from 0 to 50, and then all the other entries can be determined.

| | |
|---|---|
| 25 | 25 |
| 35 | 15 |

| | |
|---|---|
| 10 | 40 |
| 50 | 0 |

**Note:** *This is why we say that such a table has "one degree of freedom": We can make one (nearly) arbitrary choice for the value of* a, *and then have no more decisions to make.*

**6.7. (a)** First find all the column totals, then compute (total delayed)/(total flights). This gives

$$\frac{501}{3274+501} \doteq 13.3\% \text{ for Alaska Airlines, and}$$

$$\frac{787}{6438+787} \doteq 10.9\% \text{ for America West.}$$

**(b)** Table at right; for example, $11.1\% \doteq \frac{62}{497+62}$.
**(c)** Both airlines do best at Phoenix, where America West has 72.7% of its flights, and Alaska Airlines has only 6.2% of its flights. Seattle is the worst city for both; Alaska Airlines has 56.8% of its flights there, versus only 3.6% for America West. The large percent of "easy" (Phoenix) flights for America West and the large percent of "hard" (Seattle) flights for Alaska Airlines make America West look better.

| | Percent delayed | |
|---|---|---|
| | Alaska Airlines | America West |
| Los Angeles | 11.1% | 14.4% |
| Phoenix | 5.2 | 7.9 |
| San Diego | 8.6 | 14.5 |
| San Francisco | 16.9 | 28.7 |
| Seattle | 14.2 | 23.3 |
| All flights | 13.3% | 10.9% |

**6.8. (a)** At right. **(b)** Overall, $\frac{19}{160} \doteq 11.9\%$ of white defendants and $\frac{17}{166} \doteq 10.2\%$ of black defendants got the death penalty. However, for white victims the percents are 12.6% and 17.5% (respectively); when the victim is black, they are 0% and 5.8%. **(c)** In cases involving white victims, 14% of defendants got the death penalty; when the victim was black, only 5.4% of defendants got the death penalty. White defendants killed whites 94.3% of the time, but are less likely to get the death penalty than blacks who killed whites.

| | Death penalty? | |
|---|---|---|
| | Yes | No |
| White defendant | 19 | 141 |
| Black defendant | 17 | 149 |

**6.9.** (a) The first column adds to 2625.

**6.10.** (b) The ten counts in the table add to 4877.

**6.11.** (b) $\frac{2625}{4877} \doteq 0.5382 \doteq 54\%$.

**6.12.** (a) The marginal distribution of sex is found by adding down the columns to eliminate the "chance of marriage" variable.

**6.13.** (b) $\frac{1174}{2625} \doteq 0.4472 \doteq 45\%$.

**6.14.** (c) The conditional distribution of chance of marriage given sex is the entries in a given column, divided by that column total.

**6.15.** (c) 1930 respondents said they would almost certainly be married; $\frac{1174}{1930} \doteq 0.6083 \doteq 61\%$.

**6.16.** (b) The conditional distribution of sex given chance of marriage is the entries in a given row, divided by that row total.

**6.17.** (b) There would be five bars—one for each "chance of marriage" category.

**6.18.** (b) We are lumping together dissimilar groups, the typical mistake in cases of Simpson's paradox. To illustrate this effect in this situation, suppose that there were 100 part-time and 100 full-time students, with individual category counts and average GPAs shown. Then the average GPA for full-time and part-time students would be 3.00 and 3.06, respectively.

| | Full-time (GPA) | Part-time (GPA) |
|---|---|---|
| Science | 50 (2.8) | 10 (2.7) |
| Nonscience | 50 (3.2) | 90 (3.1) |

**6.19.** The table on the right gives the two marginal distributions. The marginal distribution of marital status is found by taking, e.g., $\frac{337}{8235} \doteq 4.1\%$. The marginal distribution of job grade is found by taking, e.g., $\frac{955}{8235} \doteq 11.6\%$.

| Single | Married | Divorced | Widowed |
|---|---|---|---|
| 4.1% | 93.9% | 1.5% | 0.5% |
| **Grade 1** | **Grade 2** | **Grade 3** | **Grade 4** |
| 11.6% | 51.5% | 30.2% | 6.7% |

As rounded here, both sets of percents add up to 100%. If students round to the nearest whole percent, the marital status numbers add up to 101%. If they round to two places after the decimal, the job grade percents add up to 100.01%.

**6.20.** The percent of single men in grade 1 jobs is $\frac{58}{337} \doteq 17.2\%$. The percent of grade 1 jobs held by single men is $\frac{58}{955} \doteq 6.07\%$.

**6.21.** Divide the entries in the first column by the first column total; e.g., $17.2\% \doteq \frac{58}{337}$. These should add to 100% (except for rounding error).

| Job grade | % of single men |
|---|---|
| 1 | 17.2% |
| 2 | 65.9% |
| 3 | 14.8% |
| 4 | 2.1% |

**6.22. (a)** We need to compute percents to account for the fact that the study included many more married men than single men, so that we would expect their numbers to be higher in every job grade (even if marital status had no relationship with job level). **(b)** A table of percents is above; descriptions of the relationship may vary. Single and widowed men had higher percents of level 1 jobs; single men had the lowest (and widowed men the highest) percents of level 4 jobs.

| Job level | Single | Married | Divorced | Widowed |
|---|---|---|---|---|
| 1 | 17.2% | 11.3% | 11.9% | 19.0% |
| 4 | 2.1% | 6.9% | 5.6% | 9.5% |

**6.23.** Age is the main lurking variable: Married men would generally be older than single men, so they would have been in the work force longer, and therefore had more time to advance in their careers.

**6.24. (a)** To find the marginal distribution of opinion, we need to know the total numbers of people with each opinion: $\frac{49}{133} \doteq 36.8\%$ said "higher," $\frac{32}{133} \doteq 24.1\%$ said "the same," and $\frac{52}{133} \doteq 39.1\%$ said "lower." The numbers are summarized in the first table on the right. The main finding is probably that about 39% of users think the recycled product is of lower quality. This is a serious barrier to sales. **(b)** There were 36 buyers and 97 nonbuyers among the respondents, so (for example) $\frac{20}{36} \doteq 55.6\%$ of buyers rated the quality as higher. Similar arithmetic with the buyers and nonbuyers rows gives the two conditional distributions of opinion, shown in the second table on the right. We see that buyers are much more likely to consider recycled filters higher in quality, though 25% still think they are lower in quality. We cannot draw any conclusion about causation: It may be that some people buy recycled filters because they start with a high opinion of recycled products, or it may be that use persuades people that the quality is high.

| Higher | The same | Lower |
|---|---|---|
| 36.8% | 24.1% | 39.1% |

| | Higher | The same | Lower |
|---|---|---|---|
| Buyers | 55.6% | 19.4% | 25.0% |
| Nonbuyers | 29.9% | 25.8% | 44.3% |

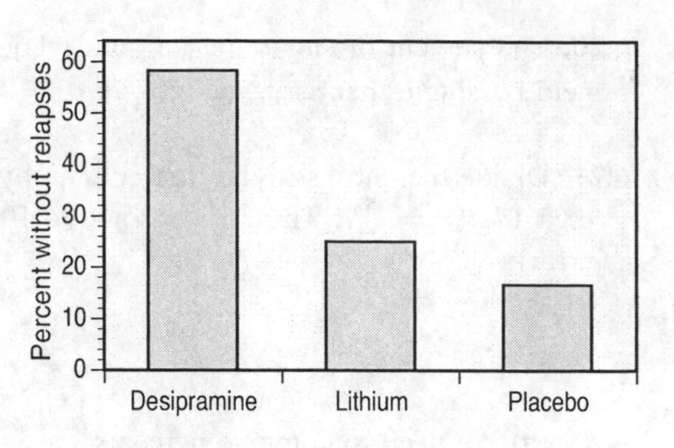


**6.25. (a)** $\frac{14}{24} \doteq 58.33\%$ of desipramine users did not have a relapse, while $\frac{6}{24} = 25\%$ of lithium users and $\frac{4}{24} \doteq 16.67\%$ of those who received placebos succeeded in breaking their addictions. Desipramine seems to be effective. Note that use of percents is not as crucial here as in other cases because each drug was given to 24 addicts. **(b)** Because random assignment was used, causation is indicated.

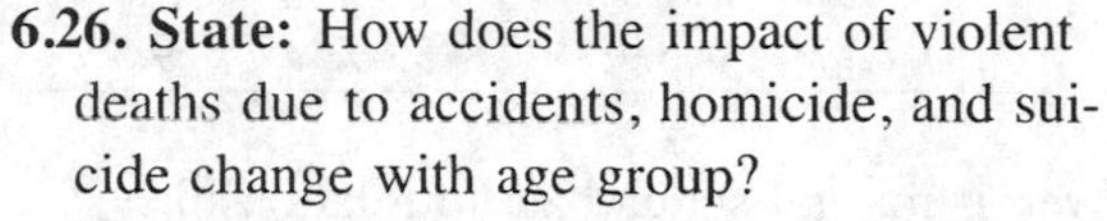

**6.26. State:** How does the impact of violent deaths due to accidents, homicide, and suicide change with age group?
**Formulate:** Compute and compare the percents of such deaths in each age group.
**Solve:** Divide the counts of such deaths by the column totals (the number of deaths in each age group). We are most interested in the *total* percent of such deaths, but it is somewhat useful to examine each subcategory separately, as has been done in the table and bar graph.

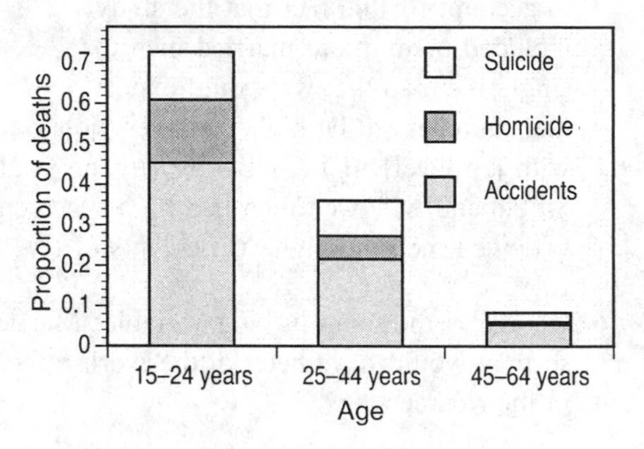


| | 15 to 24 years | 25 to 44 years | 45 to 64 years |
|---|---|---|---|
| Accidents | $\frac{14{,}966}{33{,}022} \doteq 45.3\%$ | $\frac{27{,}844}{128{,}924} \doteq 21.6\%$ | $\frac{23{,}669}{437{,}058} \doteq 5.4\%$ |
| Homicide | $\frac{5148}{33{,}022} \doteq 15.6\%$ | $\frac{7367}{128{,}924} \doteq 5.7\%$ | $\frac{2756}{437{,}058} \doteq 0.6\%$ |
| Suicide | $\frac{3921}{33{,}022} \doteq 11.9\%$ | $\frac{11{,}251}{128{,}924} \doteq 8.7\%$ | $\frac{10{,}057}{437{,}058} \doteq 2.3\%$ |
| Total | 72.8% | 36.0% | 8.3% |

**Conclude:** Total deaths and deaths from natural causes go up with age, as we would expect. Deaths from violent causes decrease as we move from 15–24 years to 25–44 years, and decrease even more in the 45–64 age-group. (Some students might observe that the first age-group is smaller—only 10 years—while the others are 20 years. This is important to note in comparing the *number* of deaths, but is not relevant for comparing the *percent* of violent deaths.)

**6.27. State:** How does the participation of women change with level of degree?

**Formulate:** Calculate and compare the conditional distributions of sex for each degree level.

**Solve:** We compute, for example, $\frac{431}{675} \doteq 63.9\%$—the number of women earning associate's degrees, divided by the total number of associate's degrees. The table on the right shows the percent of women at each degree level, which is all we need for comparison. (A bar graph of these percents could also be constructed.)

| Degree | % female |
|---|---|
| Associate's | 63.9% |
| Bachelor's | 58.2% |
| Master's | 58.1% |
| Professional | 47.2% |
| Doctorate | 46.7% |

**Conclude:** Women earn a majority of associate's, bachelor's, and master's degrees, but fall slightly below 50% for professional and doctoral degrees.

**6.28. State:** Are people who get angry easily more likely to have heart disease?

**Formulate:** Compute and compare the risk of CHD among the three anger groups. (That is, find the conditional distributions of CHD for each group.)

**Solve:** The most important numbers for comparison are the percents of each anger group that experienced CHD:

$$\frac{53}{3110} \doteq 1.7\% \quad \text{of the low-anger group}$$
$$\frac{110}{4731} \doteq 2.3\% \quad \text{of the moderate-anger group}$$
$$\frac{27}{633} \doteq 4.3\% \quad \text{of the high-anger group}$$

(We could also construct a bar graph of these percents.)

**Conclude:** Risk of CHD increases with proneness to sudden anger. It might be good to point out to students that results like these are typically reported in the media with a reference to the *relative risk* of CHD; for example, because $4.3\%/1.7\% \doteq 2.5$, we might read that "subjects in the high-anger group had 2.5 times the risk of those in the low-anger group."

**6.29. State:** Do eggs hatch less well at cooler temperatures?

**Formulate:** Compare the conditional distribution of hatching given temperature.

**Solve:** Shown is the data presented as a two-way table; in order of increasing temperature, the proportions hatching are

| | Temperature | | |
|---|---|---|---|
| | Cold | Neutral | Hot |
| Hatched | 16 | 38 | 75 |
| Did not hatch | 11 | 18 | 29 |
| Total | 27 | 56 | 104 |

$$\frac{16}{27} \doteq 59.3\%, \quad \frac{38}{56} \doteq 67.9\%, \quad \frac{75}{104} \doteq 72.1\%.$$

(We could also construct a bar graph of these percents.)

**Conclude:** The percent hatching increases with temperature; the cold temperature did not prevent hatching, but made it less likely. The difference between the percents hatching at hot and neutral temperatures is fairly small, and may not be big enough to be called significant. (Statistical tests say that it is not.)

**6.30.** **(a)** At Hospital A, 99% of good-condition patients and 96.2% of poor-condition patients survive. For Hospital B, both numbers are slightly lower: 98.75% (good condition) and 96% (poor condition). **(b)** Combining all patients produces the table on the right, which has a 97% survival rate at Hospital A and a 98% survival rate at Hospital B. **(c)** More than 70% of Hospital A's patients arrive in poor condition, compared to 25% at Hospital B, so A's survival rate is lower overall because these patients are more likely to die in the hospital.

| | Hospital A | Hospital B |
|---|---|---|
| Died | 63 | 16 |
| Survived | 2037 | 784 |
| Total | 2100 | 800 |

**6.31.** **(a)** At right. **(b)** $\frac{490}{700} = 70\%$ of male applicants are admitted, while only $\frac{280}{500} = 56\%$ of females are admitted. **(c)** 80% of male business school applicants are admitted, compared with 90% of females; in the law school, 10% of males are admitted, compared with 33.3% of females. **(d)** A majority (6/7) of male applicants apply to the business school, which admits 82.5% of all applicants. Meanwhile, a majority (3/5) of women apply to the law school, which admits only 27.5% of its applicants.

| | Admit | Deny |
|---|---|---|
| Male | 490 | 210 |
| Female | 280 | 220 |

**6.32.** Examples will vary, of course; here (below) is one very simplistic possibility. The key is to be sure that the three-way table has a lower percent of overweight people among the smokers than among the nonsmokers.

| **Smoker** | Early Death | |
|---|---|---|
| | Yes | No |
| Overweight | 1 | 0 |
| Not overweight | 4 | 2 |

| **Nonsmoker** | Early Death | |
|---|---|---|
| | Yes | No |
| Overweight | 3 | 6 |
| Not overweight | 1 | 3 |

| **Combined** | Early Death | |
|---|---|---|
| | Yes | No |
| Overweight | 4 | 6 |
| Not overweight | 5 | 5 |

# Chapter 7 Solutions

**7.1.** Student answers may vary; for comparison, recent *U.S. News* rankings have used measures such as academic reputation (measured by surveying college and university administrators), retention rate, graduation rate, class sizes, faculty salaries, student-faculty ratio, percent of faculty with highest degree in their fields, quality of entering students (ACT/SAT scores, high school class rank, enrollment-to-admission ratio), financial resources, and the percent of alumni who give to the school.

**7.2.** Unmet need is greatest at private institutions, especially for-profit ones. A pie chart would be incorrect because these numbers do not represent parts of a single whole. (If the numbers given had been *total* unmet need, rather than *average* unmet need, and if we had information about *all* types of institutions, we would have been able to make a pie chart.)

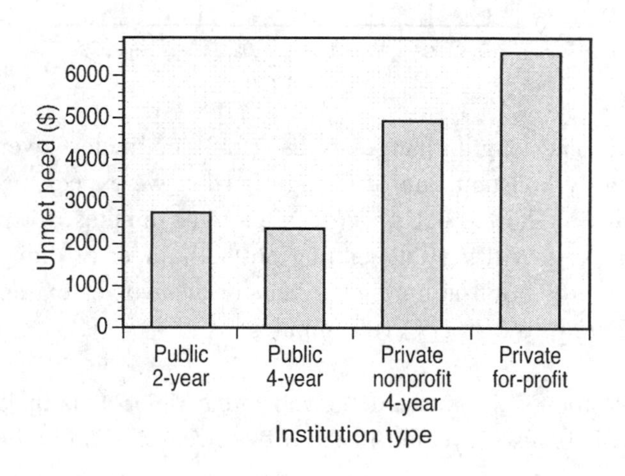


**7.3.** While income from theater showings has been relatively flat over time, video and DVD sales have grown tremendously. (Of course, starting from 0, they initially had nowhere to go but up.) In 1995 and 2000, video/DVD sales were roughly double theater income, and in 2004, they brought in nearly three times as much.

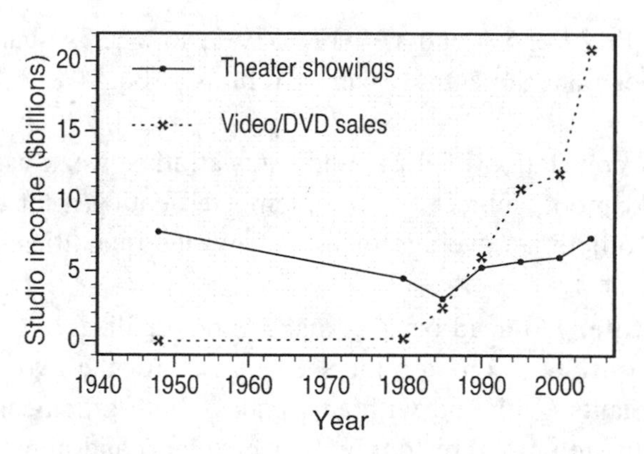

**7.4.** Either a bar graph or a pie chart can be used. Theater showings account for about $\frac{7.4}{44.9} \doteq 16.5\%$ of studio income. (Note that in order to answer this question, we must assume that there are no other sources of income apart from those listed—the same assumption we make in creating the pie chart.)

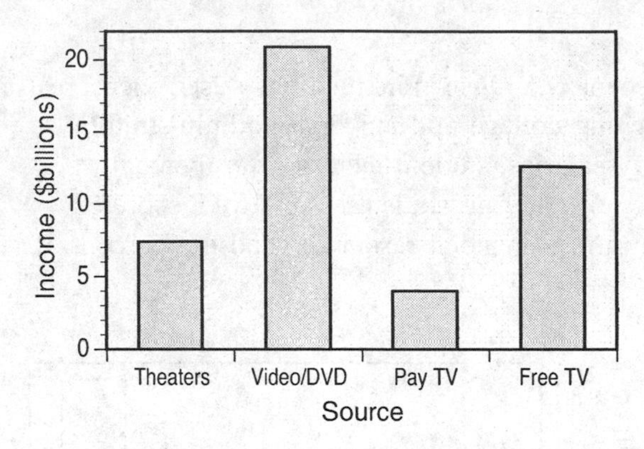


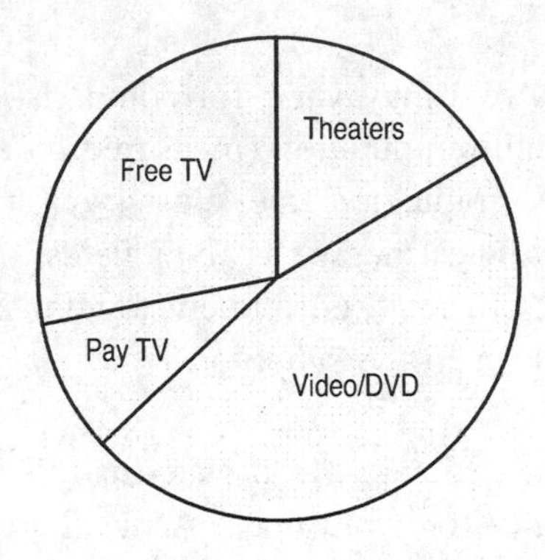


**7.5.** **(a)** The length changes from 1 to 3 centimeters over each 10-minute time interval. This roughly constant rate of change is what we expect for a line. **(b)** The regression equation is $\hat{y} = -2.39 + 0.158x$. **(c)** After 1440 minutes, we predict a length of about 225 cm. (Answers will vary depending on the number of digits used for the slope and intercept.) This prediction is unreliable because it involves extrapolation: The data we have is based on times up to 3 hours (180 minutes).

**7.6.** Women's weights are skewed to the right: This makes the mean higher than the median, and it is also revealed in the differences $M - Q_1 = 14.9$ pounds and $Q_3 - M = 24.1$ pounds.

**7.7.** $\bar{x} \doteq 7.9235\%$ and $s \doteq 17.7559\%$, so $\bar{x} \pm 3s$ spans $-45.34\%$ to $61.19\%$. This is much wider than the actual span of returns, $-34.54\%$ to $34.167\%$.

**7.8.** A correlation of 0.217 indicates a rather weak association. This might mean, for example, that among subjects who remembered eating a lot of beef, some really did eat a lot of beef, but others ate average or below-average quantities.

**7.9.** **State:** Do dead cicadas make good fertilizer?
**Formulate:** Compare the seed masses for the two groups of plants (with and without cicadas), both graphically (with stemplots, histograms, or boxplots) and numerically (with appropriate statistics).
**Solve:** Back-to-back stemplots show little difference overall. (Both shapes are somewhat irregular, but neither is clearly higher or lower.) Means and medians are also similar:

| Cicada plants | | Control plants |
|---:|:---:|:---|
| 0 | 1 | |
| | 1 | 3 |
| 4 | 1 | 445 |
| 7 | 1 | 77 |
| 99 | 1 | 89999 |
| 111100 | 2 | 0111 |
| 3333332222 | 2 | 2 |
| 5544 | 2 | 4444445555 |
| 7777666 | 2 | 66666 |
| 999 | 2 | 89 |
| 110 | 3 | |
| | 3 | |
| 5 | 3 | |

| | $\bar{x}$ | $M$ |
|---|---|---|
| Cicada group | 0.2426 mg | 0.2380 mg |
| Control group | 0.2221 mg | 0.2410 mg |

**Conclude:** The data give little reason to believe that cicadas make good fertilizer (at least on the basis of this response variable).

**7.10.** See also the solution to Exercise 4.41. **(a)** The scatterplot of 2003 returns against 2002 returns shows (ignoring the outlier) a strong negative association. That is, the funds that did best in 2003 are those that did worst in 2002. **(b)** The correlation for all 23 points is $r \doteq -0.6230$; with the outlier removed, the correlation is $r^* \doteq -0.8722$. The outlier deviates from the linear pattern of the other points; removing it makes the negative association stronger, and so moves $r$ closer to $-1$.

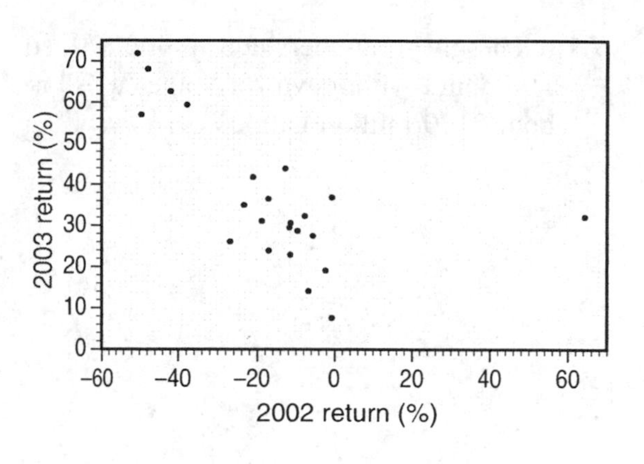


**7.11.** **(a)** The distribution is roughly symmetric; the possible outliers are 0.109 mg and 0.351 mg. (This stemplot is also given in the solution to Exercise 7.9.) **(b)** The means and standard deviations are:

| | $\bar{x}$ | $s$ |
|---|---|---|
| All plants | 0.2426 mg | 0.04759 mg |
| Without extremes | 0.2433 mg | 0.03959 mg |

The standard deviation decreases without the extreme values because the data is less spread out without them. The mean changes very little because the effect of removing the low value is balanced out by removing the high value.

| Stem | Leaves |
|---|---|
| 1 | 0 |
| 1 | |
| 1 | 4 |
| 1 | 7 |
| 1 | 99 |
| 2 | 001111 |
| 2 | 2222333333 |
| 2 | 4455 |
| 2 | 6667777 |
| 2 | 999 |
| 3 | 011 |
| 3 | |
| 3 | 5 |

**7.12.** **(a)** Software gives these results:

| | Equation | $r^2$ |
|---|---|---|
| All 23 funds | $29.2512 - 0.4501x$ | 0.3881 |
| Without Fidelity Gold | $18.1106 - 0.9429x$ | 0.7608 |

The first line is solid in the plot, the second is the dashed line. **(b)** The least-squares line makes the sum of the squares of the vertical deviations of the points from the line as small as possible. The line for the 22 other funds is so far below Fidelity Gold that the squared deviation is very large. The line must pivot up toward Fidelity Gold in order to minimize the sum of squares of all 23 deviations.

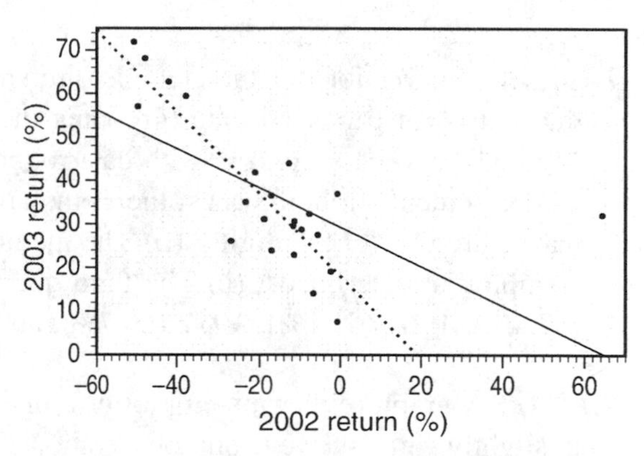


**7.13.** The quartiles are $Q_1 = 0.217$ and $Q_3 = 0.276$, so $IQR = 0.059$, and outliers are those numbers below $Q_1 - 1.5 \times IQR = 0.1285$ and $Q_3 + 1.5 \times IQR = 0.3645$. By this rule, the smallest mass (0.109 mg) is an outlier.

**7.14.** The given numbers add to 402,870, so the amount withdrawn for "other uses" is about 5130 million gallons per day.

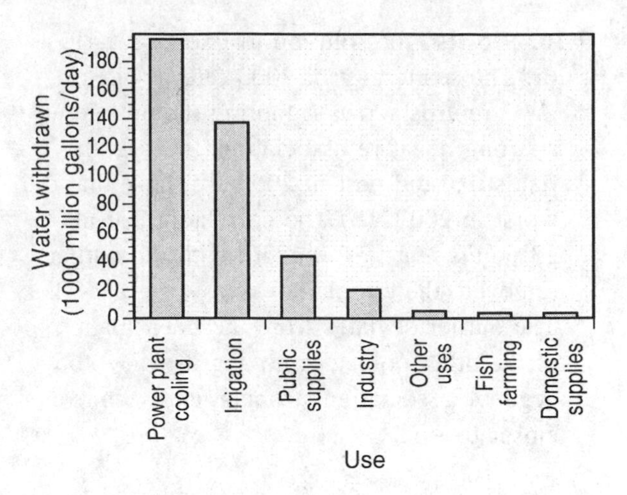


**7.15.** A bar graph is one possible display; a pie graph could also be used, but it would need to include a slice showing the remaining 36.4% of the market as "other brands." (The given percents add up to 63.6%.)

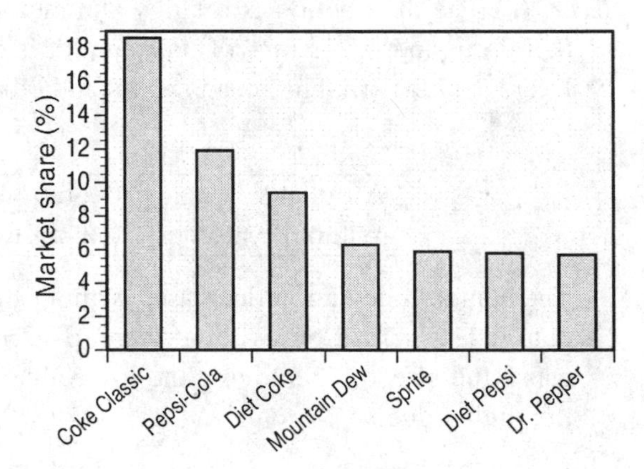


**7.16.** **(a)** Two versions of the stemplot are shown on the right; the first is for truncated data (dropping the digit after the decimal) and the second is with data rounded to the nearest whole percent. In both cases, the stems are split two ways; the leaves are the "ones" digits. **(b)** The median is $M = 50.7\%$. (The corresponding leaf on each stemplot is underlined.) **(c)** The third quartile is $Q_3 = 57.4\%$; there were landslides in 1956 (57.4%), 1964 (61.1%), 1972 (60.7%), and 1984 (58.8%).

| Stem | Leaves |
|---|---|
| 4 | 33 |
| 4 | 7999 |
| 5 | 0<u>0</u>13 |
| 5 | 578 |
| 6 | 01 |

| Stem | Leaves |
|---|---|
| 4 | 33 |
| 4 | 89 |
| 5 | 0001<u>1</u>4 |
| 5 | 579 |
| 6 | 11 |

**7.17.** **(a)** A graph (either a stemplot or a histogram) shows that the distribution is slightly right-skewed; one observation is somewhat low, but not really an outlier. **(b)** Because of the slight right skew, we might expect the median to be slightly larger, but the low observation will tend to counteract that. We find that $\bar{x} \doteq 563.1$ and $M = 560$ km$^3$ of water. **(c)** Because the distribution is not too badly skewed, one could choose the mean and standard deviation—$s \doteq 136.5$ km$^3$ of water—or use the five-number summary:

$$\text{Min} = 290,\ Q_1 = 445,\ M = 560,\ Q_3 = 670,\ \text{Max} = 900$$

(all in km$^3$ of water).

| Stem | Leaves |
|---|---|
| 2 | 9 |
| 3 | |
| 3 | 6999 |
| 4 | 1222234 |
| 4 | 5678 |
| 5 | 00114 |
| 5 | 5566889 |
| 6 | 0001344 |
| 6 | 778889 |
| 7 | 011 |
| 7 | 7 |
| 8 | 0 |
| 8 | 8 |
| 9 | 0 |

**7.18.** The time plot shows a lot of fluctuation from year to year, but also shows a recent increase: Prior to 1972, the discharge rarely rose above 600 km$^3$, but since then, it has exceeded that level more than half the time. The histogram or stemplot cannot show this change over time.

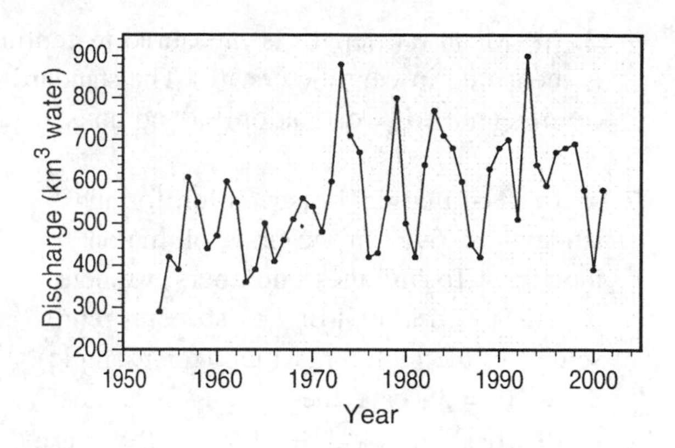


**7.19.** A stemplot is shown; a histogram could also be used. The distribution seems to be fairly Normal apart from a high outlier of 50°. The five-number summary (preferred because of the outlier) is Min $= 13°$, $Q_1 = 20°$, $M = 25°$, $Q_3 = 30°$, Max $= 50°$, while the mean and standard deviation are $\bar{x} = 25.42°$ and $s = 7.47°$.

Student descriptions of the distribution will vary. Most patients have a deformity angle in the range 15° to 35°.

| | |
|---|---|
| 1 | 34 |
| 1 | 66788 |
| 2 | 000111123 |
| 2 | 55556666888 |
| 3 | 00012224 |
| 3 | 88 |
| 4 | |
| 4 | |
| 5 | 0 |

**7.20.** The median ($M = 25°$) does not change when the outlier is removed. The mean changes from 25.42° to 24.76°, and the standard deviation changes from 7.47° to 6.34°.

**7.21.** **(a)** MA angle is the explanatory variable, so it should be on the horizontal axis of the scatterplot. (This scatterplot has the same scale on both axes because both variables are measured in degrees. The regression line is included for the next exercise.) **(b)** The scatterplot shows a moderate to weak positive linear association, with one clear outlier (the patient with HAV angle 50°). **(c)** MA angle can be used to give (very rough) estimates of HAV angle, but the spread is so wide that the estimates would not be very reliable. (Also see the solution to the next problem.)

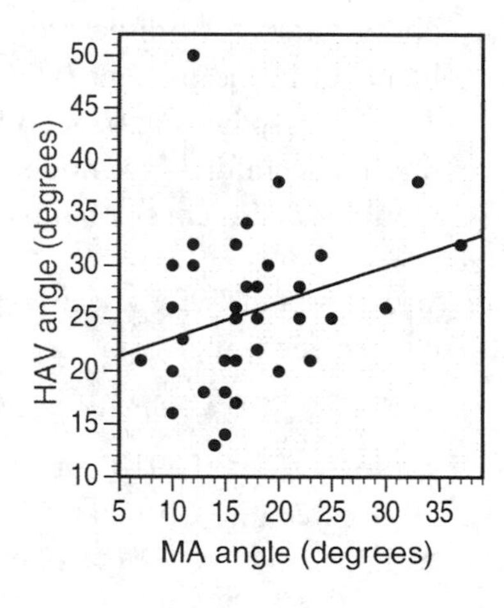


**7.22.** **(a)** The regression line is $\hat{y} = 19.7 + 0.339x$. **(b)** For $x = 25°$, we predict $\hat{y} = 28.2°$. **(c)** The scatterplot shows a lot of spread, so predictions based on this line will not be very reliable. This is confirmed by the value of $r^2$; it is only 9.1%.

**Minitab output**

```
The regression equation is HAV = 19.7 + 0.339 MA

Predictor         Coef        Stdev     t-ratio         p
Constant        19.723        3.217        6.13     0.000
MA              0.3388       0.1782        1.90     0.065

s = 7.224         R-sq = 9.1%        R-sq(adj) = 6.6%
```

**7.23.** **(a)** Mean tail length is measured in centimeters. **(b)** The first quartile of tail length is measured in centimeters. **(c)** The standard deviation of tail length is measured in centimeters. **(d)** Correlation has no units.

**7.24.** **(a)** The marginal distribution for all students is given in the first column on the right. To find these numbers, we note that there are a total of 184 students represented in the table, of which (for example) $29 + 10 = 39$ gave the reason "save time," so this percent is $\frac{39}{184} \doteq 21.20\%$. **(b)** These two conditional distributions are found in the other two columns in the table. For example, $\frac{29}{115} = 25.22\%$ of American students said, "save time."

| | All students | American students | Asian students |
|---|---|---|---|
| Save time | 21.20% | 25.22% | 14.49% |
| Easy | 21.20 | 24.35 | 15.94 |
| Low price | 27.72 | 14.78 | 49.28 |
| Far from store | 8.15 | 9.57 | 5.80 |
| No pressure | 7.07 | 8.70 | 4.35 |
| Other reason | 14.67 | 17.39 | 10.14 |

**7.25.** **State:** How do parent opinions of schools vary among these racial/ethnic groups?
**Formulate:** We will compare the groups using graphs and appropriate conditional distributions.
**Solve:** Student analyses will vary, as will choices of graphs (if any). Some possible observations: All three groups were basically identical in the percent rating schools as "poor." Hispanics appear to be more likely to rate their children's schools as "excellent," but less likely to call the schools "good."
**Conclude:** Student conclusions will vary as well.

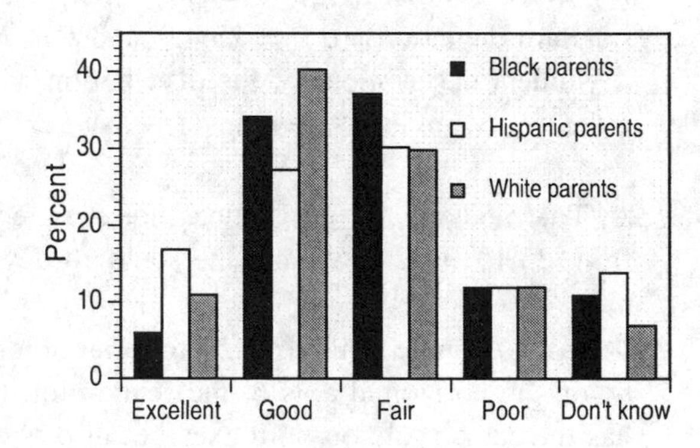


**7.26.** **(a)** About 59% of seeds weigh more than 500 g: If $W$ is the weight of a randomly chosen seed, then

$$P(W > 500 \text{ mg}) = P(Z > \frac{500 - 525}{110}) \doteq P(Z > -0.23).$$

Table A gives 0.5910 for this probability; software gives 0.5899. **(b)** From Table A, the 10th percentile of a standard Normal distribution is about $-1.28$, so the 10th percentile for weight is $525 - 1.28 \times 110 \doteq 384.2$ g. Software gives the value 384.03 g.

**7.27.** **(a)** About 3.5% of bolts will withstand a stress of 90 ksi: If $S$ is the breaking stress of a randomly chosen bolt, then

$$P(S > 90 \text{ ksi}) = P(Z > \frac{90 - 75}{8.3}) \doteq P(Z > 1.81).$$

Table A gives 0.0351 for this probability; software gives 0.0354. **(b)** From Table A, the 25th and 75th percentiles of a standard Normal distribution are about $\pm 0.675$, so the middle 50% of breaking strengths is the range $75 \pm 0.675 \times 8.3 \doteq 75 \pm 5.6 \doteq 69.4$ to 80.6 ksi. (Software gives essentially the same answer.)

**7.28.** The association is negative (as day increases, weight decreases), so $r$ should be negative. The plot shows a very strong linear relationship, so $r$ should be close to $-1$.

**Note:** *In fact,* $r \doteq -0.998$. *The scatterplot includes the regression line for Exercise 7.29.*

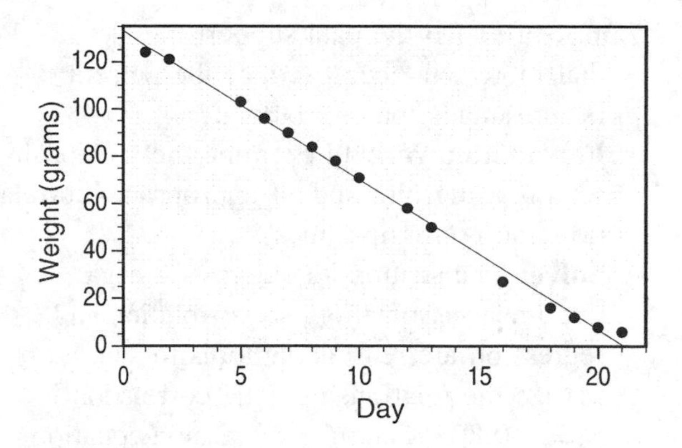


**7.29.** **(a)** The regression equation is $\hat{y} = 133.2 - 6.31x$. On the average, the weight of the soap decreases by about 6.31 grams each day. **(b)** We estimate the weight of the soap on day 4 as $133.2 - 6.31 \times 4 \doteq 108$ grams. **(c)** See the solution to Exercise 7.28.

**7.30.** For day 30, we predict $133.2 - 6.31 \times 30 = -56.1$ grams, which of course makes no sense. Using a regression line for prediction outside the range of the available data is risky.

**7.31.** **(a)** Fidelity Technology Fund is more closely tied to the stock market as a whole, because its correlation is larger. **(b)** No: Correlations tell nothing about the absolute size of the variables, only the relative sizes (above/below average).

**7.32.** This distribution of stock value changes is strongly right-skewed, likely with Cisco and perhaps some others as high outliers. Note that in contrast to the Cisco Systems stock, the *minimum* change can be no smaller than $-100\%$ (if the stock loses all of its value).

**7.33.** In the mid-1990s, European and American stocks were only weakly linked, but now it is more common for them to rise and fall together. Thus investing in both types of stocks is not that much different from investing in either type alone.

**7.34.** The article is incorrect; a correlation of 0.8 means that a straight-line relationship explains about $r^2 = 64\%$ of the variation of European stock prices.

**7.35.** Two possibilities are that they might perform better simply because this is their second attempt, or because they feel better prepared because of the course (whether or not they really *are* better prepared).

**7.36. State:** Do the data support the idea that more wildebeest reduce the percent of grasslands that are burned?
**Formulate:** We will examine the relationship with a scatterplot and (if appropriate) correlation and regression lines.
**Solve:** The scatterplot suggests a negative linear association, so correlation and regression are reasonable tools to summarize the relationship. The correlation is $r \doteq -0.8035$, and the regression equation is $\hat{y} = 92.29 - 0.05762x$; the equation explains $r^2 \doteq 64.6\%$ of the variation in burned grassland.
**Conclude:** The claim is supported: When wildebeest numbers are higher, the percent of grassland burned tends to be lower.

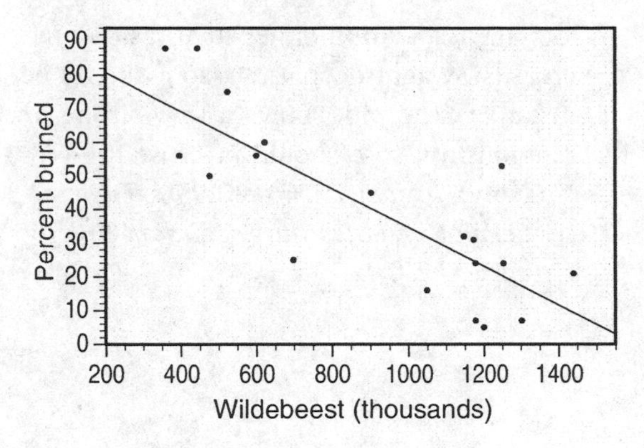


**Minitab output**

```
The regression equation is burned = 92.3 - 0.0576 beest

Predictor        Coef       Stdev    t-ratio        p
Constant        92.29       10.06       9.17    0.000
beest        -0.05762     0.01035      -5.56    0.000

s = 15.99          R-sq = 64.6%       R-sq(adj) = 62.5%
```

**7.37. State:** Do the data support the principle that "more prey attract more predators, who drive down the number of prey"?
**Formulate:** We will examine the relationship with a scatterplot and (if appropriate) correlation and regression lines.
**Solve:** The scatterplot suggests a positive linear association, albeit with lots of scatter, so correlation and regression are reasonable tools to summarize the relationship. The correlation is $r \doteq 0.6821$, and the regression equation is $\hat{y} = 0.1205 + 0.008569x$; the equation explains $r^2 \doteq 46.5\%$ of the variation in the proportion killed.
**Conclude:** The analysis supports the idea that the proportion of perch killed rises with the number of perch present.

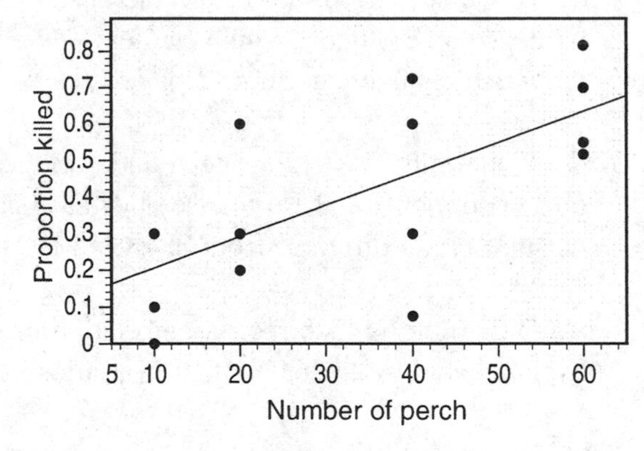


**7.38.** The regression equation is $\hat{y} = 92.29 - 0.05762x$. Students may choose different values of $x$ to illustrate extrapolation, but it is worth pointing out to them that it is not necessary to choose excessively large values of $x$. By referring to the scatterplot in the solution to Exercise 7.36, we can see that this equation will give negative estimates for values of $x$ which are slightly larger than 1600 thousand wildebeest—a number that is not too much larger than the highest count in our data (1440).

**7.39.** A stemplot is shown; a histogram would also be a good choice. The distribution is roughly Normal, though with enough irregularity that students may not be willing to call it Normal. The two low numbers and one high number are not extreme enough to be called outliers.

The mean, standard deviation, and five-number summary are $\bar{x} = 15.48$ days, $s = 5.989$ days, and Min $= 1$, $Q_1 = 11$, $M = 16$, $Q_3 = 20$, Max $= 31$ days. The median date is therefore May 5.

| | |
|---|---|
| 0 | 11 |
| 0 | |
| 0 | 455 |
| 0 | 77 |
| 0 | 8999 |
| 1 | 0000000111111111 |
| 1 | 2222233 |
| 1 | 4445555 |
| 1 | 66666666777777 |
| 1 | 8899999999 |
| 2 | 0001111 |
| 2 | 2222333333 |
| 2 | 455 |
| 2 | 67 |
| 2 | |
| 3 | 1 |

**7.40. (a)** At right. **(b)** The regression formula is $\hat{y} = 159.27 - 0.07332x$. The slope is negative, suggesting that the ice breakup day is decreasing (by 0.07332 day per year). **(c)** The regression line is not very useful for prediction, as it accounts for only about 10% ($r^2 \doteq 0.1001$) of the variation in ice breakup time.

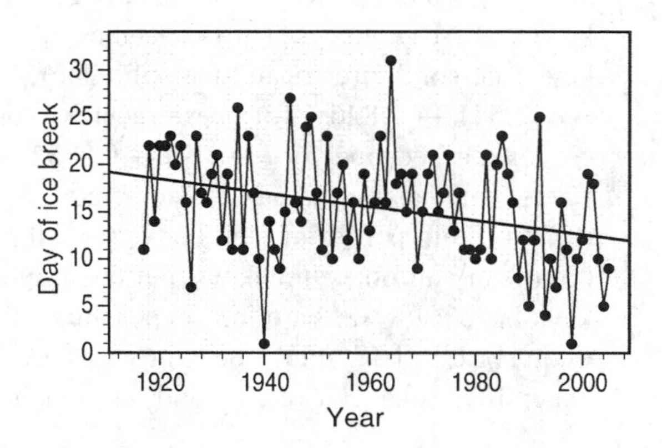


**7.41.** The five-number summaries are:

| | Min | $Q_1$ | $M$ | $Q_3$ | Max |
|---|---|---|---|---|---|
| 1917–1939 | 7 | 12 | 19 | 22 | 26 |
| 1940–1959 | 1 | 11 | 15.5 | 19.75 | 27 |
| 1960–1979 | 9 | 13.5 | 16.5 | 19 | 31 |
| 1980–2005 | 1 | 9 | 11 | 18 | 25 |

and the boxplots are shown on the right. There is no clearly discernible pattern in the boxes, but the minimum values suggest a cyclic pattern (the minimum is 1 in every other group of years).

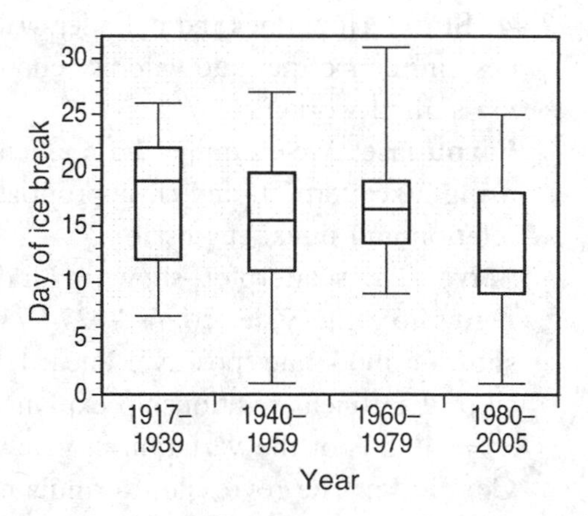

**7.42.** **(a)** The timeplot shows a noticeable change beginning a few years after the ban. **(b)** For 1966–1972, the regression formula is $\hat{y} = 195.56 - 0.09893x$; for the postban years, the line is $\hat{y} = -84.558 + 0.04321x$. One might use the second line for predictions for a short time after 1981, but it should be done cautiously because of the dangers of extrapolation and the fact that for the second regression, $r^2$ is only about 64%.

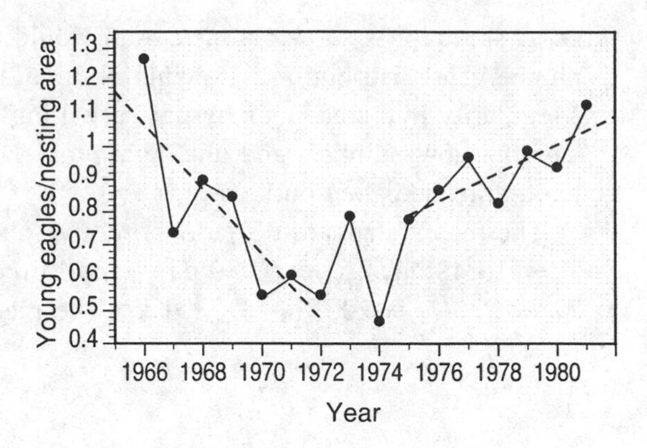


**7.43.** **(a)** For lean monkeys, the mean lean body mass is 8.6833 kg, while the mean is 10.5167 kg for obese monkeys. **(b)** For lean monkeys (the solid circles, and the solid line), $\hat{y} = 0.541 + 0.0826x$; for obese monkeys (open circles, dashed line), $\hat{y} = 0.371 + 0.0852x$. Energy increases at about the same rate (0.08 kJ/min per kg of lean body mass) for both lean and obese monkeys, but obese monkeys have a lower "baseline" expenditure (the intercept 0.371 kJ/min), meaning that they expend less energy overall—and, presumably, the excess energy they take in becomes fat.

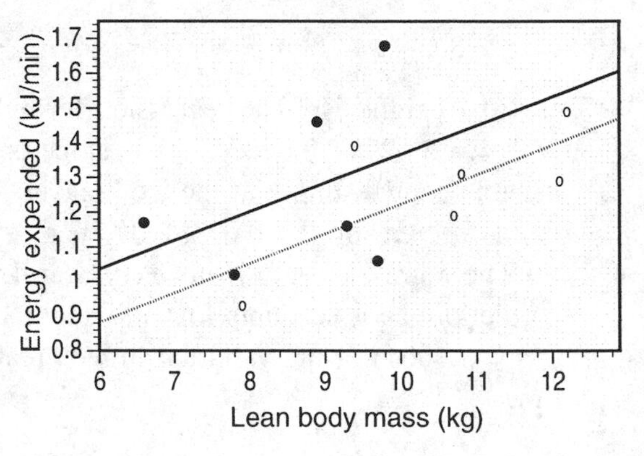


**7.44.** **State:** How does the cylinder wall thickness influence the gate velocity chosen by the skilled workers?
**Formulate:** We examine the relationship using a scatterplot, and (if appropriate) correlation and linear regression.
**Solve:** The scatterplot, shown with the regression line $\hat{y} = 70.44 + 274.78x$, shows a moderate, positive, linear relationship. The linear relationship explains about $r^2 \doteq 49.3\%$ of the variation in gate velocity.
**Conclude:** The regression formula might be used as a rule of thumb for new workers to follow, but the wide spread in the scatterplot suggests that there may be other factors that should be taken into account in choosing the gate velocity.

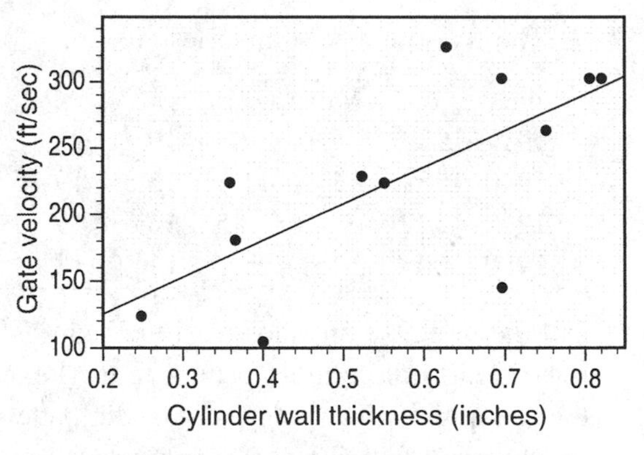


**7.45.** **(a)** Weeds per meter is explanatory, corn yield is the response. **(b)** The stemplots give some evidence that yield decreases when there are more lamb's-quarter plants.

| 0 wpm | | 1 wpm | | 3 wpm | | 9 wpm | |
|---|---|---|---|---|---|---|---|
| 14 | | 14 | | 14 | | 14 | 2 |
| 14 | | 14 | | 14 | | 14 | |
| 15 | | 15 | | 15 | 3 | 15 | |
| 15 | | 15 | 7 | 15 | 69 | 15 | |
| 16 | | 16 | 1 | 16 | | 16 | 233 |
| 16 | 57 | 16 | 67 | 16 | | 16 | |
| 17 | 2 | 17 | | 17 | | 17 | |
| 17 | 7 | 17 | | 17 | 6 | 17 | |

**7.46.** **(a)** The regression equation is

$$\hat{y} = 166 - 1.10x.$$

Each additional lamb's-quarter per meter decreases yield by about 1.1 bushels/acre. **(b)** We predict $\hat{y} = 166 - 1.10(6) = 159.4$ bushels/acre.

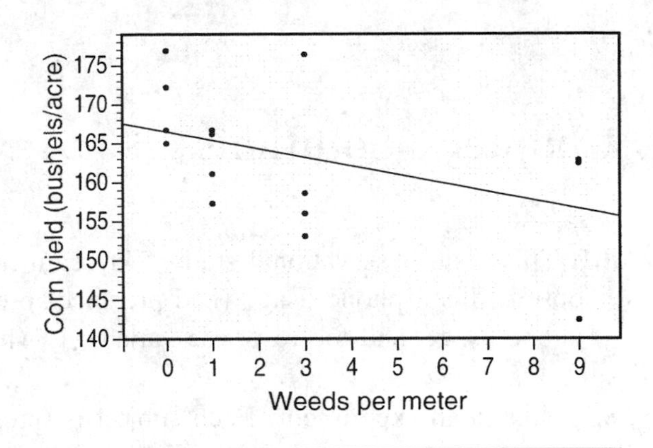


---

For solutions to the EESEE Case Studies (Exercises 47–53), see the instructor's version of EESEE.

# Chapter 8 Solutions

**8.1.** This is an observational study: No treatment was assigned to the subjects; we merely observed cell phone usage (and presence/absence of cancer). The explanatory variable is cell phone usage, and the response variable is whether or not a subject has brain cancer.

**8.2.** This is an experiment: Each subject is (presumably randomly) assigned to a group, each with its own treatment (computer animation or reading the textbook). The explanatory variable is the teaching method, and the response variable is the change in each student's test score.

**8.3.** An adolescent who watches a lot of television probably is more likely to spend less time doing homework, playing sports, or having social interactions with peers. He or she may also have less contact with or guidance from his/her parents.

**8.4.** **(a)** The population is (all) college students. **(b)** The sample is the 104 students at the researcher's college.

**8.5.** The population is all households in the United States. The sample is the households from which responses are received (about 97% of the 250,000 households contacted—roughly 242,500 households).

**8.6.** The population is all 45,000 people who made credit card purchases. The sample is the 137 people who returned the survey form.

**8.7.** It is a convenience sample; she is only getting opinions from students who are at the student center at a certain time of day. This might underrepresent some group: commuters, graduate students, or nontraditional students, for example.

**8.8.** **(a)** For example, a call-in poll, or a survey form published in the campus newspaper. **(b)** For example, a convenience sample method such as interviewing students as they enter the student center, or as they leave the parking lot.

**8.9.** Number from 01 to 33 alphabetically (down the columns). With the applet: Population = 1 to **33**, select a sample of size **3**, then click Reset and Sample. With Table B, enter at line 117 and choose

16=Fairington, 32=Waterford Court, 18=Fowler.

See note on page 59 about using Table B.

**8.10.** Number from 01 to 28 alphabetically (down the columns). With the applet: Population = 1 to **28**, select a sample of size **6**, then click Reset and Sample. With Table B, enter at line 139 and choose

04=Bonds, 10=Fleming, 17=Liao, 19=Naber, 12=Goel, 13=Gomez.

See note on page 59 about using Table B.

**8.11.** **(a)** Assign labels 0001 through 1410. **(b)** Beginning at line 105, we choose plots 0769, 1315, 0094, 0720, and 0906.

**8.12.** Label the students 01, . . . , 30 and use Table B. Then label the faculty 0, . . . , 9 and use the table again. (You could also label the faculty from 01 to 10, but that would needlessly require two-digit labels.)

**Note:** *Students often try some fallacious method of choosing both samples simultaneously. We simply want to choose two separate SRSs: one from the students and one from the faculty.* *See note on page 59 about using Table B.*

**8.13.** Label the 500 midsize accounts from 001 to 500, and the 4400 small accounts from 0001 to 4400. On line 115, we first encounter numbers 417, 494, 322, 247, and 097 for the midsize group, then 3698, 1452, 2605, 2480, and 3716 for the small group. See note on page 59 about using Table B.

**8.14.** The higher no-answer was probably the second period—more families are likely to be gone for vacations, or to be outside enjoying the warmer weather, and so on. Nonresponse of this type might underrepresent those who are more affluent (and are able to travel). In general, high nonresponse rates always make results less reliable, because we do not know what information we are missing.

**8.15.** The first wording brought the higher numbers in favor of a tax cut; "new government programs" has considerably less appeal than the list of specific programs given in the second wording.

**8.16.** With the election close at hand, the polling organization wants to increase the accuracy of its results. Larger samples provide better information about the population.

**8.17.** (a) This is an observational study: Behavior (alcohol consumption) is observed, but no treatment is imposed.

**8.18.** (c) The study shows an association between the two, but not a cause-and-effect relationship.

**8.19.** (b) The sample is the group about which we have information.

**8.20.** (a) The population is the group about which we wish to learn.

**8.21.** (c) The sample is the group from which we received responses, not the group from which we solicited responses.

**8.22.** (b) A voluntary response sample is typically biased, so we can draw few conclusions about the population.

**8.23.** (a) Each member of the population needs a three-digit label, and we need 440 of them—not 441 labels, as in (b).

**8.24.** (c) Take two digits at a time, and ignore unused and duplicate labels.

**8.25.** (a) Take four digits at a time, and ignore unused labels.

**8.26.** (b) Those without phones or with unlisted numbers—39% of the population—cannot be included in the sample.

**8.27.** This is an observational study; the subjects chose their own "treatments" (how much to drink). The explanatory variable is alcohol consumption, and the response variable is whether or not a subject dies. (There may have been other variables, but these were the only ones mentioned in the problem.)

**8.28.** This is an experiment, because the treatment is selected (randomly, we assume) by the interviewer. The explanatory variable (treatment) is the level of identification, and the response variable is whether or not the interview is completed.

**8.29.** **(a)** In order to be an experiment, the treatments (choice of anesthetic) would have to be randomly assigned. Instead, a patient's anesthetic is selected by his or her doctor(s). **(b)** We should consider the type of surgery, and the age, sex, and condition of the patient.

**8.30.** **(a)** The population is (something like) adult residents of the United States. **(b)** The nonresponse rate is $\frac{869}{2000} = 43.45\%$. **(c)** This question will likely have response bias; specifically, many people will give an inaccurate count of how many movies they have seen in the past year.

**8.31.** **(a)** The population is adult residents of the United States. The sample size is 1002. **(b)** Perhaps people are more inclined to respond with the first or last option they hear. Rotating the order of the options would cancel out any effect on the response of such inclinations.

**8.32.** Online polls, call-in polls, and voluntary response polls in general, tend to attract responses from those who have strong opinions on the subject, and therefore are often not representative of the population as a whole. On the other hand, there is no reason to believe that randomly chosen adults would overrepresent any particular group, so the responses from such a group give a more reliable picture of public opinion.

**8.33.** Those who feel most strongly tend to respond to any such straw poll. In this case, women who are unhappy with their treatment by men dominated the response, so 72% is an overestimate (too high) of the fraction of women who are content with affection only.

**8.34.** People likely claim to wear their seat belts because they know they should; they are embarrassed or ashamed to say that they do not always wear seat belts. Such bias is likely in most surveys about seat belt use (and similar topics).

**8.35.** Numbering from 01 to 40 alphabetically (down the columns), we enter Table B at line 117 and choose

| | | | | |
|---|---|---|---|---|
| 38–Washburn | 16–Garcia | 32–Rodriguez | 18–Helling | 37–Wallace |
| 06–Cabrera | 23–Morgan | 19–Husain | 03–Batista | 25–Nguyen |

See note on page 59 about using Table B.

**8.36.** With the applet: Population = 1 to **371**, select a sample of size **25**, then click Reset and Sample. Using line 129 of Table B, the first 5 codes are 367, 288, 229, 131, and 303.

**8.37.** The response rate was $\frac{5029}{45{,}956} \doteq 0.1094$, so the nonresponse rate was $0.8906 \doteq 89.1\%$.

**8.38.** **(a)** Assign labels 0001 through 5024, enter the table at line 104, and select: 1388, 0746, 0227, 4001, and 1858.
See note on page 59 about using Table B. **(b)** More than 171 respondents have run red lights. We would not expect very many people to claim they *have* run red lights when they have not, but some people will deny running red lights when they have.

**8.39.** Each student has a 10% chance: 3 of 30 over-21 students, and 2 of 20 under-21 students. This is not an SRS because not every group of 5 students can be chosen; the only possible samples are those with 3 older and 2 younger students.

**8.40.** If one always begins at the same place, then the results would not really be random.

**8.41.** **(a)** False. Such regularity holds only in the long run. If it were true, you could look at the first 39 digits and know whether or not the 40th was a 0. **(b)** True. All pairs of digits (there are 100, from 00 to 99) are equally likely. **(c)** False. Four random digits have chance 1/10000 to be 0000, so this sequence will occasionally occur. 0000 is no more or less random than 1234 or 2718, or any other four-digit sequence.

**8.42.** Assign labels 001 through 290 to the men, and 001 through 110 to the women. Entering the table at line 130, first choose the men (174, 095, and 178), and then continue on to choose the women (019, 007, and 041). See note on page 59 about using Table B.

**8.43.** Sample separately in each stratum; that is, assign separate labels, then choose the first sample, then continue on in the table to choose the next sample, etc. Beginning with line 162 in Table B, we choose:

| Forest type | Labels | Parcels selected |
|---|---|---|
| Climax 1 | 01 to 36 | 34, 14, 15, 36 |
| Climax 2 | 01 to 72 | 23, 36, 21, 11, 55, 27, 14 |
| Climax 3 | 01 to 31 | 28, 31, 09 |
| Secondary | 01 to 42 | 03, 41, 37, 16 |

**8.44. (a)** We will choose one of the first 40 at random and then the addresses 40, 80, 120, and 160 places down the list from it. Beginning on line 120, the addresses selected are 35, 75, 115, 155, and 195. (Only the first number is chosen from the table.) **(b)** All addresses are equally likely; each has chance 1/40 of being selected. To see this, note that each of the first 40 has chance 1/40 because one is chosen at random. But each address in the second 40 is chosen exactly when the corresponding address in the first 40 is, so each of the second 40 also has chance 1/40. And so on.

This is not an SRS because the only possible samples have exactly one address from the first 40, one address from the second 40, and so on. An SRS could contain any 5 of the 200 addresses in the population. Note that this view of systematic sampling assumes that the number in the population is a multiple of the sample size.

**8.45. (a)** This design would omit households without telephones or with unlisted numbers. Such households would likely be made up of poor individuals (who cannot afford a phone), those who choose not to have phones, and those who do not wish to have their phone numbers published. **(b)** Those with unlisted numbers would be included in the sampling frame when a random-digit dialer (RDD) is used. (Additionally, RDDs exclude cell phones, although students may not be aware of this fact. For a discussion of this issue, see `http://www.mysterypollster.com/main/2004/10/arianna_huffing.html`.)

**8.46. (a)** The wording is clear, but will almost certainly be slanted toward a high positive response. (Would anyone hear the phrase "brain cancer" and *not* be inclined to agree that a warning label is a good idea?) **(b)** The question makes the case for a national health care system, and so will slant responses toward "yes." **(c)** This survey question is most likely to produce a response similar to: "Uhh...yes? I mean, no? I'm sorry, could you repeat the question?" (And, if the person is able to understand the question, it is slanted in favor of day-care subsidies.)

**8.47. (a)** Random-digit dialing randomly generates a phone number and dials it; this means that it can conceivably contact any person who has a telephone. (Of course, it could also call businesses, fax machines, modems, etc.) **(b)** If those performing surveys always asked their questions of the person who answered the phone, then those who are more likely to answer the phone would be overrepresented in the sample. Such people may be more likely to have some particular personality trait, for example; this could introduce bias into the sample.

**8.49. (a)** The population is Ontario residents; the sample is the 61,239 people interviewed. **(b)** The sample size is very large, so if there were large numbers of both sexes in the sample—this is a safe assumption because we are told this is a "random sample"—these two numbers should be fairly accurate reflections of the values for the whole population.

**8.50. (a)** The sample size for Hispanics was smaller. Smaller sample sizes give less information about the population, and therefore lead to larger margins of error (with the same confidence level). **(b)** The sample size was so small, and the margin of error so large, that the results could not be viewed as an accurate reflection of the population of Cubans.

# Chapter 9 Solutions

**9.1.** Subjects: The students living in the selected dormitory. Factor: The rate structure. Treatments: Paying one flat rate, or paying peak/off-peak rates. Response variables: The amount and time of use.

**9.2.** Individuals: pine seedlings. Treatments: full light, 25% light, or 5% light. Response variable: dry weight at the end of the study.

**9.3.** The individuals are the students in the participating schools. (This needs a short discussion: for practical reasons, entire schools were assigned at random, but data were recorded on individual students and we are interested in effects on students.) There are two factors, activity intervention (yes or no) and nutrition intervention (yes or no). The treatments are the four combinations of levels of the factors (see the table on the right). The response variables are measures of physical activity and lunchtime fat consumption.

| | Nutrition | No nutrition |
|---|---|---|
| Activity | Treatment 1 | Treatment 2 |
| No activity | Treatment 3 | Treatment 4 |

**9.4.** The lurking variable is time—or rather, the changes in the economy that occur over time. Making a comparison between the treatment group and the percent finding work *last year* is not helpful; perhaps it is easier to find a job this year. (In order to draw conclusions, we would need to make the $500 bonus offer to some people and not to others, and compare the two groups.)

**9.5.** **(a)** Diagram is shown below. **(b)** If we assign labels 001, . . . , 230, then from line 103 we select:

170, 005, 227, 118, and 007

as the first five ginkgo subjects. See note on page 59 about using Table B.

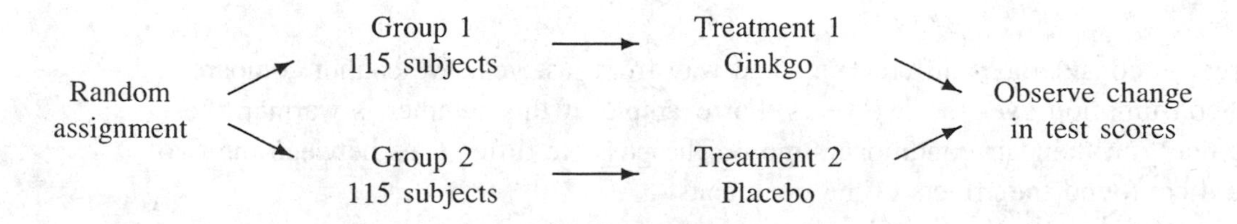

**9.6.** **(a)** Diagram is shown below. **(b)** Shown below are sample screenshots from the applet.

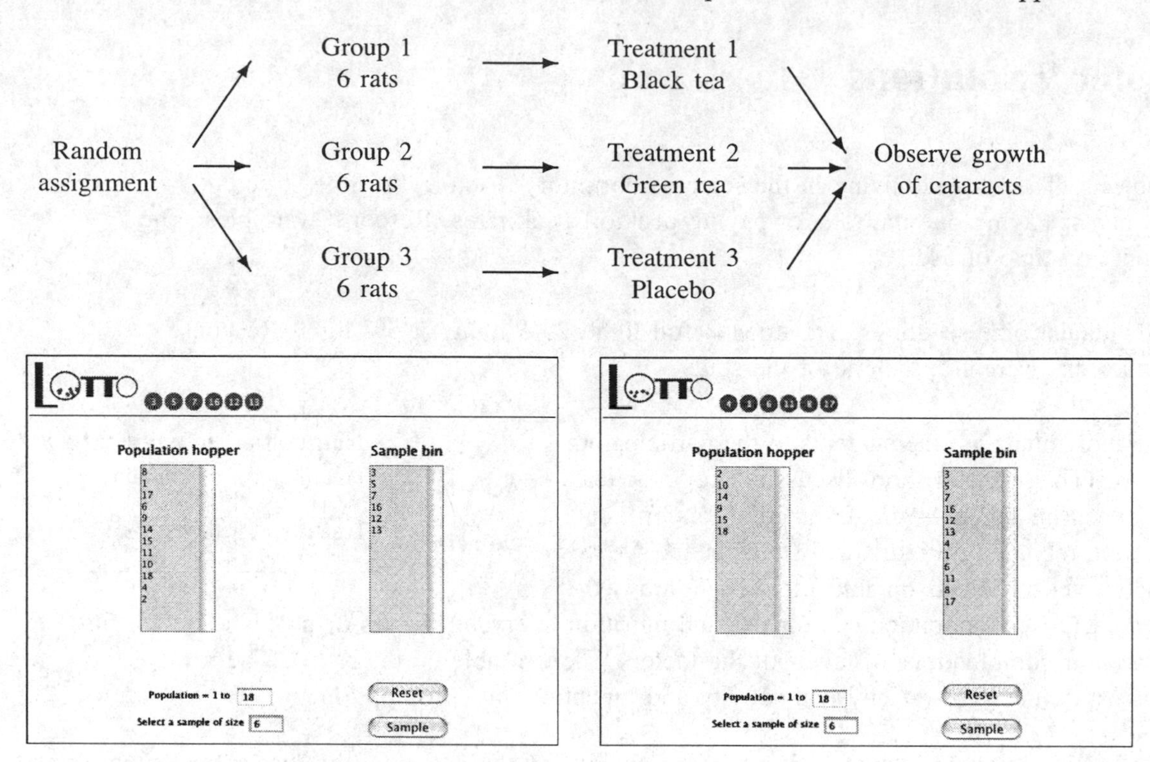


**9.7.** Diagram is shown below. See note on page 59 about using Table B.

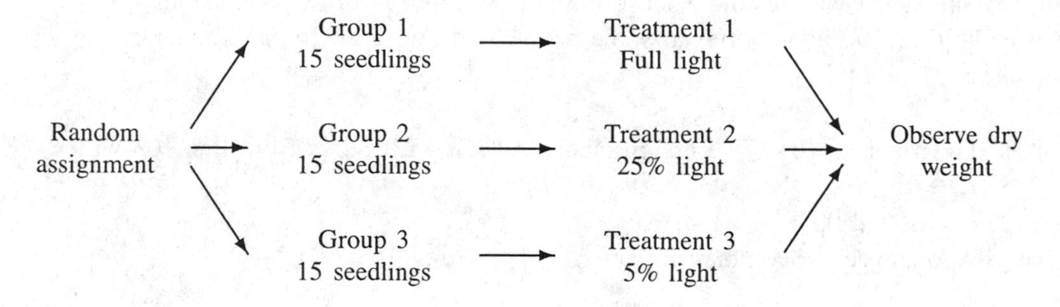


**9.8.** If this year is considerably different in some way from last year, we cannot compare electricity consumption over the two years. For example, if this summer is warmer, the customers may run their air conditioners more. The possible differences between the two years would confound the effects of the treatments.

**9.9.** The first design is an observational study: Subjects are assigned to groups based on their own habits, with no treatment (exercising or not) imposed on them. In this study, there may be other factors (e.g., personality type or genetic background) that make one more likely to exercise and less (or more) likely to have a heart attack. This means we could not conclude that exercise *causes* a reduced risk of heart attack; it may simply be a "symptom" of some other factor.

The second design is an experiment: Each subject is randomly assigned to an exercise program or to continue with his "usual habits."

**Note:** *In the second setting, some in the "usual habits" group may choose to exercise. That is not a problem. The treatment being imposed is not "exercise" or "do not exercise"; it is "exercise" or "make your own decision about whether or not to exercise."*

**9.10.** The mean Monday return for the first three weeks of the month was both different from zero and higher than the mean for the last two Mondays. However, the difference from zero was small enough that it might have occurred purely by chance (and so it gives no reason to suspect that the first three Mondays tend to produce negative returns). On the other hand, the other difference was so large that it would rarely occur by chance, leading us to conclude that the last two Mondays really do (for whatever reason) tend to yield lower returns than the first three Mondays.

**9.11.** "Randomized" means that patients were randomly assigned to receive either the standard morphine treatment or CR morphine tablets. "Double blind" means that the treatment assigned to a patient was unknown to both the patient and those responsible for assessing the effectiveness of that treatment. (It is not clear how the treatment was hidden from the patients because they would know when they received the morphine.) "Comparative" means researchers are comparing the effectiveness of two treatments, rather than simply trying to assess the effectiveness of one treatment—that is, researchers did not simply change over to CR morphine and try to judge if it was better than the standard treatment had been in the past.

**9.12.** In this case, "lack of blindness" means that the experimenter knows which subjects were taught to meditate. He or she may have some expectation about whether or not meditation will lower anxiety; this could unconsciously influence the diagnosis.

**9.13.** For each person, flip a coin to decide which hand he or she should use first (heads: right hand first; tails: left hand first). Record the difference in hand strength for each person.

**9.14.** **(a)** *Completely randomized design:* Randomly assign 15 students to Group 1 (easy mazes) and the other 15 to Group 2 (hard mazes). Compare the time estimates of Group 1 with those of Group 2. **(b)** *Matched-pairs design:* Each student does the activity twice, once with the easy mazes, and one with the hard mazes. Randomly decide (for each student) which set of mazes is used first. Compare each student's "easy" and "hard" time estimate (for example, by looking at each "hard" minus "easy" difference). *Alternate matched-pairs design:* Again, all students do the activity twice. Randomly assign 15 students to Group 1 (easy first) and 15 to Group 2 (hard first).

**9.15.** For each block (pair of lecture sections), randomly assign one section to be taught using standard methods and the other to be taught with multimedia. Then (at the end of the term) compare final-exam scores and student attitudes.

The diagram below is *part* of the whole block diagram; there would also be three other pieces like this (one for each of the other instructors). The randomization will vary with the starting line in Table B—or the randomization can be done by flipping a coin for each block.

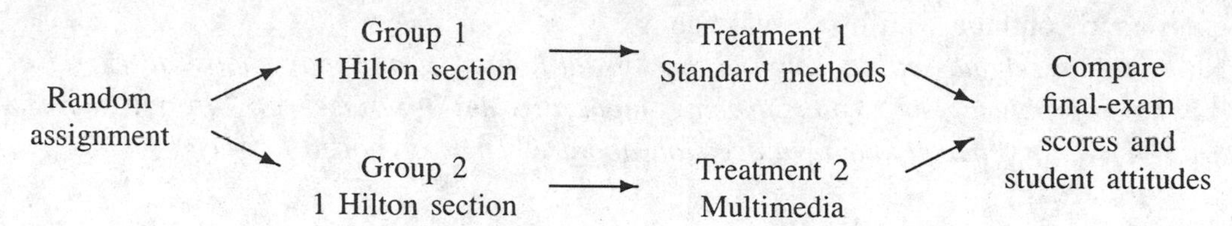


**9.16.** (a) This is an observational study: No treatment was assigned to the subjects; we merely observed cell phone usage (and presence/absence of cancer).

**9.17.** (b) This is an experiment (a treatment is imposed), but there is no control group for comparison.

**9.18.** (b) There are two factors, each with two levels, which yields the four treatments listed.

**9.19.** (a) We choose randomly from all subjects at once (rather than grouping them in blocks), and each subject gets one treatment (there is no pairing).

**9.20.** (c) The response variable is the effect we want to observe: How blood pressure changes in response to the various treatments.

**9.21.** (a) Each of the 36 subjects needs a label.

**9.22.** (b) The communities are paired up, then one is chosen to have the advertising campaign.

**9.23.** (a) The choice should be made randomly.

**9.24.** (b) This was a (matched pairs) experiment, but in order to give useful information, the subjects should be chosen from those who might be expected to buy this car.

**9.25.** Treatments were not assigned; that is, the subjects were not told what they could or could not drink.

**9.26.** **(a)** Explanatory variable: treatment method; response: survival times. **(b)** No treatment is actively imposed; the women (or their doctors) choose which treatment to use. **(c)** Doctors may decide which treatment to recommend based in part on how advanced the case is. Some might be more likely to recommend the older treatment for advanced cases, in which case the chance of recovery is lower. Other doctors might view the older treatment as not being worth the effort and recommend the newer method as a way of providing *some* hope for recovery while minimizing the trauma and expense of major surgery.

**9.27.** Diagram is shown below. The last stage ("observe heart health") might be described in more detail.

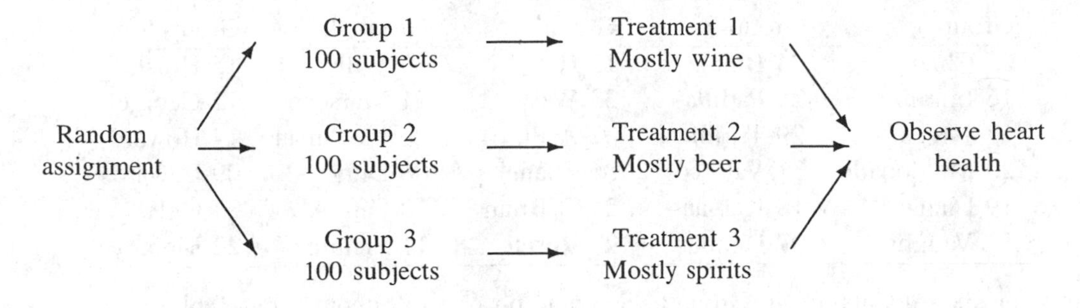


**9.28.** **(a)** A diagram is shown below. **(b)** Label the subjects from 01 through 20. From line 131, we choose

05, 19, 04, 20, 16, 18, 07, 13, 02, and 08;

that is, Dubois, Travers, Cheng, Ullmann, Quinones, Thompson, Fluharty, Lucero, Afifi, and Gerson for one group, and the rest for the other. See note on page 59 about using Table B.

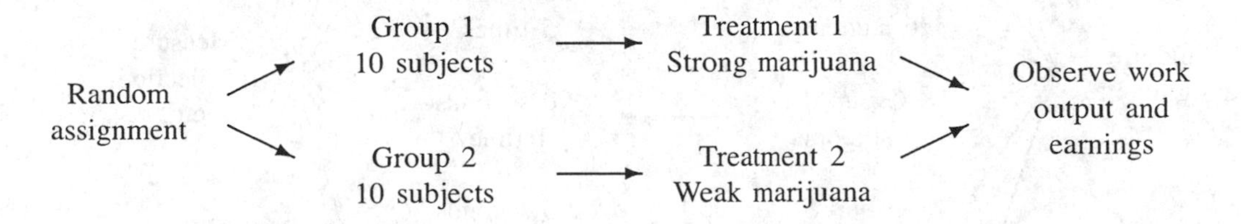


**9.29.** Use a completely randomized design. Labeling the men from 01 through 39, and starting on line 107 of Table B, we make the assignments shown in the table on the right. See note on page 59 about using Table B.

| | |
|---|---|
| Group 1 | 20, 11, 38, 31, 07, 24, 17, 09, 06 |
| Group 2 | 36, 15, 23, 34, 16, 19, 18, 33, 39 |
| Group 3 | 08, 30, 27, 12, 04, 35 |
| Group 4 | 02, 32, 25, 14, 29, 03, 22, 26, 10 |
| Group 5 | Everyone else |

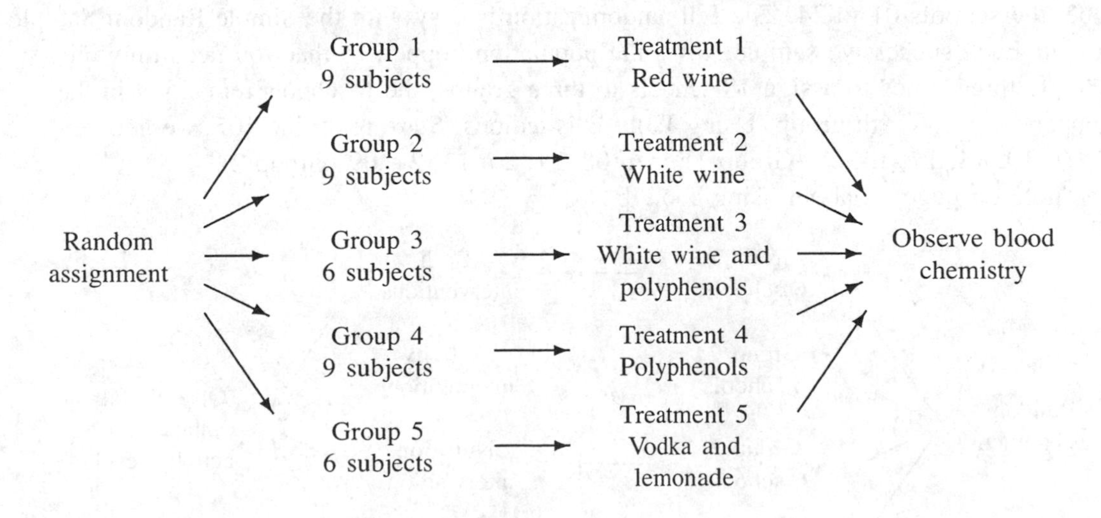

**9.30.** Assign six students to each treatment. The diagram is shown below; if we assign labels 01 through 36, then line 130 gives:

| Group 1 | Group 2 | Group 3 | Group 4 | Group 5 |
|---|---|---|---|---|
| 05 Chao | 04 Bikalis | 13 Han | 35 Willis | 15 Hruska |
| 16 Imrani | 25 Padilla | 33 Wei | 21 Marsden | 12 George |
| 17 James | 29 Trujillo | 02 Asihiro | 26 Plochman | 14 Howard |
| 20 Maldonado | 31 Valasco | 36 Zhang | 08 Durr | 09 Edwards |
| 19 Liang | 18 Kaplan | 23 O'Brian | 10 Farouk | 24 Ogle |
| 32 Vaughn | 07 Denman | 27 Rosen | 11 Fleming | 22 Montoya |

The other six students are in Group 6. See note on page 59 about using Table B.

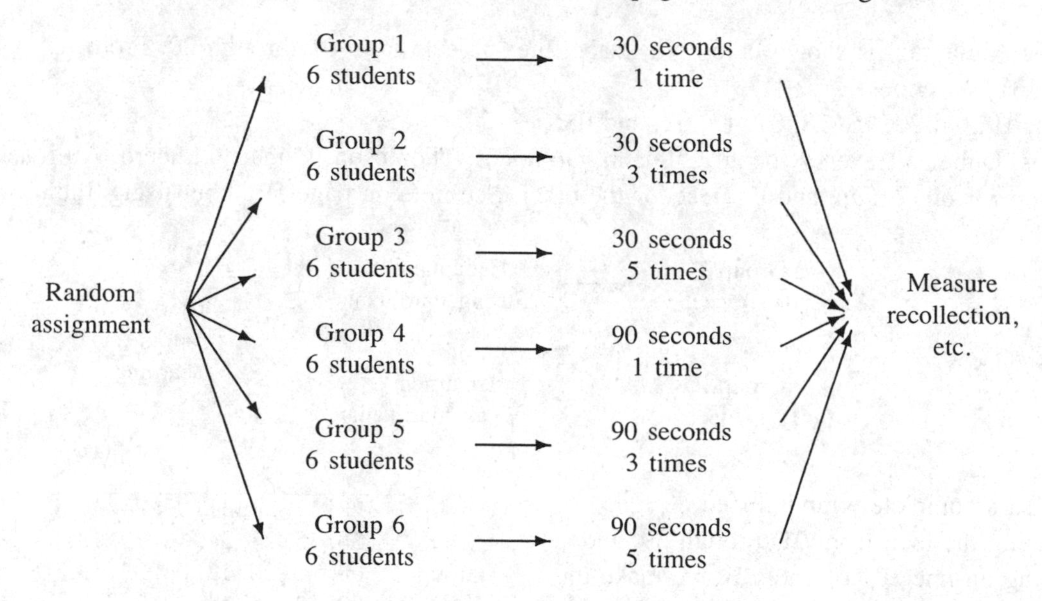


**9.31.** The outline of the completely randomized design is shown below. For the randomization, label the schools 01 to 24. The full randomization is easy with the Simple Random Sample applet: Each successive sample leaves the population hopper, so that you need only click Sample three times to assign 18 schools to three groups; the 6 schools remaining in the hopper are the fourth group. Using Table B is tedious. Starting at line 105, we get:

07, 19, 14, 17, 13, 15 (Group 1), then 08, 21, 20, 11, 24, 09 (Group 2).

See note on page 59 about using Table B.

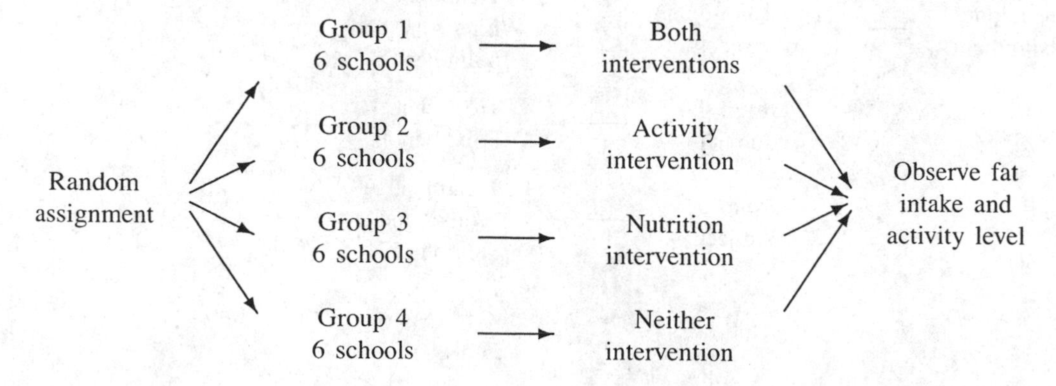

**9.32. (a)** There are 40 subjects, so we assign 10 subjects to each treatment. A diagram is shown below. **(b)** Assign labels 01 through 40 (in alphabetical order). The full randomization is easy with the Simple Random Sample applet: Each successive sample leaves the population hopper, so that you need only click Sample three times to assign 30 subjects to three groups; the 10 subjects remaining in the hopper are the fourth group. Line 130 of Table B gives the following subjects for Group 1:

05, 16, 17, 40, 20, 19, 32, 04, 25, and 29;

that is, Chai, Hammond, Herrera, Xiang, Irwin, Hurwitz, Reed, Broden, Lucero, and Nho. See note on page 59 about using Table B.

| | Antidepressant | No drug |
|---|---|---|
| Stress management | Treatment 1 | Treatment 2 |
| None | Treatment 3 | Treatment 4 |

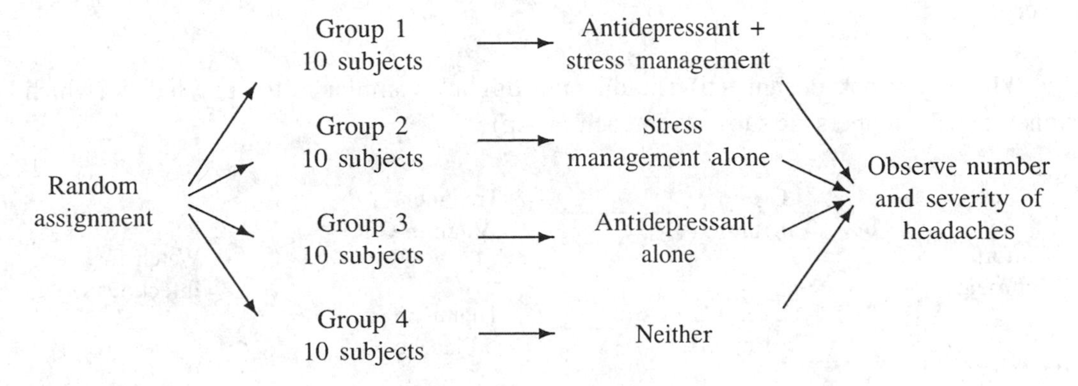


**9.33. (a)** There are three factors (roller type, dyeing cycle time, and temperature), each with two levels, for a total of $2^3 = 8$ treatments. The experiment therefore requires 24 fabric specimens. **(b)** In the interest of space, only the top half of the diagram is shown below. The other half consists of Groups 5 to 8, for which the treatments have natural bristle rollers instead of metal rollers.

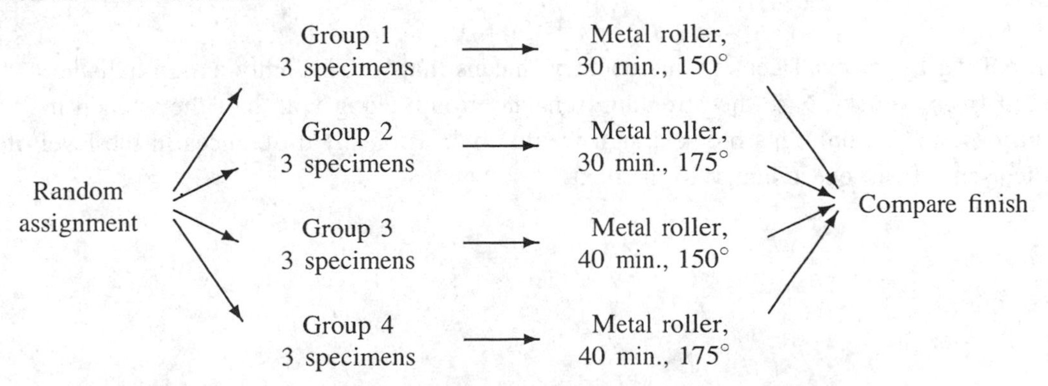


**9.34. (a)** The subjects are randomly chosen Starbucks customers. Each subject tastes two cups of coffee, in identical unlabeled cups. One contains regular mocha frappucino, the other the new light version. The cups are presented in random order, half the subjects get regular then light, the other half light then regular. Each subject says which cup he or she prefers. **(b)** We must assign 10 customers to get regular coffee first. Label the subjects 01 to 20. Starting at line 141, the "regular first" group is:

12, 16, 02, 08, 17, 10, 05, 09, 19, 06.

See note on page 59 about using Table B.

**9.35.** The sketches requested in the problem are not shown here; random assignments will vary among students. **(a)** Label the circles 1 to 6, then randomly select three (using Table B, or simply by rolling a die) to receive the extra $CO_2$. Observe the growth in all six regions, and compare the mean growth within the three treated circles with the mean growth in the other three (control) circles. **(b)** Select pairs of circles in each of three different areas of the forest. For each pair, randomly select one circle to receive the extra $CO_2$ (using Table B or by flipping a coin). For each pair, compute the difference in growth (treated minus control).

**9.36.** Each player will be put through the sequence (100 yards, four times) twice—once with oxygen and once without. For each player, randomly determine whether to use oxygen on the first or second trial. Allow ample time (perhaps a day or two) between trials for full recovery.

**9.37.** **(a)** This is a block design. **(b)** The diagram might be similar to the one below (which assumes equal numbers of subjects in each group).

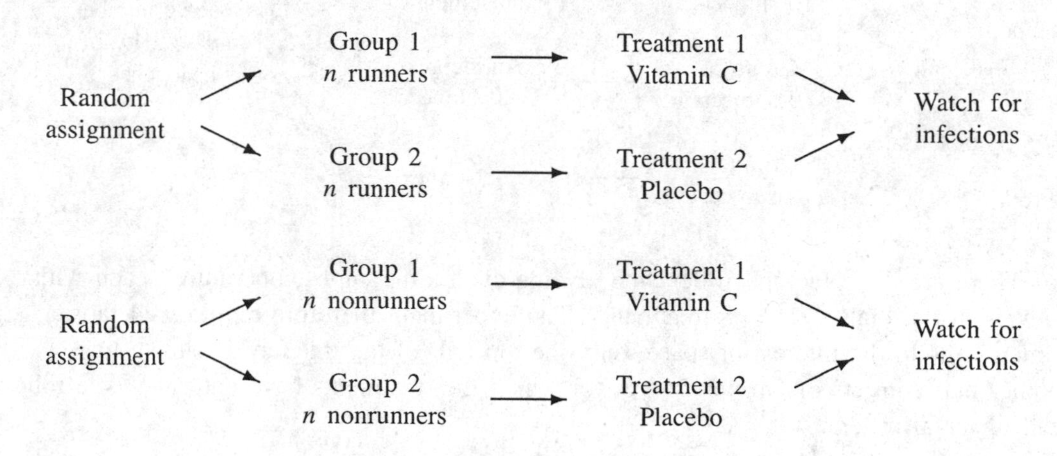


**9.38.** Blocking by medical center (and country) means that we randomly assign half the women from country A to the strontium renelate group, along with half the women in country B, and so on. This block design would control for any differences in the level of medical care from one country to the next.

**9.39.** Divide the men and women into three groups of equal size. Diagram below.

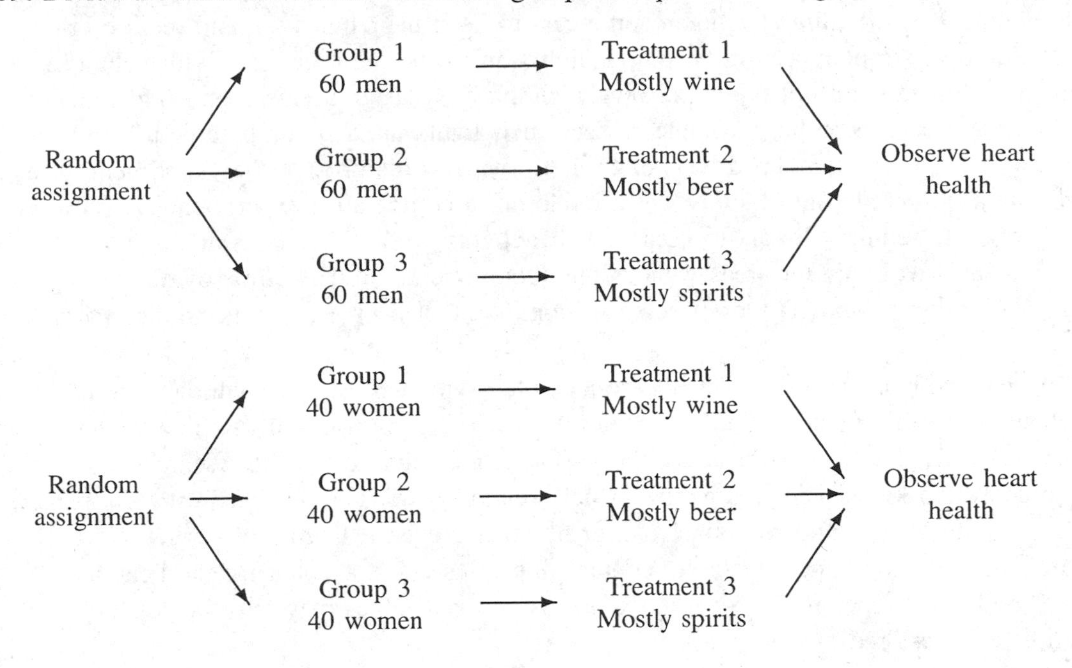


**9.40.** **(a)** The diagram is not shown here, but would consist of two copies of the diagram for Exercise 9.30: one with six groups of four women each, and the other with six groups of two men each. **(b)** The most straightforward approach to the randomization is first to assign (e.g.) all of the men and then assign the women: Label the men 01, . . . , 12, and use Table B to choose two men (12, 04) for Treatment 1, then two more (02 and 08) for Treatment 2, etc. When all men are assigned, label the women 01, . . . , 24, assign four (16, 19, 22, 05) to Treatment 1, and so on. In the table, the first row is the men and women assigned to Treatment 1, etc.

| | | |
|---|---|---|
| 12 Zhang<br>04 Edwards | 16 O'Brian<br>19 Trujillo | 22 Vaughn<br>05 Denman |
| 02 Chao<br>08 Ogle | 13 Liang<br>17 Plochman | 09 Han<br>07 Fleming |
| 10 Rosen<br>05 Howard | 02 Bennett<br>01 Alomar | 14 Maldonado<br>08 George |
| 09 Padilla<br>06 Kaplan | 21 Valasco<br>20 Tullock | 11 Imrani<br>24 Willis |
| 01 Asihiro<br>07 Montoya | 06 Farouk<br>23 Wei | 03 Bikalis<br>04 Clemente |
| 03 Durr<br>11 Wilder | 10 Hruska<br>12 James | 15 Marsden<br>18 Solomon |

**9.41.** In a controlled scientific study, the effects of factors other than the nonphysical treatment (e.g., the placebo effect, differences in the prior health of the subjects) can be eliminated or accounted for, so that the differences in improvement observed between the subjects can be attributed to the differences in treatments.

**9.43.** Any experiment randomized in this way assigns all the women to one treatment and all the men to the other. That is, sex is completely confounded with treatment. If women and men respond differently to the treatment, the experiment will be strongly biased. The direction of the bias is random, depending on the coin toss.

**9.44. (a)** The response variable should be "number of accidents," or something similar. Ideally, one would like to require at random some cars to keep their lights on, and require others in the same geographic area to keep their lights off. This might be done with volunteers. Though volunteers are not typical drivers, a simple CR design seems promising. A less effective approach is to have volunteers keep their lights on, and compare their accident records to those of "similar" drivers or to their own records prior to the experiment. The latter is an observed control study, not a randomized comparative experiment. Yet another approach is to require all cars to keep their headlights on in some areas and compare accident rates with similar areas without this requirement. **(b)** The effect of running lights may be lessened when (if) they become so common that people no longer notice them.

**9.45. (a)** The explanatory variable is the beta-carotene/vitamin(s) taken each day; the response variable is whether or not colon cancer develops. **(b)** Diagram is shown below; equal group sizes are convenient but not necessary. **(c)** Neither the subjects nor the researchers who examined them knew who was getting which treatment. **(d)** The observed differences were no more than what might reasonably occur by chance even if there is no effect due to the treatments. **(e)** Fruits and vegetables contain fiber; this could account for the benefits of those foods. Also, people who eat lots of fruits and vegetables may have healthier diets overall (e.g., less red meat).

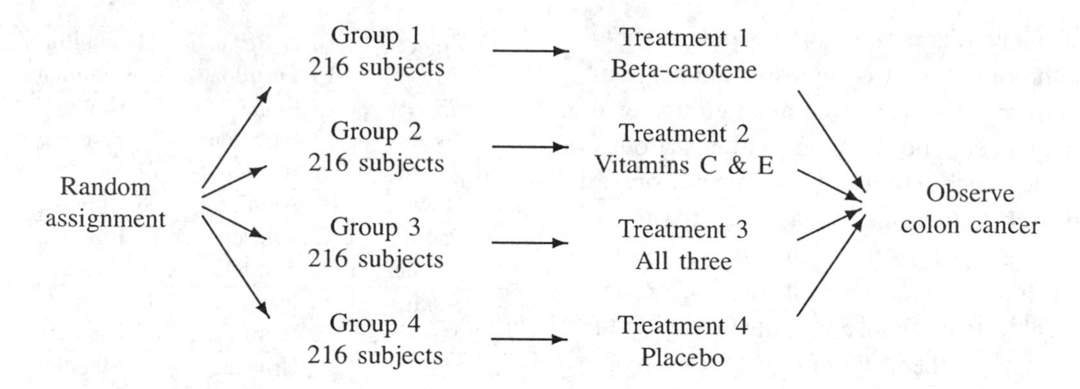


**9.46. (a)** "Randomized" means that patients were randomly assigned to receive either Saint-John's-wort or a placebo. "Double blind" means that the treatment assigned to a patient was unknown to both the patient and those responsible for assessing the effectiveness of that treatment. "Placebo-controlled" means that some of the subjects were given placebos. Even though these possess no medical properties, some subjects may show improvement or benefits just as a result of participating in the experiment; the placebos allow those doing the study to observe this effect. **(b)** Diagram below.

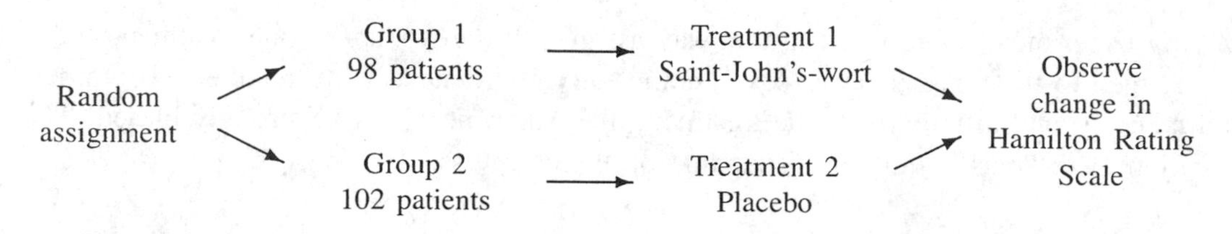

**9.47.** **(a)** In an observational study, we simply observe subjects who have chosen to take supplements and compare them with others who do not take supplements. In an experiment, we *assign* some subjects to take supplements and assign the others to take no supplements (or better yet, assign the others to take a placebo). **(b)** "Randomized" means that the assignment to treatments is made randomly, rather than by some other method (e.g., asking for volunteers). "Controlled" means that some subjects were used as a "control" group—probably meaning that they received placebos—which gives a basis for comparison to observe the effects of the treatment. **(c)** Subjects who choose to take supplements have other characteristics that are confounded with the effect of the supplements; one of those characteristics is that people in this group are more likely to make healthy lifestyle choices (about smoking, drinking, eating, exercise, etc.). When we randomly assign subjects to a treatment, the effect of those characteristics is erased, because some of those subjects will take the supplement, and some will take the placebo.

**9.48.** Results will vary, but probability computations reveal that more than 97.7% of samples will have 9 to 16 older employed subjects (and 99.6% of samples have 8 to 17 older employed subjects). Additionally, if students average their 20 samples, nearly all students (more than 99%) should find that the average number of older employed subjects is between 11.3 and 13.7.

**Note:** *$X$, the number of older employed subjects in the sample, has a hypergeometric distribution with parameters $N = 50$, $r = 25$, $n = 25$, so that $P(9 \le X \le 16) \doteq 0.977$. The theoretical average number of older employed subjects in the sample is 12.5.*

# Data Ethics Solutions

**1.** These three proposals are clearly in increasing order of risk. Most students will likely consider that (a) qualifies as minimal risk, and most will agree that (c) goes beyond minimal risk.

**2.** **(a)** A nonscientist might raise different viewpoints and concerns from those considered by scientists. **(b)** Answers will vary.

**3.** It is good to state the purpose of the research plainly ("To study how people's religious beliefs and their feelings about authority are related"). Stating the research *thesis* (that orthodox religious belief are associated with authoritarian personalities) would cause bias.

**6.** They cannot be anonymous because the interviews are conducted in person in the subject's home. They are certainly kept confidential. More information can be found at the GSS Web site: `www.norc.org/projects/gensoc.asp`.

**7.** This offers anonymity, because names are never revealed. (However, faces are seen, so there may be some chance of someone's identity becoming known. We also must trust that the caller-ID system is not used to identify the source of incoming calls.)

**8.** **(a)** Those being surveyed should be told the kind of questions they will be asked and the approximate amount of time required. **(b)** Giving the name and address of the organization may give the respondents a sense that they have an avenue to complain should they feel offended or mistreated by the pollster. **(c)** At the time that the questions are being asked, knowing who is paying for a poll may introduce bias, perhaps due to nonresponse (not wanting to give what might be considered a "wrong" answer). When information about a poll is made public, though, the poll's sponsor should be announced.

# Chapter 10 Solutions

**10.1.** In the long run, of a large number of Texas Hold'em games in which you hold a pair, the fraction in which you can make four of a kind will be about 88/1000 (or 11/125). It *does not* mean that exactly 88 out of 1000 such hands would yield four of a kind; that would mean, for example, that if you've been dealt 999 such hands and only had four of a kind 87 times, then you could count on getting four of a kind the next time you held a pair.

**10.2.** Obviously, results will vary with the type of thumbtack used, but the key is that students understand the procedure: The approximate probability is the fraction of times their thumbtack landed point-up (that is, they should divide their count by 100). The result can be reported as a fraction, a decimal, or a percent.

**10.3.** **(a)** There are 4 zeros among the first 50, for a proportion of 0.08. **(b)** Answers will vary, but more than 99% of all students should get between 7 and 33 heads out of 200 flips.

**10.4.** **(a)** 0. **(b)** 1. **(c)** 0.01. **(d)** 0.6 (or 0.99, but "more often than not" is a rather weak description of an event with probability 0.99).

**10.5.** **(a)** $S = \{\text{all numbers between 0 and 24}\}$ (assuming we measure time in hours). **(b)** $S = \{\text{all numbers greater than or equal to 0}\}$, or $S = \{0, 0.01, 0.02, 0.03, \ldots\}$. **(c)** $S = \{\text{A, B, C, D, F}\}$ (students might also include "+" and "–"). **(d)** $S = \{\text{yes, no}\}$.

**10.6.** **(a)** The table on the right illustrates the 16 possible pair combinations in the sample space. **(b)** Each of the 16 outcomes has probability 1/16.

| | ⚀ | ⚁ | ⚂ | ⚃ |
|---|---|---|---|---|
| ⚀ | ⚀⚀ | ⚀⚁ | ⚀⚂ | ⚀⚃ |
| ⚁ | ⚁⚀ | ⚁⚁ | ⚁⚂ | ⚁⚃ |
| ⚂ | ⚂⚀ | ⚂⚁ | ⚂⚂ | ⚂⚃ |
| ⚃ | ⚃⚀ | ⚃⚁ | ⚃⚂ | ⚃⚃ |

**10.7.** For the sample space, add 1 to each pair-total in the table shown in the previous solution: $S = \{3, 4, 5, 6, 7, 8, 9\}$. As all faces are equally likely and the dice are independent, each of the 16 possible pairings is equally likely, so (for example) the probability of a total of 5 is 3/16, because 3 pairings add to 4 (and then we add 1). The complete set of probabilities is shown in the table on the right.

| Total | Probability |
|---|---|
| 3 | 1/16 |
| 4 | 2/16 |
| 5 | 3/16 |
| 6 | 4/16 |
| 7 | 3/16 |
| 8 | 2/16 |
| 9 | 1/16 |

**10.8.** **(a)** Both rules are satisfied: All probabilities are between 0 and 1 (0% and 100%), and the percents add to 100%. (We also should note that the four groups described are nonoverlapping, and account for all possible classifications of potential customers.) **(b)** 35% (20% + 15%) are currently undergraduates.

**10.9.** **(a)** The given probabilities have sum 0.89, so $P(\text{other language}) = 0.11$. **(b)** $P(\text{not English}) = 1 - 0.59 = 0.41$. (Or, add the other three probabilities.)

**10.10.** Model 1: Not legitimate (probabilities have sum $\frac{6}{7}$). Model 2: Legitimate. Model 3: Not legitimate (probabilities have sum $\frac{7}{6}$). Model 4: Not legitimate (probabilities cannot be more than 1).

**10.11.** **(a)** $A = \{7, 8, 9\}$, so $P(A) = 0.058 + 0.051 + 0.046 = 0.155$. **(b)** $B = \{1, 3, 5, 7, 9\}$, so $P(B) = 0.301 + 0.125 + 0.079 + 0.058 + 0.046 = 0.609$. **(c)** $A \text{ or } B = \{1, 3, 5, 7, 8, 9\}$, so $P(A \text{ or } B) = 0.301 + 0.125 + 0.079 + 0.058 + 0.051 + 0.046 = 0.660$. This is different from $P(A) + P(B)$ because $A$ and $B$ are not disjoint.

**10.12.** **(a)** The eight probabilities have sum 1 (and account for all possible responses to the question). **(b)** "$X < 7$" means "the student watched TV fewer than 7 days in the past week," or "the student did not watch TV every day in the past week." $P(X < 7) = 1 - 0.57 = 0.43$ (or, add the first 7 probabilities). **(c)** "Watched TV at least once" is "$X > 0$. $P(X > 0) = 1 - 0.04 = 0.96$ (or, add the last 7 probabilities).

**10.13.** **(a)** $P(X \le 0.4) = 0.4$. **(b)** $P(X < 0.4) = 0.4$. **(c)** $P(0.3 \le X \le 0.5) = 0.2$.

**10.14.** **(a)** The area of a triangle is $\frac{1}{2}bh = \frac{1}{2}(2)(1) = 1$. **(b)** $P(Y < 1) = 0.5$. **(c)** $P(Y < 0.5) = 0.125$.

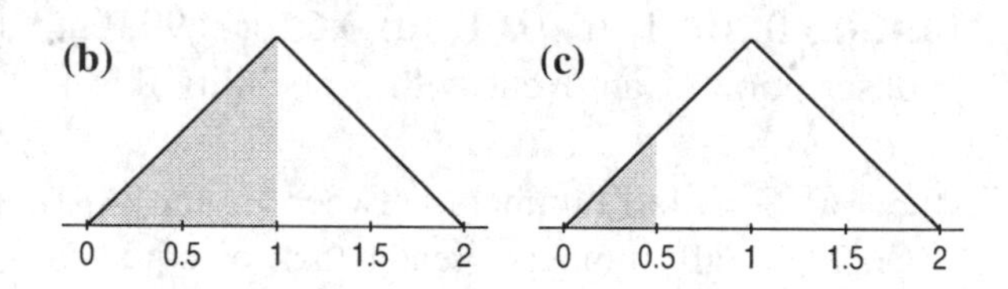


**10.15.** **(a)** The event is $\{X \ge 10\}$. **(b)** $P(X \ge 10) = P\left(\frac{X-6.8}{1.6} \ge \frac{10-6.8}{1.6}\right) = P(Z \ge 2) \doteq 0.025$ (using the 68–95–99.7 rule) or 0.0228 (using Table A).

**10.16.** **(a)** $X \ge 3$ means the student's grade is either an A or a B. $P(X \ge 3) = 0.35 + 0.45 = 0.8$. **(b)** "Poorer than C" means either D ($X = 1$) or F ($X = 0$), so we want $P(X < 2) = P(X \le 1) = 0.02 + 0.02 = 0.04$.

**10.17.** $P(\text{student's score was higher than 25}) = P(Y > 25) = P\left(\frac{Y-20.9}{4.8} > \frac{25-20.9}{4.8}\right) \doteq P(Z > 0.85) \doteq 0.1977$ (using Table A), or 0.1965 (using software).

**10.18.** **(b)** A personal probability might take into account specific information about one's own driving habits, or about the kind of traffic one usually drives in. **(c)** Most people believe that they are better-than-average drivers (whether or not they have any evidence to support that belief).

**10.19.** (a) Probabilities express the approximate fraction of occurrences out of many trials.

**10.20.** (b) The set $\{0, 1, 2, 3, 4, 5, 6, 7, 8\}$ lists all possible counts.

**10.21.** (b) This is a discrete (but not equally likely) model.

**10.22.** (b) The other probabilities add to 0.96, so this must be 0.04.

**10.23.** (c) $P(\text{type O or type B}) = P(\text{type O}) + P(\text{type B}) = 0.45 + 0.11 = 0.56$.

**10.24.** (a) $P(\text{not type O}) = 1 - P(\text{type O}) = 1 - 0.45 = 0.55$.

**10.25.** (b) There are 10 equally likely possibilities, so $P(\text{zero}) = 1/10$.

**10.26.** (c) "7 or greater" means 7, 8, or 9—3 of the 10 possibilities.

**10.27.** (a) 80% have 0, 1, or 2 cars; the rest have more than 2.

**10.28.** (c) $Y > 120$ standardizes to $Z > 1.33$, for which Table A gives 0.0918.

**10.29.** Note that in this experiment, factors other than the nickel's characteristics might affect the outcome. For example, if the surface used is not quite level, there will be a tendency for the nickel to fall in the "downhill" direction.

**10.30.** **(a)** There are sixteen possible outcomes:

{ HHHH, HHHM, HHMH, HMHH, MHHH, HHMM, HMHM, HMMH,
MHHM, MHMH, MMHH, HMMM, MHMM, MMHM, MMMH, MMMM }

**(b)** The sample space is {0,1,2,3,4}.

**10.31.** **(a)** Legitimate. **(b)** Not legitimate (the total is more than 1). **(c)** Legitimate (even if the deck of cards is not!).

**10.32.** **(a)** The given probabilities have sum 0.72, so this probability must be 0.28. **(b)** $P(\text{at least a high school education}) = 1 - P(\text{has not finished HS}) = 1 - 0.12 = 0.88$. (Or, add the other three probabilities.)

**10.33.** Because the two events are disjoint, we simply add the two probabilities:

$P(\text{death was agriculture- or manufacturing-related}) = 0.134 + 0.119 = 0.253.$

Meanwhile, $P(\text{death from some other cause}) = 1 - 0.253 = 0.747$.

**10.34.** The probabilities of 2, 3, 4, and 5 are unchanged (1/6), so $P$(⚀ or ⚅) must still be 1/3. If $P$(⚅) $= 0.2$, then $P$(⚀) $= \frac{1}{3} - 0.2 = 0.1\overline{3}$ (or $\frac{2}{15}$).

| Face | ⚀ | ⚁ | ⚂ | ⚃ | ⚄ | ⚅ |
|---|---|---|---|---|---|---|
| Probability | $0.1\overline{3}$ | 1/6 | 1/6 | 1/6 | 1/6 | 0.2 |

**10.35.** **(a)** – **(c)** Results will vary, but after $n$ tosses, the distribution of the proportion $\hat{p}$ is approximately Normal with mean 0.5 and standard deviation $1/(2\sqrt{n})$, while the distribution of the count of heads is approximately Normal with mean $0.5n$ and standard deviation $\sqrt{n}/2$, so using the 68–95–99.7 rule, we have the results shown in the table on the right. Note that the range for $\hat{p}$ gets narrower, while the range for the count gets wider.

| $n$ | 99.7% Range for $\hat{p}$ | 99.7% Range for count |
|---|---|---|
| 40 | $0.5 \pm 0.237$ | $20 \pm 9.5$ |
| 120 | $0.5 \pm 0.137$ | $60 \pm 16.4$ |
| 240 | $0.5 \pm 0.097$ | $120 \pm 23.2$ |
| 480 | $0.5 \pm 0.068$ | $240 \pm 32.9$ |

**10.36.** Each of the 90 guests has probability $1/90$ of winning the prize. The probability that the winner is a woman is the sum of $1/90$ 42 times, one for each woman. The probability is $42/90 = 0.4\bar{6}$.

**10.37.** In computing the probabilities, we have dropped the trailing zeros from the land area figures. **(a)** $P(\text{area is forested}) = \frac{4176}{9094} \doteq 0.4592$. **(b)** $P(\text{area is not forested}) \doteq 1 - 0.4592 = 0.5408$.

**10.38.** **(a)** All probabilities are between 0 and 1, and they add to 1. (We must assume that no one takes more than one language.) **(b)** The probability that a student is studying a language other than English is $0.41 = 1 - 0.59$ (or add all the other probabilities). **(c)** This probability is $0.38 = 0.26 + 0.09 + 0.03$.

**10.39.** **(a)** The given probabilities add to 0.84, so other colors must account for the remaining 0.16. **(b)** $P(\text{Silver or white}) = 0.18 + 0.17 = 0.35$, so $P(\text{neither silver nor white}) = 1 - 0.35 = 0.65$.

**10.40.** **(a)** The sum of the given probabilities is 0.76, so $P(\text{blue}) = 0.24$. **(b)** $P(\text{not brown}) = 1 - 0.13 = 0.87$. **(c)** $P(\text{yellow, orange, or red}) = 0.14 + 0.20 + 0.13 = 0.47$.

**10.41.** Cindy chose 5 colors, so each color has probability $1/5$ (because she chose "equal numbers" of each color).

**10.42.** **(a)** It is legitimate because every person must fall into exactly one category, and the probabilities add to 1. **(b)** $0.125 = 0.000 + 0.003 + 0.060 + 0.062$ is the probability that a randomly chosen American is Hispanic. **(c)** $0.309 = 1 - 0.691$ is the probability that a randomly chosen American is not a non-Hispanic white.

**10.43.** **(a)** $X$ is discrete, because it has a finite sample space. **(b)** "At least one nonword error" is the event $\{X \geq 1\}$ (or $\{X > 0\}$). $P(X \geq 1) = 1 - P(X = 0) = 0.9$. **(c)** $\{X \leq 2\}$ is "no more than two nonword errors," or "fewer than three nonword errors." $P(X \leq 2) = P(X = 0) + P(X = 1) + P(X = 2) = 0.1 + 0.2 + 0.3 = 0.6$. $P(X < 2) = P(X = 0) + P(X = 1) = 0.1 + 0.2 = 0.3$.

**Note:** *The more precise notation* $\{X \geq 1\}$ *is clearer in print than just* $X \geq 1$. *We recommend that you* not *use the precise notation for students at this level.*

**10.44.** **(a)** All 9 digits are equally likely, so each has probability 1/9:

| Value of $W$ | 1 | 2 | 3 | 4 | 5 | 6 | 7 | 8 | 9 |
|---|---|---|---|---|---|---|---|---|---|
| Probability | $\frac{1}{9}$ | $\frac{1}{9}$ | $\frac{1}{9}$ | $\frac{1}{9}$ | $\frac{1}{9}$ | $\frac{1}{9}$ | $\frac{1}{9}$ | $\frac{1}{9}$ | $\frac{1}{9}$ |

**(b)** $P(W \geq 6) = \frac{4}{9} \doteq 0.444$—twice as big as the Benford's law probability.

**10.45.** **(a)** There are 10 pairs. Just using initials: {(A, D), (A, M), (A, S), (A, R), (D, M), (D, S), (D, R), (M, S), (M, R), (S, R)}. **(b)** Each has probability $1/10 = 10\%$. **(c)** Mei-Ling is chosen in 4 of the 10 possible outcomes: $4/10 = 40\%$. **(d)** There are 3 pairs with neither Sam nor Roberto, so the probability is $3/10$.

**10.46.** **(a)** BBB, BBG, BGB, GBB, GGB, GBG, BGG, GGG. Each has probability 1/8. **(b)** Three of the eight arrangements have two (and only two) girls, so $P(X = 2) = 3/8 = 0.375$. **(c)** See table.

| Value of $X$ | 0 | 1 | 2 | 3 |
|---|---|---|---|---|
| Probability | 1/8 | 3/8 | 3/8 | 1/8 |

**10.47.** The possible values of $Y$ are $1, 2, 3, \ldots, 12$, each with probability $1/12$. Aside from drawing a diagram showing all the possible combinations, one can reason that the first (regular) die is equally likely to show any number from 1 through 6. Half of the time, the second roll shows 0, and the other half it shows 6. Each possible outcome therefore has probability $\frac{1}{6} \cdot \frac{1}{2}$.

**10.48.** **(a)** This is a continuous random variable because the set of possible values is an interval. **(b)** The height should be $\frac{1}{2}$ because the area under the curve must be 1. The density curve is at right. **(c)** $P(Y \leq 1) = \frac{1}{2}$.

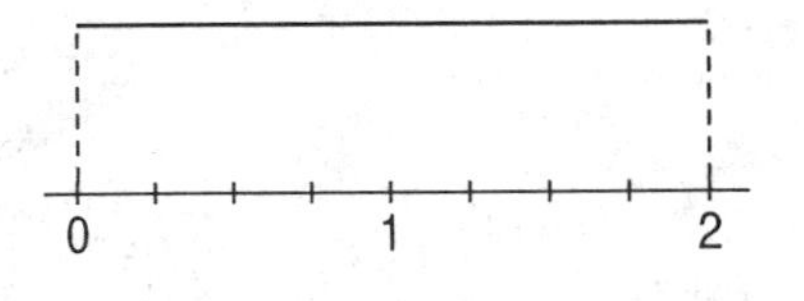


**10.49.** **(a)** $P(0.52 \leq \hat{p} \leq 0.60) = P\left(\frac{0.52-0.56}{0.019} \leq \frac{\hat{p}-0.56}{0.019} \leq \frac{0.60-0.56}{0.019}\right) = P(-2.11 \leq Z \leq 2.11) = 0.9826 - 0.0174 = 0.9652$. **(b)** $P(\hat{p} \geq 0.72) = P\left(\frac{\hat{p}-0.56}{0.019} \geq \frac{0.72-0.56}{0.019}\right) = P(Z \geq 8.42)$; this is basically 0.

**10.50.** For these probabilities, compute the areas of the appropriate rectangle under the density shown above (Exercise 10.48). **(a)** $P(0.5 < Y < 1.3) = 0.4$. **(b)** $P(Y \geq 0.8) = 0.6$.

**10.51.** **(a)** $P(Y > 300) = P(Z > 0) = 0.5$. **(b)** $P(Y > 370) = P(Z > 2) = 0.025$.

**10.52.** **(a)** Because there are 10,000 equally likely four-digit numbers (0000 through 9999), the probability of an exact match is $\frac{1}{10,000}$. **(b)** There is a total of $24 = 4 \cdot 3 \cdot 2 \cdot 1$ arrangements of the four digits 5, 9, 7, and 4 (there are four choices for the first digit, three for the second, two for the third), so the probability of a match in any order is $\frac{24}{10,000}$.

**10.53.** $P(8.9 \leq \bar{x} \leq 9.1) = P\left(\frac{8.9-9}{0.075} \leq \frac{\bar{x}-9}{0.075} \leq \frac{9.1-9}{0.075}\right) \doteq P(-1.33 \leq Z \leq 1.33) = 0.9082 - 0.0918 = 0.8164$. (Software give 0.8176.)

**10.54.** For an "exact match" bet, the mean amount won on a \$1 bet is $\$5000 \times \frac{1}{10,000} = \$0.50$, making it a slightly better bet than an "any order" bet, for which the mean amount won is $\$200 \times \frac{24}{10,000} = \$0.48$.

**10.55.** **(a)** Most answers will be between 35% and 65%. **(b)** Based on 10,000 simulated trials—more than students are expected to do—there is about an 80% chance of having a longest run of four or more (i.e., either making or missing four shots in a row), a 54% chance of getting five or more, a 31% chance of getting six or more, and a 16% chance of getting seven or more. The average ("expected") longest run length is about six.

**10.56.** **(a)** With $n = 20$, nearly all answers will be 0.40 or greater. With $n = 80$, nearly all answers will be between 0.50 and 0.80. With $n = 320$, nearly all answers will be between 0.58 and 0.72.

# Chapter 11 Solutions

**11.1.** Both 283 and 311 pushes per minute are statistics (related to one sample: the subjects with placebo, and the same subjects with caffeine).

**11.2.** 68% is a parameter (related to the population of all registered voters in Indianapolis); 73% is a statistic (related to the sample of registered voters among those called).

**11.3.** 2.5003 cm is a parameter (related to the population, i.e., the whole lot); 2.5009 cm is a statistic (related to the sample of 100 ball bearings).

**11.4.** $\frac{28}{1} = 28$; $\frac{28+40}{2} = 34$; $\frac{28+40+28}{3} = 32$; $\frac{28+40+28+33}{4} = 32.25$; $\frac{28+40+28+33+20}{5} = 29.8$. The plot (not shown) looks like the left side of Figure 11.1.

**11.5.** Although the probability of having to pay for a total loss for 1 or more of the 12 policies is very small, if this were to happen, it would be financially disastrous. On the other hand, for thousands of policies, the law of large numbers says that the average claim on many policies will be close to the mean, so the insurance company can be assured that the premiums they collect will (almost certainly) cover the claims.

**11.6. (a)** $\mu = 694/10 = 69.4$. **(b)** The table below shows the results for line 116. Note that we need to choose 5 digits, because the digit 4 appears twice. (When choosing an SRS, no student should be chosen more than once.) **(c)** The results for the other lines are in the table; the histogram is shown on the right below. (Students might choose different intervals than those shown here.) The center of the histogram is a bit lower than 69.4 (it is closer to about 67), but for a small group of $\bar{x}$-values, we should not expect the center to be in exactly the right place.

**Note:** *You might consider having students choose different samples from those prescribed in this exercise, and then pooling the results for the whole class. With more values of* $\bar{x}$*, a better picture of the sampling distribution begins to develop.*

| Line | Digits | Scores | $\bar{x}$ |
|---|---|---|---|
| 116 | 14459 | 62 + 72 + 73 + 62 = 269 | 67.25 |
| 117 | 3816 | 58 + 74 + 62 + 65 = 259 | 64.75 |
| 118 | 7319 | 66 + 58 + 62 + 62 = 248 | 62 |
| 119 | 95857 | 62 + 73 + 74 + 66 = 275 | 68.75 |
| 120 | 3547 | 58 + 73 + 72 + 66 = 269 | 67.25 |
| 121 | 7148 | 66 + 62 + 72 + 74 = 274 | 68.5 |
| 122 | 1387 | 62 + 58 + 74 + 66 = 260 | 65 |
| 123 | 54580 | 73 + 72 + 74 + 82 = 301 | 75.25 |
| 124 | 7103 | 66 + 62 + 82 + 58 = 268 | 67 |
| 125 | 9674 | 62 + 65 + 66 + 72 = 265 | 66.25 |

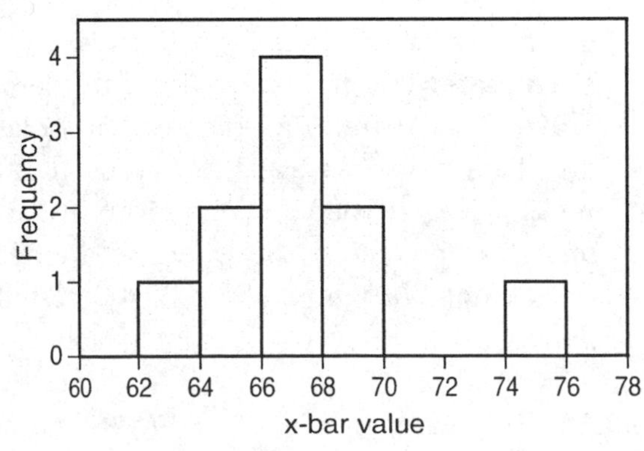

**11.7.** **(a)** $\bar{x}$ is not systematically higher than or lower than $\mu$; that is, it has no particular tendency to underestimate or overestimate $\mu$. **(b)** With large samples, $\bar{x}$ is more likely to be close to $\mu$, because with a larger sample comes more information (and therefore less uncertainty).

**11.8.** **(a)** $\sigma/\sqrt{3} \doteq 5.7735$ mg. **(b)** Solve $\sigma/\sqrt{n} = 5$: $\sqrt{n} = 2$, so $n = 4$. The average of several measurements is more likely than a single measurement to be close to the mean.

**11.9.** **(a)** If $X$ has a $N(300, 35)$ distribution, we have $P(X > 300) = 0.5$ and $P(X > 335) = P(Z > 1) \doteq 0.16$ (using the 68–95–99.7 rule). **(b)** The average of four independent NAEP scores has mean $\mu = 300$ and standard deviation $\sigma/\sqrt{4} = 17.5$. (Specifically, it has [approximately] a Normal distribution with that mean and standard deviation.) **(c)** $P(\bar{x} > 300) = 0.5$ and $P(\bar{x} > 335) = P(Z > 2) = 0.025$ (using the 68–95–99.7 rule).

**11.10.** No: The histogram of the sample values will look like the population distribution, whatever it might happen to be. (For example, if we roll a fair die many times, the histogram of sample values should look relatively flat—probability close to 1/6 for each value 1, 2, 3, 4, 5, and 6.) The central limit theorem says that the histogram of *sample means* (from many large samples) will look more and more Normal.

**11.11.** **(a)** $\mu_{\bar{x}} = 0.5$ and $\sigma_{\bar{x}} = \sigma/\sqrt{50} = 0.7/\sqrt{50} \doteq 0.09899$. **(b)** Because this distribution is only approximately normal, it would be quite reasonable to use the 68–95–99.7 rule to give a rough estimate: 0.6 is about one standard deviation above the mean, so the probability should be about 0.16 (half of the 32% that falls outside ±1 standard deviation). Alternatively, $P(\bar{x} > 0.6) \doteq P(Z > \frac{0.6-0.5}{0.09899}) = P(Z > 1.01) = 0.1562$.

**11.12.** **(a)** Ramon's score is about the 64th percentile: $P(X \leq 1100) \doteq P(Z \leq \frac{1100-1026}{209}) = P(Z \leq 0.35) = 0.6368$ (software: 0.6384). **(b)** $\bar{x} = 1100$ is about the 99.9th percentile: $\bar{x}$ is approximately Normal with mean 1026 and standard deviation $209/\sqrt{70} \doteq 24.9803$, so $P(\bar{x} \leq 1100) \doteq P(Z \leq 2.96) = 0.9985$. **(c)** The first answer is less accurate: The distribution of an individual's score (like Ramon's) might not be Normal, but the central limit theorem says that the distribution of $\bar{x}$ will be close to Normal.

**11.13.** **State:** What is the probability that the average loss will be no greater than $275?
**Formulate:** Use the central limit theorem to approximate this probability.
**Solve:** The central limit theorem says that, in spite of the skewness of the population distribution, the average loss among 10,000 policies will be approximately $N(\$250, \sigma/\sqrt{10,000}) = N(\$250, \$10)$. Because $275 is 2.5 standard deviations above the mean, the probability of seeing an average loss of no more than $275 is about 0.9938.
**Conclude:** We can be about 99.4% certain that average losses will not exceed $275 per policy.

**11.14.** The center line is at $\mu = 75^\circ$ F; the control limits should be at $\mu \pm 3\sigma/\sqrt{4}$, which means $74.25^\circ$ F and $75.75^\circ$ F.

**11.15. (a)** The center is 11.5, and the control limits are $\mu \pm 3\sigma/\sqrt{4} = 11.5 \pm 0.3 = 11.2$ and 11.8. **(b)** Graphs are at right and below. Points outside control limits are marked with an "X." **(c)** Set B is from the in-control process. The process mean shifted suddenly for Set A; it appears to have changed on about the 11th or 12th sample. The mean drifted gradually for the process in Set C.

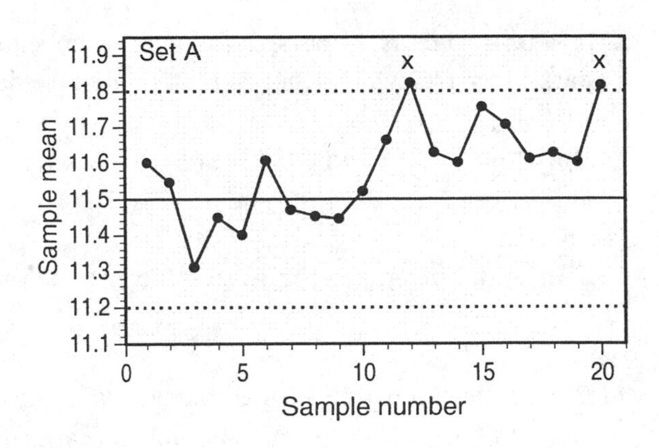


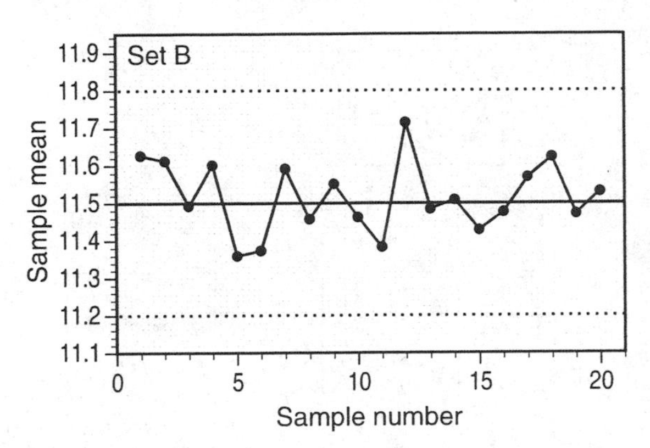


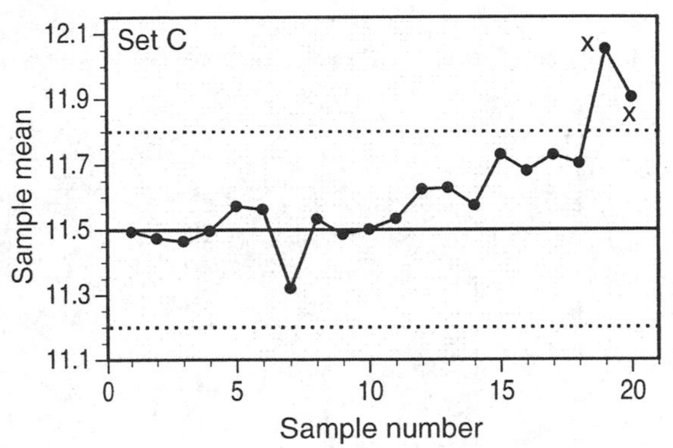


**11.16.** The natural tolerances are $\mu \pm 3\sigma = 73.5^\circ$ to $76.5^\circ$. The middle 95% of response temperatures will fall in the range $\mu \pm 2\sigma = 74^\circ$ to $76^\circ$.

**11.17.** (c) This is a proportion of the people interviewed in the sample of 60,000 households.

**11.18.** (b) 56% is a proportion of all registered voters (the population).

**11.19.** (b) The law of large numbers says that the mean from a large sample is close to the population mean. Statement (c) is also true, but is based on the central limit theorem, not on the law of large numbers.

**11.20.** (a) The mean of the sample means ($\bar{x}$) is the same as the population mean ($\mu$).

**11.21.** (c) The standard deviation of the distribution of $\bar{x}$ is $\sigma/\sqrt{n}$.

**11.22.** (a) "Unbiased" means that the estimator is right "on the average."

**11.23.** (c) The central limit theorem says that the mean from a large sample has (approximately) a Normal distribution. Statement (a) is also true, but is based on the law of large numbers, not on the central limit theorem.

**11.24.** (a) The mean $\bar{x}$ of the four inspected parts has a $N(40.150 \text{ mm}, 0.0015)$ distribution, so 40.148 mm is about 1.33 standard deviations below the mean; Table A gives a probability of 0.0918 below this point.

**11.25.** 65 inches is a statistic (related to the sample of female college students). 64 inches is a parameter (related to the population of all young women).

**11.26.** Both 40.2% and 31.7% are statistics (related, respectively, to the samples of small-class and large-class black students).

**11.27.** On the average, Joe loses 40 cents each time he plays (that is, he spends \$1 and gets back 60 cents).

**11.28.** In the long run, the gambler earns an average of 94.7 cents per bet. In other words, the gambler loses (and the house gains) an average of 5.3 cents for each \$1 bet.

**11.29.** Sketches will vary; one result is shown below, left.

***For 11–29.***

***For 11–30.***

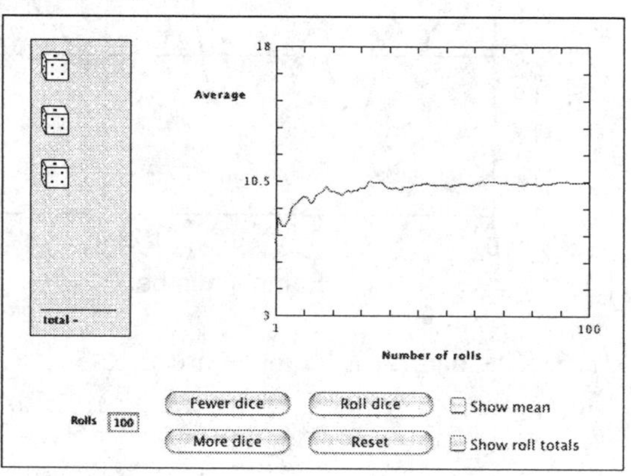


**11.30.** The mean is 10.5 (= $3 \times 3.5$ because a single die has a mean of 3.5). Sketches will vary, as will the number of rolls; one result is shown above, right.

**11.31.** If $\bar{x}$ is the mean number of strikes per square kilometer, then $\mu_{\bar{x}} = 6$ strikes/km$^2$ and $\sigma_{\bar{x}} = 2.4/\sqrt{10} \doteq 0.7589$ strikes/km$^2$.

**11.32. State:** How large an SRS is needed to reduce the standard deviation of $\bar{x}$ to 0.5 inch?
**Formulate:** Use the formula for the standard deviation of the mean, and solve for the sample size.
**Solve:** We need to choose $n$ so that $2.8/\sqrt{n} = 0.5$. That means $\sqrt{n} = 5.6$, so $n = 31.36$. Because $n$ must be a whole number, take $n = 32$.
**Conclude:** A sample of size 32 will give a standard deviation (slightly below) 0.5 inch.

**11.33. (a)** 99.7% of all observations fall within 3 standard deviations, so we want $3\sigma/\sqrt{n} = 0.5$. The standard deviation of $\bar{x}$ must therefore be $1/6 = 0.1\overline{6}$ inch. **(b)** We need to choose $n$ so that $2.8/\sqrt{n} = \frac{1}{6}$. That means $\sqrt{n} = 16.8$, so $n = 282.24$. Because $n$ must be a whole number, take $n = 283$.

**11.34.** **(a)** For the height $H$ of an individual student, $P(69 < H < 71) \doteq P(\frac{69-70}{2.8} < Z < \frac{71-70}{2.8}) = P(-0.36 < Z < 0.36) = 0.6406 - 0.3594 = 0.2812$. (With software: 0.2790.) **(b)** In Exercise 11.32, we decided to sample $n = 32$ students, so $\bar{x}$ has a $N(70 \text{ in}, 0.4950 \text{ in})$ distribution. Therefore, $P(69 < \bar{x} < 71) \doteq P(\frac{69-70}{0.4950} < Z < \frac{71-70}{0.4950}) = P(-2.02 < Z < 2.02) = 0.9783 - 0.0217 = 0.9566$. If we use a standard deviation of 0.5 in (our goal in Exercise 11.32), we get $P(-2 < Z < 2)$, which is either 0.9544 (Table A) or 0.95 (68–95–99.7 rule).

**11.35.** **(a)** The mean of five untreated specimens has a standard deviation of $2.3/\sqrt{5} \doteq 1.0286$ lbs, so $P(\bar{x}_u > 50) = P(Z > \frac{50-58}{1.0286}) = P(Z > -7.78)$, which is basically 1.
**(b)** The mean of five treated specimens has a standard deviation of $1.6/\sqrt{5} \doteq 0.7155$ lbs, so $P(\bar{x}_t > 50) = P(Z > \frac{50-30}{0.7155}) = P(Z > 27.95)$, which is basically 0.

**11.36.** Let $X$ be Shelia's measured glucose level. **(a)** $P(X > 140) = P(Z > 1.5) = 0.0668$. **(b)** If $\bar{x}$ is the mean of four measurements (assumed to be independent), then $\bar{x}$ has a $N(125, 10/\sqrt{4}) = N(125 \text{ mg/dl}, 5 \text{ mg/dl})$ distribution, and $P(\bar{x} > 140) = P(Z > 3) = 0.0013$.

**11.37.** **(a)** For the emissions $E$ of a single car, $P(E > 0.3) \doteq P(Z > \frac{0.3-0.2}{0.05}) = P(Z > 2) = 0.0228$ (or 0.025, using the 68–95–99.77 rule). **(b)** The average $\bar{x}$ is Normal with mean 0.3 g/mi and standard deviation $0.05/\sqrt{25} = 0.01$ g/mi. Therefore, $P(\bar{x} > 0.3) \doteq P(Z > \frac{0.3-0.2}{0.01}) = P(Z > 10)$, which is basically 0.

**11.38.** The mean of four measurements has a $N(125 \text{ mg/dl}, 5 \text{ mg/dl})$ distribution, and $P(Z > 1.645) = 0.05$ if $Z$ is $N(0, 1)$, so $L = 125 + 1.645 \cdot 5 = 133.225$ mg/dl.

**11.39.** The mean NOX level for 25 cars has a $N(0.2 \text{ g/mi}, 0.01 \text{ g/mi})$ distribution, and $P(Z > 2.326) = 0.01$ if $Z$ is $N(0, 1)$, so $L = 0.2 + 2.326 \cdot 0.01 \doteq 0.2233$ g/mi.

**11.40.** **State:** What are the probabilities of an average return over 10%, or less than 5%?
**Formulate:** Use the central limit theorem to approximate this probability.
**Solve:** The central limit theorem says that over 40 years, $\bar{x}$ (the mean return) is approximately Normal with mean $\mu = 8.7\%$ and standard deviation $\sigma_{\bar{x}} = 20.2\%/\sqrt{40} \doteq 3.194\%$. Therefore, $P(\bar{x} > 10\%) = P(Z > 0.41) = 0.3409$, and $P(\bar{x} < 5\%) = P(Z < -1.16) = 0.1230$. (Software gives 0.3420 and 0.1233.)
**Conclude:** There is about a 34% chance of getting average returns over 10%, and a 12% chance of getting average returns less than 5%.
**Note:** *We have to assume that returns in separate years are independent.*

**11.41.** **(a)** $\bar{x}$ is approximately $N(2.2, 1.4/\sqrt{52}) = N(2.2 \text{ accidents}, 0.1941 \text{ accidents})$. **(b)** $P(\bar{x} < 2) \doteq P(Z < -1.03) = 0.1515$. (Software gives the same answer.) **(c)** Let $A$ be the number of accidents in a year; then $\bar{x} = A/52$. $P(A < 100) = P(\bar{x} < \frac{100}{52}) \doteq P(Z < -1.43) = 0.0764$ (software: 0.0769). [Alternatively, we might use the *continuity correction* (which adjusts for the fact that counts must be whole numbers) and find $P(A < 99.5) = P(\bar{x} < \frac{99.5}{52}) = P(Z < -1.48) = 0.0694$ (software: 0.0700).]

**11.42. State:** What is the probability that the total weight of the passengers exceeds 4000 lb?
**Formulate:** Use the central limit theorem to approximate this probability.
**Solve:** If $W$ is total weight, and $\bar{x} = W/19$, then the central limit theorem says that $\bar{x}$ is approximately Normal with mean 190 lb and standard deviation $35/\sqrt{19} \doteq 8.0296$ lb. Therefore,

$$P(W > 4000) = P(\bar{x} > \tfrac{4000}{19}) \doteq P(Z > \tfrac{210.5263-190}{35/\sqrt{19}}) = P(Z > 2.56) = 0.0052$$

(software: 0.0053).
**Conclude:** There is very little chance—about 0.5%—that the total weight exceeds 4000 lb.

**11.43. (a)** Starting at line 101, we choose 19, 22, 39, 50, and 34. Three of these circles are empty, so $\hat{p} = 0.6$. **(b)** The table (below, left) shows all ten samples, indicating which circles are filled (the shaded numbers). **(c)** Histogram is shown below, right. **(d)** Four were exactly correct. Considering the small number of samples, 0.6 is roughly in the center. In a large number of samples, 0.6 should be in the center because this random sample should be unbiased. See also the solution to the next exercise.

| Sample | # empty | $\hat{p}$ |
|---|---|---|
| 19, 22, 39, 50, 34 | 3 | 0.6 |
| 73, 67, 64, 71, 50 | 4 | 0.8 |
| 45, 46, 77, 17, 09 | 4 | 0.8 |
| 52, 71, 13, 88, 89 | 5 | 1 |
| 95, 59, 29, 40, 07 | 2 | 0.4 |
| 68, 41, 73, 50, 13 | 2 | 0.4 |
| 82, 73, 95, 78, 90 | 3 | 0.6 |
| 60, 94, 07, 20, 24 | 4 | 0.8 |
| 36, 00, 91, 93, 65 | 3 | 0.6 |
| 38, 44, 84, 87, 89 | 3 | 0.6 |

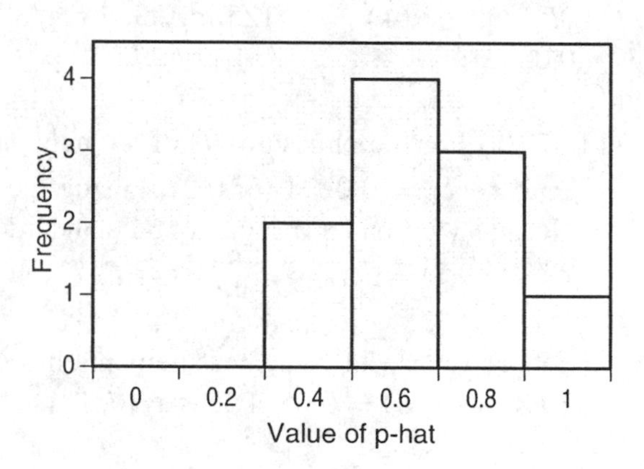


**11.44. (a)** The histogram should be centered at about 0.6. For reference, the theoretical histogram is shown below on the left; student results should have a similar appearance (but will no doubt have more irregularity). **(b)** The histogram should be centered at about 0.2. The theoretical histogram is shown below on the right.

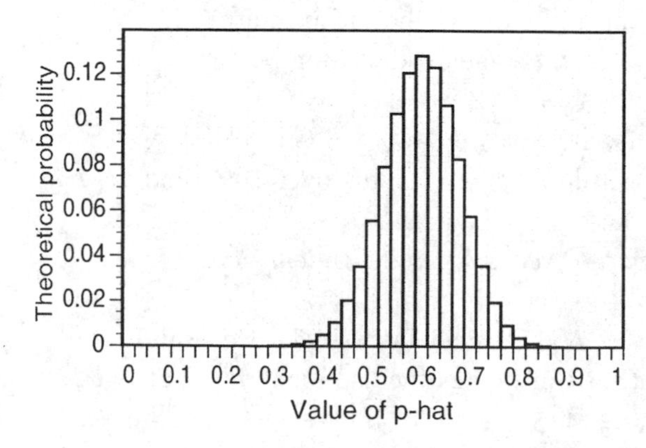


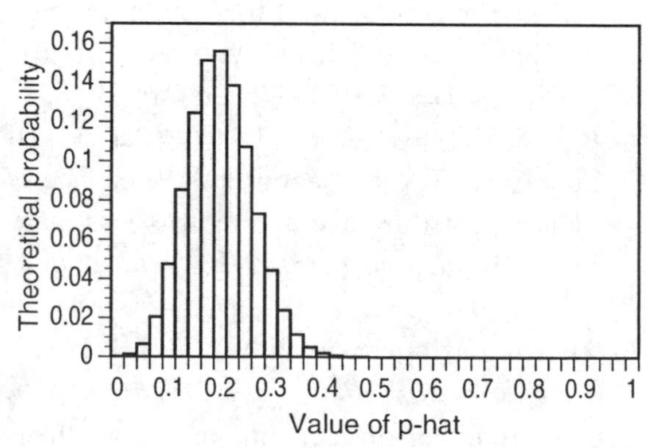


**11.45.** The center line is $\mu = 4.22$ and the control limits are $\mu \pm 3\sigma/\sqrt{5} = 4.05$ and 4.39.

**11.46. State:** Do the average losses on major joint replacements suggest that further investigation is needed?
**Formulate:** Construct an $\bar{x}$ chart and identify any out-of-control points.
**Solve:** The center line is the mean ($6400) and the control limits are $\mu \pm 3\sigma/\sqrt{8} = \$5657$ to $7142. The last two points are above the upper control limit. Overall, the plot suggests that the mean is gradually drifting upward.
**Conclude:** The hospital should investigate the apparent increasing trend in these losses to determine if anything can be done to bring losses back down to their former levels.

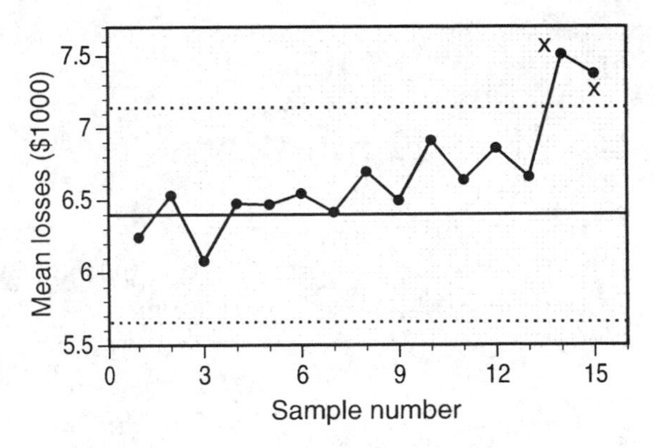


**11.47.** For an in-control process, the pH would almost always fall in the range $\mu \pm 3\sigma = 3.84$ to 4.60.

**11.48.** The center line is $\mu = 0.8750$ inch, and the control limits are $\mu \pm 3\sigma/\sqrt{5} \doteq 0.8750 \pm 0.0016 = 0.8734$ and 0.8766 inch.

**11.49. (a)** Assuming (as we do in process control) that the distribution is Normal, an individual tension $X$ has a $N(275 \text{ mV}, 43 \text{ mV})$ distribution, and we have $P(100 \le X \le 400) = P(-4.07 \le Z \le 2.91) = 0.9982$ (using Table A or software), so about 99.8% of all monitors meet the specifications. **(b)** Now we have $P(150 \le X \le 350) = P(-2.91 \le Z \le 1.74) = 0.9591 - 0.0018 = 0.9573$ (software: 0.9576), so about 95.7% (or 95.8%) of all monitors meet the tighter specifications.

**11.50.** With $X$ having a $N(250 \text{ mV}, 43 \text{ mV})$ distribution, we have $P(150 \le X \le 350) = P(-2.33 \le Z \le 2.33) = 0.9901 - 0.0099 = 0.9802$ (software: 0.9800), so about 98% meet the specifications.

# Chapter 12 Solutions

**12.1.** If we assume that each site is independent of the others (and that they can be considered as a random sample from the collection of sites referenced in scientific journals), then $P$(all seven are still good) $= 0.87^7 \doteq 0.3773$.

**12.2.** **(a)** $P$(win the jackpot) $= \left(\frac{1}{20}\right)\left(\frac{9}{20}\right)\left(\frac{1}{20}\right) = 0.001125$. **(b)** The other symbol can show up on the middle wheel, with probability $\left(\frac{1}{20}\right)\left(\frac{11}{20}\right)\left(\frac{1}{20}\right) = 0.001375$, or on either of the outside wheels, with probability $\left(\frac{19}{20}\right)\left(\frac{9}{20}\right)\left(\frac{1}{20}\right) = 0.021375$ (each). **(c)** Combining all three cases from part (b), we have $P$(exactly two bells) $= 0.001375 + 2 \cdot 0.021375 = 0.044125$.

**12.3.** This would not be surprising: Assuming that all the authors are independent (for example, none were written by siblings or married couples), we can view the nine names as being a random sample, so that the number $N$ of occurrences of the ten most common names would have a binomial distribution with $n = 9$ and $p = 0.056$. Then $P(N = 0) = (1 - 0.056)^9 \doteq 0.5953$.

**12.4.** It is unlikely that these events are independent. In particular, it is reasonable to expect that college graduates are less likely to be construction workers. Using the concept of conditional probability introduced later in this chapter,

$$P(\text{construction worker} \mid \text{college-educated}) < 0.06.$$

**12.5.** The Venn diagram is shown on the right.

**(a)** 30%: $P(\text{country but not gospel}) = P(C) - P(C \text{ and } G)$
$= 0.4 - 0.1 = 0.3.$

**(b)** 40%: $P(\text{neither}) = 1 - P(C \text{ or } G)$
$= 1 - (0.4 + 0.3 - 0.1) = 0.4.$

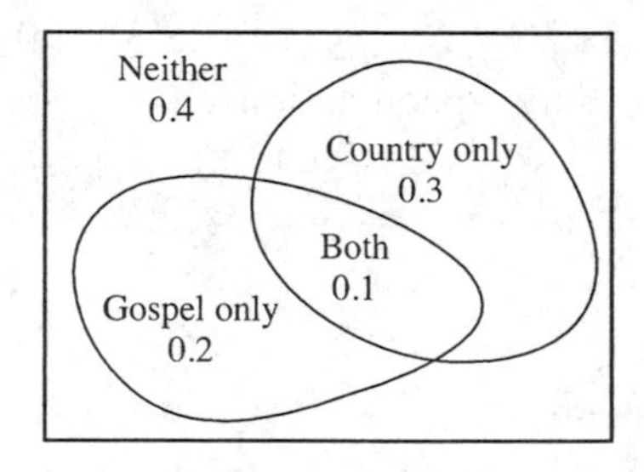


**12.6.** **(a)** $P(A \text{ does not occur}) = 1 - P(A) = 0.3$. **(b)** "At least 25 years old and not local" means $A$ and not $B$: $P(A \text{ and not } B) = P(A) - P(A \text{ and } B) = 0.65$.

**12.7.** Let $G = \{\text{student likes Gospel}\}$ and $C = \{\text{student likes country}\}$. See also the Venn diagram in the solution to Exercise 12.5. $P(G \mid C) = P(G \text{ and } C)/P(C) = 0.1/0.4 = 0.25$.

**12.8.** $P(B \mid \text{not } A) = \dfrac{P(B \text{ and not } A)}{P(\text{not } A)} = \dfrac{P(B) - P(B \text{ and } A)}{1 - P(A)} = \dfrac{0.2}{0.3} = \dfrac{2}{3}.$

**12.9.** Let $S$ be the event "game is a strategy game," while $T$ is "game is not a family/children's game." Then $P(T) = 1 - 0.203 = 0.797$, and

$$P(S \mid T) = \frac{P(S \text{ and } T)}{P(T)} = \frac{P(S)}{P(T)} = \frac{0.269}{0.797} \doteq 0.3375.$$

(Note that "$S$ and $T$" is equivalent to $S$.)

**12.10.** Let $H$ be the event that an adult belongs to a club, and $T$ be the event that he/she goes at least twice a week. We have been given $P(H) = 0.1$ and $P(T \mid H) = 0.4$, so $P(T) = P(H)\,P(T \mid H) = 0.04$—about 4% of all adults go to health clubs at least twice a week. (We assume here that someone cannot attend a health club without being a member.)

**12.11. Formulate:** Express the information in terms of events and their probabilities: We were given $P(\text{educated}) = P(A) = 0.28$ and $P(\text{prosperous} \mid \text{educated}) = P(B \mid A) = 0.13$. We want to find $P(\text{educated and prosperous}) = P(A \text{ and } B)$.
**Solve:** By the general multiplication rule: $P(A \text{ and } B) = P(A)\,P(B \mid A) = (0.28)(0.13) = 0.0364$.
**Conclude:** 3.64% of adults are both educated and prosperous.

**12.12.** **(a)** and **(b)** These probabilities are on the right. **(c)** The product of these conditional probabilities gives the probability of a flush in spades by the general multiplication rule: We must draw a spade, and then another, and then a third, a fourth, and a fifth. The product of these probabilities is about 0.0004952.

$$P(\text{1st card } \spadesuit) = \tfrac{13}{52} = \tfrac{1}{4} = 0.25$$
$$P(\text{2nd card } \spadesuit \mid 1 \spadesuit \text{ picked}) = \tfrac{12}{51} = \tfrac{4}{17} \doteq 0.2353$$
$$P(\text{3rd card } \spadesuit \mid 2 \spadesuit\text{s picked}) = \tfrac{11}{50} = 0.22$$
$$P(\text{4th card } \spadesuit \mid 3 \spadesuit\text{s picked}) = \tfrac{10}{49} \doteq 0.2041$$
$$P(\text{5th card } \spadesuit \mid 4 \spadesuit\text{s picked}) = \tfrac{9}{48} = \tfrac{3}{16} = 0.1875$$

**(d)** Because there are four possible suits in which to have a flush, the probability of a flush is four times that found in (c), or about 0.001981.

**12.13. Formulate:** Let $N$ be the event "a spelling error is a nonword error," let $W$ be "a spelling error is a word error," and let $C$ be "the proofreader catches the error." Restating the given information as probabilities, we have

$P(N) = 0.25$, $P(W) = 0.75$,
$P(C \mid N) = 0.9$, and $P(C \mid W) = 0.7$.

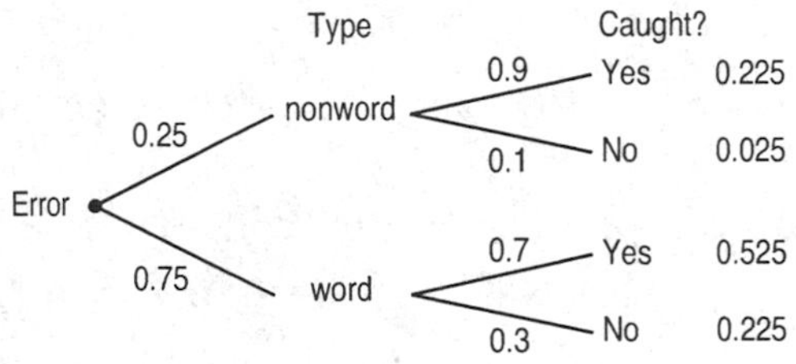

Type
Caught?
Error
0.25 nonword
0.9 Yes 0.225
0.1 No 0.025
0.75 word
0.7 Yes 0.525
0.3 No 0.225

Because all spelling errors are either nonword or word errors, the first two probabilities add to 1. We want to find the unconditional probability $P(C)$.
**Solve:** The tree diagram on the right organizes this information. The numbers on the right side of the tree are found by the multiplication rule; for example, $P$("nonword error" and "caught") $= P(N \text{ and } C) = P(N)\,P(C \mid N) = (0.25)(0.9) = 0.225$. Then $P(C)$ is the total probability of the paths in this tree that end in the error being caught: $P(C) = 0.225 + 0.525 = 0.75$.
**Conclude:** A proofreader should catch about 75% of all errors.

**12.14.** **(a)** At right.
**(b)** $P(\text{positive}) = 0.009985 + 0.00594$
$= 0.015925.$

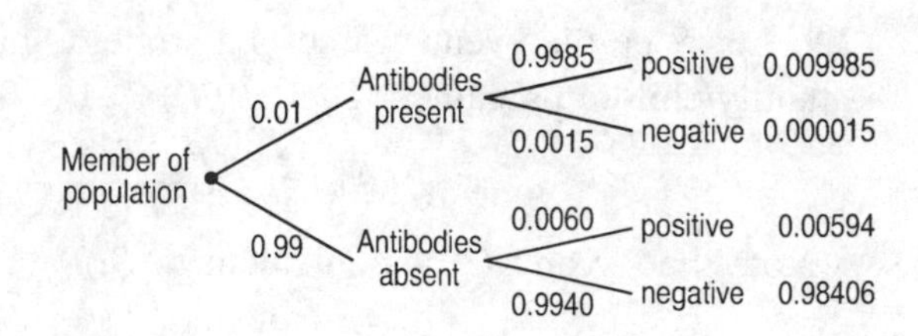


**12.15.** $P(\text{nonword} \mid \text{error found}) = P(N \mid C) = \dfrac{P(N \text{ and } C)}{P(C)} = \dfrac{0.225}{0.75} = 0.3$, so 30% of the errors caught are nonword errors.

**12.16.** $P(\text{has antibody} \mid \text{positive}) = \frac{0.009985}{0.015925} \doteq 0.627.$

**12.17.** (b) This probability is $0.98^3 \doteq 0.9412$.

**12.18.** (b) This probability is $1 - 0.98^3 \doteq 0.0588$.

**12.19.** (c) $P(\text{neither is positive}) = P(\text{first negative})P(\text{second negative}) = (0.1)(0.2) = 0.02.$

**12.20.** (a) There were 11,479 male victims out of a total of 14,099: $\frac{11,479}{14,099} \doteq 0.8142$.

**12.21.** (b) Of 8275 accident victims, 6457 were males: $\frac{6457}{8275} \doteq 0.7803$.

**12.22.** (c) Of 11,479 male victims, 6457 died in accidents: $\frac{6457}{11,479} \doteq 0.5625$.

**12.23.** (c) We want the fraction of suicides among all women's deaths, so $P(A)$ should be in the denominator, as it is in $P(B \mid A) = \dfrac{P(B \text{ and } A)}{P(A)}$.

**12.24.** (b) $P(W \text{ or } S) = P(W) + P(S) - P(W \text{ and } S) = 0.52 + 0.24 - 0.11 = 0.65.$

**12.25.** (c) $P(W \text{ and } D) = P(W)\,P(D \mid W) = (0.86)(0.028) \doteq 0.024.$

**12.26.** (b) $P(D) = P(W \text{ and } D) + P(B \text{ and } D) + P(A \text{ and } D)$
$= (0.86)(0.028) + (0.12)(0.044) + (0.02)(0.035) \doteq 0.030.$

**12.27.** $P(8 \text{ losses}) = 0.75^8 \doteq 0.1001.$

**12.28.** $P(\text{none are O-negative}) = (1 - 0.072)^{10} \doteq 0.4737$, so $P(\text{at least one is O-negative}) \doteq 1 - 0.4737 = 0.5263$.

**12.29.** **(a)** About 0.33: $P(\text{no calls reach a live person}) \doteq (1 - 0.2)^5 = 0.8^5 = 0.32768$.
**(b)** About 0.66: $P(\text{no NY calls reach a live person}) \doteq 0.92^5 \doteq 0.65908$.

**12.30.** **(a)** $(0.65)^3 \doteq 0.2746$ (under the random walk theory). **(b)** $(0.65)^3 + (0.35)^3 = 0.3175$.

**12.31.** This computation would be correct only if the events "a randomly selected person is at least 75" and "a randomly selected person is a woman" were independent. This is probably not true; in particular, because women have a greater life expectancy than men, this fraction is probably greater than 3%.

**12.32.** **(a)** $X$ can be 0, 1, 2, or 3. **(b)** See the top two lines of the table below. To find the probabilities, multiply 0.27 for "F" and 0.73 for "D"; for example, $P(\text{DDF}) = (0.73)(0.73)(0.27) \doteq 0.1439$. **(c)** The distribution is given in the bottom two lines of the table. For example, $P(X = 0) = (0.73)(0.73)(0.73) \doteq 0.3890$, and in the same way, $P(X = 3) = 0.27^3 \doteq 0.1597$. For $P(X = 1)$, note that each of the three arrangements that give $X = 1$ have probability $(0.73)(0.73)(0.27) = 0.143883$, so $P(X = 1) = 3(0.143883) \doteq 0.4316$. Similarly, $P(X = 2) = 3(0.73)(0.27)(0.27) \doteq 0.1597$.

| Arrangement | DDD | DDF | DFD | FDD | FFD | FDF | DFF | FFF |
|---|---|---|---|---|---|---|---|---|
| Probability | 0.3890 | 0.1439 | 0.1439 | 0.1439 | 0.0532 | 0.0532 | 0.0532 | 0.0197 |
| Value of $X$ | 0 | | 1 | | | 2 | | 3 |
| Probability | 0.3890 | | 0.4316 | | | 0.1597 | | 0.0197 |

**12.33.** Venn diagram on the right.

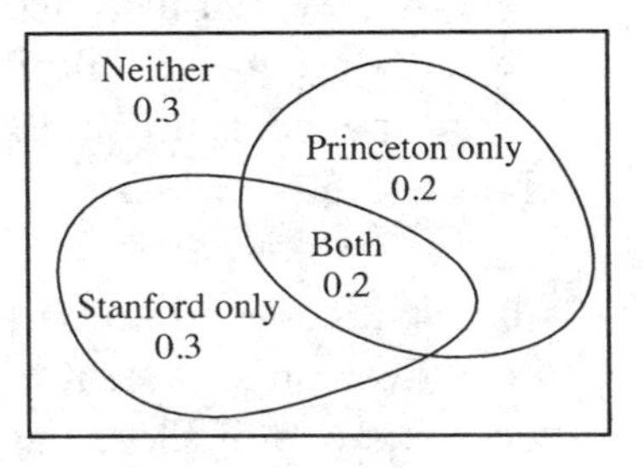


**(a)** $P(\text{neither admits Ramon}) = 1 - P(P \text{ or } S)$
$= 1 - (0.4 + 0.5 - 0.2) = 0.3.$

**(b)** $P(S \text{ and not } P) = P(S) - P(P \text{ and } S) = 0.3.$

**(c)** These two events are independent because $P(P \text{ and } S) = P(P)\,P(S)$.

**12.34. Formulate:** Let $I$ be the event "infection occurs" and let $F$ be "the repair fails." We have been given $P(I) = 0.03$, $P(F) = 0.14$, and $P(I \text{ and } F) = 0.01$. We want to find $P(\text{not } I \text{ and not } F)$.

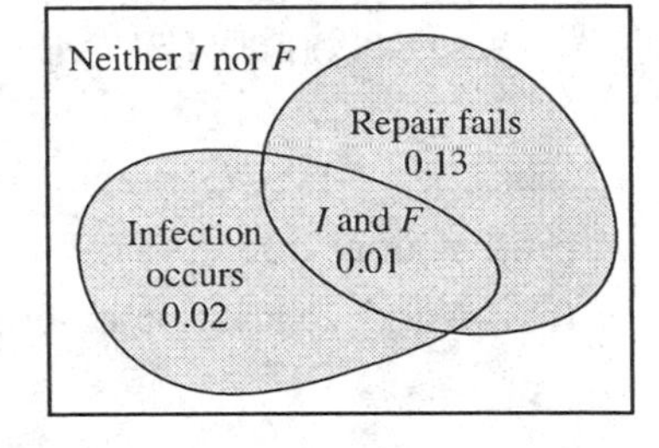


**Solve:** First use the general addition rule:

$$P(I \text{ or } F) = P(I) + P(F) - P(I \text{ and } F)$$
$$= 0.03 + 0.14 - 0.01 = 0.16.$$

This is the shaded region in the Venn diagram on the right. Now observe that the desired probability is the complement of "$I$ or $F$" (the *unshaded* region):

$$P(\text{not } I \text{ and not } F) = 1 - P(I \text{ or } F) = 0.84.$$

**Conclude:** 84% of operations succeed and are free from infection.

**12.35.** Note that in this diagram, events $A$, $B$, and $C$ should not overlap and should account for all possibilities (that is, those three events fill the entire diagram). Meanwhile, $D$ intersects all three of the others. The probabilities $P(A \text{ and } D)$, $P(B \text{ and } D)$, and $P(C \text{ and } D)$ give the probability of each overlapping region, and the portion of each event $A$, $B$, and $C$ outside of $D$ must account for the rest of that event's probability. As can be seen from the diagram, $P(D) = 0.4 = 0.1 + 0.1 + 0.2$.

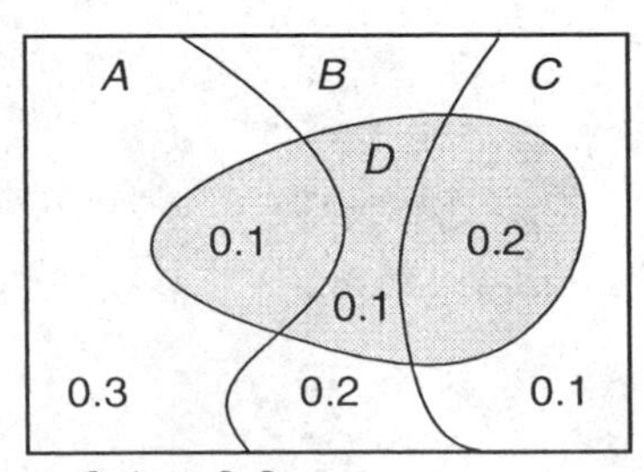

**12.36.** $P(\text{Spanish} \mid \text{studying another language}) = \frac{0.26}{1-0.59} \doteq 0.6341$.

**12.37. (a)** $P(\text{income} \geq \$50,000) = 0.206 + 0.068 + 0.020 = 0.294$.
**(b)** $P(\text{income} \geq \$100,000 \mid \text{income} \geq \$50,000) = 0.088/0.294 \doteq 0.2993$.

**12.38.** The event $\{Y < 1/2\}$ is the bottom half of the square, while $\{Y > X\}$ is the upper left triangle of the square. They overlap in a triangle with area $1/8$, so

$$P(Y < \tfrac{1}{2} \mid Y > X) = \frac{P(Y < \frac{1}{2} \text{ and } Y > X)}{P(Y > X)} = \frac{1/8}{1/2} = \frac{1}{4}.$$

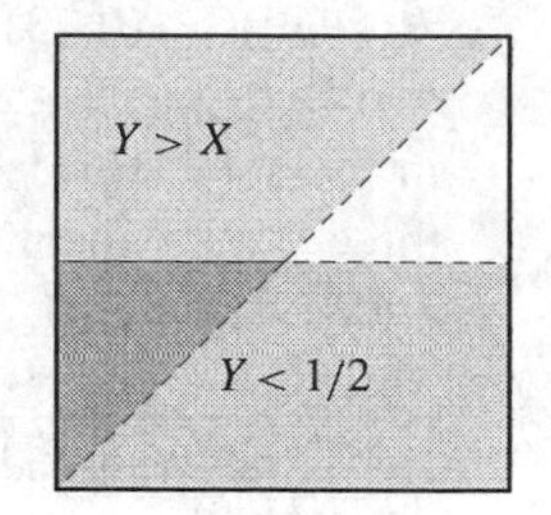


**12.39. (a)** $P(\text{two boys} \mid \text{at least one boy}) = \dfrac{P(\text{two boys})}{P(\text{at least one boy})} = \dfrac{0.25}{0.75} = \dfrac{1}{3}$.
**(b)** $P(\text{two boys} \mid \text{older child is a boy}) = \dfrac{P(\text{two boys})}{P(\text{older child is a boy})} = \dfrac{0.25}{0.50} = \dfrac{1}{2}$.
Note that we can also find this by reasoning that $P(\text{two boys} \mid \text{older child is a boy}) = P(\text{younger child is a boy} \mid \text{older child is a boy})$. Because the two children's genders are independent, this probability is the same as the unconditional probability $P(\text{younger child is a boy}) = 0.5$.

**12.40.** First, concentrate on (say) spades. The probability that the first card dealt is one of those five cards (A♠, K♠, Q♠, J♠, or 10♠) is 5/52. The conditional probability that the second is one of those cards, given that the first was, is 4/51. Continuing like this, we get 3/50, 2/49, and finally 1/48; the product of these five probabilities gives $P(\text{royal flush in } \spadesuit) \doteq 0.00000038477$. Multiplying by four gives $P(\text{royal flush}) \doteq 0.000001539$.

**12.41.** Let $W$ be the event "the person is a woman" and $P$ be "the person earned a professional degree." **(a)** $P(W) = \frac{1119}{1944} \doteq 0.5756$. **(b)** $P(W \mid P) = \frac{39/1944}{83/1944} = \frac{39}{83} \doteq 0.4699$.
**(c)** $W$ and $P$ are *not* independent; if they were, the two probabilities in (a) and (b) would be equal.

**12.42.** Let $M$ be the event "the person is a man" and $B$ be "the person earned a bachelor's degree." **(a)** $P(M) = \frac{825}{1944} \doteq 0.4244$. **(b)** $P(B \mid M) = \frac{559/1944}{825/1944} = \frac{559}{825} \doteq 0.6776$.
**(c)** $P(M \text{ and } B) = P(M)\,P(B \mid M) \doteq (0.4244)(0.6776) \doteq 0.2876$. This agrees with the directly computed probability: $P(M \text{ and } B) = \frac{559}{1944} \doteq 0.2876$.

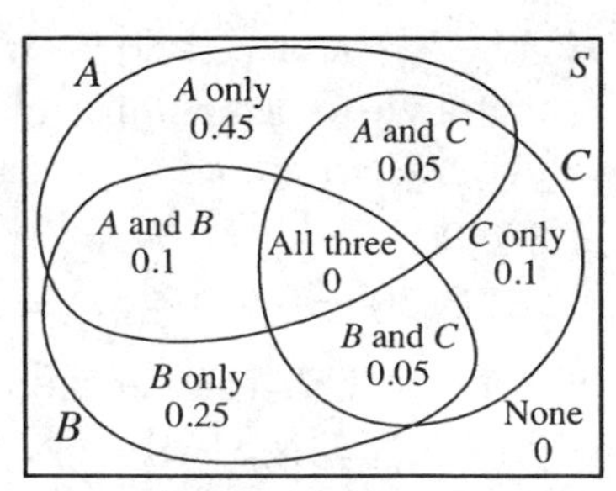


**12.43.** To find the probabilities in this Venn diagram, begin with $P(A \text{ and } B \text{ and } C) = 0$ in the center of the diagram. Then the two-way intersections $P(A \text{ and } B)$, $P(A \text{ and } C)$, and $P(B \text{ and } C)$ go in the remainder of the overlapping areas; if $P(A \text{ and } B \text{ and } C)$ had been something other than 0, we would have subtracted this from each of the two-way intersection probabilities to find, for example, $P(A \text{ and } B \text{ and not } C)$. Next, determine $P(A \text{ only})$ so that the total probability of the regions that make up the event $A$ is 0.6. Finally, $P(\text{none}) = P(\text{not } A \text{ and not } B \text{ and not } C) = 0$ because the total probability inside the three sets $A$, $B$, and $C$ is 1.

**12.44.** We seek $P(\text{at least one offer}) = P(A \text{ or } B \text{ or } C)$; we can find this as $1 - P(\text{no offers}) = 1 - P(\text{not } A \text{ and not } B \text{ and not } C)$. We see in the Venn diagram of Exercise 12.43 that this probability is 1.

**12.45.** This is $P(A \text{ and } B \text{ and not } C)$. As was noted in Exercise 12.43, because $P(A \text{ and } B \text{ and } C) = 0$, this is the same as $P(A \text{ and } B) = 0.1$.

**12.46.** $P(B \mid C) = \dfrac{P(B \text{ and } C)}{P(C)} = \frac{0.05}{0.2} = 0.25$. $P(C \mid B) = \dfrac{P(B \text{ and } C)}{P(B)} = \frac{0.05}{0.4} = 0.125$.

**12.47.** **(a)** $P(\text{first } \boxdot \text{ appears on toss 2}) = \left(\frac{5}{6}\right)\left(\frac{1}{6}\right) = \frac{5}{36}$.

**(b)** $P(\text{first } \boxdot \text{ appears on toss 3}) = \left(\frac{5}{6}\right)\left(\frac{5}{6}\right)\left(\frac{1}{6}\right) = \frac{25}{216}$.

**(c)** $P(\text{first } \boxdot \text{ appears on toss 4}) = \left(\frac{5}{6}\right)^3\left(\frac{1}{6}\right)$.

$P(\text{first } \boxdot \text{ appears on toss 5}) = \left(\frac{5}{6}\right)^4\left(\frac{1}{6}\right)$.

$P(\text{first } \boxdot \text{ appears on toss } k) = \left(\frac{5}{6}\right)^{k-1}\left(\frac{1}{6}\right)$.

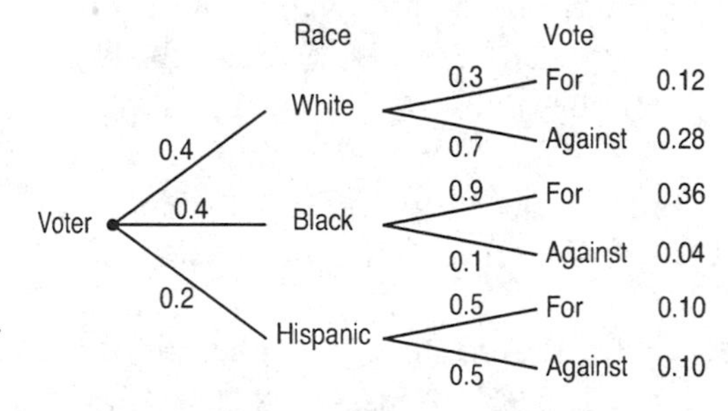


**12.48. Formulate:** Let $W$, $B$, and $H$ be the events that a randomly selected voter is (respectively) white, black, and Hispanic. We have been given

$$P(W) = 0.4,\quad P(B) = 0.4,\quad P(H) = 0.2.$$

If $F$ = "a voter votes for the candidate," then

$$P(F \mid W) = 0.3,\quad P(F \mid B) = 0.9,\quad P(F \mid H) = 0.5.$$

We want to find $P(F)$.

**Solve:** The tree diagram on the right organizes the information. The numbers on the right side of the tree are found by the general multiplication rule; for example,

$$P(\text{"white" and "for"}) = P(W \text{ and } F) = P(W)\,P(F \mid W) = (0.4)(0.3) = 0.12.$$

We find $P(F)$ by adding all the numbers next to the branches ending in "for":

$$P(F) = 0.12 + 0.36 + 0.10 = 0.58.$$

**Conclude:** The black candidate expects to get 58% of the vote.

**12.49. Formulate:** Let $R$, $M$, and $P$ be the events that a customer pumps (respectively) regular, midgrade, and premium gasoline. We have been given

$$P(R) = 0.4, \ P(M) = 0.35, \ P(P) = 0.25.$$

If $T$ = "the customer pays at least \$30," then

$$P(T \mid R) = 0.3, \ P(T \mid M) = 0.5, \ P(T \mid P) = 0.6.$$

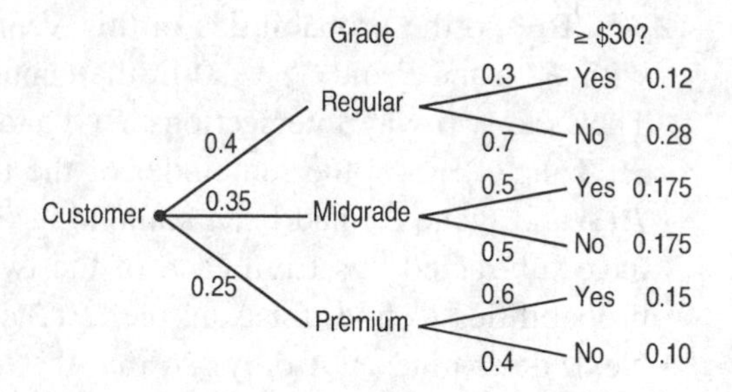


We want to find $P(T)$.

**Solve:** The tree diagram on the right organizes the information. The numbers on the right side of the tree are found by the general multiplication rule; for example,

$$P(\text{"regular" and "}\geq \$30\text{"}) = P(R \text{ and } T) = P(R)\,P(T \mid R) = (0.4)(0.3) = 0.12.$$

We find $P(T)$ by adding all the numbers next to the branches ending in "yes":

$$P(T) = 0.12 + 0.175 + 0.15 = 0.445.$$

**Conclude:** The probability that the next customer pays at least \$30 is 0.445.

**12.50.** $P(B \mid F) = \dfrac{P(B \text{ and } F)}{P(F)} = \frac{0.36}{0.58} \doteq 0.6207$—about 62%.

**12.51.** $P(P \mid T) = \dfrac{P(P \text{ and } T)}{P(T)} = \frac{0.15}{0.445} \doteq 0.3371$—about 34%.

**12.52. (a)** The percentage of calls resulting in a contribution can be found by considering all the branches of the tree that end in a contribution, meaning that we compute, for example,

$$P(\text{recent donor}) \cdot P(\text{makes pledge} \mid \text{recent}) \cdot P(\text{contributes} \mid \text{recent, made pledge}).$$

This gives $(0.5)(0.4)(0.8) + (0.3)(0.3)(0.6) + (0.2)(0.1)(0.5) = 0.224$.

**(b)** $P(\text{recent donor} \mid \text{contributed}) = \dfrac{P(\text{contributing recent donor})}{P(\text{contributed})} = \dfrac{(0.5)(0.4)(0.8)}{0.224} \doteq 0.7143.$

**12.53.** Each unemployment rate is computed as shown on the right. (Alternatively, subtract the number employed from the number in the labor force, then divide that difference by the number in the labor force.) Because these rates (probabilities) are different, education level and being employed are not independent.

| | |
|---|---|
| Did not finish HS | $1 - \frac{11{,}408}{12{,}470} \doteq 0.0852$ |
| HS/no college | $1 - \frac{35{,}857}{37{,}834} \doteq 0.0523$ |
| Some college | $1 - \frac{32{,}977}{34{,}439} \doteq 0.0425$ |
| College graduate | $1 - \frac{39{,}293}{40{,}390} \doteq 0.0272$ |

**12.54. (a)** Add up the numbers in the first and second columns. We find that there are 186,937 thousand (that is, almost 187 million) people aged 25 or older, of which 125,133 thousand are in the labor force, so $P(L) = \frac{125{,}133}{186{,}937} \doteq 0.6694$.
**(b)** $P(L \mid C) = \frac{P(L \text{ and } C)}{P(C)} = \frac{40{,}390}{51{,}852} \doteq 0.7789$. **(c)** $L$ and $C$ are *not* independent; if they were, the two probabilities in (a) and (b) would be equal.

**12.55. (a)** Add up the numbers in the third column. We find that there are 119,535 thousand (that is, over 119 million) employed people aged 25 or older. Therefore, $P(C \mid E) = \frac{P(C \text{ and } E)}{P(E)} = \frac{39{,}293}{119{,}535} \doteq 0.3287$. **(b)** Use the total number of college graduates in the population: $P(E \mid C) = \frac{P(C \text{ and } E)}{P(C)} = \frac{39{,}293}{51{,}852} \doteq 0.7578$.

**12.56.** **(a)** Rachel and Jonathan's children can have alleles AA, BB, or AB, so they can have blood type A, B, or AB. (The table on the right shows the possible combinations.) **(b)** Either note that the four combinations in the table are equally likely, or compute:

| | A | B |
|---|---|---|
| A | AA | AB |
| B | AB | BB |

$$P(\text{type A}) = P(\text{A from Rachel and A from Jonathan}) = P(\text{A}_R)P(\text{A}_J) = 0.5^2 = 0.25$$
$$P(\text{type B}) = P(\text{B from Rachel and B from Jonathan}) = P(\text{B}_R)P(\text{B}_J) = 0.5^2 = 0.25$$
$$P(\text{type AB}) = P(\text{A}_R)P(\text{B}_J) + P(\text{B}_R)P(\text{A}_J) = 2 \cdot 0.25 = 0.5.$$

**12.57.** **(a)** Sarah and David's children can have alleles BB, BO, or OO, so they can have blood type B or O. (The table on the right shows the possible combinations.) **(b)** Either note that the four combinations in the table are equally likely, or compute $P(\text{type O}) = P(\text{O from Sarah and O from David}) = 0.5^2 = 0.25$, and $P(\text{type B}) = 1 - P(\text{type O}) = 0.75$.

| | B | O |
|---|---|---|
| B | BB | BO |
| O | BO | OO |

**12.58.** **(a)** Any child of Isabel and Carlos has a 50% chance of being type A (alleles AA or AO), and each child inherits alleles independently of other children, so $P(\text{both are type A}) = 0.5^2 = 0.25$. **(b)** For one child, we have $P(\text{type A}) = 0.5$ and $P(\text{type AB}) = P(\text{type B}) = 0.25$, so that $P(\text{both have same type}) = 0.5^2 + 0.25^2 + 0.25^2 = 0.375 = \frac{3}{8}$.

| | A | O |
|---|---|---|
| A | AA | AO |
| B | AB | BO |

**12.59.** **(a)** Any child of Jasmine and Tyrone has an equal (1/4) chance of having blood type AB, A, B, or O. Therefore, $P(\text{type O}) = 0.25$.
**(b)** $P(\text{all three have type O}) = 0.25^3 = 0.015625 = \frac{1}{64}$.
**(c)** $P(\text{first has type O, next two do not}) = 0.25 \cdot 0.75^2 = 0.140625 = \frac{9}{64}$.

| | A | O |
|---|---|---|
| B | AB | BO |
| O | AO | OO |

# Chapter 13 Solutions

**13.1.** Yes: (1) We have a fixed number of observations ($n = 15$). (2) It is reasonable to believe that each call is independent of the others. (3) "Success" means reaching a live person, "failure" is any other outcome. (4) Each randomly dialed number has chance $p = 0.2$ of reaching a live person.

**13.2.** Not binomial: There is no fixed number of attempts ($n$).

**13.3.** Not binomial: Because the student receives instruction after incorrect answers, her probability of success is likely to increase.

**13.4.** The number who say they never have time to relax has (approximately) a binomial distribution with parameters $n = 500$ and $p = 0.14$.

**13.5.** **(a)** $C$, the number caught, is binomial with $n = 10$ and $p = 0.7$. $M$, the number missed, is binomial with $n = 10$ and $p = 0.3$. **(b)** We find $P(M = 3) = \binom{10}{3}(0.3)^3(0.7)^7 = 120(0.027)(0.08235) \doteq 0.2668$. With software, we find $P(M \geq 3) \doteq 0.6172$.

**13.6.** Let $N$ be the number of live persons contacted among the 15 calls observed. Then $N$ has the binomial distribution with $n = 15$ and $p = 0.2$ (see also the solution to Exercise 13.1).
**(a)** $P(N = 3) = \binom{15}{3}(0.2)^3(0.8)^{12} \doteq 0.2501$.
**(b)** $P(N \leq 3) = P(N = 0) + \cdots + P(N = 3) \doteq 0.6482$.

```
binompdf(15,.2,3
          .2501388953
binomcdf(15,.2,3
          .6481621047
```

The TI-83 screen on the right illustrates the use of that calculator's `binompdf` and `binomcdf` functions (found in the DISTR menu) to compute these probabilities. The first of these finds individual binomial probabilities, and the second finds cumulative probabilities (that is, it sums the probability from 0 up to a given number). Excel offers similar features with its BINOMDIST function. Calculators that do not have binomial probabilities may have a built-in function to compute, e.g., $\binom{15}{3}$.

**13.7.** Let $X$ be the number of returns (out of 20) with AGI of \$100,000 or more. Then $X$ has a binomial distribution with $n = 20$ and $p = 0.087$, so

$$P(X = 0 \text{ or } X = 1) = \binom{20}{0}(0.087)^0(0.913)^{20} + \binom{20}{1}(0.087)^1(0.913)^{19} \doteq 0.4706,$$

and $P(X > 1) = 1 - P(X = 0 \text{ or } X = 1) = 0.5294$.

**13.8.** **(a)** With $n = 15$ and $p = 0.2$, we have $\mu = np = 3$ calls.
**(b)** $\sigma = \sqrt{np(1-p)} = \sqrt{2.4} \doteq 1.5492$ calls.
**(c)** With $p = 0.08$, $\sigma = \sqrt{1.104} \doteq 1.0507$ calls; with $p = 0.01$, $\sigma = \sqrt{0.1485} \doteq 0.3854$ calls. As $p$ approaches 0, the standard deviation decreases (that is, it also approaches 0).

**13.9.** **(a)** The mean of $C$ is $(10)(0.7) = 7$ errors caught, and for $M$ the mean is $(10)(0.3) = 3$ errors missed. **(b)** The standard deviation of $C$ (or $M$) is $\sigma = \sqrt{(10)(0.7)(0.3)} \doteq 1.4491$ errors. **(c)** With $p = 0.9$, $\sigma = \sqrt{(10)(0.9)(0.1)} \doteq 0.9487$ errors; with $p = 0.99$, $\sigma \doteq 0.3146$ errors. $\sigma$ decreases toward 0 as $p$ approaches 1 (because $1 - p$ gets close to zero).

**13.10.** Let $X$ be the number of 1's and 2's; then $X$ has a binomial distribution with $n = 90$ and $p = 0.477$ (in the absence of fraud). This should have a mean of 42.93 and standard deviation $\sigma \doteq \sqrt{22.4524} = 4.7384$. Therefore,

$$P(X \leq 29) \doteq P\left(Z \leq \frac{29-42.93}{4.7384}\right) = P(Z \leq -2.94) = 0.0016.$$

```
binomcdf(90,.477
,29)
      .0020818796
```

(Using software, we find that the exact value is 0.0021.) This probability is quite small, so we have reason to be suspicious.

**13.11.** If $H$ is the number of home runs, with a binomial distribution with $n = 509$ and $p = 0.116$, then $H$ has mean $\mu = np \doteq 59.044$ and standard deviation $\sigma \doteq \sqrt{52.195} = 7.2246$ home runs. Therefore,

$$P(H \geq 70) \doteq P\left(Z \geq \frac{70-59.044}{7.2246}\right) = P(Z \geq 1.52) = 0.0643.$$

```
1-binomcdf(509,.
116,69)
      .0763741347
```

(Using software, we find that the exact value is 0.0764.)

**13.12.** **(a)** $\mu = (1500)(0.12) = 180$ blacks and $\sigma = \sqrt{158.4} \doteq 12.5857$ blacks. **(b)** The Normal approximation is quite safe: $np = 180$ and $n(1-p) = 1320$ are both more than 10. We compute $P(165 \leq X \leq 195) \doteq P(\frac{165-180}{12.5857} \leq Z \leq \frac{195-180}{12.5857}) \doteq P(-1.19 \leq Z \leq 1.19) \doteq 0.7660$. (Exact computation of this probability gives 0.7820. Other answers are given in the table.)

| | | *Continuity correction* | |
|---|---|---|---|
| Table Normal | Software Normal | Table Normal | Software Normal |
| 0.7660 | 0.7667 | 0.7814 | 0.7819 |

**13.13.** (b) He has 3 independent eggs, each with probability $1/4$ of containing salmonella.

**13.14.** (b) $P(S > 0) = 1 - P(S = 0) = 1 - 0.75^3 \doteq 0.5781$.

**13.15.** (c) The selections are not independent; once we choose one student, it changes the probability that the next student is a business major.

**13.16.** (b) We must choose 5 of the 7 shots to be "made"; $\binom{7}{2} = 21$.

**13.17.** (c) This probability is $0.7^5 \cdot 0.3^2 \doteq 0.015$.

**13.18.** (b) This probability is $\binom{7}{5}0.7^5 \cdot 0.3^2 \doteq 0.318$.

**13.19.** (c) This probability is $\binom{40}{4}0.1^4 \cdot 0.9^{36} \doteq 0.2059$.

**13.20.** (a) The mean is $np = (40)(0.1) = 4$.

**13.21.** (b) The mean is $np = (400)(0.1) = 40$ and the standard deviation is $\sqrt{np(1-p)} = \sqrt{36} = 6$.

**13.22.** **(a)** No: There is no fixed number of observations. **(b)** A binomial distribution is reasonable here; a "large city" will have a population much larger than 1000 (the sample size), and each randomly selected juror has the same (unknown) probability $p$ of opposing the death penalty. **(c)** In a "Pick 3" game, Joe's chance of winning the lottery is the same every week, so assuming that a year consists of 52 weeks (observations), this would be binomial.

**13.23.** **(a)** A binomial distribution is *not* an appropriate choice for field goals made, because given the different situations the kicker faces, his probability of success is likely to change from one attempt to another. **(b)** It would be reasonable to use a binomial distribution for free throws made, because we have $n = 150$ attempts, presumably independent (or at least approximately so), with chance of success $p = 0.8$ each time.

**13.24.** **(a)** $X$, the number of auction site visitors, is binomial with $n = 12$ and $p = 0.5$. **(b)** $P(X = 8) = \binom{12}{8}(0.5)^8(0.5)^4 \doteq 0.1208$. Using software, we find $P(X \geq 8) = 0.1938$.

**13.25.** **(a)** $n = 20$ and $p = 0.25$. **(b)** $\mu = np = 5$ correct guesses. **(c)** $P(X = 5) = \binom{20}{5}(0.25)^5(0.75)^{15} \doteq 0.2023$.

**13.26.** **(a)** $n = 5$ and $p = 0.65$. **(b)** The possible values of $X$ are 0 through 5. **(c)** At right. For example,

$$P(X=0) = \binom{5}{0}(0.65)^0(0.35)^5 \doteq 0.00525$$

$$P(X=1) = \binom{5}{1}(0.65)^1(0.35)^4 \doteq 0.04877$$

| $X$ | Prob. |
|---|---|
| 0 | 0.00525 |
| 1 | 0.04877 |
| 2 | 0.18115 |
| 3 | 0.33642 |
| 4 | 0.31239 |
| 5 | 0.11603 |

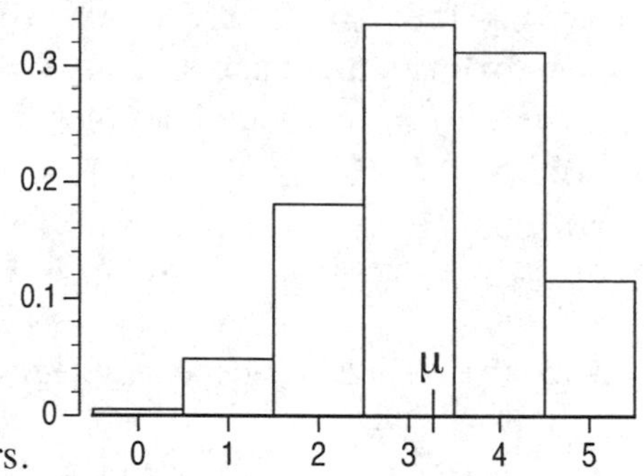

**(d)** $\mu = np = 3.25$ and $\sigma = \sqrt{np(1-p)} \doteq 1.0665$ years.

**13.27.** Let $N$ be the number of households with 3 or more cars. Then $N$ has a binomial distribution with $n = 12$ and $p = 0.2$. **(a)** $P(N = 0) = \binom{12}{0}(0.2)^0(0.8)^{12} = 0.8^{12} \doteq 0.0687$. $P(N \geq 1) = 1 - P(N = 0) \doteq 0.9313$. **(b)** $\mu = np = 2.4$ and $\sigma = \sqrt{np(1-p)} \doteq 1.3856$ households. **(c)** $P(N > 2.4) = 1 - P(N \leq 2) \doteq 0.4417$.

**13.28.** **(a)** $X$, the number of positive tests, has a binomial distribution with parameters $n = 1000$ and $p = 0.004$. **(b)** $\mu = np = (1000)(0.004) = 4$ positive tests. **(c)** To use the Normal approximation, we need $np$ and $n(1-p)$ both bigger than 10, and as we saw in (b), $np = 4$.

**13.29.** **(a)** $\mu = np = (25000)(0.123) = 3075$ dropouts. **(b)** First, we compute $\sigma \doteq 51.9305$ dropouts. Using the Normal approximation, $P(X \geq 3500) \doteq P(Z > 8.18)$—this is so small that we might as well call it 0.

**13.30.** **(a)** With $n = 100$, the mean and standard deviation are $\mu = 75$ and $\sigma \doteq 4.3301$ questions, so $P(X \leq 70) \doteq P(Z < -1.15) = 0.1251$ (software gives 0.1495 using the binomial distribution; also see line 1). **(b)** With $n = 250$, we have $\mu = 187.5$ and $\sigma \doteq 6.8465$ questions, and a score of 70% or less means 175 or fewer correct answers, so $P(X \leq 175) \doteq P(Z < -1.83) = 0.0336$ (software gives 0.0418 using the binomial distribution; also see line 2).

| | | *Continuity correction* | |
|---|---|---|---|
| Table Normal | Software Normal | Table Normal | Software Normal |
| 0.1251 | 0.1241 | 0.1492 | 0.1493 |
| 0.0336 | 0.0339 | 0.0401 | 0.0398 |

**13.31.** **(a)** The mean is $\mu = (1200)(0.124) = 148.8$ Hispanics, and the standard deviation is $\sigma \doteq 11.4170$ Hispanics. **(b)** $\mu \pm 2\sigma$ gives the range 125.97 to 171.63. (To be safe, we should round "away from the center" to give the range 125 to 172.) **(c)** In order to have $np = 0.124n$ at least 200, we need $n \geq \frac{200}{0.124} \doteq 1612.9$, so sample at least 1613 adults.

**13.32.** **(a)** $\mu = np = (15)(0.25) = 3.75$ leaking tanks. **(b)** $P(X \geq 10) = P(X = 10) + P(X = 11) + \cdots + P(X = 15) \doteq 0.0008$. **(c)** With $n = 1000$, $\mu = 250$ and $\sigma \doteq 13.6931$ leaking tanks, so $P(X \geq 275) \doteq P(Z \geq \frac{275-250}{13.6931}) = P(Z \geq 1.83) = 0.0336$ (software gives 0.0378 using the binomial distribution; also see the table).

| | | *Continuity correction* | |
|---|---|---|---|
| Table Normal | Software Normal | Table Normal | Software Normal |
| 0.0336 | 0.0339 | 0.0367 | 0.0368 |

**13.33.** **(a)** If $R$ is the number of red-blossomed plants out of a sample of 8, then $P(R = 6) = \binom{8}{6}(0.75)^6(0.25)^2 \doteq 0.3115$, using a binomial distribution with $n = 8$ and $p = 0.75$. **(b)** With $n = 80$, the mean number of red-blossomed plants is $np = 60$. **(c)** If $R_2$ is the number of red-blossomed plants out of a sample of 80, then $P(R_2 \geq 50) \doteq P(Z \geq -2.58) = 0.9951$ (software gives 0.9954 using the binomial distribution; also see the table).

| | | *Continuity correction* | |
|---|---|---|---|
| Table Normal | Software Normal | Table Normal | Software Normal |
| 0.9951 | 0.9951 | 0.9966 | 0.9966 |

**13.34.** 35% to 50% of a sample of 500 is 175 to 250 students. The mean and standard deviation are $\mu = 205$ and $\sigma \doteq 10.9977$ students, so the desired probability is

$$P(175 \leq X \leq 250) = P(\tfrac{175-205}{10.9977} \leq Z \leq \tfrac{250-205}{10.9977}) = P(-2.73 \leq Z \leq 4.09) = 0.9968$$

(software gives 0.9974 using the binomial distribution; also see the table).

| | | *Continuity correction* | |
|---|---|---|---|
| Table Normal | Software Normal | Table Normal | Software Normal |
| 0.9968 | 0.9968 | 0.9972 | 0.9972 |

**13.35.** We have $\mu = 5000$ and $\sigma = 50$ heads, so using the Normal approximation, we compute $P(X \geq 5067) \doteq P(Z \geq 1.34) = 0.0901$ (or 0.0918 with the continuity correction). If Kerrich's coin were "fair," we would see 5067 or more heads in about 9% of all repetitions of the experiment of flipping the coin 10,000 times, or about once every 11 attempts. This is *some* evidence against the coin being fair, but it is not by any means overwhelming.

**13.36.** Each time we choose a sample of size 10, the probability that we have exactly 1 bad CD is 0.3874; therefore, out of 20 samples, the number of times that we have exactly 1 bad CD has a binomial distribution with parameters $n = 20$ and $p = 0.3874$. This means that most students—99.8% of them—will find that between 2 and 14 of their 20 samples have exactly 1 bad CD. (If anyone has an answer outside of that range, that would be significant evidence that he or she did the exercise incorrectly.)

# Chapter 14 Solutions

**14.1.** **(a)** The standard deviation of $\bar{x}$ is $\sigma/\sqrt{1000} \doteq 1.8974$. **(b)** $m = 2(1.8974) \doteq 3.8$ (or "$\pm 3.8$"). **(c)** The confidence intervals drawn may vary, of course, but they should be $2m = 7.6$ units wide. **(d)** 95%.

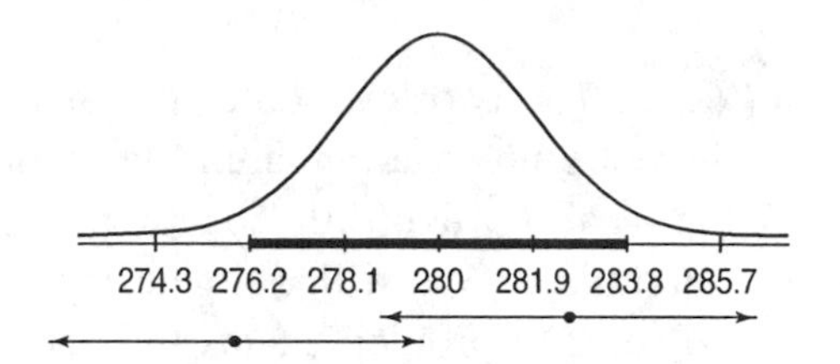


**14.2.** **(a)** $51\% \pm 3\% = 48\%$ to $54\%$. **(b)** "95% confidence" means that this interval was found using a procedure that produces correct results (i.e., includes the true population proportion) 95% of the time.

**14.3.** Shown below are sample output screens for (a) 10 and (b) 1000 SRSs. In 99.4% of all repetitions of part (a), students should see between 5 and 10 hits (that is, at least 5 of the 10 SRSs capture the true mean $\mu$). Out of 1000 80% confidence intervals, nearly all students will observe between 76% and 84% capturing the mean.

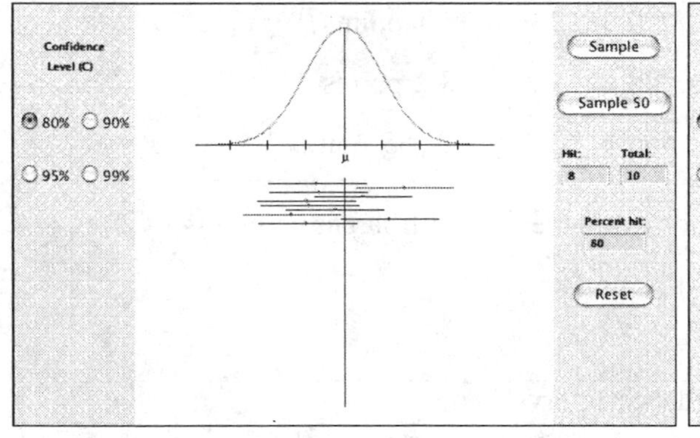


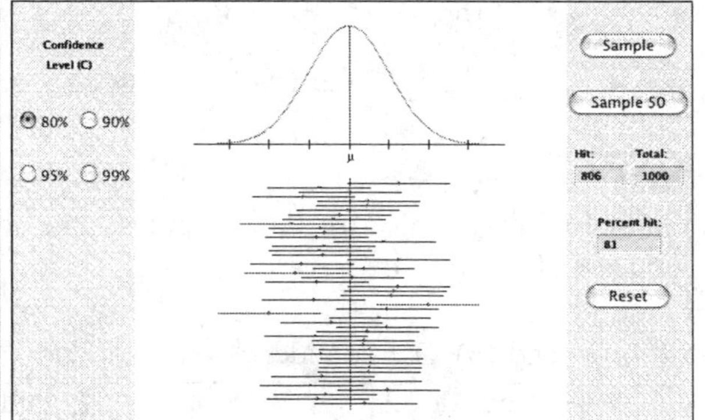


**14.4.** Search Table A for 0.0125 (half of the 2.5% that is *not* included in a 97.5% confidence interval). This area corresponds to $z^* = 2.24$. Software gives $z^* = 2.2414$.

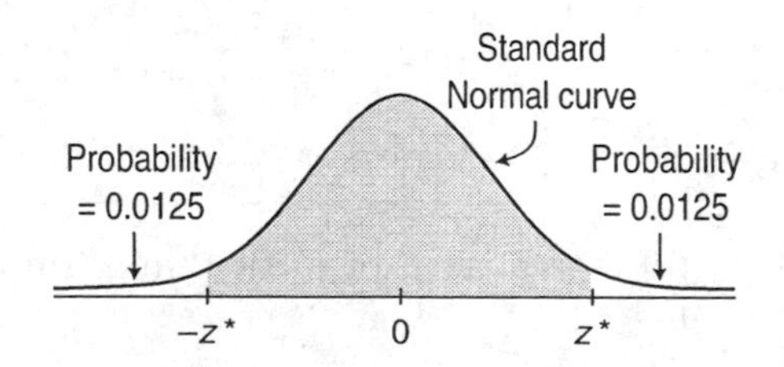


**14.5.** **State:** What is the concentration of the active ingredient in this batch?
**Formulate:** We will estimate the true concentration in this batch of the product—the mean $\mu$ of the distribution of all measurements—by giving a 95% confidence interval.
**Solve:** We assume that the three measurements can be considered an SRS of all such measurements. We have been told that repeated measurements follow a Normal distribution with standard deviation 0.0068 g/l. The mean of the sample is

$$\bar{x} = \frac{0.8403 + 0.8363 + 0.8447}{3} = 0.8404\overline{3} \text{ g/l.}$$

For 95% confidence, the critical value is $z^* = 1.960$, so the 95% confidence interval for $\mu$ is

$$\bar{x} \pm z^* \frac{\sigma}{\sqrt{n}} = 0.8404\bar{3} \pm 1.960\left(\frac{0.0068}{\sqrt{3}}\right) = 0.8404\bar{3} \pm 0.00770 = 0.8327 \text{ to } 0.8481 \text{ g/l.}$$

**Conclude:** We are 95% confident that the concentration of active ingredient in this batch is between 0.8327 and 0.8481 g/l.

**14.6.** **(a)** The two low scores (72 and 74) are both possible outliers, but there are no other apparent deviations from Normality. **(b) State:** What is the mean IQ $\mu$ of all seventh-grade girls in this school district? **Formulate:** We will estimate $\mu$ by giving a 99% confidence interval. **Solve:** The problem states that these girls are an SRS of the population. In part (a), we saw that the scores appear to come from a Normal distribution. With $\bar{x} \doteq 105.84$, our 99% confidence interval for $\mu$ is

$$105.84 \pm 2.576\left(\frac{15}{\sqrt{31}}\right) \doteq 105.84 \pm 6.94 = 98.90 \text{ to } 112.78 \text{ IQ points.}$$

**Conclude:** We are 99% confident that the mean IQ of seventh-grade girls in this district is between 98.90 and 112.78.

| Stem | Leaves |
|---|---|
| 7 | 24 |
| 7 | |
| 8 | |
| 8 | 69 |
| 9 | 13 |
| 9 | 68 |
| 10 | 023334 |
| 10 | 578 |
| 11 | 11222444 |
| 11 | 89 |
| 12 | 0 |
| 12 | 8 |
| 13 | 02 |

**14.7.** **(a)** – **(c)** The confidence intervals are:

| $n$ | Confidence interval | m.e. |
|---|---|---|
| 1000 | $22 \pm 1.960\frac{50}{\sqrt{1000}} \doteq 22 \pm 3.099 = 18.9$ to 25.1 points | 3.1 |
| 250 | $22 \pm 1.960\frac{50}{\sqrt{250}} \doteq 22 \pm 6.198 = 15.8$ to 28.2 points | 6.2 |
| 4000 | $22 \pm 1.960\frac{50}{\sqrt{4000}} \doteq 22 \pm 1.550 = 20.45$ to 23.55 points | 1.55 |

**(d)** The margin of error ("m.e." in the table above) decreases with larger samples (by a factor of $1/\sqrt{n}$).

**14.8.** **(a)** and **(b)** The confidence intervals are:

| Conf. level | Confidence interval | m.e. |
|---|---|---|
| 95% | $22 \pm 1.960\frac{50}{\sqrt{1000}} \doteq 22 \pm 3.099 = 18.9$ to 25.1 points | 3.099 |
| 90% | $22 \pm 1.645\frac{50}{\sqrt{1000}} \doteq 22 \pm 2.601 = 19.4$ to 24.6 points | 2.601 |
| 99% | $22 \pm 2.576\frac{50}{\sqrt{1000}} \doteq 22 \pm 4.073 = 17.93$ to 26.07 points | 4.073 |

**(c)** The margin of error ("m.e." in the table above) increases with increasing confidence level.

**14.9.** $n = \left(\frac{(1.960)(50)}{2}\right)^2 = 2401.$

**14.10.** $n = \left(\frac{(2.576)(15)}{5}\right)^2 \doteq 59.72$—take $n = 60$.

**14.11.** (c) Table C (or software) shows that $z^* = 2.326$ for 98% confidence.

**14.12.** (c) Assuming (as is typical) that the margin of error is given with 95% confidence, this is the correct meaning.

**14.13.** (b) The standard deviation is $\sigma/\sqrt{n} = \sigma/\sqrt{3} \doteq 0.000577$ gram.

**14.14.** (a) The margin of error is $1.96\sigma/\sqrt{3} = (1.96)(0.000577) \doteq 0.00113$.

**14.15.** (c) The margin of error is $2.576\sigma/\sqrt{8} = (2.576)(0.000354) \doteq 0.00091$.

**14.16.** (c) $n = \left(\frac{(1.960)(0.001)}{0.0005}\right)^2 \doteq 15.37$—take $n = 16$.

**14.17.** (a) Even without computations, we can say that the margin of error would have to be larger when the sample size is smaller. By examining the formula for margin of error—in particular, the fact that it depends on the square root of $n$—we see that with one-fourth the sample size, the margin of error would double.

**14.18.** (a) Provided "the population is much larger than the sample," the margin of error depends only on the sample size.

**14.19.** (b) Greater confidence (with the same sample size) requires a larger margin of error. (If the confidence interval was based on a Normal distribution—we don't know that it was—the 95% confidence interval would be $\frac{1.96}{1.645} \doteq 1.19$ times larger than the 90% interval.)

**14.20.** (c) A larger sample size (with the same confidence level) gives a smaller margin of error. (In fact, the margin of error would be smaller by a factor of $\sqrt{\frac{1060}{1500}} \doteq 0.84$.)

**14.21.** The 99% confidence interval for mean BSRI masculinity score is

$$\bar{x} \pm z^* \frac{\sigma}{\sqrt{n}} = 5.91 \pm 2.576 \left(\frac{0.79}{\sqrt{148}}\right) = 5.91 \pm 0.167 = 5.743 \text{ to } 6.077.$$

**14.22.** The 90% confidence interval for mean BSRI femininity score is

$$\bar{x} \pm z^* \frac{\sigma}{\sqrt{n}} = 5.29 \pm 1.645 \left(\frac{0.78}{\sqrt{148}}\right) = 5.29 \pm 0.105 = 5.185 \text{ to } 5.395.$$

**14.23.** Lower confidence requires a smaller margin of error. To be specific: A 90% interval (as in Exercise 14.22) is based on covering the central 90% of a standard Normal distribution. It is shorter than a 99% interval (Exercise 14.21), which is based on covering the central 99%. This fact determines the two critical values, $z^* = 1.645$ for 90% confidence and $z^* = 2.576$ for 99% confidence.

**14.24.** $n = \left(\frac{(2.576)(0.79)}{0.2}\right)^2 \doteq 103.5$—take $n = 104$.

**14.25.** **(a)** The stemplot does look reasonably Normal. **(b) State:** What is the mean percent change $\mu$ in spinal mineral content of nursing mothers?

| | |
|---|---|
| −8 | 3 |
| −7 | 80 |
| −6 | 88552 |
| −5 | 97633221 |
| −4 | 9977430 |
| −3 | 86310 |
| −2 | 755322110 |
| −1 | 800 |
| −0 | 83 |
| 0 | 234 |
| 1 | 7 |
| 2 | 2 |

**Formulate:** We will estimate $\mu$ by giving a 99% confidence interval.
**Solve:** The problem states that we may consider these women to be an SRS of the population. In part (a), we saw that the data appear to come from a Normal distribution. We find $\bar{x} = -3.587\%$, so the 99% confidence interval for $\mu$ is

$$\bar{x} \pm 2.576\left(\frac{2.5\%}{\sqrt{47}}\right) = -3.587\% \pm 0.939\% = -4.526\% \text{ to } -2.648\%.$$

**Conclude:** We are 99% confident that the mean percent change in spinal mineral content is between −4.526% and −2.648%.

**14.26.** **(a)** A stemplot (right) or histogram shows that the distribution is noticeably skewed to the left. The data do not appear to follow a Normal distribution. **(b) State:** What is the mean load $\mu$ required to pull apart pieces of Douglas fir?

| | |
|---|---|
| 23 | 0 |
| 24 | 0 |
| 25 | |
| 26 | 5 |
| 27 | |
| 28 | 7 |
| 29 | |
| 30 | 149 |
| 31 | 389 |
| 32 | 033577 |
| 33 | 0126 |

**Formulate:** We will estimate $\mu$ by giving a 90% confidence interval.
**Solve:** The problem states that we are willing to take this sample to be an SRS of the population. In spite of the shape of the stemplot, we are told to suppose that this distribution is Normal with standard deviation 3000 lb. We find $\bar{x} = 30,841$ lb, so the 90% confidence interval for $\mu$ is

$$\bar{x} \pm 1.645\left(\frac{3000}{\sqrt{20}}\right) = 30,841 \pm 1103.5 = 29,737 \text{ to } 31,945 \text{ lb}.$$

**Conclude:** We are 90% confident that the mean load required to pull apart pieces of Douglas fir is between 29,737 and 31,945 pounds.

**14.27.** **(a)** We must assume that the 10 students can be considered to be an SRS of the population of students, and that odor thresholds are Normally distributed. A stemplot gives no reason to doubt the second condition: It is reasonably symmetric for such a small sample. **(b) State:** What is the mean DMS odor threshold $\mu$ among all students?

| | |
|---|---|
| 2 | 034 |
| 2 | |
| 3 | 01124 |
| 3 | 6 |
| 4 | 3 |

**Formulate:** We will estimate $\mu$ by giving a 95% confidence interval.
**Solve:** We must assume that we have an SRS of the population, and that the underlying distribution is Normal with standard deviation 7 $\mu$g/l. The mean is $\bar{x} = 30.4$ $\mu$g/l, so the 95% confidence interval for $\mu$ is

$$\bar{x} \pm 1.960\left(\frac{7}{\sqrt{10}}\right) = 30.4 \pm 4.34 = 26.06 \text{ to } 34.74\ \mu\text{g/l}.$$

**Conclude:** We are 95% confident that the mean DMS odor threshold among all students is between 26.06 and 34.74 $\mu$g/l.

**14.28.** $n = \left(\frac{(1.960)(3000)}{1000}\right)^2 \doteq 34.57$—take $n = 35$.

**14.29.** **(a)** The distribution is slightly skewed to the right. The appearance of the stemplot changes depending on how many ways we split the stems.
**(b)** The 95% confidence interval is

$$224.002 \pm 1.960\left(\frac{0.060}{\sqrt{16}}\right) = 224.002 \pm 0.029$$
$$= 223.973 \text{ to } 224.031 \text{ mm.}$$

| Stem | Leaves |
|---|---|
| 2239 | 01 |
| 2239 | 66788889 |
| 2240 | 01 |
| 2240 | 589 |
| 2241 | 2 |

| Stem | Leaves |
|---|---|
| 2239 | 01 |
| 2239 | |
| 2239 | |
| 2239 | 667 |
| 2239 | 88889 |
| 2240 | 01 |
| 2240 | |
| 2240 | 5 |
| 2240 | |
| 2240 | 89 |
| 2241 | |
| 2241 | 2 |

**14.30.** **(a)** The margin of error for 99% confidence is $2.576\left(\frac{65}{\sqrt{269}}\right) \doteq 10.2090$ minutes, so the interval is $137 \pm 10.2090 = 126.8$ to 147.2 minutes. **(b)** We need to know if this sample (i.e., the students in the class where the survey was performed) can be considered an SRS of the population of all first-year students at this university.

**14.31.** **(a)** The outlying patient has an HAV angle of 50 degrees. **(b)** Without the outlier, the mean is $\bar{x} \doteq 24.76$ degrees. The margin of error is $1.960\left(\frac{6.3}{\sqrt{37}}\right) \doteq 2.03$ degrees, so the confidence interval is $24.76 \pm 2.03$, or about 22.7 to 26.8 degrees.

**14.32.** The margin of error for 99% confidence is slightly smaller (because of the larger sample size). It is now $2.576\left(\frac{65}{\sqrt{270}}\right) \doteq 10.1901$ minutes, so the interval is $248 \pm 10.1901 = 237.8$ to 258.2 minutes, compared with 126.8 to 147.2 minutes in Exercise 14.30. This one outlier has a huge impact on the interval.

**14.33.** **(a)** The 98% confidence interval is

$$10.0023 \pm 2.326\left(\frac{0.0002}{\sqrt{5}}\right) \doteq 10.0023 \pm 0.00021 = 10.0021 \text{ to } 10.0025 \text{ g.}$$

**(b)** $n = \left(\frac{(2.326)(0.0002)}{0.0001}\right)^2 \doteq 21.64$—take $n = 22$.

**14.34.** No: The interval refers to the mean NAEP score, not to individual scores, which will be much more variable. (Indeed, if more than 95% of young men score below 276.2, then very few can, for example, determine the price of a meal from a menu.)

**14.35.** The mistake is in saying that 95% of other polls would have results close to the results of this poll. Other surveys should be close to *the truth*—not necessarily close to the results of this survey. (Additionally, there is the suggestion that 95% means exactly "19 out of 20.")

**14.36.** The sample size for adults ages 18 to 29 is smaller, so the margin of error is larger than 3 percentage points.

**14.37.** The sample size for women was more than twice as large as that for men. Larger sample sizes give more information, and therefore lead to smaller margins of error (with the same confidence level).

**14.38. (a)** In 99% of all repetitions of this experiment, at least 40 of the 50 confidence intervals will capture $\mu$. Out of 1000 90% confidence intervals, nearly all students will observe between 87% and 93% capturing the mean. Sample output is shown on the right.

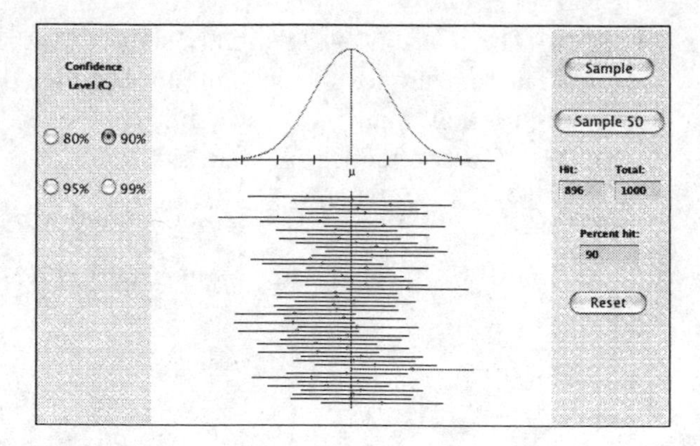


**(b)** When the switch is made from 90% to 95% confidence, the intervals become longer; to be more confident, we need a larger margin of error. In 99% of all repetitions of this experiment, at least 44 of the 50 confidence intervals will capture $\mu$. Out of 1000 95% confidence intervals, nearly all students will observe between 93% and 97% capturing the mean.

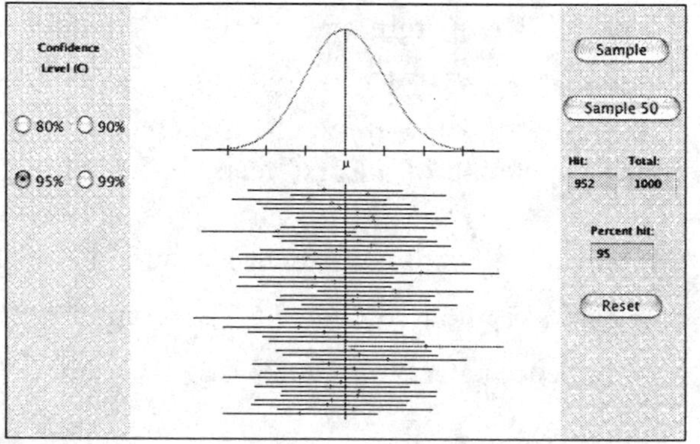


**(c)** In 99% of all repetitions of this experiment, at least 47 of the 50 confidence intervals will capture $\mu$. Out of 1000 99% confidence intervals, nearly all students will observe at least 98% capturing the mean.

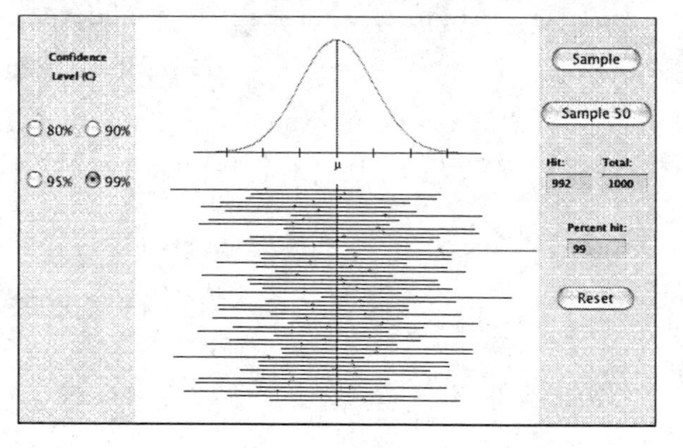


**14.39.** To verify the critical value for 95% confidence, the applet gives the first result below (on the left). For 92.5% confidence, the critical value is 1.780.

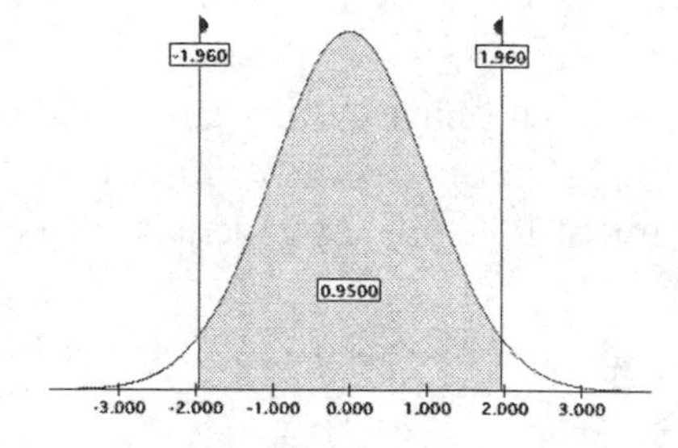


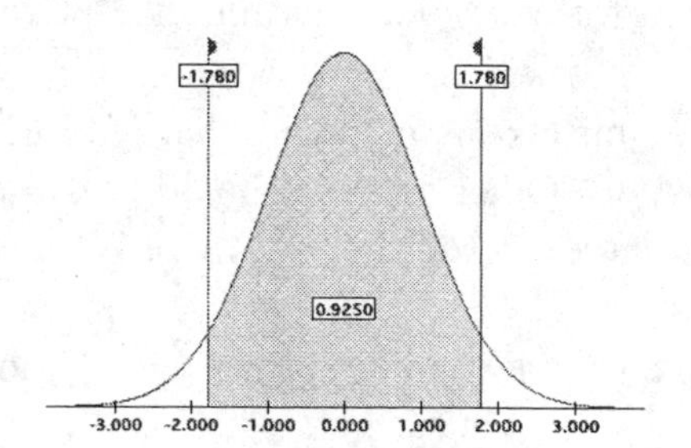

# Chapter 15 Solutions

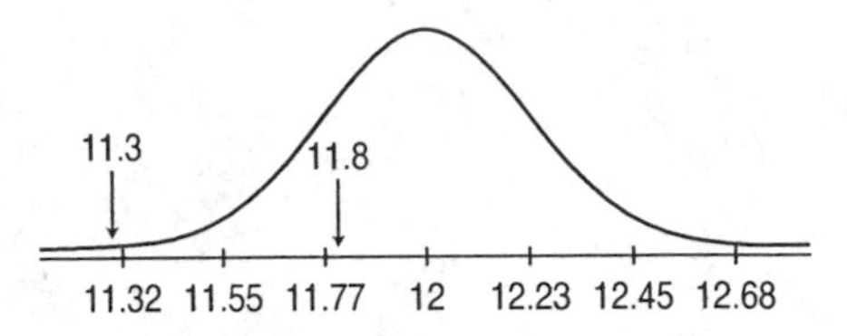


**15.1.** **(a)** If $\mu = 12$, the distribution is approximately Normal with mean $\mu = 12$ g/dl and standard deviation $\sigma/\sqrt{50} \doteq 0.2263$ g/dl. **(b)** A result like $\bar{x} = 11.3$ g/dl lies out toward the low tail of the curve, while 11.8 g/dl is fairly close to the middle. If $\mu = 12$ g/dl, observing a value similar to 11.8 g/dl would not be too surprising, but 11.3 g/dl is less likely, and it therefore provides some evidence that $\mu < 12$ g/dl.

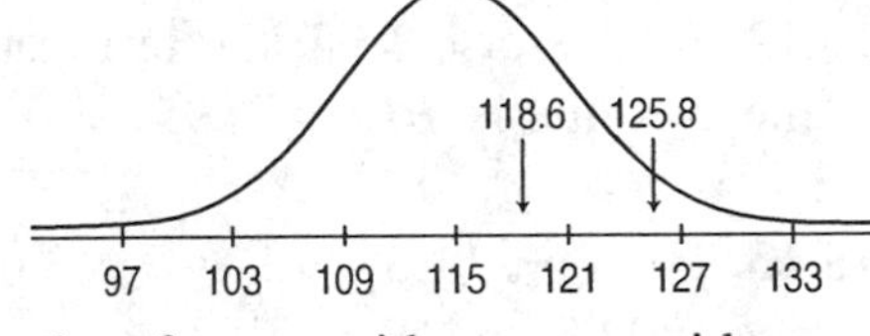


**15.2.** **(a)** If $\mu = 115$, the distribution is approximately Normal with mean $\mu = 115$ and standard deviation $\sigma/\sqrt{25} = 6$. **(b)** The actual result lies out toward the high tail of the curve, while 118.6 is fairly close to the middle. If $\mu = 115$, observing a value similar to 118.6 would not be too surprising, but 125.8 is less likely, and it therefore provides some evidence that $\mu > 115$.

**15.3.** $H_0$: $\mu = 12$ g/dl; $H_a$: $\mu < 12$ g/dl.

**15.4.** $H_0$: $\mu = 115$; $H_a$: $\mu > 115$.

**15.5.** $H_0$: $\mu = 51$ mpg; $H_a$: $\mu < 51$ mpg.

**15.6.** $H_0$: $\mu = 20$ min; $H_a$: $\mu \neq 20$ min.

**15.7.** Hypotheses should be stated in terms of $\mu$, not $\bar{x}$.

**Note:** *Students who think about this problem a bit more might also point out that 1000 g (2.2 lb) is a dangerously low birth weight; babies smaller than this are classified as extremely low birth weight (ELBW).*

**15.8.** For $\bar{x} = 0.3$, $z = \frac{0.3-0}{1/\sqrt{10}} \doteq 0.95$.

**15.9.** For $\bar{x} = 11.3$ g/dl, $z = \frac{11.3-12}{1.6/\sqrt{50}} \doteq -3.09$. For $\bar{x} = 11.8$ g/dl, $z = \frac{11.8-12}{1.6/\sqrt{50}} \doteq -0.88$.

**15.10.** For $\bar{x} = 118.6$, $z = \frac{118.6-115}{30/\sqrt{25}} = 0.60$. For $\bar{x} = 125.8$, $z = \frac{125.8-115}{30/\sqrt{25}} = 1.80$.

**15.11.** The applet's output for $n = 18$, $\sigma = 60$, and $\bar{x} = 17$ is shown on the right. (This Normal curve has mean 0 and standard deviation $\sigma/\sqrt{18} \doteq 14.14$.)

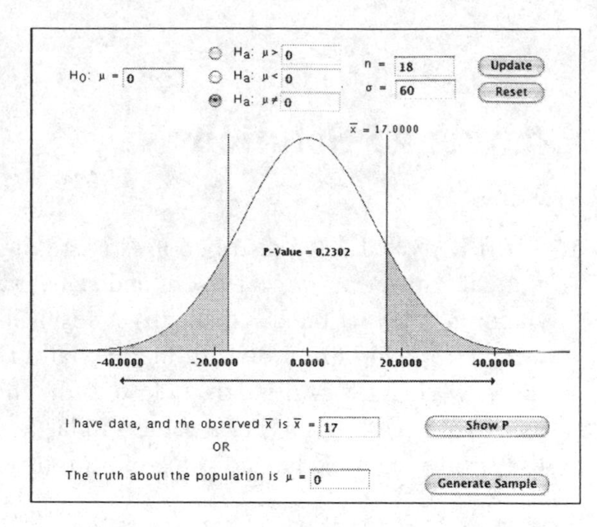


**15.12.** In Exercise 15.8, the test statistic $z$ was found to be 0.95, so for the alternative $\mu > 0$, the $P$-value is $P(Z \geq 0.95) = 0.1711$.

**15.13.** For $\bar{x} = 11.3$ g/dl, $z = -3.09$ and $P = P(Z < -3.09) = 0.0010$. For $\bar{x} = 11.8$ g/dl, $z = -0.88$ and $P = P(Z < -0.88) = 0.1894$. The first $P$-value tells us that values of $\bar{x}$ similar to 11.3 g/dl would rarely occur when $H_0$ is true, while the second $P$-value is larger, indicating that results similar to this one give little reason to doubt $H_0$.

**15.14.** For $\bar{x} = 118.6$, the $P$-value is $P(\bar{x} > 118.6) = P(Z > 0.6) = 0.2743$. For $\bar{x} = 125.8$, $P = P(\bar{x} > 125.8) \doteq P(Z > 1.80) = 0.0359$. A small $P$-value (such as 0.0359) tells us that values of $\bar{x}$ similar to 125.8 would rarely occur when $H_0$ is true, while $P = 0.2743$ indicates that results similar to 118.6 give little reason to doubt $H_0$.

**15.15.** For $\bar{x} = 11.8$ g/dl, we found $z = -0.88$ and $P = 0.1894$; this is not significant at $\alpha = 0.05$ or $\alpha = 0.01$.

**15.16.** For $\bar{x} = 125.8$, we found $z = 1.80$ and $P = 0.0359$; this is significant at $\alpha = 0.05$, but not at $\alpha = 0.01$.

**15.17. (a)** The results observed in this study would rarely have occurred by chance if vitamin C were ineffective. **(b)** $P < 0.01$ means that results similar to those observed would occur less than 1% of the time if vitamin C supplements had no effect.

**15.18.** We test $H_0$: $\mu = 5$ mg versus $H_a$: $\mu < 5$ mg. The test statistic is $z = \frac{4.62-5}{0.92/\sqrt{45}} \doteq -2.77$, and the $P$-value is $P = P(Z < -2.77) = 0.0028$. This is very strong evidence that $\mu < 5$ mg.

**15.19. State:** Do student SATM scores improve on their second attempt?
**Formulate:** Let $\mu$ be the mean change in SATM score. We test $H_0$: $\mu = 0$ versus $H_a$: $\mu > 0$; the alternative is one-sided because we expect scores to increase.
**Solve:** We were told the 46 students were "randomly" chosen, and that we "know" that changes in score follow a Normal distribution with standard deviation 50 points. We find

that $\bar{x} = 13.1087$ points, so the test statistic is $z = \frac{\bar{x}-0}{50/\sqrt{46}} \doteq 1.78$, and the $P$-value is $P = P(Z > 1.78) = 0.0375$.
**Conclude:** A mean change as large as 13.1087 would occur about 4% of the time if there were no change in scores ($\mu = 0$). This is fairly strong evidence (significant at $\alpha = 0.05$) that the mean change in test score is positive.

**15.20. State:** Does the use of fancy type fonts slow down the reading of text?
**Formulate:** Let $\mu$ be the mean reading time for Gigi. We test $H_0$: $\mu = 22$ sec versus $H_a$: $\mu > 22$ sec; the alternative is one-sided because we expect that the fancy font will increase reading times.
**Solve:** Assume we have a Normal distribution and an SRS. We find that $\bar{x} = 27.088$ sec, so the test statistic is $z = \frac{27.088-22}{6/\sqrt{25}} \doteq 4.24$, and the $P$-value is $P = P(Z > 4.24) \doteq 0$.
**Conclude:** A mean reading time as large as 27.088 seconds would almost never occur if Gigi did not affect reading time ($\mu = 22$ sec). This is very strong evidence (significant at $\alpha = 0.01$, or much smaller) that it takes more than 22 seconds to read text printed in Gigi.

**15.21.** For a one-sided alternative (on the positive side), $z$ is statistically significant at $\alpha = 0.005$ if $z > 2.576$.

**15.22.** For a two-sided alternative, $z$ is statistically significant at $\alpha = 0.005$ if $|z| > 2.807$—that is, $z < -2.807$ or $z > 2.807$.

**15.23. (a)** $z = \frac{0.4365-0.5}{0.2887/\sqrt{100}} \doteq -2.20$. **(b)** This result is significant at the 5% level because $z < -1.960$. **(c)** It is not significant at 1% because $z \geq -2.576$. **(d)** This value of $z$ is between 2.054 and 2.326, so the $P$-value is between 0.02 and 0.04 (because the alternative is two-sided).

**15.24. (a)** Yes: $P = 0.06$ indicates that the results observed are not significant at the 5% level, so the 95% confidence interval will include 10. **(b)** No: Because $P < 0.1$, we can reject $H_0$: $\mu = 10$ at the 10% level. The 90% confidence interval would include only those values $a$ for which we could *not* reject $H_0$: $\mu = a$ at the 10% level.

**15.25. (a)** No: 34 falls in the 95% confidence interval (28 to 35). **(b)** Yes: 26 falls outside of the 95% confidence interval.

**Note:** *We assume a two-sided alternative.*

**15.26.** (a) The null hypothesis is that the hotel managers' population mean $\mu$ is the same as that for all adult men.

**15.27.** (b) The researcher suspects that hotel managers score higher; the alternative hypothesis reflects that belief.

**15.28.** (c) $z = \frac{5.91-4.88}{0.79/\sqrt{48}} \doteq 9.03$.

**15.29.** (b) The two-sided $P$-value is $2P(Z > 1.30) = 2(0.0968) = 0.1936$.

**15.30.** (b) With a two-sided alternative, the strength of the evidence is the same regardless of the sign (plus or minus) of the $z$ statistic.

**15.31.** (c) $z$ is positive, as we would expect if $H_a$ were true, so the $P$-value is $P = P(Z > 1.30) = 0.0968$.

**15.32.** (a) $z$ is negative, while we would expect it to be positive if $H_a$ were true, so $P = P(Z > -1.30) = 1 - P(Z < -1.30) = 0.9032$.

**15.33.** (a) While $z = 9.03$ cannot be found in the table, we can tell that the probability outside the range $-9.03$ to $9.03$ is very small.

**15.34.** (b) To be significant at level $\alpha$, we need $P < \alpha$.

**15.35.** (a) Because $59,000 falls in the 90% confidence interval, the mean is not significantly different from $59,000 at the 10% level, and would not be significantly different for any smaller levels of significance. (Or equivalently, any higher-confidence intervals would be wider, and would therefore also include $59,000.)

**15.36. State:** Is there evidence that the mean threshold for untrained tasters is greater than 25 $\mu$g/l?
**Formulate:** Let $\mu$ be the mean threshold for untrained tasters. We test $H_0$: $\mu = 25$ $\mu$g/l versus $H_a$: $\mu > 25$ $\mu$g/l; the alternative is one-sided because we expect that untrained noses are less sensitive (have a higher threshold).
**Solve:** Assume we have a Normal distribution and an SRS. We find that $\bar{x} = 30.4$ $\mu$g/l, and the test statistic is $z = \frac{30.4-25}{7/\sqrt{10}} \doteq 2.44$, so the $P$-value is $P = P(Z > 2.44) = 0.0073$.
**Conclude:** A mean threshold as large as 30.4 $\mu$g/l would occur less than 1% of the time if $\mu$ were 25 $\mu$g/l. This is very strong evidence (significant at $\alpha = 0.01$) that the students' mean threshold is greater than 25 $\mu$g/l.

**15.37. State:** Does the mean IQ in this district differ from 100?
**Formulate:** Let $\mu$ be the mean IQ for all seventh-grade girls in this district. We test $H_0$: $\mu = 100$ versus $H_a$: $\mu \neq 100$; the alternative is two-sided because we had no prior belief about the direction of the difference. (That is, before looking at the data, we had no reason to expect the mean to be more or less than 100.)
**Solve:** Assume we have a Normal distribution and an SRS. In Exercise 14.6, we found that $\bar{x} = 105.84$, so the test statistic is $z = \frac{105.84-100}{15/\sqrt{31}} \doteq 2.17$, and the $P$-value is $P = 2P(Z > 2.17) = 0.0300$.
**Conclude:** A mean IQ 5.84 points away from 100 would occur only 3% of the time if the population mean IQ were 100. This is strong evidence (significant at the 5% level) that the mean IQ differs from (is greater than) 100.

**15.38. State:** Do hotel managers have a different mean femininity score from men in general?
**Formulate:** Let $\mu$ be the mean femininity score $\mu$ of the population of hotel managers. We test $H_0$: $\mu = 5.19$ versus $H_a$: $\mu \neq 5.19$; the alternative is two-sided because we had no prior belief about the direction of the difference. (That is, before looking at the data, we had no

reason to expect that the mean for hotel managers would be higher or lower than 5.19.)
**Solve:** Assume we have a Normal distribution and an SRS. With $\bar{y} = 105.84$, the test statistic is $z = \frac{5.29-5.19}{0.78/\sqrt{148}} \doteq 1.56$, and the $P$-value is $P = 2P(Z > 1.56) = 0.1188$.
**Conclude:** A mean femininity score 0.1 units away from 5.19 would occur almost 12% of the time if the population mean femininity score were 5.19. There is only weak evidence that hotel managers have different mean femininity score than the general male population. Particularly when the large sample ($n = 148$) is taken into account, we suspect that managers don't differ much from males in general (in this respect).

**15.39. State:** Do nursing mothers lose bone mineral on the average?
**Formulate:** Let $\mu$ be the mean percent change in spinal mineral content for the population of nursing mothers. We test $H_0$: $\mu = 0\%$ versus $H_a$: $\mu < 0\%$; the alternative is one-sided because we suspect that nursing will reduce mineral content.
**Solve:** Assume we have a Normal distribution and an SRS. We find that $\bar{x} = -3.587\%$, so the test statistic is $z = \frac{\bar{x}-0}{2.5/\sqrt{47}} \doteq -9.84$, and the $P$-value is extremely small ($P = P(Z < -9.84) \doteq 0$).
**Conclude:** This is overwhelming evidence that, on the average, nursing mothers lose bone mineral.

**15.40.** For $\bar{x} = 17$ with $n = 75$, the test statistic is $z = \frac{17-0}{60/\sqrt{75}} \doteq 2.45$, and the $P$-value is $P = P(Z \leq -2.45 \text{ or } Z \geq 2.45) = 0.0071 \cdot 2 = 0.0142$. This is fairly strong evidence against $H_0$.

**15.41.** The 90% confidence interval for $\mu$ (the mean femininity score of all managers in the population) is 5.185 to 5.395. This interval includes the hypothesized value $\mu = 5.19$, so we know that the result is not significant in a two-sided test at the 10% level. We think that $\mu$ is not far from 5.19.

**15.42.** For $z^* = 2$ the $P$-value would be $2P(Z > 2) = 0.0456$, and for $z^* = 3$ the $P$-value would be $2P(Z > 3) = 0.0026$.
**Note:** *In other words, the Supreme Court uses $\alpha$ no bigger than about* 0.05.

**15.43. (a)** The alternative hypothesis expresses the effect we expect to be true or hope to find when we plan our study. If we have no reason to expect in advance of the data that women will rate a movie more highly than men, we should use a two-sided alternative. Choosing the alternative to match the data makes it more likely that the test will find an effect. That's cheating. **(b)** If the one-sample $z$ statistic is $z = 2.1$, the two-sided $P$-value is the probability of a result this far from zero in either direction,

$$P = 2P(Z \geq 2.1) = 2(1 - 0.9821) = 0.0358.$$

The two-sided $P$-value is double the one-sided value, showing again that the one-sided alternative makes it easier to find an effect.

**15.44.** Because a $P$-value is a probability, it can never be greater than 1. The correct $P$-value is $P(Z > 1.33) = 0.0918$.

**15.45.** Let $\mu = \mu_{\text{placebo}} - \mu_{\text{no treatment}}$ be the mean difference between the two groups. If the placebo reduces activity, then $\mu$ would be negative, so the hypotheses are $H_0$: $\mu = 0$ versus $H_a$: $\mu < 0$.

**15.46.** $\mu$ is the mean difference (fortified minus unfortified) in blood folic acid levels. If eating fortified cereal raises the level of folic acid, then $\mu$ would be positive, so the hypotheses are $H_0$: $\mu = 0$ versus $H_a$: $\mu > 0$.

**15.47.** If the presence of pig skulls were not an indication of wealth, then differences similar to those observed in this study would occur less than 1% of the time by chance.

**15.48.** $P = 0.031$ means that if cicada bodies had no effect—if nitrogen levels differed only because of natural variation among the plants—then only 3.1% of all samples would produce results similar to the ones found in this experiment.

**15.49.** While there was some difference in richness and total stem densities between the two areas, those differences were so small that they could easily occur by chance if the population means were identical.

**15.50.** **(a)** Below (subject counts may vary). **(b)** The observed difference in polyp occurrence between the two groups was so small that it might reasonably be expected to occur purely by chance if we assumed that diet had no effect.

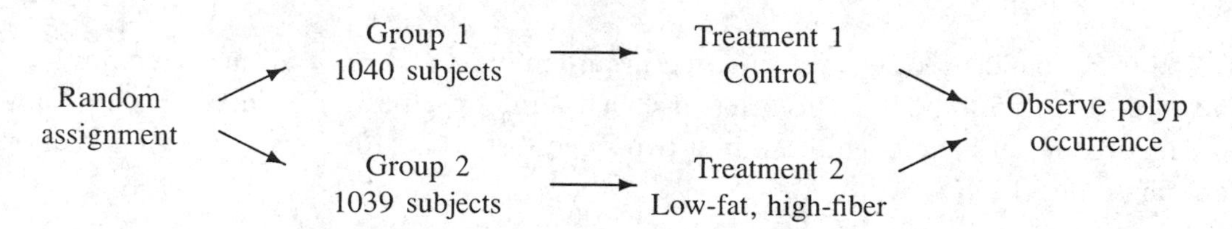


**15.51.** In the sketch, the "significant at 1%" region includes only the dark shading ($z > 2.326$). The "significant at 5%" region of the sketch includes both the light and dark shading ($z > 1.645$).

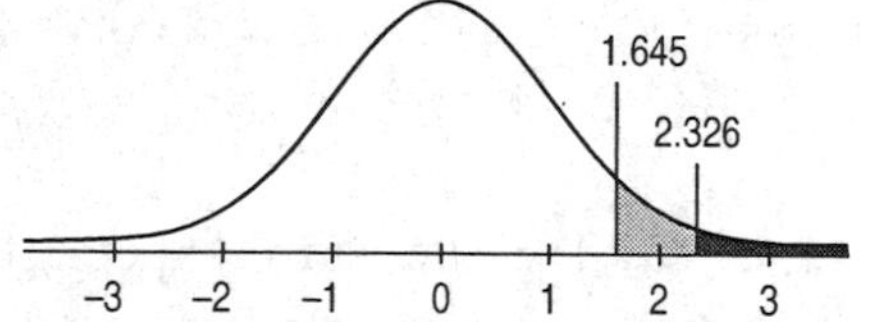


When a test is significant at the 1% level, it means that if the null hypothesis were true, outcomes similar to those seen are expected to occur less than once in 100 repetitions of the experiment or sampling. "Significant at the 5% level" means we have observed something that occurs in less than 5 out of 100 repetitions (when $H_0$ is true). Something that occurs "less than once in 100 repetitions" also occurs "less than 5 times in 100 repetitions," so significance at the 1% level implies significance at the 5% level (or any higher level).

The opposite statement does not hold: Something that occurs "less than 5 times in 100 repetitions" is not necessarily as rare as something that occurs "less than once in 100 repetitions," so a test that is significant at 5% is not necessarily significant at 1%.

**15.52.** No: "$P = 0.03$" *does* mean that $H_0$ is unlikely, but only in the sense that the evidence (from the sample) would not occur very often if $H_0$ were true. $P$ is a probability associated with the sample, not with the null hypothesis; either $H_0$ is true or it isn't.

**15.53.** Yes. That's the heart of why we care about statistical significance. Significance tests allow us to discriminate between random differences ("chance variation") that might occur when the null hypothesis is true, and differences that are unlikely to occur when $H_0$ is true.

**15.54.** In Exercise 14.26, we found the interval to be 29,737 to 31,945 pounds. **(a)** Because 32,000 pounds is not in this interval, we would reject $H_0$: $\mu = 32,000$ pounds at the 10% level (in favor of $H_a$: $\mu \neq 32,000$ pounds). **(b)** Because 31,500 pounds is in this interval, we cannot reject $H_0$: $\mu = 31,500$ pounds at the 10% level.

**15.55.** Student results will vary; below are two sample screens. The first shows 20 shots by a player whose true shooting percentage is only 50%; we are fairly convinced this player does not shoot 80% after only 20 shots. The second screen shows 40 shots for the a player who really does shoot 80%.

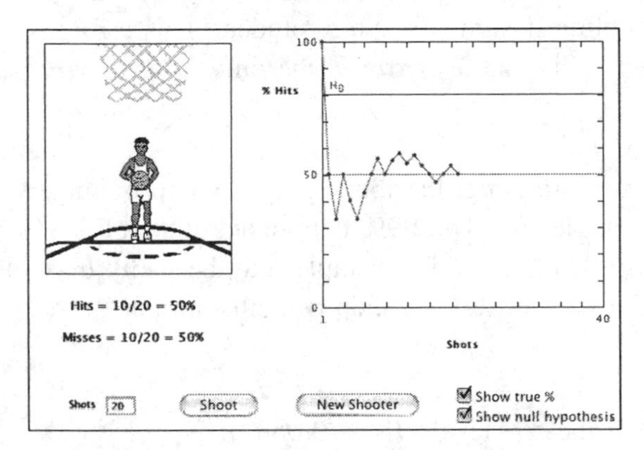


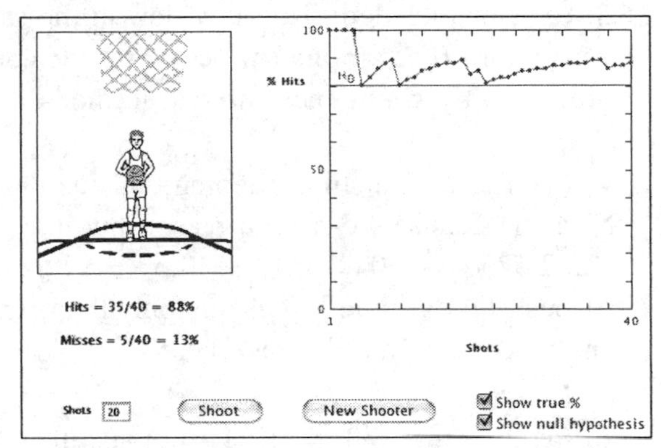


**15.56.** The cutoffs for significance at the $\alpha = 0.0125$ level are $\pm 2.24$; Max should choose positive or negative based on the direction of his alternative hypothesis (use the rejection region $z < -2.24$ if the alternative is $\mu < \mu_0$, $z > 2.24$ for the alternative $\mu > \mu_0$).

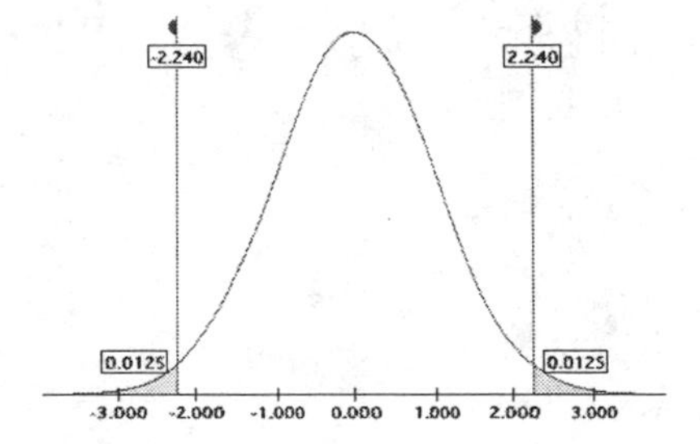

# Chapter 16 Solutions

**16.1.** **(a)** Yes: $(1.96)(\$1125/\sqrt{958}) \doteq \$71$, and $\$8740 \pm \$71 = \$8669$ to $\$8811$. **(b)** No: Because the numbers are based on voluntary response rather than an SRS, the confidence interval methods of this chapter cannot be used; the interval does not apply to the whole population.

**16.2.** **(a)** $\bar{x} \pm 1.96\sigma/\sqrt{880} = 1.92 \pm 0.1209 = 1.80$ to $2.04$ motorists. **(b)** The large sample size means that, because of the central limit theorem, the sampling distribution of $\bar{x}$ is roughly Normal even if the distribution of responses is not. **(c)** Only people with listed phone numbers were represented in the sample, and the low response rate ($10.9\% \doteq \frac{5029}{45,956}$) means that even that group may not be well represented by this sample.

**16.3.** **(a)** Not included: This is a flaw in the sampling design. **(b)** Not included: This error arises from the sampling process. **(c)** Included: This random error is the only error addressed by confidence interval methods.

**16.4.** **(a)** The central limit theorem tells us that the sampling distribution of $\bar{x}$ is approximately Normal because we have a reasonably large sample. **(b)** The 99% confidence interval is $\bar{x} \pm 2.576\sigma/\sqrt{250} = \$237 \pm 10.59 = \$226.4$ to $\$247.6$. **(c)** The sample may be badly biased: At best, this sample represents only the opinions of those who shop in malls similar to the one where the sample was chosen.

**16.5.** **(a)** $z = \frac{544-518}{114/\sqrt{50}} \doteq 1.61$—not significant at the 5% level ($P = 0.0537$).
**(b)** $z = \frac{545-518}{114/\sqrt{50}} \doteq 1.67$—significant at 5% level ($P = 0.0475$),

**16.6.** The full applet output for $n = 5$ is below on the left; on the right are the Normal curves drawn for $n = 15$ and $n = 40$. The reported $P$-values (0.1867, 0.0606, and 0.0057) agree with the "hand-computed" values given in the solution to the next exercise.

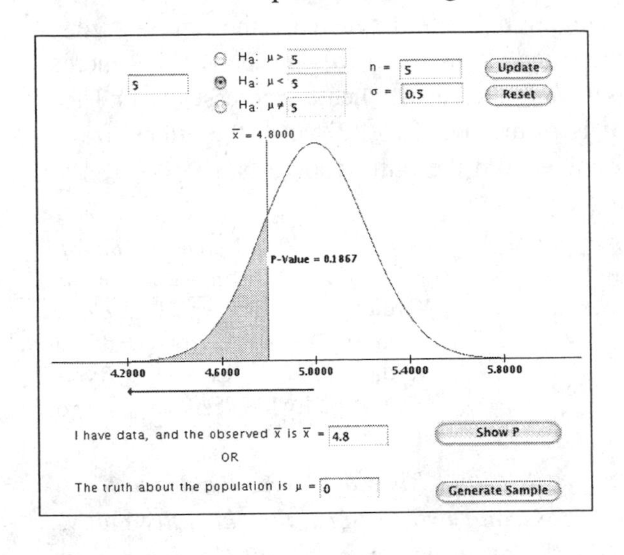


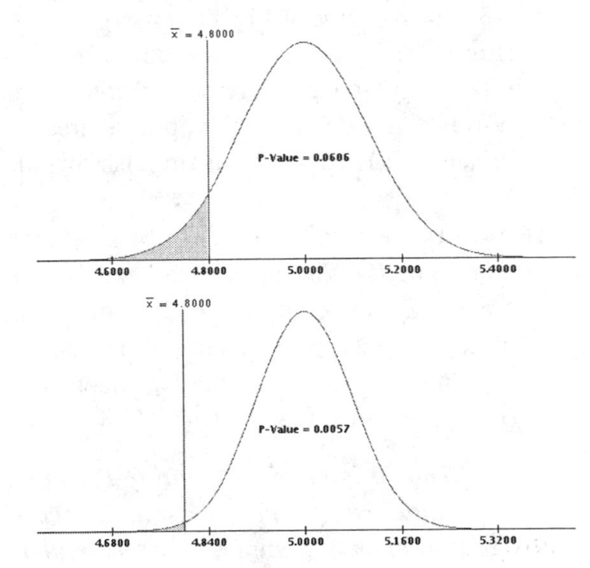


**16.7.** The $z$ statistics and the $P$-values are given in the table on the right. In each case, the computation is

$$z = \frac{4.8 - 5}{0.5/\sqrt{n}} \quad \text{and} \quad P = P(Z < z).$$

| | $n$ | $z$ | $P$ |
|---|---|---|---|
| **(a)** | 5 | −0.89 | 0.1867 |
| **(b)** | 15 | −1.55 | 0.0606 |
| **(c)** | 40 | −2.53 | 0.0057 |

**16.8.** The confidence intervals are given in the table on the right. In each case, the interval is

$$4.8 \pm 1.960\left(\frac{0.5}{\sqrt{n}}\right).$$

| | |
|---|---|
| $n = 5$ | 4.362 to 5.238 |
| $n = 15$ | 4.547 to 5.053 |
| $n = 40$ | 4.645 to 4.955 |

**16.9.** **(a)** "Statistically insignificant" means that the differences observed were no more than might have been expected to occur by chance even if SES had no effect on LSAT results. **(b)** If the results are based on a small sample, then even if the null hypothesis were not true, the test might not be sensitive enough to detect the effect. Knowing the effects were small tells us that the test was not insignificant merely because of a small sample size.

**16.10.** **(a)** No: In a sample of size 500, we expect to see about 5 people who have a $P$-value of 0.01 or less [$5 = (500)(0.01)$]. These four *might* have ESP, or they may simply be among the "lucky" ones we expect to see. **(b)** The researcher should repeat the procedure on these four to see whether they again perform well.

**16.11.** Recall that effect size $= \dfrac{\text{true mean response} - \text{hypothesized response}}{\text{standard deviation of response}}$. The hypothesized response is 115, and the standard deviation is 30. **(a)** The effect size is $\frac{130-115}{30} = 0.5$, so from the table in the text, we need a sample of size $n = 35$ to have 90% power against the alternative $\mu = 130$. **(b)** The effect size is $\frac{139-115}{30} = 0.8$, so we need a sample of size $n = 14$ to have 90% power against the alternative $\mu = 139$.

**16.12.** The $z$ test will reject $H_0$ 78% of the time if the true mean score is 270 (instead of the null-hypothesized value 275).

**16.13.** **(a)** To achieve higher power without changing $\alpha$, we must increase the sample size. (Larger samples give more power against the same alternative.) **(b)** The power will increase. (Generally, power increases when $\alpha$ increases, and decreases when $\alpha$ decreases.) **(c)** The power against $\mu = 265$ would be greater: It is further from $\mu_0$ (275), so the effect size is greater—it is easier to distinguish this alternative from the null hypothesis.

**16.14.** **(a)** We should take $\alpha$ to be small; 0.01 is preferable to 0.20. With $\alpha = 0.20$, we will wrongly convict an innocent person 20% of the time. For more thoughts on balancing Type I and Type II errors in this setting, see the two quotations below. **(b)** Diagram on the right.

| | *Defendant is:* Innocent | Guilty |
|---|---|---|
| Verdict: "Guilty" | Type I error | Correct decision |
| Verdict: "Not guilty" | Correct decision | Type II error |

*"That it is better 100 guilty Persons should escape than that one innocent Person should suffer, is a Maxim that has been long and generally approved."*
*–Benjamin Franklin*

*"... that 'tis much more Prudence to acquit two Persons, tho' actually guilty, than to pass Sentence of Condemnation on one that is virtuous and innocent."*
*–Voltaire*

**16.15.** **(a)** $H_0$: The patient is healthy (or "the patient should not see a doctor"); $H_a$: The patient is ill (or "the patient should see a doctor"). A Type I error is a false positive—sending a healthy patient to the doctor. A Type II error means a false negative—clearing a patient who should be referred to a doctor. **(b)** One might wish to lower the probability of a false negative so that most ill patients are treated, especially for serious diseases that require fast treatment. On the other hand, if resources (for example, money or medical personnel) are limited, or for less serious health problems, lowering the probability of false positives might be desirable.

**Note:** *For (a), there is no clear choice for which should be the null hypothesis in this case. Because these are "routine medical tests," it seems reasonable to assume the subjects have no specific medical complaints, so that we choose $H_0$ to be "the patient is healthy." However, for some conditions, the cost of mistakenly determining that someone is healthy might be too great, leading us to choose $H_0$ to be "the patient is ill."*

**16.16.** Shown is the applet output for $n = 5$. For the three specified sample sizes, the applet reports the following:

| $n$ | Power |
|---|---|
| 5 | 0.378 |
| 15 | 0.749 |
| 40 | 0.981 |

As sample size increases (while $\alpha$ and the alternative remain the same), power increases. If we want to "almost always" reject $H_0$ when the true mean pH is 4.7, we should choose a sample size like $n = 40$.

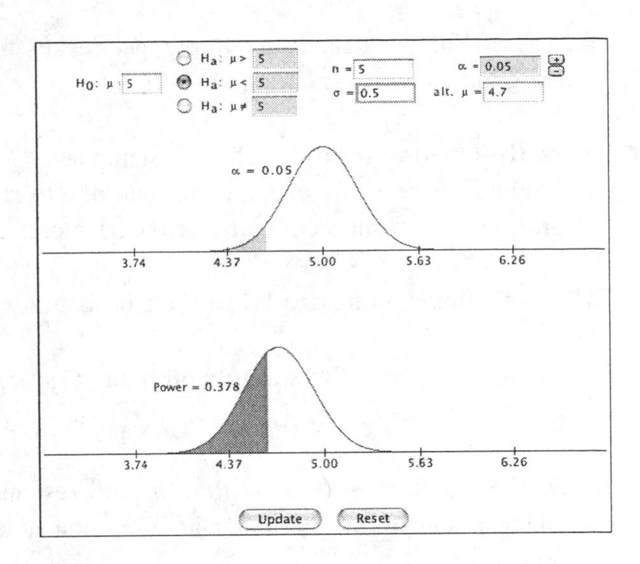


**16.17. (a)** The test statistic is $z = \frac{\bar{x}-5}{0.5/\sqrt{15}}$. Because the alternative is $\mu < 5$, we reject $H_0$ at the 5% level when $z < -1.645$. **(b)** This requires some algebra:

$$\frac{\bar{x}-5}{0.5/\sqrt{15}} < -1.645 \quad \text{when} \quad \bar{x} - 5 < .645\left(\frac{0.5}{\sqrt{15}}\right) \doteq -0.2124,$$

so we reject $H_0$ when $\bar{x} < 4.7877$. **(c)** When $\mu = 4.7$, the power is

$$P(\text{reject } H_0) = P(\bar{x} < 4.7877) = P\left(\frac{\bar{x}-4.7}{0.5/\sqrt{15}} < \frac{4.7877-4.7}{0.5/\sqrt{15}}\right) = P(Z < 0.68)$$

for which Table A gives 0.7517.

**16.18. (a)** $P(\text{Type I error}) = P(\bar{x} > 0) = P(Z > 0) = 0.50$. **(b)** $P(\text{Type II error when } \mu = 0.3) = P(\bar{x} \le 0) = P(Z \le \frac{0-0.3}{1/\sqrt{9}}) = P(Z \le -0.9) = 0.1841$. **(c)** $P(\text{Type II error when } \mu = 1) = P(Z \le \frac{0-1}{1/\sqrt{9}}) = P(Z \le -3) = 0.0013$.

**16.19.** (c) This is a convenience sample consisting of students with a particular interest in filmmaking which may make their opinions different from those of "typical" college-age adults.

**16.20.** (a) In describing an experiment, "uncontrolled" means that there was no control group.

**16.21.** (b) This voluntary response sample collects only the opinions of those who visit this site and feel strongly enough to respond.

**16.22.** (c) The announced margin of error accounts only for random sampling error.

**16.23.** (a) Dishonest responses are likely for questions like this.

**16.24.** (a) In order to detect small differences, we need large samples. (That is, small samples have low power against alternatives that are not very different from the null hypothesis.)

**16.25.** (a) Without a random sample, our results might be completely useless. (Of course, it is also good to avoid calculation errors!)

**16.26.** (b) Quoting from the chapter summary: "The margin of error in a confidence interval accounts for only the chance variation due to random sampling. In practice, errors due to nonresponse or undercoverage are often more serious."

**16.27.** (a) The significance level is the probability of a Type I error—wrongly rejecting $H_0$.

**16.28.** (b) The power is the probability of rejecting $H_0$ when a specific alternative ($\mu = 3$, in this case) is true.

**16.29.** We would like to know that the 148 respondents were chosen at random from all general managers of three-star and four-star hotels. We would also like to know the rate of nonresponse.

**16.30.** We don't have an SRS; even though the students were randomly chosen, the colleges were not. Differences among the colleges (the types of students they attract, the statistics professors, etc.) will confound any differences due to the textbooks.

**16.31.** **(a)** These results come from a convenience sample, rather than a random sample. Women sampled from a shopping mall do not represent the larger population of all women. **(b)** While this sample might not represent *all* women, it may be reasonable to view the women in the sample as an SRS of women who shop at large suburban malls.

**16.32.** Opinion—even expert opinion—unsupported by data is the weakest type of evidence, so the third description is level C. The second description refers to experiments (clinical trials) and large samples; that is the strongest evidence (level A). The first description is level B: stronger than opinion, but not as strong as experiments with large numbers of subjects.

**16.33.** Any type of error other than random sampling error; for example, poorly worded questions, a poorly chosen sample, nonresponse.

**16.34.** **(a)** Margin of error decreases. **(b)** The $P$-value decreases (the evidence against $H_0$ becomes stronger). **(c)** The power increases (the test becomes better at distinguishing between the null and alternative hypotheses).

**16.35.** A significance test answers only question (b). The $P$-value states how likely the observed effect (or a stronger one) is if chance alone is operating. The observed effect may be significant (very unlikely to be due to chance) and yet not be of practical importance. And the calculation leading to significance *assumes* a properly designed study.

**16.36.** Many people might be reluctant to discuss such intimate details of their personal lives (although this may be somewhat offset by some who might be inclined to brag or exaggerate). The margin of error allows only for random sampling error, not bias.

**16.37.** This is not information taken from an SRS, or from any kind of sample. We have information about all states—the whole population of interest.

**16.38.** The effect is greater if the sample is small. Quoting from "Cautions about the $z$ procedures": "Outliers or extreme skewness make the $z$ procedures untrustworthy unless the sample is large."

**16.39.** **(a)** Any number of things could go wrong with this convenience sample. Depending on the time of day or the day of the week, certain types of shoppers would or would not be present. **(b)** The distribution is strongly right-skewed, violating the assumption of Normality. (The sample size may be large enough to overcome this skewness, but it should make us cautious nonetheless.)

| | |
|---|---|
| 0 | 389 |
| 1 | 023557788999 |
| 2 | 0023445667888 |
| 3 | 24689 |
| 4 | 1244568 |
| 5 | 0249 |
| 6 | 1 |
| 7 | 0 |
| 8 | 256 |
| 9 | 3 |

**16.40.** When many variables are examined, "significant" results will show up by chance, so we should not take it for granted that the variables identified are really indicative of future success.

**16.41.** **(a)** The probability that one test rejects $H_0$ at $\alpha = 0.05$ when $H_0$ is true is 0.05. **(b)** Out of 77 tests, we can expect to see about 3 or 4 [$3.85 = (77)(0.05)$] significant tests at the 5% level.

**Note:** *Using a binomial distribution, we find that when all null hypotheses are true, there is a 90% chance of seeing two or more significant results.*

**16.42.** **(a)** The response rate is $\frac{1468}{13000} \doteq 0.1129$, or about 11.3%. **(b)** The reported margin of error is probably unreliable, because we know nothing about the 88.7% of organizations that did *not* respond; they may be more (or less) male-dominated than those that responded.

**16.43.** We might conclude that customers prefer Design A, but perhaps not "strongly." Because the sample size is so large, this statistically significant difference may not be of any practical importance.

**Note:** *For a two-sided alternative,* $P = 0.02$ *means that* $z \doteq 2.326$, *which we find (using methods from Chapter 21) would arise from* $\hat{p} = 0.516$*—hardly suggesting a "strong" preference.*

**16.44.** **(a)** $P < 0.01$ means that there is strong evidence that the correlation between exotic birds and native extinctions really is greater than zero in the population of all ocean islands. Specifically, the correlation in the sample was so large that it would happen in less than 1% of all samples drawn from a population in which the true correlation is zero. **(b)** The sample is reasonably large ($n = 220$), so it is possible that small correlations could be significant. But we know that the actual correlation was $r = 0.62$, which is quite strong for data collected in the field. This is large enough to be important. (In fact, the $P$-value is much smaller than 0.01. The study authors would have done better to give the actual $P$-value.)

**16.45.** **(a)** The difference observed in the study would occur in less than 1% of all samples if the two populations actually have the same proportion remaining on welfare. **(b)** The interval is constructed using a method that is correct (i.e., contains the actual proportion) 95% of the time. **(c)** No: Treatments were not randomly assigned, but instead were chosen by the mothers. Mothers who choose to attend a job-training program may be more inclined to get themselves off of welfare.

**16.46.** A Type I error means that we conclude the correlation is different from 0 when it really is 0. A Type II error means that we conclude the correlation is 0 when it is not.

**16.47.** A low-power test may do a good job of *not* incorrectly rejecting the null hypothesis (that is, avoiding a Type I error), but it will often accept $H_0$ even when it is false, simply because it is difficult to distinguish between $H_0$ and "nearby" alternatives.

**16.48.** $P(\text{Type I error}) = \alpha = 0.05$. $P(\text{Type II error}) = 1 - \text{Power} = 1 - 0.78 = 0.22$.

**16.49.** The power is $1 - P(\text{Type II error}) = 1 - 0.14 = 0.86$.

**16.50.** **(a)** $|z| \geq 2.576$ is equivalent to $z \leq -2.576$ or $z \geq 2.576$, so we reject $H_0$ if $\bar{x} \leq 0.84989$ or $\bar{x} \geq 0.87011$ [these two numbers are $0.86 \pm (2.576)(0.0068/\sqrt{3})$]. In other words, we reject $H_0$ if $\bar{x}$ is *not* between 0.84989 and 0.87011. **(b)** The power against $\mu = 0.845$ is

$$1 - P(\tfrac{0.84989-0.845}{0.0068/\sqrt{3}} < Z < \tfrac{0.87011-0.845}{0.0068/\sqrt{3}}) \doteq 1 - P(1.25 < Z < 6.40) \doteq 1 - 0.1056 = 0.8944.$$

**(c)** $P(\text{Type II error}) = 1 - \text{Power} = 0.1056$.

**16.51.** **(a)** We reject $H_0$ if $\bar{x} \leq 124.54$ or $\bar{x} \geq 131.46$; these numbers are $128 \pm (1.96)(15/\sqrt{72})$. The power against $\mu = 134$ is

$$1 - P\left(\tfrac{124.54-134}{15/\sqrt{72}} \leq Z \leq \tfrac{131.46-134}{15/\sqrt{72}}\right) \doteq 1 - P(-5.35 \leq Z \leq -1.43) \doteq 0.9236.$$

**(b)** Power: 0.9236—the same as in (a), because 122 and 134 are equal distances below and above 128. More than 90% of the time, this test will detect a difference of 6 (in either the positive or negative direction). **(c)** The power would be higher because greater differences are easier to detect than smaller ones.

# Chapter 17 Solutions

**17.1.** This is an experiment, because each subject is (randomly, we assume) assigned to a treatment. The explanatory variable is the price history seen by the subject (steady prices or fluctuating prices), and the response variable is the price the subject expects to pay.

**17.2.** The population is all words in Tom Clancy's novels. The sample is the 250 words recorded. The variable is the number of letters in a word.

**Note:** *The sample is not "250"; it is "250 words."*

**17.3.** **(a)** Label the students from 0001 to 3478 (or 0000 to 3477). Another possibility is to assign two four-digit labels to each student (for a total of 6956 labels). **(b)** Taking four digits at a time from line 105 gives

2940, 0769, 1481, 2975, and 1315.

If two labels are used for each student, we choose 2940, 0769, 1481, 6077, and 2975. See note on page 59 about using Table B. **(c)** The response variable is how much money the students earn in the summer. (Presumably, the questionnaire asks some question to get this information—perhaps, "How much did you earn last summer?")

**17.4.** Label from 01 through 27; beginning at line 111 of Table B, we choose

27 (951), 12 (619), 04 (323), 11 (562), 19 (805), 02 (213), and 06 (415).

**17.5.** **(a)** The control group should have 24 trees with no beehives. Diagram is shown below. **(b)** Label the trees 01 through 72. From line 137 of Table B, the first four active-hive trees are 53, 64, 56, and 68. **(c)** The response variable is elephant damage.

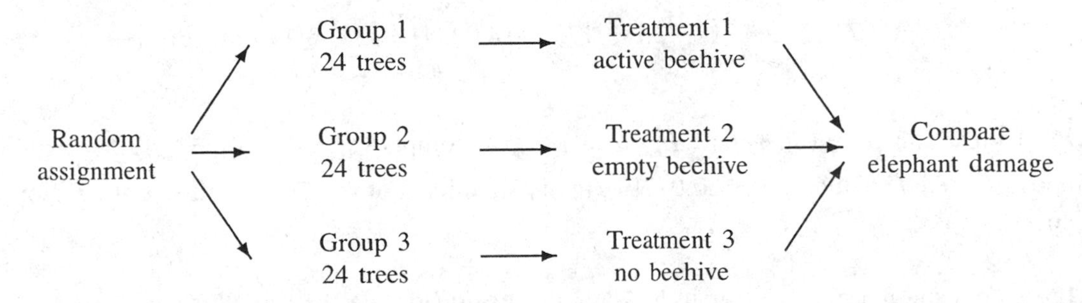

**17.6.** **(a)** The outline is shown below. **(b)** To use Table B, label the subjects 001 through 235, and choose three digits at a time. The first 5 subjects chosen from line 110 are
006, 051, 004, 127, and 123.
See note on page 59 about using Table B.

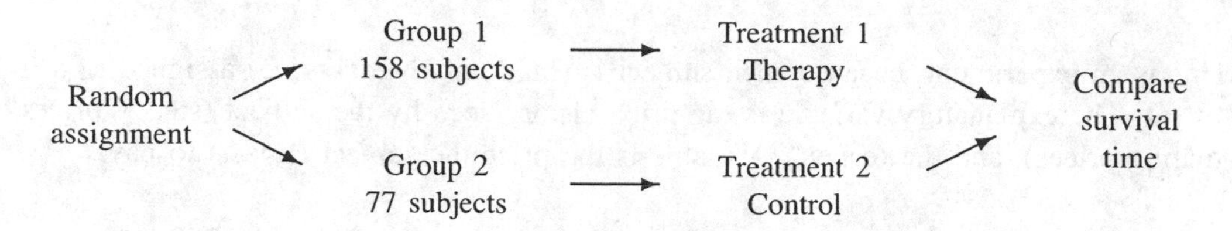


**17.7.** Both are statistics (relating to the samples used to form the treatment and control groups).

**17.8.** The intended population is television viewers (or perhaps just basketball fans). There is little that can be determined from this "sample" because the station heard only from persons who wanted to see the local game; they have no way on knowing how many NBA fans were happy with the station's choice, or how many viewers would have rather watched the local game but didn't feel strongly enough to call and complain.

**17.9.** Subjects who err in their responses are more likely to underestimate either their marijuana usage or the number of accidents they have caused (or both). That is, few people would want to exaggerate either of those quantities. It seems reasonable to expect more truthfulness (or accuracy) regarding accidents than marijuana usage, so we expect that marijuana usage will be underreported to a greater degree than accidents caused. This will have the effect of weakening the association, because the number of accidents caused by those who claim to use marijuana rarely or never will be inflated.

**17.10.** The 90% confidence interval is

$$172 \pm 1.645\left(\frac{41}{\sqrt{14}}\right) \doteq 172 \pm 18.0254 = 154 \text{ to } 190 \text{ mg/dl.}$$

**17.11.** To test $H_0$: $\mu = 188$ versus $H_a$: $\mu < 188$, we compute $z = \frac{172-188}{41/\sqrt{14}} \doteq -1.46$, for which the one-sided $P$-value is $P = 0.0721$. This is significant at $\alpha = 0.10$, but not at 0.05 or 0.01.

**17.12.** To cut the margin of error in half, we need to quadruple the sample size: $n = 4 \cdot 14 = 56$. For $\pm 5$ mg/dl, we compute $n = \left(\frac{(1.645)(41)}{5}\right)^2 \doteq 181.95$—take $n = 182$.

**17.13.** Now $z = \frac{172-188}{41/\sqrt{56}} \doteq -2.92$ (it is double the value in Exercise 17.11 because the margin of error was halved). The one-sided $P$-value is $P = 0.0018$. This is significant at $\alpha = 0.10$, 0.05, or 0.01. Even small differences can be significant with large sample sizes.

**17.14. State:** What is the mean concentration of dieldrin in the population of male minke whales?
**Formulate:** We will estimate $\mu$ by giving a 95% confidence interval.
**Solve:** We must assume that we have an SRS of the population, and that the underlying distribution is Normal with standard deviation 50 ng/g. With $\bar{x} = 357$ ng/g, our 95% confidence interval for $\mu$ is

$$357 \pm 1.960\left(\frac{50}{\sqrt{8}}\right) \doteq 357 \pm 34.65 = 322.35 \text{ to } 391.65 \text{ ng/g}.$$

**Conclude:** We are 95% confident that the mean dieldrin concentration among male minke whales is between 322.35 and 391.65 ng/g.

**17.15. State:** Is there evidence that the mean dieldrin concentration in minke whale blubber exceeds 100 ng/g?
**Formulate:** Let $\mu$ be the mean dieldrin concentration. We test $H_0$: $\mu = 100$ ng/g versus $H_a$: $\mu > 100$ ng/g; the alternative is one-sided because we are concerned only with concentrations that exceed the FDA limit.
**Solve:** Assume we have a Normal distribution and an SRS. With $\bar{x} = 357$ ng/g, the test statistic is $z = \frac{357-100}{50/\sqrt{8}} \doteq 14.54$. This is so large that it should not be necessary to consult Table C or use software to realize that $P \doteq 0$.
**Conclude:** This is overwhelming evidence against $H_0$; we conclude that the mean dieldrin level is above 100 ng/g.

**17.16.** For 80% confidence, the margin of error is $1.282\left(\frac{50}{\sqrt{8}}\right) \doteq 22.6628$, while for 90% confidence, the margin is $1.645\left(\frac{50}{\sqrt{8}}\right) \doteq 29.0798$. Therefore, the intervals are 334.34 to 379.66 ng/g (80%) and 327.92 to 386.08 ng/g (90%). Margin of error grows with increasing confidence.

**17.17. State:** What is the mean age-20 IQ score $\mu$ for very low birth weight (VLBW) males?
**Formulate:** We will estimate $\mu$ by giving a 95% confidence interval.
**Solve:** We must assume that we have an SRS of the population. The problem states that IQ scores follow a Normal distribution. We have $\bar{x} = 87.6$, so the 95% confidence interval for $\mu$ is

$$\bar{x} \pm 1.960\left(\frac{15}{\sqrt{113}}\right) = 87.6 \pm 2.7657 = 84.8 \text{ to } 90.4.$$

**Conclude:** We are 95% confident that the mean age-20 IQ for VLBW males is between 84.8 and 90.4.

**17.18. State:** Is there evidence that the mean age-20 IQ score for very low birth weight (VLBW) males is less than 100?
**Formulate:** Let $\mu$ be the mean age-20 IQ score for this population. We test $H_0$: $\mu = 100$ versus $H_a$: $\mu < 100$; the alternative is one-sided because we suspect that VLBW babies have lower IQs.
**Solve:** Assume we have a Normal distribution and an SRS. With $\bar{x} = 87.6$, the test statistic is $z = \frac{87.6-100}{15/\sqrt{113}} \doteq -8.79$. This is so far below 0 that it should not be necessary to consult

Table C or use software to realize that $P \doteq 0$.

**Conclude:** This is overwhelming evidence against $H_0$; we conclude that the male VLBW population has a mean age-20 IQ below 100.

**17.19.** **(a)** The treatment (being classified as very low birth weight) was not assigned. (Nor could it be!) **(b)** IQ could be affected by other factors, including socioeconomic and hereditary factors that are associated with low birth weight.

**17.20.** **(a)** {F, M} or {female, male}. **(b)** {6, 7, ..., 20}. **(c)** All numbers between 2.5 and 6 l/min. **(d)** All numbers (or all whole numbers) between __ and __ bpm. (Choices of upper and lower limits will vary.)

**17.21.** **(a)** The given probabilities have sum 0.81, so $P(\text{other topic}) = 0.19$. **(b)** $P(\text{adult or scam}) = 0.145 + 0.142 = 0.287$.

**Note:** *An underlying assumption here is that each piece of spam falls into exactly one category.*

**17.22.** **(a)** "More than one person lives in this household" is the event $\{Y > 1\}$. The probability is $1 - P(Y = 1) = 1 - 0.27 = 0.73$. **(b)** $P(2 < Y \leq 4) = P(Y = 3 \text{ or } Y = 4) = 0.16 + 0.14 = 0.3$. **(c)** $P(Y \neq 2) = 1 - P(Y = 2) = 1 - 0.33 = 0.67$.

**17.23.** **(a)** All probabilities are between 0 and 1; the probabilities add to 1. **(b)** $P(X \leq 3) = 0.48 + 0.38 + 0.08 = 1 - (0.01 + 0.05) = 0.94$. **(c)** $P(X < 3) = 0.48 + 0.38 = 0.86$. **(d)** Write either $X \geq 4$ or $X > 3$. The probability is $0.05 + 0.01 = 0.06$.

**17.24.** Obviously, there are many possible answers; the key is that the events $A$ and $B$ must be able to occur together.

**17.25.** The mean monthly fee for 500 households has approximately a $N(\$38, \$10/\sqrt{500}) = N(\$38, \$0.4472)$ distribution, so $P(\bar{x} > \$39) \doteq P(Z > 2.24) \doteq 0.0125$ (software: 0.0127).

**17.26.** **(a)** $P(Z > \frac{105-100}{15}) \doteq P(Z > 0.33) \doteq 0.3707$. (Using software with $z = 1/3$ gives 0.3694.) **(b)** $\mu_{\bar{x}} = 100$; $\sigma_{\bar{x}} = 15/\sqrt{60} \doteq 1.93649$. **(c)** $P(Z > \frac{105-100}{1.93649}) \doteq P(Z > 2.58) = 0.0049$. **(d)** The answer to (a) could be quite different; (b) would be the same (it does not depend on Normality at all). The answer we gave for (c) would still be fairly reliable because of the central limit theorem.

**17.27.** **(a)** Out of 100 scores, nearly all should be in the range $\mu \pm 3\sigma = 92$ to 452. **(b)** The sample mean $\bar{x}$ has a $N(\mu, \sigma/\sqrt{100}) = N(272, 6)$ distribution, so nearly all such means should be in the range 254 to 290.

**17.28.** To cut the range of values of $\bar{x}$ in half, we need to halve the standard deviation of the distribution of $\bar{x}$, which requires increasing the sample size by a factor of 4, to $n = 400$. Those 400 individual scores will be as variable as the 100 individual scores (or more variable because there are now four times as many opportunities to observe extreme scores).

**17.29. State:** Is there good reason to think that the mean apartment size is less than 1250 square feet?
**Formulate:** Let $\mu$ be the mean apartment size in this development. We test $H_0$: $\mu = 1250$ ft$^2$ versus $H_a$: $\mu < 1250$ ft$^2$; the alternative is one-sided because the tenants are concerned only that their apartments are too small. (They would not complain if their apartments were larger than advertised.)
**Solve:** Assume we have a Normal distribution and an SRS. The average apartment size in our sample is $\bar{x} = 1240.83$ ft$^2$, so the test statistic is $z = \frac{1240.83-1250}{5/\sqrt{18}} \doteq -7.78$. This is so far below 0 that it should not be necessary to consult Table C or use software to realize that $P \doteq 0$.
**Conclude:** We have overwhelming evidence against $H_0$; we conclude that the mean apartment size is less than 1250 square feet.

**17.30. State:** Is there evidence that the mean body temperature for all healthy adults is not equal to 98.6°?
**Formulate:** Let $\mu$ be the mean body temperature. We test $H_0$: $\mu = 98.6°$ versus $H_a$: $\mu \neq 98.6°$; the alternative is two-sided because we had no suspicion (before looking at the data) that $\mu$ might be higher or lower than 98.6°.
**Solve:** Assume we have a Normal distribution and an SRS. The average body temperature in our sample is $\bar{x} = 98.203°$, so the test statistic is $z = \frac{98.203-98.6}{0.7/\sqrt{20}} \doteq -2.54$. The two-sided $P$-value is $P = 2P(Z < -2.54) = 0.0110$.
**Conclude:** We have fairly strong evidence—significant at $\alpha = 0.05$, but not at $\alpha = 0.01$—that mean body temperature is not equal to 98.6°. (Specifically, the data suggests that mean body temperature is lower.)

**17.31. State:** What is the mean apartment size $\mu$ in this development?
**Formulate:** We will estimate $\mu$ by giving a 95% confidence interval.
**Solve:** Assume we have a Normal distribution and an SRS. With $\bar{x} = 1240.83$ ft$^2$, our 95% confidence interval for $\mu$ is

$$1240.83 \pm 1.960 \left(\frac{5}{\sqrt{18}}\right) \doteq 1240.83 \pm 2.31 = 1238.52 \text{ to } 1243.14 \text{ ft}^2.$$

**Conclude:** We are 95% confident that the mean apartment size is between 1238.52 and 1243.14 ft$^2$.

**17.32. State:** What is the mean body temperature $\mu$ for healthy adults?
**Formulate:** We will estimate $\mu$ by giving a 90% confidence interval.
**Solve:** Assume we have a Normal distribution and an SRS. With $\bar{x} = 98.203°$, our 90% confidence interval for $\mu$ is

$$98.203 \pm 1.645 \left(\frac{0.7}{\sqrt{20}}\right) \doteq 98.203 \pm 0.257 = 97.95° \text{ to } 98.46°.$$

**Conclude:** We are 90% confident that the mean body temperature for healthy adults is between 97.95°and 98.46°.

**17.33.** **(a)** Possible response variables: Whether or not a subject has a job within some period of time, whether or not the subject stayed in that job, number of hours worked during some period, length of time before subject became employed. For the design, randomly assign about one-third of the group (3355 subjects) to each treatment, and observe the chosen response variables after a suitable amount of time. **(b)** The simplest approach is to label from 00001 through 10065, and then take five digits at a time from the table. (This means we have to skip about 90% of the five-digit sets, because only those beginning with 0 [and a few beginning with 1] are useful.) With this approach, the first three subjects are 06565, 00795, and 08727 (the last of these is on line 129). More efficient labelings are possible and will lead to different samples.

**17.34.** **(a)** Diagram is shown below. **(b)** Using line 123 from Table B, the first four subjects are 102, 063, 035, and 090. See note on page 59 about using Table B.

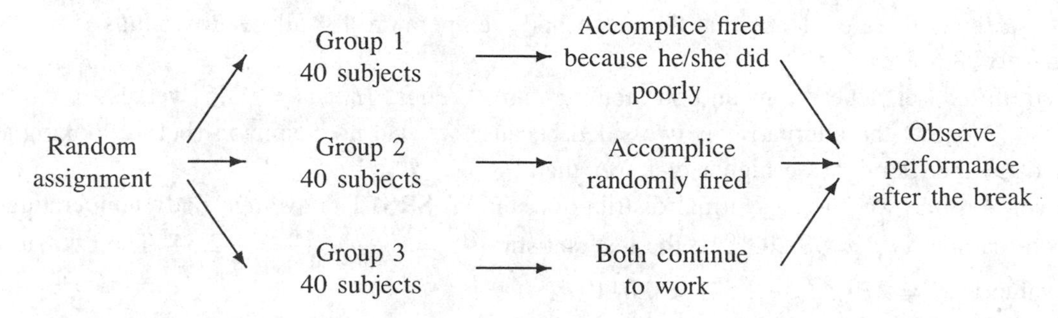


**17.35.** **(a)** $P = 0.45$ says that a response this large or larger would be seen in sample data almost half the time when in fact there is *no* effect in the entire population of rats. That is, a response this size would often happen just by chance. **(b)** The four $P$-values say that the differences that were observed were so small that they would often happen just by the chance variation caused by choosing rats for the sample. That is, there were differences in the *sample* rats, but they were so small that they aren't evidence of any differences in the entire *population* of rats.

**17.36.** $P = 0.04$ means that such results would occur by chance only 4% of the time, which suggests that the difference in reported pain is more than coincidence. $P = 0.72$ means that the difference in median survival time could easily happen by chance.

**17.37.** We expect the number of fires to vary somewhat over time. If we assume that the mean number of fires has not changed over time (so that all variation is due to chance), then there would be less than a 1% chance of observing fire counts similar to those that have occurred since 1910. Therefore, we conclude that the mean number of fires is increasing over time.

This straight-line relationship between number of fires and time explains 61% of the variation in the number of fires; that is, we can make fairly good estimates of how many fires will occur in a given year.

**17.38. (a)** One possible population: all full-time undergraduate students in the fall term on a list provided by the registrar. **(b)** A stratified sample with 125 students from each year is one possibility. **(c)** Mailed questionnaires might have high nonresponse rates. Telephone interviews exclude those without phones, and may mean repeated calling for those who are not home. Face-to-face interviews might be more costly than your funding will allow. Some students might be sensitive about responding to questions about sexual harassment.

**17.39.** Placebos do work with real pain, so the placebo response tells nothing about physical basis of the pain. In fact, placebos work poorly in hypochondriacs. The survey is described in the April 3, 1979, edition of the *New York Times*.

**17.40.** Parents who fail to return the consent form may be more likely to place less priority on education, and therefore may give their children less help with homework, and so forth. Including those children in the control group is likely to lower that group's score.

**Note:** *This is a generalization, to be sure: We are not saying that* every *such parent does not value education, only that the percent of this group that highly values education will almost certainly be lower than that same percent of the parents who return the form.*

**17.41. (a)** Increase. **(b)** Decrease. **(c)** Decrease. **(d)** Decrease.

**Note:** *The first statement is an argument in favor of the system, while the other three statements suggest reasons to oppose pursuing its development.*

**17.42. (a)** The table on the right shows the six treatments—three levels of Factor A (discount level) and two levels of Factor B (fraction of shoes on sale). **(b)** Diagram is shown below. From line 111 of Table B, the first 10 subjects (group 1) are 48, 60, 51, 30, 41, 27, 12, 38, 50, and 59.

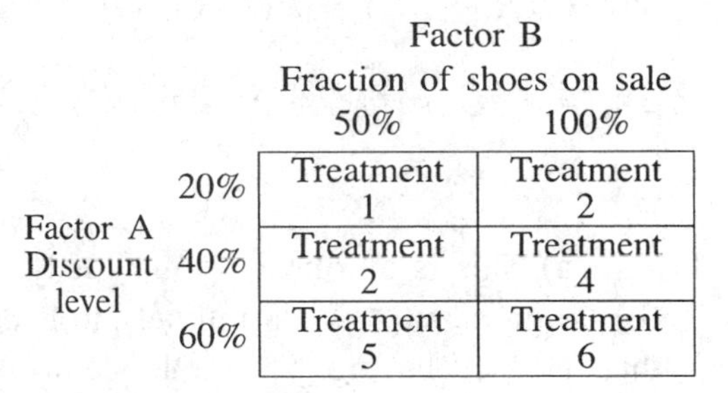

| Factor A Discount level | Factor B Fraction of shoes on sale: 50% | 100% |
|---|---|---|
| 20% | Treatment 1 | Treatment 2 |
| 40% | Treatment 2 | Treatment 4 |
| 60% | Treatment 5 | Treatment 6 |

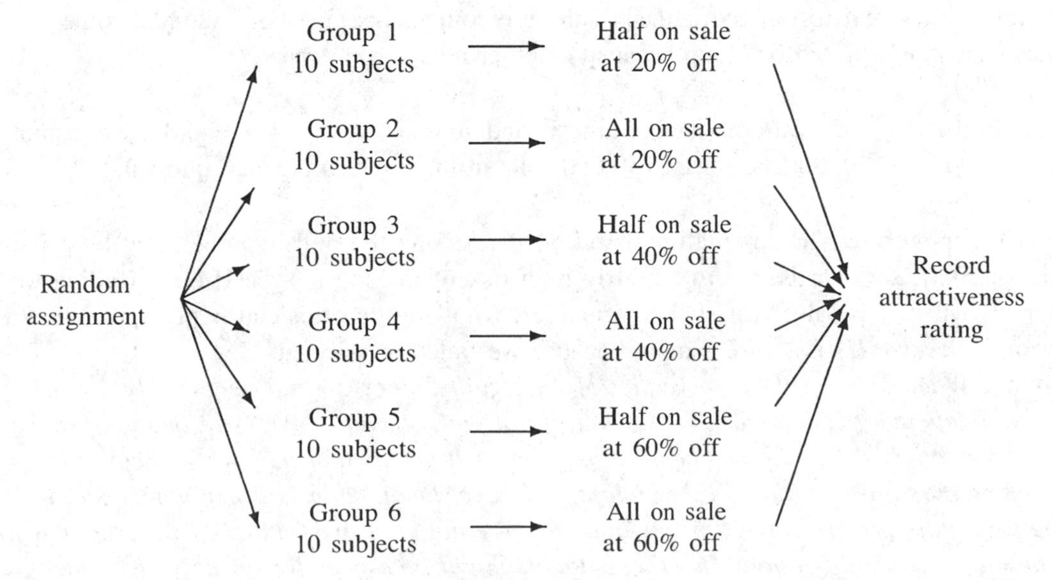

**17.43.** **(a)** The factors are storage method (three levels: fresh, room temperature for one month, refrigerated for one month) and preparation method (two levels: cooked immediately, or after one hour). There are therefore six treatments (summarized in the table on the right). The response variables are the tasters' color and flavor ratings. **(b)** Randomly allocate $n$ potatoes to each of the six groups, then compare ratings. (Diagram not shown.) **(c)** For each taster, randomly choose the order in which the fries are tasted.

| | Cooked immediately | Wait one hour |
|---|---|---|
| Fresh | Treatment 1 | Treatment 2 |
| Stored | Treatment 3 | Treatment 4 |
| Refrigerated | Treatment 5 | Treatment 6 |

**17.44.** **(a)** All probabilities are greater than or equal to 0, and their sum is 1. **(b)** Let $R_1$ be Taster 1's rating and $R_2$ be Taster 2's rating. Add the probabilities on the diagonal (upper left to lower right): $P(R_1 = R_2) = 0.03 + 0.08 + 0.25 + 0.20 + 0.06 = 0.62$. **(c)** $P(R_1 > R_2) = 0.19$. This is the sum of the ten numbers in the "lower left" part of the table; the bottom four numbers from the first column, the bottom three from the second column, the bottom two from the third column, and the last number in the fourth column. These entries correspond to, e.g., "Taster 2 gives a rating of 1, and Taster 1 gives a rating more than 1." $P(R_2 > R_1) = 0.19$; this is the sum of the ten numbers in the "upper right" part of the table. We could also find this by noting that this probability and the other two in this exercise must add to 1 (because they account for all of the entries in the table). Alternatively, noting that the matrix is symmetric (relative to the main diagonal), we must have $P(R_1 > R_2) = P(R_2 > R_1)$.

**17.45.** $P(\text{A}) = P(\text{B}) = \cdots = P(\text{F}) = \frac{0.72}{6} = 0.12$ and $P(1) = P(2) = \cdots = P(8) = \frac{1-0.72}{8} = 0.035$.

**17.46.** **(a)** This is an observational study: Behavior is observed, but no treatment is imposed. **(b)** "Significant" means unlikely to happen by chance. In this study, researchers determined that the fact that light-to-moderate drinkers had a lower death rate than the other groups is evidence of a real difference, rather than mere coincidence. **(c)** For example, some nondrinkers might avoid drinking because of other health concerns.

**17.47.** With the two-sided alternative hypothesis and significance level $\alpha = 0.01$, we cannot reject $H_0$: $\mu = \$150,000$ because $150,000 falls in the 99% confidence interval.

**17.48.** A low-power test has a small probability of rejecting the null hypothesis, at least for some alternatives. That is, we run a fairly high risk of making a Type II error (failing to reject $H_0$ when it is false) for such alternatives. Knowing that this can happen, we should not conclude that $H_0$ is "true" simply because we failed to reject it.

**Note:** *When a jury returns a verdict of "not guilty," they are not necessarily declaring that "the defendant is innocent." A verdict of not guilty means, "We were unable to reject the null hypothesis that the defendant is innocent." It means that they were unconvinced of the defendant's guilt—although they might still have doubts about his/her innocence. In the same way, failing to reject* $H_0$ *means that we were not convinced that* $H_a$ *was true, but we might still have doubts about* $H_0$*. These doubts might be especially strong with a low-power test.*

**17.49.** A Type I error means that we conclude the mean IQ is less than 100 when it really is 100 (or more). A Type II error means that we conclude the mean IQ is 100 (or more) when it really is less than 100.

**17.50.** Let $A$ be the event "income $\geq$ \$1 million" and $B$ be "income $\geq$ \$100,000." Then "$A$ and $B$" is the same as $A$, so

$$P(A \mid B) = \frac{P(A)}{P(B)} = \frac{\frac{181{,}000}{130{,}424{,}000}}{\frac{11{,}415{,}000}{130{,}424{,}000}} = \frac{181{,}000}{11{,}415{,}000} \doteq 0.01586.$$

**17.51.** Let $R_1$ be Taster 1's rating and $R_2$ be Taster 2's rating. $P(R_1 = 3) = 0.01 + 0.05 + 0.25 + 0.05 + 0.01 = 0.37$, so

$$P(R_2 > 3 \mid R_1 = 3) = \frac{P(R_2 > 3 \text{ and } R_1 = 3)}{P(R_1 = 3)} = \frac{0.05 + 0.01}{0.37} \doteq 0.1622.$$

**17.52.** **(a)** If $N$ is the number of games, then (under the given assumptions) $N$ has a binomial distribution with $n = 12$ and $p = 0.67$. **(b)** $P(N \geq 9) \doteq 0.4027$, and $P(N \geq 8) \doteq 0.6410$.

**17.53.** **(a)** $X$ has a binomial distribution with $n = 1555$ and $p = 0.2$. **(b)** $P(X \leq 300) \doteq P(Z \leq -0.7) = 0.2420$ (or see the table).

| | | | *Continuity correction* | |
|---|---|---|---|---|
| Exact prob. | Table Normal | Software Normal | Table Normal | Software Normal |
| 0.25395 | 0.2420 | 0.2428 | 0.2514 | 0.2528 |

**Note:** *Actually, X has a hypergeometric distribution, but the size of the population (all Internet users) is so much larger than the sample that the binomial distribution is an extremely good approximation.*

**17.54.** If $X$ has a binomial distribution with parameters $n = 77$ and $p = 0.05$, then

$$P(X = 0 \text{ or } X = 1) = 0.95^{77} + 77 \cdot 0.95^{76} 0.05^{1} \doteq 0.0973.$$

Therefore, $P(X \geq 2) = 1 - 0.0973 = 0.9027$.

**17.55.** For two consecutive years: $\left(\frac{1}{2}\right)^2 = 0.25$. For four consecutive years: $\left(\frac{1}{2}\right)^4 = 0.0625$.

**17.56.** **(a)** $\mu = (1500)(0.7) = 1050$ and $\sigma = \sqrt{315} \doteq 17.7482$ students.
**(b)** $P(X \geq 1000) \doteq P(Z \geq -2.82) = 0.9976$ (0.9978 with continuity correction).

**17.57.** The college will admit the top 110 students on its waiting list if the number of acceptances from the initial group of 1500 admitted students is 1090 or less. $P(X \leq 1090) \doteq P(Z \leq 2.25) \doteq 0.9878$; there is a very good chance that the top 110 students from the waiting list will be admitted.

**17.58.** A person who has just turned 50 has probability 0.99561 of surviving one more year, at which point he or she has probability 0.99527 of surviving an additional year, etc. Overall:

$$P(\text{survive to age 55}) = (0.99561)(0.99527)(0.99488)(0.99443)(0.99390) \doteq 0.97436.$$

(Note that surviving to age 55 means reaching the beginning of one's 56th year.)

**17.59.** Let $T$ be the event "test is positive" and $G$ be the event "subject has the abnormal CF gene." Then $P(T) = P(G)\,P(T \mid G) = (0.04)(0.9) = 0.036$.

**17.60.** Let $T$ be the event "test is positive" and $C$ be the event "Jason is a carrier." Since the given information says that the test is never positive for noncarriers, it clearly must be the case that $P(C \mid T) = 1$ (assuming no human error).

To confirm this, note that (if there is no human error), we have $P(T \text{ and } C^c) = 0$, and $P(T) = P(T \text{ and } C) + P(T \text{ and } C^c) = P(T \text{ and } C) = P(T)\,P(T \mid C) = (0.04)(0.9) = 0.036$. Therefore, $P(C \mid T) = \dfrac{P(C \text{ and } T)}{P(T)} = \dfrac{0.036}{0.036} = 1$.

**17.61.** Let $F$ be "adult is a full-time student," $P$ be "adult is a part-time student," $N$ be "adult is not a student," and $A$ be "adult accesses Internet from some place other than work or home."

We were given $P(F) = 0.041$ and $P(P) = 0.029$, so that $P(N) = 1 - 0.041 - 0.029 = 0.93$. Also, $P(A \mid F) = 0.58$, $P(A \mid P) = 0.30$, and $P(A \mid N) = 0.21$. Therefore $P(A) = P(F)\,P(A \mid F) + P(P)\,P(A \mid P) + P(N)\,P(A \mid N) \doteq 0.22778$—about 22.8%.

**17.62.** **(a)** We have been given $P(A) = 0.10$, $P(C) = 0.20$, and $P(A \mid C) = 0.05$.
**(b)** $P(A \text{ and } C) = P(C)P(A \mid C) = 0.01$.

**17.63.** We seek $P(C \mid A) = P(C \text{ and } A)/P(A) = 0.01/0.10 = 0.10$, so 10% of A students are involved in accidents each year.

**17.64.** The tree diagram is shown on the right. The probability that the grandchild of people in the top 20% is also in the top 20% is

$$(0.42)(0.42) + (0.52)(0.15) + (0.06)(0.07) = 0.2586.$$

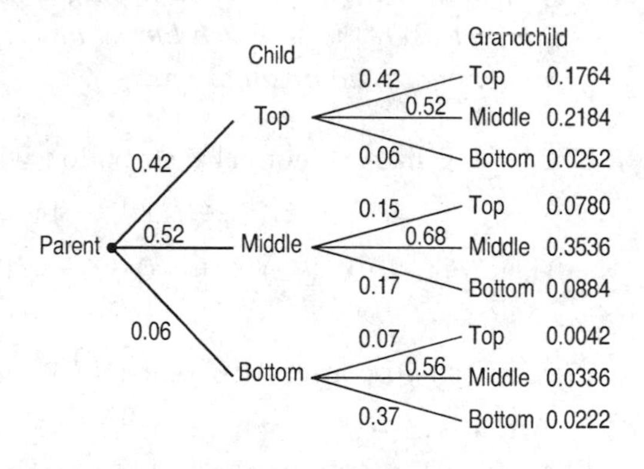


---

For solutions to the EESEE Case Studies (Exercises 65–72), see the instructor's version of EESEE.

---

**17.73. (a)** Below. The two extra patients can be randomly assigned to two of the three groups. **(b)** No one involved in administering the treatments or assessing their effectiveness knew which subjects were in which group. **(c)** The pain scores in Group A were so much lower than the scores in Group C that such a difference would not often happen by chance if NSAIDs were not effective. However, the difference between Group A and Group B could be due to chance. We can conclude that NSAIDs after surgery provide real pain relief, but there seems to be no additional benefit to having them before the surgery.

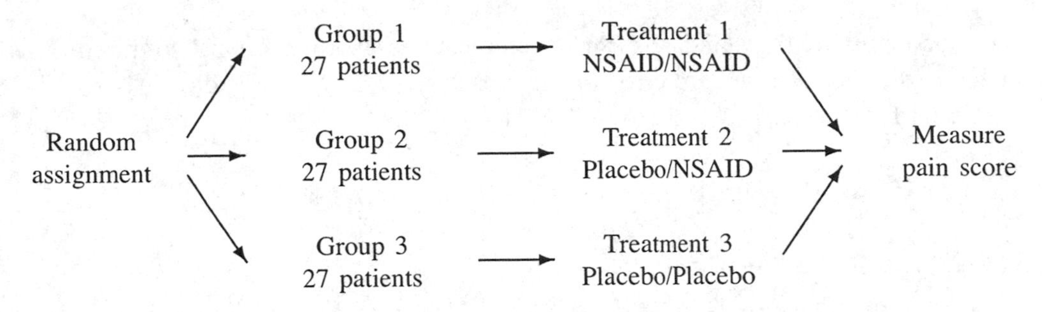

# Chapter 18 Solutions

**18.1.** $s/\sqrt{n} = 21.88/\sqrt{20} \doteq 4.8925$ minutes.

**18.2.** "Mean plus or minus the standard error of the mean" is "$89.01 \pm 5.36$," so the mean is $\bar{x} = 89.01$ mg/dl, and the standard error of the mean, $s/\sqrt{n}$, is 5.36 mg/dl. If $s/\sqrt{6} = 5.36$, then the standard deviation is $s = 5.36\sqrt{6} \doteq 13.13$ mg/dl.

**18.3.** **(a)** $t^* = 2.015$. **(b)** $t^* = 2.518$.

**18.4.** Use df $= 24$. **(a)** $t^* = 2.064$. **(b)** $t^* = 0.685$.

**18.5.** **(a)** Use df $= 9$: $t^* = 2.262$. **(b)** Use df $= 19$: $t^* = 2.861$. **(c)** Use df $= 6$: $t^* = 1.440$.

**18.6.** **(a)** A stemplot shows that the data are not skewed and have no outliers. (There is a gap between 1.12 and 1.18, but as 1.18 appears three times, we would not consider it an outlier.) **(b)** Calculate $\bar{x} \doteq 1.1182$ and $s \doteq 0.04378$. We have $n = 11$, so df $= n - 1 = 10$. The critical value for a 95% confidence interval is $t^* = 2.228$, and the interval for $\mu$ is

$$x \pm t^*\left(\frac{s}{\sqrt{n}}\right) = 1.1182 \pm 2.228\left(\frac{0.04378}{\sqrt{11}}\right) = 1.1182 \pm 0.0294 = 1.089 \text{ to } 1.148.$$

| Stem | Leaf |
|---|---|
| 10 | 77 |
| 10 | 88 |
| 11 | 11 |
| 11 | 22 |
| 11 | |
| 11 | |
| 11 | 888 |

**(c)** Because this interval does not include 1, we can reject $H_0$: $\mu = 1$ in favor of the two-sided alternative.

**18.7.** **State:** What is the mean percent $\mu$ of nitrogen in ancient air?
**Formulate:** We will estimate $\mu$ with a 90% confidence interval.
**Solve:** We are told to view the observations as an SRS. A stemplot shows some left-skewness; however, for such a small sample, the data are not unreasonably skewed. There are no outliers. With $\bar{x} = 59.5889\%$ and $s = 6.2553\%$ nitrogen, and $t^* = 1.860$ (df $= 8$), the 90% confidence interval for $\mu$ is

$$59.5889 \pm 1.860\left(\frac{6.2553}{\sqrt{9}}\right) = 59.5889 \pm 3.8783 = 55.71\% \text{ to } 63.47\%.$$

| Stem | Leaf |
|---|---|
| 4 | 9 |
| 5 | 1 |
| 5 | |
| 5 | 4 |
| 5 | |
| 5 | |
| 6 | 0 |
| 6 | 33 |
| 6 | 445 |

**Conclude:** We are 90% confident that the mean percent of nitrogen in ancient air is between 55.71% and 63.47%.

**18.8.** **(a)** df $= 14$. **(b)** $t = 1.82$ is between 1.761 and 2.145, for which the one-sided $P$-values are 0.05 and 0.025, respectively. (Software reports that $P = 0.0451$.) **(c)** $t = 1.82$ is significant at $\alpha = 0.05$ but not at $\alpha = 0.01$.

**18.9.** **(a)** df = 24. **(b)** $t = 1.12$ is between 1.059 and 1.318, so $0.20 < P < 0.30$. (Software reports that $P = 0.2738$.) **(c)** $t = 1.12$ is not significant at either $\alpha = 0.10$ or $\alpha = 0.05$.

**18.10.** **State:** Is there evidence that the percent of nitrogen in ancient air was different from the present 78.1%?
**Formulate:** We test $H_0$: $\mu = 78.1\%$ versus $H_a$: $\mu \neq 78.1\%$. We use a two-sided alternative because, prior to seeing the data, we had no reason to believe that the percent of nitrogen in ancient air would be higher or lower.
**Solve:** We addressed the conditions for inference in Exercise 18.7. In that solution, we found $\bar{x} = 59.5889\%$ and $s = 6.2553\%$ nitrogen, so $t = \frac{59.5889-78.1}{6.2553/\sqrt{9}} \doteq -8.88$. For df = 8, this is beyond anything shown in Table C, so $P < 0.001$ (software gives $P = 0.00002$).
**Conclude:** We have very strong evidence ($P < 0.001$) that Cretaceous air contained less nitrogen than modern air.

**18.11.** **(a)** Let $\mu$ be the mean difference in healing rates. The null hypothesis is $\mu = 0$ ("no difference"). The alternative hypothesis says that the control limb heals faster; that is, the healing rate is greater for the control limb than for the experimental limb. Therefore, $H_a$ is either $\mu < 0$ (if we take experimental rate minus control rate) or $\mu > 0$ (if we take control rate minus experimental rate). **(b)** The stemplot (for control rate minus experimental rate) shows no major deviations from Normality. **(c)** **Solve:** The mean and standard deviation of the set of differences are $\bar{x} \doteq 5.7143$ $\mu$m/hr and $s \doteq 10.5643$ $\mu$m/hr, so $t = \frac{5.7143-0}{10.5643/\sqrt{14}} \doteq 2.02$ with df = 13, for which $0.025 < P < 0.05$ (software reports 0.032). If subtraction was done in the other order, $\bar{x}$ and $t$ are negative, but $P$ is the same.

| Stem | Leaves |
|---|---|
| −1 | 0 |
| −0 | |
| −0 | 43 |
| 0 | 113334 |
| 0 | 7 |
| 1 | 02 |
| 1 | |
| 2 | 2 |
| 2 | |
| 3 | 1 |

**Conclude:** This is fairly strong evidence (significant at 5% but not at 1%) that altering the electric field reduces the healing rate.

**Minitab output**

```
Test of mu = 0.00 vs mu > 0.00

Variable     N      Mean    StDev   SE Mean        T     P-Value
HealRate    14      5.71    10.56      2.82     2.02       0.032
```

**18.12.** With $\bar{x} \doteq 5.7143$ $\mu$m/hr, $s \doteq 10.5643$ $\mu$m/hr, and $t^* = 1.771$ (df = 13), the 90% confidence interval for $\mu$ is

$$5.7143 \pm 1.771\left(\frac{10.5643}{\sqrt{14}}\right) = 5.7143 \pm 5.0003 = 0.71 \text{ to } 10.71\ \mu\text{m/hr}.$$

**18.13. (a)** The outlier (31 $\mu$m/hr, from newt #8) is the only significant departure from Normality visible in the stemplot. **(b)** "The healing rate is higher in the control limbs" means $\mu > 0$, because we computed control rate minus experimental rate, so we test $H_0$: $\mu = 0$ versus $H_a$: $\mu > 0$. For all 12 newts, $\bar{x} \doteq 6.4167$ and $s \doteq 10.7065$ $\mu$m/hr, so

$$t = \frac{6.4167 - 0}{10.7065/\sqrt{12}} \doteq 2.076 \quad (\text{df} = 11, \ P = 0.031).$$

Omitting the outlier yields $\bar{x} \doteq 4.1818$ and $s \doteq 7.7565$ $\mu$m/hr, so

$$t = \frac{4.1818 - 0}{7.7565/\sqrt{11}} \doteq 1.788 \quad (\text{df} = 10, \ P = 0.052).$$

With the outlier present, the test is significant at $\alpha = 0.05$, but that is no longer the case with it removed (although there is still somewhat strong evidence against $H_0$).

| Stem | Leaves |
|---|---|
| −1 | 3 |
| −0 | 6 |
| −0 | |
| 0 | 12 |
| 0 | 5789 |
| 1 | 012 |
| 1 | |
| 2 | |
| 2 | |
| 3 | 1 |

**18.14. (a)** The sample size is very large, so the only potential hazard is extreme skewness. As scores range only from 0 to 500, there is a limit to how skewed the distribution could be. **(b)** From Table C, we take $t^* = 2.581$ (df = 1000), or with software, we take $t^* \doteq 2.5792$. For either value of $t^*$, the 99% confidence interval is $\bar{x} \pm t^*\text{SE} \doteq 240 \pm 2.84 = 237.2$ to 242.8. **(c)** Because the 99% confidence interval for $\mu$ does not include 243, we can reject $H_0$: $\mu = 243$ in favor of the two-sided alternative at the 1% significance level. (The evidence is a bit stronger than that: We would typically test $H_0$ against the one-sided alternative $\mu < 243$; for this test we find $P = 0.0032$.)

**18.15.** (b) In real-life settings, we almost never know the true value of $\sigma$.

**18.16.** (c) $t = \dfrac{8 - 10}{4/\sqrt{20}} \doteq -2.24$

**18.17.** (a) The degrees of freedom are df $= n - 1 = 19$.

**18.18.** (a) For df = 19, 2.25 falls between the critical values 2.205 and 2.539 in Table C. This is a one-sided test, so $P$ equals the upper tail probability, placing it between 0.01 and 0.02.

**18.19.** (c) Use a $t$ distribution with df $= n - 1 = 14$.

**18.20.** (a) For a two-sided test with $n = 15$ and $\alpha = 0.005$, we need df $= n - 1 = 14$ and upper tail probability equal to $\alpha/2 = 0.0025$.

**18.21.** (c) For a one-sided test with $n = 15$ and $\alpha = 0.005$, we need df $= n - 1 = 14$ and upper tail probability equal to $\alpha = 0.005$.

**18.22.** (a) We have df = 14 and $t^* = 2.571$, so the 95% confidence interval for $\mu$ is

$$85 \pm 2.571\left(\frac{12}{\sqrt{6}}\right) = 85 \pm 12.5953 = 72.4 \text{ to } 97.6 \text{ mg/dl}.$$

**18.23.** (b) The two samples are independent; there is no matching between a male student and a female student.

**18.24.** (c) Robustness means that $t$ procedures are approximately correct provided the data are an SRS.

**18.25.** For the student group: $t = \frac{0.08-0}{0.37/\sqrt{12}} \doteq 0.749$ (rather than 0.49). For the nonstudent group: $t = \frac{0.35-0}{0.37/\sqrt{12}} \doteq 3.277$ (rather than 3.25—this difference might be due to rounding error). From Table C, the first $P$-value is between 0.4 and 0.5 (software gives 0.47), and the second $P$-value is between 0.005 and 0.01 (software gives 0.007).

**18.26.** **(a)** As the exercise suggests, there are no serious departures from Normality. **(b)** Calculate $\bar{x} = 13.15375$ and $s \doteq 0.53024$. Software with df = 47 (so $t^* = 2.0117$) gives the 95% confidence interval as 13.000% to 13.308%. For Table C, we use df = 40, so $t^* = 2.021$ and the 95% confidence interval is

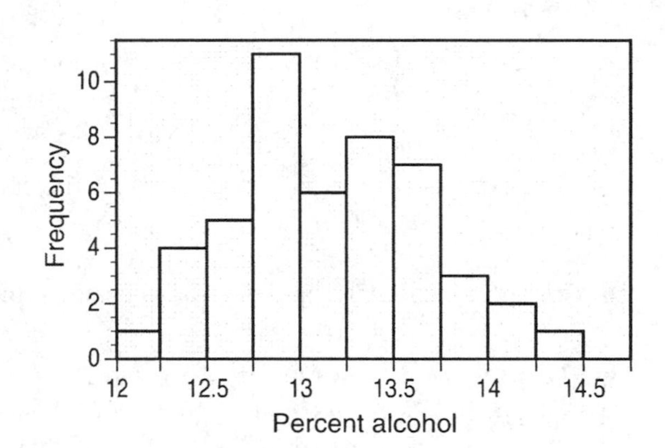


$$\bar{x} \pm t^* \frac{s}{\sqrt{n}} = 13.15375 \pm 2.021 \left(\frac{0.53024}{\sqrt{48}}\right)$$
$$= 13.15375 \pm 0.1547$$

or 12.999% to 13.308%. **(c)** Because the interval does not include 12%, we could reject $H_0$: $\mu = 12\%$. We could not reject $\mu = 13\%$—although the two-sided $P$-value would be very close to 0.05, because 13% is *just barely* in the interval.

**18.27.** **(a)** The distribution looks reasonably symmetric; other than the low (9.4 ft) and high (22.8 ft) outliers, it appears to be nearly normal. The mean is $\bar{x} \doteq 15.59$ ft and the standard deviation is $s = 2.550$ ft. **(b)** Using df = 40 from Table C, $t^* = 2.021$, so the interval is

$$\bar{x} \pm t^* \left(\frac{s}{\sqrt{44}}\right) \doteq 15.59 \pm 0.78 = 14.81 \text{ to } 16.37 \text{ ft.}$$

Using software, we can find $t^* = 2.0167$ for df = 43, which (after rounding) also gives $15.59 \pm 0.78$ ft. Because 20 ft does not fall in (or even near) this interval, we reject this claim ($\mu = 20$ ft). **(c)** We need to know what population we are examining: Were these all full-grown sharks? Were they all male? (That is, is $\mu$ the mean adult male shark length? Or something else?) Also, can these numbers be considered an SRS from this population?

| Stem | Leaves |
|---|---|
| 9 | 4 |
| 10 | |
| 11 | |
| 12 | 12346 |
| 13 | 22225668 |
| 14 | 3679 |
| 15 | 237788 |
| 16 | 122446788 |
| 17 | 688 |
| 18 | 23677 |
| 19 | 17 |
| 20 | |
| 21 | |
| 22 | 8 |

**18.28.** **(a)** Stems can be split two ways or five ways; both stemplots are shown on the right. The second one suggests that the two highest counts might be outliers, but they are not too extreme; the use of $t$ procedures should be fairly safe. **(b)** With $\bar{x} = 12.8\overline{3}$ and $s \doteq 4.6482$, the 90% confidence interval for $\mu$ is

| Stem | Leaves |
|---|---|
| 0 | 699 |
| 1 | 01124 |
| 1 | 55 |
| 2 | 02 |

| Stem | Leaves |
|---|---|
| 0 | 6 |
| 0 | 99 |
| 1 | 011 |
| 1 | 2 |
| 1 | 455 |
| 1 | |
| 1 | |
| 2 | 0 |
| 2 | 2 |

$$12.8333 \pm 1.796 \left(\frac{4.6482}{\sqrt{12}}\right) = 12.8333 \pm 2.4099 = 10.423 \text{ to } 15.243$$

**18.29.** Table C gives $t^* = 2.626$ for df = 100, while software gives $t^* = 2.5832$ for df = 667. The 99% confidence interval is $9.88 \pm t^* \left(\frac{17.847}{\sqrt{668}}\right) = 8.07$ to 11.69 days (or 8.10 to 11.66 days, using the software critical value).

```
TInterval
 (22.964,27.878)
 x̄=25.42105263
 Sx=7.474755999
 n=38
```

**18.30. Solve:** The mean is $\bar{x} \doteq 25.42°$ and the standard deviation is 7.47°, and $t^*$ is either 2.042 (using df = 30 from Table C) or 2.0262 (using software). The confidence interval is nearly identical in both cases:

$$\bar{x} \pm t^* \left(\frac{s}{\sqrt{38}}\right) = 22.95° \text{ to } 27.89° \quad (t^* = 2.042), \text{ or}$$
$$= 22.96° \text{ to } 27.88° \quad (t^* = 2.0262).$$

**Conclude:** We are 95% confident that the mean HAV angle among such patients is between 22.95° and 27.89°.

**18.31.** The distribution is right-skewed, but $t$ procedures are robust for large samples.

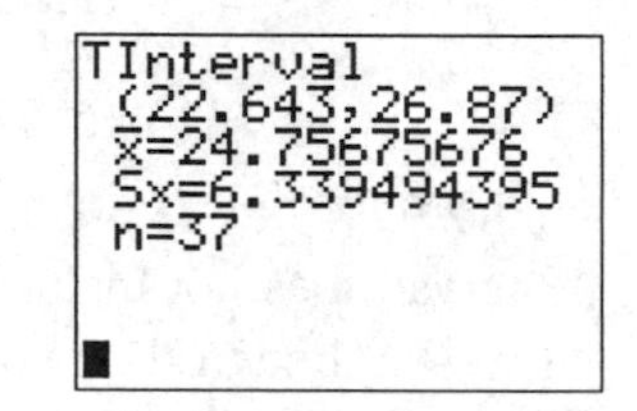


**18.32. (a)** Without the outlier, the mean is $\bar{x}^* \doteq 24.76°$ while the standard deviation drops to 6.34°. $t^*$ is either 2.042 (using df = 30 from Table C) or 2.0281 (using software). The confidence interval is

$$\bar{x} \pm t^* \left(\frac{s}{\sqrt{37}}\right) = 22.63° \text{ to } 26.89° \quad (t^* = 2.042), \text{ or}$$
$$= 22.64° \text{ to } 26.87° \quad (t^* = 2.0281).$$

**(b)** The width of the interval decreases (because the outlier raised both $\bar{x}$ and $s$).

**18.33.** We find $\bar{x} = 44.44\ \mu g$ and $s = 20.74\ \mu g$, and for df = 4, we have $t^* = 2.776$. Therefore, the 95% confidence interval is $\bar{x} \pm t^* \left(\frac{s}{\sqrt{5}}\right) \doteq 18.69$ to $70.19\ \mu g$.

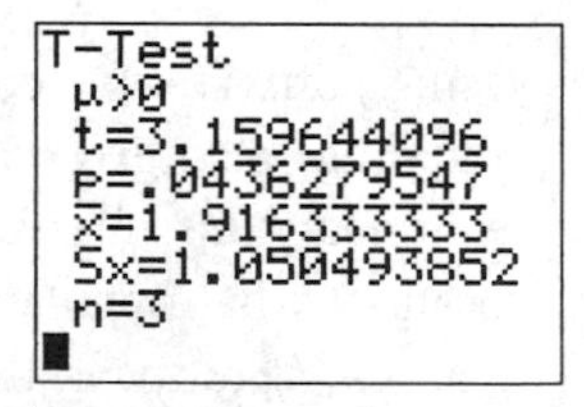


**18.34. (a)** We test $H_0$: $\mu = 0$ versus $H_a$: $\mu > 0$, where $\mu$ is the mean difference (treated minus control). We use a one-sided alternative because the researchers have reason to believe that $CO_2$ will increase growth rate. **(b)** The mean difference is $\bar{x} = 1.916$, and the standard deviation is 1.050, so the $t$ statistic is $t = \frac{1.916}{1.050/\sqrt{3}} \doteq 3.16$ with df = 2. This is significant at $\alpha = 0.05$, as the TI-83 and Minitab outputs confirm ($P = 0.044$). **(c)** For small samples, the $t$ procedures should be used only for samples from a Normal population; we have no way to assess Normality for these data.

**Minitab output**

```
T-Test of the Mean

Test of mu = 0.000 vs mu > 0.000

Variable     N      Mean    StDev    SE Mean          T    P-Value
diff         3     1.916    1.050      0.607       3.16      0.044
```

**18.35.** **(a)** Weather conditions that change from day to day can affect spore counts. So the two measurements made on the same day form a matched pair. **(b)** Take the differences, kill room counts minus processing counts. For these differences, $\bar{x} = 1824.5$ and $s \doteq 834.1$ CFUs/m$^3$. For the population mean difference, the 90% confidence interval for $\mu$ is

$$1824.5 \pm 2.353\left(\frac{834.1}{\sqrt{4}}\right) = 1824.5 \pm 981.3 = 843.2 \text{ to } 2805.8 \text{ CFUs/m}^3.$$

The interval is wide because the sample is small (four days), but we are confident that mean counts in the kill room are quite a bit higher. **(c)** The data are counts, which are at best only approximately Normal, and we have only a small sample ($n = 4$).

**18.36.** **(a)** Use df = 26:

$$114.9 \pm 2.056\left(\frac{9.3}{\sqrt{27}}\right) = 111.2 \text{ to } 118.6 \text{ mm Hg.}$$

**(b)** The essential assumption is that the 27 men tested can be regarded as an SRS from a population, such as all healthy white males in a stated age-group. The assumption that blood pressure in this population is Normally distributed is *not* essential because $\bar{x}$ from a sample of size 27 will be roughly Normal in any event, provided the population is not too greatly skewed and has no outliers.

**18.37.** **(a)** A subject's responses to the two treatments would not be independent. **(b)** We find $t = \frac{-0.326-0}{0.181/\sqrt{6}} \doteq -4.41$; with df = 5, this yields $P = 0.0069$—significant evidence of a difference.

**18.38.** **(a)** The mean and standard deviation are $\bar{x} \doteq 48.25$ and $s \doteq 40.24$ thousand barrels of oil. From Table C, we take $t^* = 2.000$ (df = 60); using software we can obtain $t^* = 1.998$ for df = 63. The 95% confidence interval for $\mu$ is

$$48.25 \pm 2.000\left(\frac{40.24}{\sqrt{64}}\right) = 48.25 \pm 10.06 = 38.19 \text{ to } 58.31$$

(software value: $48.25 \pm 10.05 = 38.20$ to $58.30$ thousand barrels of oil). **(b)** The stemplot confirms the skewness and outliers described in the exercise. The two intervals have similar widths, but the new interval is higher (by 2000 barrels). While $t$ procedures are fairly robust, we should be cautious about trusting our result from (a) because of the strong skew and outliers; the computer-based method is presumably more reliable for this situation.

| | |
|---|---|
| 0 | 00001111111111 |
| 0 | 22222223333333333333 |
| 0 | 44444445555555 |
| 0 | 6666667 |
| 0 | 8899 |
| 1 | 01 |
| 1 | |
| 1 | 5 |
| 1 | |
| 1 | 9 |
| 2 | 0 |

**18.39.** The data contain two extreme high outliers, 5973 and 8015. These may distort the $t$ statistic. (This exercise did not call for a stemplot, but it is shown here because it makes the outliers easily visible.)

| | |
|---|---|
| 0 | 1123788 |
| 1 | 00115677899 |
| 2 | 01112458 |
| 3 | |
| 4 | |
| 5 | 9 |
| 6 | |
| 7 | |
| 8 | 0 |

**18.40. State:** Is the mean percent of beetle-infected seeds $\mu$ large enough to be helpful in controlling velvetleaf plants?
**Formulate:** We will construct a 90% confidence interval for $\mu$.
**Solve:** A stemplot (right) shows a single-peaked and roughly symmetric distribution. We assume that the 28 plants can be viewed as an SRS of the population. Calculate that $\bar{x} \doteq 4.0786$ and $s \doteq 2.0135$. Using df $= 27$, the 90% confidence interval for $\mu$ is

| | |
|---|---|
| 0 | 07 |
| 1 | 9 |
| 2 | 24689 |
| 3 | 666778 |
| 4 | 0000336 |
| 5 | 157 |
| 6 | |
| 7 | 00 |
| 8 | 57 |

$$4.0786 \pm 1.703 \left(\frac{2.0135}{\sqrt{28}}\right) = 4.0786 \pm 0.648 = 3.43\% \text{ to } 4.73\%.$$

**Conclude:** The beetle infects less than 5% of seeds, so it is unlikely to be effective in controlling velvetweed.

**18.41. State:** Is there evidence that the mean dimension $\mu$ is not 224 mm?
**Formulate:** We test $H_0$: $\mu = 224$ mm versus $H_a$: $\mu \neq 224$ mm. We use a two-sided alternative because, prior to seeing the data, we had no reason to believe that the mean dimension would be higher or lower (and we are concerned with variation in either direction).

| | |
|---|---|
| 2239 | 01 |
| 2239 | 6688899 |
| 2240 | 002 |
| 2240 | 69 |
| 2241 | 02 |

**Solve:** The stemplot shows a slightly skewed distribution, but there are no apparent outliers, so the $t$ procedures are acceptable. We find $\bar{x} \doteq 224.002$ mm and $s \doteq 0.0618$ mm, so $t = \frac{224.002-224}{s/\sqrt{16}} \doteq 0.13$. With df $= 15$, we see that $P > 0.50$ (software gives $P \doteq 0.90$).
**Conclude:** We have very little reason to doubt that $\mu = 224$ mm.

**18.42. (a)** Fund and index performances are certainly not independent; for example, a good year for one is likely to be a good year for the other.
**(b) State:** Does the VIG Fund's performance differ significantly from that of the EAFE index?
**Formulate:** Let $\mu$ be the mean difference (fund minus EAFE). We test $H_0$: $\mu = 0$ versus $H_a$: $\mu \neq 0$, taking a two-sided alternative because the VIG Fund could outperform or underperform the benchmark. (The case could be made for a one-sided alternative, but as we shall see, the choice of $H_a$ does not matter.)

| | |
|---|---|
| −1 | 6 |
| −1 | 22 |
| −0 | 877 |
| −0 | 43110 |
| 0 | 01223 |
| 0 | 5678 |
| 1 | 124 |
| 1 | 9 |

**Solve:** A stemplot shows no reason to doubt Normality. We must assume that the data we have can be viewed as an SRS. We find $\bar{x} \doteq 0.8467\%$ and $s \doteq 8.9871\%$, so $t = \frac{0.8467-0}{8.9871/\sqrt{24}} \doteq 0.46$, for which $P > 0.5$ (software gives 0.65).
**Conclude:** We have very little reason to doubt that $\mu = 0$; VIG Fund performance is not significantly different from its benchmark.

**Minitab output**

```
T-Test of the Mean

Test of mu = 0.00 vs mu not = 0.00

Variable     N      Mean    StDev   SE Mean        T    P-Value
diff        24      0.85     8.99      1.83     0.46       0.65
```

**18.43.** **(a)** For each subject, randomly select (e.g., by flipping a coin) which knob (right or left) that subject should use first.

| | |
|---|---|
| −5 | 2 |
| −4 | 853 |
| −3 | 511 |
| −2 | 94 |
| −1 | 66621 |
| −0 | 74331 |
| 0 | 02 |
| 1 | 1 |
| 2 | 03 |
| 3 | 8 |

**(b) State:** Do right-handed people work faster with right-handed threads?
**Formulate:** We test $H_0$: $\mu = 0$ sec versus $H_a$: $\mu < 0$ sec, where $\mu$ is the mean of (right-thread time – left-thread time), so that $\mu < 0$ is equivalent to "right-hand time is less than left-hand time."
**Solve:** A stemplot of the differences gives no reason to avoid the $t$ procedures. We assume that our subjects can be viewed as an SRS. We find that $\bar{x} = -13.32$ sec and $s \doteq 22.936$ sec, so $t = \frac{-13.32-0}{22.936/\sqrt{25}} \doteq -2.90$. With df $= 24$, we find that $P = 0.0039$.
**Conclude:** We have good evidence (significant at $\alpha = 0.01$) that the mean difference really is negative; i.e., the mean time for right-hand-thread knobs is less than the mean time for left-hand-thread knobs.

**18.44.** **State:** Do the generic and reference drugs differ in mean absorption level?

| | |
|---|---|
| −2 | 3 |
| −1 | 5 |
| −1 | 31 |
| −0 | 5 |
| −0 | 321 |
| 0 | 012334 |
| 0 | 577 |
| 1 | 1 |
| 1 | 6 |
| 2 | 0 |

**Formulate:** We test $H_0$: $\mu = 0$ versus $H_a$: $\mu \neq 0$, where $\mu$ is the mean difference in absorption (Generic minus Reference). The alternative is two-sided because we have no prior expectation of a direction for the difference.
**Solve:** We assume that the subjects can be considered an SRS. A stemplot of the differences (right) looks reasonably Normal with no outliers, so the $t$ procedures should be safe. We find $\bar{x} = 37$ and $s \doteq 1070.6$, and compute $t = \frac{37}{1070.6/\sqrt{20}} \doteq 0.15$. With df $= 19$, we see that $P > 0.5$ (software gives 0.88).
**Conclude:** We cannot conclude that the two drugs differ in mean absorption level.

**Note:** *We should be cautious about how we state this conclusion. There is much variation in our sample; a 95% confidence interval for* $\mu$ *is*

$$37 \pm 2.093\left(\frac{1070.6}{\sqrt{20}}\right) = 37 \pm 501.06 = -464 \text{ to } 538.$$

*So while we cannot reject* $H_0$, *we are hardly convinced that* $\mu = 0$.

**18.45.** With df $= 24$, the critical value is $t^* = 1.711$, so the interval for $\mu$ is

$$-13.32 \pm (1.711)\left(\frac{22.936}{\sqrt{25}}\right) \doteq -13.32 \pm 7.85 \doteq -21.2 \text{ to } -5.5 \text{ sec.}$$

We have $\bar{x}_{RH} = 104.12$ and $\bar{x}_{LH} = 117.44$, so that $\bar{x}_{RH}/\bar{x}_{LH} = 88.7\%$. Right-handers working with right-handed knobs can accomplish the task in about 90% of the time needed by those working with left-handed knobs.

**Note:** *The exercise asked us to find* $\bar{x}_{RH}/\bar{x}_{LH}$, *but an alternative approach would be to compute (right-hand time)/(left-hand time) for each subject, for which the mean is 91.7%.*

# Chapter 19 Solutions

**19.1.** This is a matched-pairs design.

**19.2.** This involves two independent samples. (There is originally a single sample, but it is split into two independent groups: those who have done volunteer work and those who have not.)

**19.3.** This involves a single sample.

**19.4.** This involves two independent samples (because the result of, e.g., the first measurement using the new method is independent of the first measurement using the old method).

**19.5.** **(a)** If SEM $= s/\sqrt{n}$, then $s = \text{SEM} \times \sqrt{n}$. Arithmetic gives the table on the right. **(b)** The smaller sample has $n = 6$, so the conservative df is 5.

| Location | $n$ | $\bar{x}$ | $s$ |
|---|---|---|---|
| Oregon | 6 | 26.9 | 3.82 |
| California | 7 | 11.9 | 7.09 |

**19.6.** **(a)** A $t$ distribution with reasonably large df is quite similar to a standard Normal distribution. So, as long as the samples were not too small, we know that the value $t = 8.37$ would have a very small $P$-value. **(b)** The smaller sample is 61 students, so we use df = 60.

**19.7.** **(a)** The "compressed" stemplot shows no particular cause for concern. The "intermediate" stemplot shows the skewness and outlier described in the text. Note that these stemplots do not allow for easy comparison of the two distributions because the software used to create them used different scales (leaf units). **(b)** We wish to test $H_0$: $\mu_C = \mu_I$ versus $H_a$: $\mu_C < \mu_I$. The summary statistics are:

| | $n$ | $\bar{x}$ | $s$ |
|---|---|---|---|
| Compressed | 20 | 2.9075 | 0.1390 |
| Intermediate | 19 | 3.2874 | 0.2397 |

Compressed

```
26 | 8
27 |
27 | 6888
28 | 122
28 | 66
29 | 024
29 | 68
30 | 0
30 | 88
31 |
31 | 68
```

Intermediate

```
2 | 99
3 | 0111111
3 | 2333
3 | 4445
3 | 6
3 | 8
4 |
4 | 2
```

We compute SE $= \sqrt{\frac{0.1390^2}{20} + \frac{0.2397^2}{19}} \doteq 0.06317$ and $t = \frac{2.9075-3.2874}{0.06317} \doteq -6.013$. Regardless of the chosen df (conservative 18, or the software value 28.6), the $P$-value is very small; this is very significant evidence that the mean penetrability for compressed soil is lower than the mean for intermediate soil.

**Minitab output**

```
Twosample T for Comp vs Inter
         N       Mean     StDev   SE Mean
Comp    20      2.908     0.139     0.031
Inter   19      3.287     0.240     0.055

95% C.I. for mu Comp - mu Inter: ( -0.509,  -0.250)
T-Test mu Comp = mu Inter (vs <): T= -6.01  P=0.0000  DF=  28
```

**19.8. (a)** If the loggers had known that a study would be done, they might have (consciously or subconsciously) cut down fewer trees than they typically would, in order to reduce the impact of logging.

| Unlogged | | Logged | |
|---|---|---|---|
| 13 | 000 | 0 | 4 |
| 14 | | 0 | |
| 15 | 00 | 0 | |
| 16 | | 1 | 0 |
| 17 | | 1 | 2 |
| 18 | 0 | 1 | 455 |
| 19 | 00 | 1 | 7 |
| 20 | 0 | 1 | 88 |
| 21 | 0 | | |
| 22 | 00 | | |

**(b) State:** Does logging significantly reduce the mean number of species in a plot after 8 years?
**Formulate:** We test $H_0$: $\mu_1 = \mu_2$ versus $H_a$: $\mu_1 > \mu_2$, where $\mu_1$ is the mean number of species in unlogged plots and $\mu_2$ is the mean number of species in plots logged 8 years earlier. We use a one-sided alternative because we expect that logging reduces the number of tree species.
**Solve:** We assume that the data come from SRSs of the two populations. Stemplots (above) suggest some deviation from Normality, and a possible low outlier for the logged-plot counts. Note that these stemplots do not allow for easy comparison of the two distributions because the software used to create them used different scales (leaf units). In spite of these concerns, we proceed with the $t$ test. The means and standard deviations are given in the Minitab output below; we compute SE $= \sqrt{\frac{3.53^2}{12} + \frac{4.50^2}{9}} \doteq 1.813$ and $t = \frac{17.50-13.67}{1.813} \doteq 2.11$. With the conservative df $= 8$, we find that $P = 0.034$. Note that Minitab uses the more accurate df $= 14$ (truncated from the true computed df $= 14.8$), rather than the conservative approach. For this df, we find that $P = 0.026$. If we remove the low outlier from the logged data, a few things change: $\bar{x}_2 = 14.875$, $s_2 \doteq 2.8504$, SE $= \sqrt{\frac{3.53^2}{12} + \frac{2.85^2}{8}} \doteq 1.433$, and $t \doteq 1.832$. Now we have either $P = 0.055$ (df $= 7$) or $P = 0.042$ (df $= 17.2$).
**Conclude:** If we use all the data, we have fairly strong evidence (significant at 5% but not at 1%) that logged plots have fewer species. If we have a reason to remove the low outlier from the logged data, the evidence is weaker, although it is still significant when we use the more accurate df.

**Minitab output**

```
Twosample T for Species
Code    N       Mean       StDev    SE Mean
1      12      17.50        3.53        1.0
2       9      13.67        4.50        1.5

90% C.I. for mu 1 - mu 2: ( 0.6,  7.0)
T-Test mu 1 = mu 2 (vs >): T= 2.11  P=0.026  DF=  14
```

**19.9.** Use the means and the standard error SE $\doteq 0.06317$ found in the solution to Exercise 19.7, and critical value $t^* = 2.101$ (df $= 18$) or $t^* = 2.047$ (df $= 28.6$). The 95% confidence interval is $\bar{x}_1 - \bar{x}_2 \pm t^*\text{SE}$, which gives $-0.5126$ to $-0.2471$ (df $= 18$) or $-0.5092$ to $-0.2506$ (df $= 28.6$). Minitab's result, shown in the solution to Exercise 19.7 above, is based on the truncated df $= 28$.

**19.10.** Use the means and the standard error SE $\doteq 1.813$ found in the solution to Exercise 19.8, and critical value $t^* = 1.860$ (df $= 8$) or $t^* = 1.755$ (df $= 14.8$). The 90% confidence interval is $\bar{x}_1 - \bar{x}_2 \pm t^*\text{SE}$, which gives 0.46 to 7.20 species (df $= 8$) or 0.65 to 7.02 species (df $= 14.8$). Minitab's result, shown in the solution to Exercise 19.8 above, is based on the truncated df $= 14$.

| | $n$ | $\bar{x}$ | $s$ |
|---|---|---|---|
| Nursing | 47 | −3.58723 | 2.50561 |
| Control | 22 | 0.30909 | 1.29832 |

**19.11. (a)** The two populations are breast-feeding women and other women. **(b) Formulate:** We will test $H_0$: $\mu_1 = \mu_2$ versus $H_a$: $\mu_1 < \mu_2$; we use a one-sided alternative because we suspect that nursing mothers lose bone density.
**Solve:** Stemplots are shown in the solution to Exercise 2.36; both distributions appear to be reasonably Normal. The means and standard deviations are given in the table above. We compute $SE = \sqrt{\frac{1.29832^2}{22} + \frac{2.50561^2}{47}} \doteq 0.45847$ and $t = \frac{0.30909+3.58723}{0.45847} \doteq 8.50$. The choice of df (21 or 66.20) is irrelevant; $P$ is tiny in either case.
**Conclude:** We have very strong evidence that nursing mothers lose bone mineral.

**19.12.** We have two small samples (each $n = 4$), so $t$ procedures are not reliable unless both distributions are Normal.

**19.13.** The means are $\bar{x}_1 = 17.6\%$ and $\bar{x}_2 = 9.4998\bar{3}\%$, and the standard deviations are $s_1 \doteq 6.3401\%$ and $s_2 \doteq 1.9501\%$. With these values, we confirm the numbers in the CrunchIt! output:

$$SE = \sqrt{\frac{6.3401^2}{6} + \frac{1.9501^2}{6}} \doteq 2.7080, \qquad t = \frac{\bar{x}_1 - \bar{x}_2}{SE} = \frac{8.1002}{2.7080} \doteq 2.9912,$$

and

$$df = \frac{\left(\frac{6.3401^2}{6} + \frac{1.9501^2}{6}\right)^2}{\frac{1}{5}\left(\frac{6.3401^2}{6}\right)^2 + \frac{1}{5}\left(\frac{1.9501^2}{6}\right)^2} = \frac{53.7772}{9.0569} \doteq 5.9376.$$

**19.14.** Here are the details of the computations:

$$SE_F = \frac{12.6961}{\sqrt{31}} \doteq 2.2803$$

$$SE_M = \frac{12.2649}{\sqrt{47}} \doteq 1.7890$$

$$SE = \sqrt{SE_F^2 + SE_M^2} \doteq 2.8983$$

$$df = \frac{SE^4}{\frac{1}{30}\left(\frac{12.6961^2}{31}\right)^2 + \frac{1}{46}\left(\frac{12.2649^2}{47}\right)^2} = \frac{70.565}{1.1239} \doteq 62.8$$

$$t = \frac{55.5161 - 57.9149}{SE} \doteq -0.8276$$

**19.15.** Reading from the CrunchIt! output in Figure 19.5, we find $t = 2.9912$, $df = 5.9376$, and $P = 0.0246$; this is significant evidence (at the 5% level) that nerve response differs for the two groups of rats.

**19.16.** Reading from the software output shown in Exercise 19.14, we find that there was no significant difference in mean Self-Concept Scale scores for men and women ($t = -0.8276$, $df = 62.8$, and $P = 0.4110$).

**19.17.** **(a)** From an $F(9, 7)$ distribution, $F^* = 3.68$. **(b)** To be significant at the 10% level, $F$ would have to be greater than $F^* = 3.68$, so this is not significant at the 10% or the 5% levels. [In fact, $P$ is between $2(0.05) = 0.10$ and $2(0.10) = 0.20$.]

**19.18.** **(a)** Compare to an $F(20, 15)$ distribution. Because $2.76 < F < 3.37$, this is significant at 5% but not at 1%. **(b)** $P$ is between $2(0.01) = 0.02$ and $2(0.025) = 0.05$. With Minitab or other software, we find $P = 0.0482$.

**19.19.** **State:** Are the standard deviations of soil penetrability for compressed and intermediate soils different?

```
2-SampFTest
 σ1≠σ2
 F=2.975612588
 p=.022940971
 Sx1=.23974
 Sx2=.13898
↓n1=19
```

**Formulate:** We want to test $H_0$: $\sigma_I = \sigma_C$ versus $H_a$: $\sigma_I \neq \sigma_C$. (Note that the intermediate soil measurements had the larger standard deviation.)

**Solve:** The $F$ test statistic is $F = \dfrac{\text{larger } s^2}{\text{smaller } s^2} = \dfrac{0.2397^2}{0.1390^2} \doteq 2.98$.

Compare the calculated value $F = 2.98$ with critical values for the $F(18, 19)$ distribution. With Table D, refer to the $F(15, 15)$ distribution; there we see that 2.98 lies between the 0.025 and 0.01 critical values, so the two-sided $P$-value lies between 0.05 and 0.02. With software, we have $P = 0.0229$.

**Conclude:** The data show significantly unequal spreads (significant at $\alpha = 0.05$). Variation in intermediate soil is greater. (This conclusion can't be trusted because the $F$ test depends heavily on Normality, and the stemplots in the solution to Exercise 19.7 cast doubt on that condition.)

**19.20.** **State:** Is there a difference in the standard deviations of species counts on unlogged and logged plots?

```
2-SampFTest
 σ1≠σ2
 F=1.625912232
 p=.4465944321
 Sx1=4.5
 Sx2=3.5291
↓n1=9
```

**Formulate:** We want to test $H_0$: $\sigma_1 = \sigma_2$ versus $H_a$: $\sigma_1 \neq \sigma_2$. (Note that the logged-plot counts had the larger standard deviation.)

**Solve:** The $F$ test statistic is $F = \dfrac{\text{larger } s^2}{\text{smaller } s^2} = \dfrac{4.5^2}{3.5291^2} \doteq 1.63$.

From an $F(8, 11)$ distribution, we see that $P = 0.4466$; using an $F(8, 10)$ distribution from Table D, we can tell that $P$ is greater than 0.20.

**Conclude:** This is no reason to suspect unequal variation due to logging.

**19.21.** In Exercise 19.13, we found the standard deviations $s_1 \doteq 6.3401\%$ and $s_2 \doteq 1.9501\%$. To test $H_0$: $\sigma_1 = \sigma_2$ versus $H_a$: $\sigma_1 \neq \sigma_2$, we compute $F = \dfrac{6.3401^2}{1.9501^2} \doteq 10.57$. From an $F(5, 5)$ distribution, we see that $P = 0.0217$. The difference is significant at 5% but not at 1%.

**19.22.** (a) We have a single sample (4398 eighth-graders), and only one score from each member of the sample.

**19.23.** (c) We consider the boys and girls as being two independent samples.

**19.24.** (b) Measure the amount of pollutant in each carp using both methods, and examine the differences between those pairs of measurements.

**19.25.** (a) We have two independent samples, each of size $n = 8$, so df = 7.

**19.26.** (b) $\text{SE} = \sqrt{\frac{9^2}{8} + \frac{13^2}{8}} \doteq 5.59$, and $t = \frac{105-89}{\text{SE}} \doteq 2.86$.

**19.27.** (c) Random-digit dialing should produce something close to an SRS, and the samples are easily large enough to overcome non-Normality (especially because the scale 0 to 20 limits skewness and outliers in the distribution of scores).

**19.28.** (a) Our alternative hypothesis should express our suspicion that men are more prone to road rage than women. (We assume that a high road-rage score means a subject is *more* prone to road rage.)

**19.29.** (b) Using Table C, refer to df = 100, where we see that $3.174 < t < 3.390$. This means that $P$ is between 0.0005 and 0.001.

**19.30. State:** Is there good evidence that active learning is superior to passive learning?
**Formulate:** We test $H_0$: $\mu_A = \mu_P$ versus $H_a$: $\mu_A > \mu_P$; the one-sided alternative is suggested by the statement of the exercise—and presumably by a suspicion that active learning is better.
**Solve:** We must assume that the data comes from an SRS of the population of learning-impaired children; we cannot check this with the data. We also assume that the data are close to Normal. The back-to-back stemplot (right) shows a high outlier and some skewness in the "active" scores, but with reasonably large (and equal) sample sizes such as those we have here, we can allow some variation from Normality. With the means and standard deviations listed in the table, we find $\text{SE} \doteq 1.5278$ and $t \doteq 4.28$. With either df = 23 or df = 39.1, $P < 0.0005$.
**Conclude:** There is very strong evidence that active learning results in more correct identifications.

| | $n$ | $\bar{x}$ | $s$ |
|---|---|---|---|
| Active | 24 | 24.4167 | 6.31022 |
| Passive | 24 | 17.8750 | 4.02506 |

| Active | | Passive |
|---|---|---|
| | 1 | 223 |
| 5 | 1 | 45555 |
| 76 | 1 | 66777 |
| | 1 | 889 |
| 111100 | 2 | 00111 |
| 332 | 2 | |
| 4444 | 2 | 5 |
| 7 | 2 | 66 |
| 9888 | 2 | |
| 1 | 3 | |
| | 3 | |
| 5 | 3 | |
| | 3 | |
| | 3 | |
| | 4 | |
| | 4 | |
| 4 | 4 | |

**19.31. (a)** Back-to-back stemplots at right. **(b)** Means and standard deviations are given in the table on the right. Testing $H_0$: $\mu_G = \mu_B$ versus $H_a$: $\mu_G \neq \mu_B$, we find $\text{SE} \doteq 3.1138$ and $t \doteq 1.64$. This gives $0.10 < P < 0.20$ (df = 30) or $P = 0.1057$ (df = 56.9), so it is not strong enough evidence to reject $H_0$.

| | $n$ | $\bar{x}$ | $s$ |
|---|---|---|---|
| Girls | 31 | 105.84 | 14.271 |
| Boys | 47 | 110.96 | 12.121 |

| Girls | | Boys |
|---|---|---|
| 42 | 7 | |
| | 7 | 79 |
| | 8 | |
| 96 | 8 | |
| 31 | 9 | 03 |
| 86 | 9 | 77 |
| 433320 | 10 | 0234 |
| 875 | 10 | 556667779 |
| 44422211 | 11 | 00001123334 |
| 98 | 11 | 556899 |
| 0 | 12 | 03344 |
| 8 | 12 | 67788 |
| 20 | 13 | |
| | 13 | 6 |

**19.32. (a)** The 90% confidence interval is $(24.4167 - 17.8750) \pm t^*\text{SE}$, where $\text{SE} \doteq 1.5278$ and $t^* = 1.714$ (df = 23) or 1.685 (df = 39.05). These intervals are 3.92 to 9.16 Blissymbols, or 3.97 to 9.12 Blissymbols. **(b)** With $t^* = 1.714$ from a $t(23)$ distribution, the 90% confidence interval is $24.4167 \pm (1.714)(6.31022/\sqrt{24}) = 22.2$ to 26.6 Blissymbols. (Note that this is a one-sample question.)

**19.33.** The 95% confidence interval is $(110.96 - 105.84) \pm t^*\text{SE}$, where $\text{SE} \doteq 3.1138$ and $t^* = 2.042$ (df = 30) or 2.003 (df = 56.9). These intervals are $-1.24$ to 11.48 or $-1.12$ to 11.35.

**19.34. State:** Do men have a lower mean SSHA score than women?
**Formulate:** We test $H_0$: $\mu_w = \mu_m$ versus $H_a$: $\mu_w > \mu_m$, using a one-sided alternative because previous studies have suggested that the men's score is lower.
**Solve:** We are told that the numbers come from SRSs of men and women at the college. Using a back-to-back stemplot, we see that both distributions are slightly skewed to the right, and have one or two moderately high outliers. A $t$ procedure may be (cautiously) used in spite of the skewness, because the sum of the sample sizes is almost 40. Means and standard deviations are given in the table on the right. We find $\text{SE} \doteq 9.6327$ and $t = 2.056$, so $P = 0.0277$ (df = 17) or $P = 0.0236$ (df = 35.6).

| | $n$ | $\bar{x}$ | $s$ |
|---|---|---|---|
| Women | 18 | 141.05 | 26.4363 |
| Men | 20 | 121.25 | 32.8519 |

| Women | | Men |
|---|---|---|
| | 7 | 05 |
| | 8 | 8 |
| | 9 | 12 |
| 931 | 10 | 489 |
| 5 | 11 | 3455 |
| 966 | 12 | 6 |
| 77 | 13 | 2 |
| 80 | 14 | 06 |
| 442 | 15 | 1 |
| 55 | 16 | 9 |
| 8 | 17 | |
| | 18 | 07 |
| | 19 | |
| 0 | 20 | |

**Conclude:** We have fairly strong evidence—significant at 5% but not at 1%—that the women's mean is higher.

**19.35. State:** How much higher is the mean summer CFU count $\mu_1$ than the mean winter count $\mu_2$?
**Formulate:** We will give a 90% confidence interval for the mean difference $\mu_1 - \mu_2$.

| | $n$ | $\bar{x}$ | $s$ |
|---|---|---|---|
| Summer | 4 | 2138.5 | 906.429 |
| Winter | 4 | 209 | 136.575 |

**Solve:** We must assume that the data can be considered SRSs of summer and winter days, and that they come from Normal distributions. (With samples of size 4, there is little point in making stemplots to attempt to confirm the latter assumption.) With the means and standard deviations from the table on the right, we find $\text{SE} \doteq 458.330$. The 90% confidence interval is $\bar{x}_1 - \bar{x}_2 \pm t^*\text{SE}$, where $t^* = 2.353$ (df = 3) or $t^* = 2.312$ (df = 3.136). This gives either

$$1929.5 \pm 1078.5 = 851.0 \text{ to } 3008.0 \text{ CFUs (df} = 3\text{), or}$$

$$1929.5 \pm 1059.8 = 869.7 \text{ to } 2989.3 \text{ CFUs (df} = 3.136\text{).}$$

**Conclude:** We are 90% confident that the mean CFU count in summer is between 851 and 3008 CFUs (or between 870 and 2989 CFUs) higher than in winter.

**Note:** *The conservative interval is wider than the interval found using the more accurate df—that's what it means to be conservative. In spite of the similar df, the difference between the two intervals is more noticeable in this case because the sample sizes are so small: Small changes in the df have a greater impact on critical values for small df than for large df.*

**19.36.** This is a two-sample $t$ statistic, comparing two independent groups (supplemented and control). Using the conservative df = 5, $t = -1.05$ would have a $P$-value between 0.30 and 0.40, which (as the report said) is not significant. ($t = -1.05$ would not be significant for any df.)

**19.37.** To test $H_0$: $\mu_1 = \mu_2$ versus $H_a$: $\mu_1 \neq \mu_2$, we find $\text{SE} = \sqrt{\frac{3.10934^2}{6} + \frac{3.92556^2}{7}} \doteq 1.95263$, and $t = \frac{4.0-11.3}{\text{SE}} \doteq -3.74$. The two-sided $P$-value is either $0.01 < P < 0.02$ (df = 5) or 0.0033 (df = 10.96), agreeing with the stated conclusion (a significant difference).

| | $n$ | $\bar{x}$ | $s$ |
|---|---|---|---|
| Control | 6 | 4.0 | 3.10934 |
| Supplemented | 7 | 11.3 | 3.92556 |

**19.38.** These are paired $t$ statistics: For each bird, the number of days behind the caterpillar peak was observed, and the $t$ values were computed based on the pairwise differences between the first and second years.

For the control group, df = 5, and for the supplemented group, df = 6. The control $t$ is not significant (so the birds in that group did *not* "advance their laying date in the second year"), while the supplemented group $t$ is significant with one-sided $P = 0.0195$ (so those birds did change their laying date).

**19.39.** We find $\text{SE} = \sqrt{7^2 + 10^2} \doteq 12.2065$ g. The 90% confidence interval is $(59-32) \pm t^*\text{SE}$, where $t^*$ is either 1.860 (df = 8) or 1.7392 (df = 17.08). These lead (respectively) to the intervals 4.301 to 49.699 g, or 5.771 to 48.229 g. Because these intervals do not include 0, we can conclude that there is a significant difference at the (two-sided) 10% level. (In fact, $P = 0.0578$ for df = 8, or 0.0409 for df = 17.08.)

**19.40.** "Do Hispanic and Anglo bank customers differ" calls for two-sided tests: $H_0$: $\mu_1 = \mu_2$ versus $H_a$: $\mu_1 \neq \mu_2$ (for both reliability and empathy). The table below gives the standard errors, $t$ statistics, degrees of freedom, and $P$-values for both tests. (The conservative df would be 85, but for use with Table C, we must take df = 80.) Both results are very significant; there is strong evidence that Anglos value reliability more than Hispanics do, and that Hispanics value empathy more than Anglos do.

| | | | *Conservative* | | *Software* | |
|---|---|---|---|---|---|---|
| | $\text{SE} = \sqrt{\frac{s_1^2}{n_1} + \frac{s_2^2}{n_2}}$ | $t = \frac{\bar{x}_1 - \bar{x}_2}{\text{SE}}$ | df | $P$ | df | $P$ |
| Reliability | 0.1182 | 3.892 | 80 | < 0.001 | 143.69 | 0.00015 |
| Empathy | 0.1196 | −3.595 | 80 | < 0.001 | 171.08 | 0.00042 |

**19.41.** In both cases, we are testing $H_0$: $\mu_1 = \mu_2$ versus $H_a$: $\mu_1 > \mu_2$. The table below gives the standard errors, $t$ statistics, degrees of freedom, and $P$-values for both tests. Both analyses give significant evidence that the meteorite has a higher percent of left-handed molecules.

| | $\text{SE} = \sqrt{\frac{s_1^2}{n_1} + \frac{s_2^2}{n_2}}$ | $t = \frac{\bar{x}_1 - \bar{x}_2}{\text{SE}}$ | *Conservative* df | *Conservative* $P$ | *Software* df | *Software* $P$ |
|---|---|---|---|---|---|---|
| Analysis 1 | 0.5548 | 6.849 | 4 | $< 0.0025$ | 16.51 | 0.000003 |
| Analysis 2 | 0.3821 | 7.066 | 9 | $< 0.001$ | 14.84 | 0.000004 |

**19.42.** **(a)** The appropriate test is the matched-pairs test because a student's score on Try 1 is certainly correlated with his/her score on Try 2. **(b)** To test $H_0$: $\mu = 0$ versus $H_a$: $\mu > 0$, we compute $t = \frac{29-0}{59/\sqrt{427}} \doteq 10.16$ with df $= 426$, which is certainly significant ($P < 0.0005$). Coached students do improve their scores. The TI-83 output screen (on the right) shows that the $P$-value is, in fact, *much* smaller than 0.0005! **(c)** Table C gives $t^* = 2.626$ for df $= 100$, while software gives $t^* = 2.587$ for df $= 426$. The confidence interval is $29 \pm t^* 59/\sqrt{427} = 21.50$ to 36.50 points (or 21.61 to 36.39, using the software critical value). The TI-83 output confirms the more exact interval.

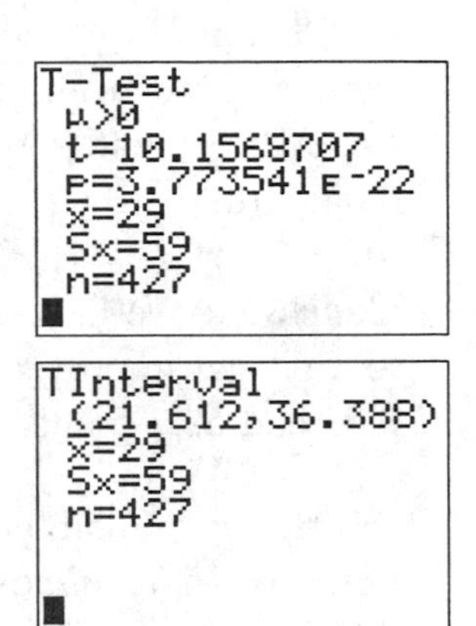


**19.43.** **(a)** The hypotheses are $H_0$: $\mu_1 = \mu_2$ versus $H_a$: $\mu_1 > \mu_2$, where $\mu_1$ is the mean gain among all coached students, and $\mu_2$ the mean gain among uncoached students. We find $\text{SE} = \sqrt{59^2/427 + 52^2/2733} \doteq 3.0235$ and $t = \frac{29-21}{3.0235} \doteq 2.646$ with conservative df $= 426$ or software df $= 534.45$. Comparing with df $= 100$ critical values in Table C, we find $0.0025 < P < 0.005$; software gives $P \doteq 0.004$ for df $= 534.45$. There is evidence that coached students had a greater average increase. **(b)** The 99% confidence interval is $8 \pm 3.0235t^*$, where $t^*$ equals 2.626 (df $= 100$, from Table C) or 2.585 (df $= 534.45$). This gives either 0.06 to 15.94 points, or 0.184 to 15.816 points. **(c)** Increasing one's score by 0 to 16 points is not likely to make a difference in being granted admission to, or receiving scholarships from, any colleges.

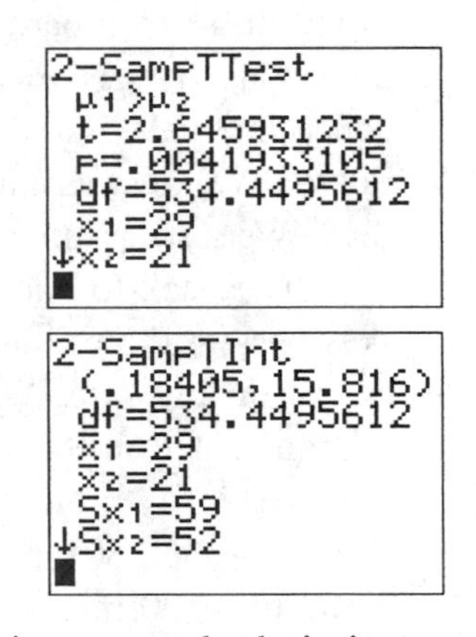


**19.44.** This was an observational study, not an experiment. The students (or their parents) chose whether or not to be coached; students who choose coaching might have other motivating factors that help them do better the second time. For example, perhaps students who choose coaching have some personality trait that also compels them to try harder the second time.

**19.45. State:** Is there evidence that the encouraging subliminal message brought about a greater improvement in math scores? What is the mean difference in gains between the two groups?

| | $n$ | $\bar{x}$ | $s$ |
|---|---|---|---|
| Treatment | 10 | 11.4 | 3.1693 |
| Control | 8 | 8.25 | 3.6936 |

| Treatment | | Control |
|---|---|---|
| | 0 | 455 |
| 76 | 0 | 7 |
| | 0 | 8 |
| 110 | 1 | 1 |
| 332 | 1 | 2 |
| 5 | 1 | 4 |
| 6 | 1 | |

**Formulate:** Compare mean gains by testing $H_0$: $\mu_1 = \mu_2$ versus $H_a$: $\mu_1 > \mu_2$, and by finding a 90% confidence interval for $\mu_1 - \mu_2$.

**Solve:** We assume that we have two SRSs, and that the distributions of score improvements are Normal. Shown on the right are stemplots of the differences ("after" minus "before") for the two groups; the samples are too small to assess Normality, but we can see that there are no outliers. With the means and standard deviations listed in the table, we find SE $\doteq$ 1.646 and $t \doteq 1.914$, for which the $P$-value is $0.025 < P < 0.05$ (df = 7) or 0.0382 (df = 13.92). The 90% confidence interval is $(11.40 - 8.25) \pm t^*\text{SE}$, where $t^* = 1.895$ (df = 7) or $t^* = 1.762$ (df = 13.92): either 0.03 to 6.27 points, or 0.25 to 6.05 points.

**Conclude:** We have evidence (significant at 5%) that the encouraging subliminal message led to a greater improvement in math scores. We are 90% confident that this increase is between 0.03 and 6.27 points (or 0.25 and 6.05 points).

**19.46. State:** Is there good evidence that the two color varieties of *Heliconia* differ in mean length? How big is the difference?

| | $n$ | $\bar{x}$ | $s$ |
|---|---|---|---|
| Red | 23 | 39.7113 | 1.7988 |
| Yellow | 15 | 36.1800 | 0.9753 |

| Red | | Yellow |
|---|---|---|
| | 34 | 56 |
| | 35 | 146 |
| | 36 | 0015678 |
| 9874 | 37 | 01 |
| 8722100 | 38 | 1 |
| 761 | 39 | |
| 65 | 40 | |
| 9964 | 41 | |
| 10 | 42 | |
| 0 | 43 | |

**Formulate:** Compare mean length by testing $H_0$: $\mu_r = \mu_y$ versus $H_a$: $\mu_r \neq \mu_y$, and by finding a 95% confidence interval for $\mu_r - \mu_y$.

**Solve:** We must assume that the data comes from an SRS. We also assume that the data are close to Normal. The back-to-back stemplots (right) show some skewness in the red lengths, but the $t$ procedures should be reasonably safe. With the means and standard deviations listed in the table, we find SE $\doteq$ 0.4518 and $t \doteq 7.817$. With either df = 14 or df = 35.1, $P < 0.001$. The 95% confidence interval is $(39.711 - 36.180) \pm t^*\text{SE}$, where $t^* = 2.145$ (df = 14) or $t^* = 2.030$ (df = 35.1): either 2.562 to 4.500 mm, or 2.614 to 4.448 mm.

**Conclude:** We have very strong evidence that the two varieties differ in mean length. We are 95% confident that the mean red length minus yellow length is between 2.562 and 4.500 mm (or 2.614 and 4.448 mm).

**19.47. State:** Is there good evidence that the Permafresh and Hylite processes result in different mean breaking strengths?

| | $n$ | $\bar{x}$ | $s$ |
|---|---|---|---|
| Permafresh | 5 | 29.54 | 1.1675 |
| Hylite | 5 | 25.20 | 2.6693 |

| Permafresh | | Hylite |
|---|---|---|
| | 22 | 1 |
| | 23 | 9 |
| | 24 | 2 |
| | 25 | |
| | 26 | |
| 6 | 27 | 0 |
| | 28 | 8 |
| 95 | 29 | |
| 70 | 30 | |

**Formulate:** As we have no advance belief that one process is stronger, use a two-sided test: $H_0$: $\mu_1 = \mu_2$ versus $H_a$: $\mu_1 \neq \mu_2$.

**Solve:** We assume that we have two SRSs, and that the distributions of breaking strengths are Normal. Shown on the right are back-to-back stemplots for the two processes; the samples are too small to assess Normality, but we can see that there are no extreme outliers. With the means and standard deviations listed in the table, we find SE $\doteq$ 1.303 and $t \doteq 3.331$, for which the $P$-value is $0.02 < P < 0.04$ (df = 4) or 0.0181 (df = 5.476).

**Conclude:** Despite the small samples, there is good evidence (significant at $\alpha = 0.05$) that the mean breaking strengths of the two processes differ.

**19.48. State:** Is there good evidence that the Permafresh and Hylite processes result in different mean wrinkle recovery angles (WRA)?

| | $n$ | $\bar{x}$ | $s$ |
|---|---|---|---|
| Permafresh | 5 | 134.8 | 1.9235 |
| Hylite | 5 | 143.2 | 2.2804 |

| Permafresh | | Hylite |
|---|---|---|
| 2 | 13 | |
| 54 | 13 | |
| 76 | 13 | |
| | 13 | |
| | 14 | 11 |
| | 14 | 3 |
| | 14 | 5 |
| | 14 | 6 |

**Formulate:** As we have no advance belief that one process is superior, use a two-sided test: $H_0$: $\mu_1 = \mu_2$ versus $H_a$: $\mu_1 \neq \mu_2$.

**Solve:** We assume that we have two SRSs, and that the distributions of WRAs are Normal. Shown on the right are back-to-back stemplots for the two processes; the samples are too small to assess Normality, but we can see that there are no extreme outliers. Both the stemplots and the means listed in the table suggest that Hylite has a substantially larger WRA. We find SE $\doteq$ 1.334 and $t \doteq -6.296$, for which the $P$-value is $0.002 < P < 0.005$ (df = 4) or 0.0003 (df = 7.779).

**Conclude:** There is very strong evidence of a difference between the population means. As we might expect, the stronger process (Permafresh) is less resistant to wrinkles.

**19.49. State:** How big is the difference in mean breaking strength for the two processes?

**Formulate:** We will find a 95% confidence interval for $\mu_1 - \mu_2$.

**Solve:** As in Exercise 19.47, we assume SRSs from Normal populations. The 95% confidence interval is $\bar{x}_1 - \bar{x}_2 \pm t^*\text{SE}$, where $t^* = 2.776$ (df = 4) or $t^* = 2.505$ (df = 5.476). This gives either

$$4.34 \pm 3.617 = 0.723 \text{ to } 7.957 \text{ pounds (df} = 4\text{), or}$$

$$4.34 \pm 3.264 = 1.076 \text{ to } 7.604 \text{ pounds (df} = 5.476\text{).}$$

As usual, the conservative interval is wider than the more accurate software result.

**Conclude:** We are 95% confident that Permafresh is stronger than Hylite by between 0.7 and 8 pounds (or 1.1 and 7.6 pounds).

**19.50. State:** How big is the difference in mean WRA for the two processes?
**Formulate:** We will find a 95% confidence interval for $\mu_1 - \mu_2$.
**Solve:** As in Exercise 19.48, we assume SRSs from Normal populations. The 95% confidence interval is $\bar{x}_1 - \bar{x}_2 \pm t^*\text{SE}$, where $t^* = 2.776$ (df = 4) or $t^* = 2.317$ (df = 7.779). This gives either

$$-8.4 \pm 3.704 = -12.104^\circ \text{ to } -4.696^\circ \text{ (df = 4), or}$$
$$-8.4 \pm 3.092 = -11.492^\circ \text{ to } -5.308^\circ \text{ (df = 7.779).}$$

As usual, the conservative interval is wider than the more accurate software result.
**Conclude:** We are 95% confident that the mean WRA for Hylite exceeds that of Permafresh by between 4.7° and 12.1° (or 5.3° and 11.5°).

**19.51.** *Because this exercise asks for a "complete analysis," without suggesting hypotheses or confidence levels, student responses may vary. This solution gives 95% confidence intervals for the means in (a) and (b), and performs a hypothesis test and gives a 95% confidence interval for part (c). Note that the first two problems call for single-sample* t *procedures (Chapter 18), while the last uses the Chapter 19 procedures. Student answers should be formatted according to the "four-step process" of the text; these answers are not, but can be used to check student results.*

We begin (as students should) with summary statistics and a display of the distributions, using either stemplots or histograms:

| | $n$ | $\bar{x}$ | $s$ |
|---|---|---|---|
| Women | 95 | 4.2737 | 2.1472 |
| Men | 81 | 6.5185 | 3.3471 |

| Women | | Men |
|---:|---:|---|
| 00000000 | 1 | 000 |
| 5555555500000 | 2 | 0000 |
| 555500000000000000000 | 3 | 0000000 |
| 500000000000000000 | 4 | 0000000000555 |
| 00000000000 | 5 | 000000005 |
| 50000000 | 6 | 00000005 |
| 00000000 | 7 | 000000005 |
| 000 | 8 | 000000000 |
| 000 | 9 | 0000 |
| 00 | 10 | 00000005 |
| | 11 | 0 |
| | 12 | 05 |
| | 13 | |
| | 14 | |
| | 15 | 000 |
| | 16 | 0 |

**(a)** The stemplot shows that the distribution of claimed drinks per day for women is right-skewed, but has no particular outliers, so with such a large sample, the $t$ procedures should be safe. Let $\mu_w$ be the mean claimed drinks per day for sophomore women. The standard error for the women's mean is $\text{SE}_w = s_w/\sqrt{95} \doteq 0.2203$, and the margin of error for 95% confidence is $t^*\text{SE}_w$, where $t^* = 1.990$ (df = 80) or $t^* = 1.9855$ (df = 94). Therefore, the 95% confidence interval for $\mu_w$ is either $4.2737 \pm 0.4384$ or $4.2737 \pm 0.4374$. With either df, we could say that we are 95% confident that, among sophomore women who drink, the mean claimed number of drinks is between 3.84 and 4.71 drinks.

**(b)** The stemplot shows that the distribution of claimed drinks per day for men has four high numbers that may be considered outliers (exaggerations). Apart from these four numbers, the distribution is fairly symmetric. The $t$ procedures should be safe, even with these high numbers included (they are not too extreme). Let $\mu_m$ be the mean claimed drinks per day for sophomore men. The standard error for the men's mean is $\text{SE}_m = s_m/\sqrt{81} \doteq 0.3719$, and the margin of error for 95% confidence is $t^*\text{SE}_m = 1.990\,\text{SE}_m = 0.7401$ (df = 80).

Therefore, we are 95% confident that, among sophomore men who drink, the mean claimed number of drinks is in the range $6.5185 \pm 0.7401 = 5.78$ to 7.26 drinks.

**(c)** For the two-sided test $H_0$: $\mu_w = \mu_m$ versus $H_a$: $\mu_w \neq \mu_m$, we find

$$\mathrm{SE} = \sqrt{\frac{2.1472^2}{95} + \frac{3.3471^2}{81}} \doteq 0.4322 \quad \text{and} \quad t = \frac{4.2737 - 6.5185}{\mathrm{SE}} \doteq -5.193.$$

Regardless of the choice of df (80 or 132.15), this is highly significant ($P < 0.001$); we have very strong evidence that the claimed number of drinks is different for men and women. To construct a 95% confidence interval for $\mu_m - \mu_w$, we take $\bar{x}_m - \bar{x}_w \pm t^*\mathrm{SE}$, with $t^* = 1.990$ (df $= 80$) or $t^* = 1.9781$ (df $= 132.15$). This gives either $2.2448 \pm 0.8601$ or $2.2448 \pm 0.8549$. After rounding either interval, we can report with 95% confidence that, on the average, sophomore men who drink claim an additional 1.4 to 3.1 drinks per day compared to sophomore women who drink.

# Chapter 20 Solutions

**20.1. (a)** The population is "all college students" (or something similar). $p$ is the proportion of the population who say they pray at least once in a while. **(b)** $\hat{p} = \frac{107}{127} \doteq 0.8425$.

**20.2. (a)** The population is "all teenagers" (or something similar). $p$ is the proportion of the population who say they play online games. **(b)** $\hat{p} = \frac{775}{1100} \doteq 0.7045$.

**20.3. (a)** The mean is $p = 0.5$, and the standard deviation is $\sqrt{\frac{p(1-p)}{n}} = \sqrt{\frac{0.25}{14{,}941}} \doteq 0.004091$. **(b)** $P(0.49 < \hat{p} < 0.51) \doteq P\left(\frac{0.49-0.5}{0.004091} < Z < \frac{0.51-0.5}{0.004091}\right) \doteq P(-2.44 < Z < 2.44) = 0.9854$.

**20.4.** If $\hat{p}$ is the sample proportion who have been on a diet, then $\hat{p}$ has approximately a $N(0.70, 0.02804)$ distribution, so $P(\hat{p} \geq 0.75) \doteq P(Z \geq 1.78) = 0.0375$ (software: 0.0373). Alternatively, as $\hat{p} \geq 0.75$ is equivalent to 201 or more dieters in the sample, we can compute this probability using the binomial distribution; these answers are shown in the table.

| | | | *Continuity correction* | |
|---|---|---|---|---|
| Exact prob. | Table Normal | Software Normal | Table Normal | Software Normal |
| 0.0329 | 0.0301 | 0.0298 | 0.0344 | 0.0347 |

**20.5.** Larger sample sizes give more accurate estimates:

For $n = 1000$: $P(0.49 < \hat{p} < 0.51) \doteq P(-0.63 < Z < 0.63) = 0.4714$.
For $n = 4000$: $P(0.49 < \hat{p} < 0.51) \doteq P(-1.26 < Z < 1.26) = 0.7924$.
For $n = 16,000$: $P(0.49 < \hat{p} < 0.51) \doteq P(-2.53 < Z < 2.53) = 0.9886$.

**20.6.** This call-in poll cannot be considered an SRS of the population ("all citizens").

**20.7.** There were only 5 or 6 "successes" in the sample (because 5/2673 and 6/2673 both round to 0.2%).

**20.8. State:** What proportion $p$ of students who retake the SAT paid for coaching?

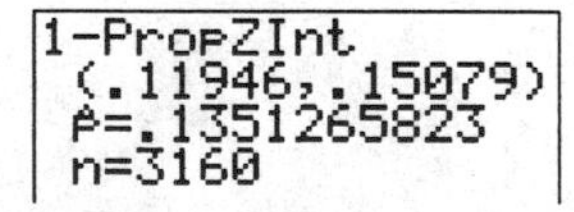


**Formulate:** We will find a 99% confidence interval for $p$.
**Solve:** We are told this is a random sample; we assume this means it is at least close to an SRS. Both the number of successes (427) and the number of failures (2306) are much greater than 15. We compute $\hat{p} = \frac{427}{3160} \doteq 0.1351$ and $\text{SE}_{\hat{p}} = \sqrt{\hat{p}(1-\hat{p})/3160} \doteq 0.006081$, so the 99% confidence interval is $0.1351 \pm (2.576)(0.006081) = 0.1194$ to $0.1508$. This agrees with the TI-83 output on the right.
**Conclude:** We are 99% confident that the proportion of coaching among students who retake the SAT is between 0.1194 and 0.1508.

**20.9.** Here, $n = 1009$ and the sample proportion is $\hat{p} = 0.70$. **(a)** The count of "successes" is $(0.70)(1009) = 706$ (rounded to the nearest whole number). **(b)** Of the large number of samples conducted by Harris's method, 95% capture the true population proportion within the stated margin of error. The other 5% miss by more than the margin of error. We have no way of knowing which samples hit and which miss. **(c)** The 95% confidence interval for $p$ is

$$\hat{p} \pm z^* \sqrt{\frac{\hat{p}(1-\hat{p})}{n}} = 0.7 \pm 1.960 \sqrt{\frac{(0.7)(0.3)}{1009}} = 0.7 \pm 0.028 = 0.672 \text{ to } 0.728.$$

The margin of error, if rounded, is $\pm 3$ percentage points as claimed. (Note: Working from $\hat{p} = \frac{706}{1009} \doteq 0.6997$ instead of $\hat{p} = 0.70$, the interval is slightly different: 0.6714 to 0.7280.)

**20.10.** **(a)** $\hat{p} = \frac{80}{80} = 1$, and the margin of error for 95% confidence (or any level of confidence) is 0: $z^* \sqrt{\frac{(1)(0)}{n}} = z^*(0) = 0$. Almost certainly, if more trials were performed, a rat would eventually make a mistake or two, meaning that its actual success rate is less than 1. **(b)** The plus four estimate is $\tilde{p} = \frac{82}{84} \doteq 0.9762$, and the plus four 95% confidence interval is

$$\tilde{p} \pm 1.960 \sqrt{\frac{\tilde{p}(1-\tilde{p})}{n+4}} = 0.9762 \pm 0.0326 = 0.9436 \text{ to } 1.0088.$$

Ignoring the upper limit, we can say we are 95% confident that the actual success rate is 0.9436 or greater.

**20.11.** **(a)** The large-sample interval should not be used because the number of "successes" is only 9. **(b)** The plus four estimate is $\tilde{p} = \frac{9+2}{98+4} \doteq 0.1078$. The 90% confidence interval is

$$\tilde{p} \pm 1.645 \sqrt{\frac{\tilde{p}(1-\tilde{p})}{n+4}} = 0.1078 \pm 0.0505 = 0.0573 \text{ to } 0.1584.$$

**20.12.** **(a)** The count of successes (5) is too small. **(b)** With the plus four method, the sample size is 2677, the success count is 7, and $\tilde{p} = \frac{7}{2677} \doteq 0.0026$. **(c)** The plus four 95% confidence interval is 0.00068 to 0.00455.

```
1-PropZInt
 (6.8E-4,.00455)
 p̂=.0026148674
 n=2677
```

**20.13.** **(a)** We find $\hat{p} = \frac{221}{270} \doteq 0.8185$ and $\text{SE}_{\hat{p}} = \sqrt{\hat{p}(1-\hat{p})/270} \doteq 0.02346$, so the margin of error for 95% confidence is $(1.96)(0.02346) \doteq 0.0460$. **(b)** For a $\pm 0.03$ margin of error, we need $n = \left(\frac{1.96}{0.03}\right)^2 p^*(1-p^*) = 4268.\overline{4} \cdot p^*(1-p^*)$. There are several ways we could take $p^*$ from the pilot study: We could simply take $p^* = \hat{p}$, or we could try values of $p^*$ that are slightly smaller than $\hat{p}$, taking into account the margin of error found in (a). The table on the right summarizes the sample size for various choices of $p^*$.

| $p^*$ | $n$ |
|---|---|
| $\hat{p}$ | 634.06 |
| 0.80 | 682.95 |
| 0.75 | 800.33 |

**20.14.** $n = \left(\frac{1.645}{0.04}\right)^2 (0.75)(0.25) \doteq 317.1$—use $n = 318$.

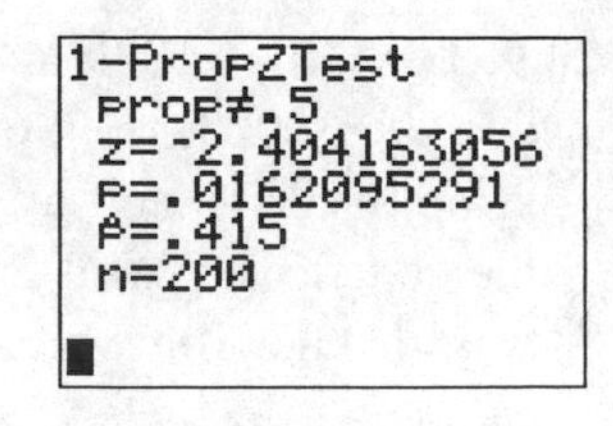


**20.15. State:** Does $\hat{p} = \frac{83}{200} = 0.415$ give significant evidence that the probability of heads from spinning a coin is different from 0.5?
**Formulate:** Let $p$ be the proportion of heads from a spun coin. We test $H_0$: $p = 0.5$ versus $H_a$: $p \neq 0.5$; the alternative is two-sided because (prior to looking at the data) we had no suspicion that coin spinning would favor heads or tails.
**Solve:** We view the 200 spins as an SRS. The expected counts $np_0$ and $n(1 - p_0)$ are both 100—large enough to proceed. With $\hat{p} = 0.415$, the test statistic is $z = (0.415 - 0.5)/\sqrt{\frac{(0.5)(0.5)}{200}} \doteq -2.40$. The $P$-value is 0.0164 (from Table A) or 0.0162 (software).
**Conclude:** We have pretty strong evidence—significant at $\alpha = 0.05$, though not at $\alpha = 0.01$—against equal probabilities.

**20.16. State:** Does $\hat{p} = \frac{22}{32} = 0.6875$ give significant evidence that the "best face" wins more than half the time?
**Formulate:** Let $p$ be the proportion of races won by the candidate with the better face. We test $H_0$: $p = 0.5$ versus $H_a$: $p > 0.5$; the alternative is one-sided because we suspect (even before seeing the data) that the better-face candidate has an advantage.
**Solve:** We view the 32 races as an SRS. The expected counts $np_0$ and $n(1 - p_0)$ are both 16—large enough to proceed. With $\hat{p} = 0.6875$, the test statistic is $z = (0.6875 - 0.5)/\sqrt{\frac{(0.5)(0.5)}{32}} \doteq 2.12$. The $P$-value is 0.0170 (from Table A) or 0.0169 (software).
**Conclude:** We have pretty strong evidence—significant at $\alpha = 0.05$, though not at $\alpha = 0.01$—that the candidate with the better face wins more than half the time.

**20.17.** **(a)** The sample size (10) is too small; it gives $np_0 = n(1 - p_0) = 5$. **(b)** The expected number of "no" responses is too small: $n(1 - p_0) = 200(0.01) = 2$.

**20.18.** (b) The mean of the distribution of $\hat{p}$ is the population proportion $p$. (That is, $\hat{p}$ is an unbiased estimate of $p$.)

**20.19.** (c) The standard deviation is $\sqrt{\frac{(0.3)(0.7)}{757}} \doteq 0.01666$.

**20.20.** (c) $\hat{p} = \frac{273}{757} \doteq 0.36$.

**20.21.** (b) The margin of error for 95% confidence is $1.96 \cdot \text{SE} = 1.96\sqrt{\frac{(0.36)(0.64)}{757}} \doteq 0.034$.

**20.22.** (c) $n = \left(\frac{1.96}{0.02}\right)^2 (0.5)(0.5) = 2401$.

**20.23.** (a) $\tilde{p} = \frac{55}{104} \doteq 0.529$ and the margin of error is $1.96\sqrt{\frac{\tilde{p}(1-\tilde{p})}{104}} \doteq 0.096$.

**20.24.** (a) The reported margin of error accounts only for random variation in the responses.

**20.25.** (a) The alternative hypothesis expresses the idea "more than half think their job prospects are good."

**20.26.** (c) $z = (0.53 - 0.5)/\sqrt{\frac{(0.5)(0.5)}{100}} = 0.6$.

**20.27.** (a) The margin of error in (almost all) publicly reported polls is with 95% confidence.

**20.28.** We estimate that $\hat{p} = \frac{19}{172} \doteq 0.1105$, $\text{SE}_{\hat{p}} \doteq 0.02390$, the margin of error is $1.960\text{SE}_{\hat{p}} \doteq 0.04685$, and the 95% confidence interval is 0.0636 to 0.1573.
With the plus four method, $\tilde{p} = \frac{21}{176} \doteq 0.1193$, $\text{SE}_{\tilde{p}} \doteq 0.02443$, the margin of error is $1.960\text{SE}_{\tilde{p}} \doteq 0.04789$, and the 95% confidence interval is 0.0714 to 0.1672.

**20.29. (a)** We find that $\tilde{p} = \frac{109}{131} \doteq 0.8321$, $\text{SE}_{\tilde{p}} \doteq 0.03266$, the margin of error is $2.576\text{SE}_{\tilde{p}} \doteq 0.08413$, and the 99% confidence interval is 0.7479 to 0.9162. **(b)** We need to know how they were chosen. (All from the same school? Public or private? Etc.) That they were all in psychology and communications courses makes it seem unlikely that they are truly representative of all undergraduates.

```
1-PropZInt
 (.74793,.91619)
 p̂=.8320610687
 n=131
```

**20.30. (a)** For the large-sample interval, we would need at least 15 successes and failures; we have only 8 and 5 failures in the two samples. For plus four intervals, we need only $n \geq 10$ (and confidence level 90% or more). **(b)** For the proportion preferring Times New Roman for Web use: $\tilde{p} = \frac{19}{29} \doteq 0.6552$, $\text{SE}_{\tilde{p}} \doteq 0.08826$, the margin of error is $1.960\text{SE}_{\tilde{p}} \doteq 0.17299$, and the 95% confidence interval is 0.4822 to 0.8282. For the proportion who prefer Gigi: $\tilde{p} = \frac{22}{29} \doteq 0.7586$, $\text{SE}_{\tilde{p}} \doteq 0.07946$, the margin of error is $1.645\text{SE}_{\tilde{p}} \doteq 0.13070$, and the 90% confidence interval is 0.6279 to 0.8893.

**20.31. State:** What proportion $p$ of female Hispanic drivers in Boston wear seat belts?
**Formulate:** We will give a 95% confidence interval for $p$.
**Solve:** We have a fairly large SRS from a much larger population, with counts 68 and 49, so we can use large-sample methods; plus four methods are also safe. For the large-sample interval: $\hat{p} = \frac{68}{117} \doteq 0.5812$, $\text{SE}_{\hat{p}} \doteq 0.04561$, the margin of error is $1.960\text{SE}_{\hat{p}} \doteq 0.08940$, and the 95% confidence interval is 0.4918 to 0.6706.
Using plus four methods: $\tilde{p} = \frac{70}{121} \doteq 0.5785$, $\text{SE}_{\tilde{p}} \doteq 0.04489$, the margin of error is $1.960\text{SE}_{\tilde{p}} \doteq 0.08798$, and the 95% confidence interval is 0.4905 to 0.6665.
**Conclude:** With either method, we are 95% confident that the proportion of female Hispanic drivers who wear seat belts is between about 0.49 and 0.67.

```
1-PropZInt
 (.4918,.67059)
 p̂=.5811965812
 n=117
```

```
1-PropZInt
 (.49053,.6665)
 p̂=.5785123967
 n=121
```

**20.32. (a)** Both large-sample and plus four methods are safe. For the large-sample interval: $\hat{p} = \frac{171}{880} \doteq 0.1943$, $\text{SE}_{\hat{p}} \doteq 0.01334$, the margin of error is $1.960\text{SE}_{\hat{p}} \doteq 0.02614$, and the 95% confidence interval is 0.1682 to 0.2205. Using plus four methods: $\tilde{p} = \frac{173}{884} \doteq 0.1957$, $\text{SE}_{\tilde{p}} \doteq 0.01334$, the margin of error is $1.960\text{SE}_{\tilde{p}} \doteq 0.02615$, and the 95% confidence interval is 0.1695 to 0.2219. **(b)** More than 171 respondents have run red lights. We would not expect very many people to claim they *have* run red lights when they have not, but some people will deny running red lights when they have.

**20.33. State:** Does $\hat{p} = \frac{68}{117} \doteq 0.5812$ give significant evidence that more than half of Hispanic female drivers in Boston wear seat belts?
**Formulate:** Let $p$ be the proportion of this population who wear seat belts. Because the exercise asks if we are convinced that more than half wear seat belts, we will test $H_0$: $p = 0.5$ versus $H_a$: $p > 0.5$; one might instead choose the two-sided alternative $p \neq 0.5$.
**Solve:** Large-sample inference procedures can be used: We view our sample as an SRS, and the expected counts $np_0$ and $n(1 - p_0)$ are both 58.5. With $\hat{p} \doteq 0.5812$, the test statistic is $z = (0.5812 - 0.5)/\sqrt{\frac{(0.5)(0.5)}{117}} \doteq 1.76$. The $P$-value is 0.0392 (from Table A) or 0.0395 (software).
**Conclude:** We have pretty strong evidence—significant at $\alpha = 0.05$, though not at $\alpha = 0.01$—that a majority of Hispanic female drivers in Boston wear seat belts. (If we had chosen a two-sided alternative, the $P$-value would be twice as big, and the evidence would not be significant at $\alpha = 0.05$.)

**20.34.** With $p^* = \hat{p} \doteq 0.5812$, we find $n = \left(\frac{1.96}{0.05}\right)^2 p^*(1 - p^*) \doteq 374.03$—so take $n = 375$.

**20.35. (a)** The failure count (5) is too small for the standard method. The plus four method only requires a confidence level of at least 90% and a sample size of at least 10 (we have $n = 23$). **(b)** Using the plus four method: $\tilde{p} = \frac{20}{27} \doteq 0.7407$, $SE_{\tilde{p}} \doteq 0.08434$, the margin of error is $1.645SE_{\tilde{p}} \doteq 0.1387$, and the 90% confidence interval is 0.6020 to 0.8795.

**20.36. (a)** Because the smallest number of total tax returns (i.e., the smallest population) is still more than 100 times the sample size, the margin of error will be (approximately) the same for all states. **(b)** Yes, it will change—the sample taken from Wyoming will be about the same size, but the sample from, for example, California will be considerably larger, and therefore the margin of error will decrease.

**20.37. (a)** Using the large-sample method: $\hat{p} = \frac{22}{148} \doteq 0.1486$, $SE_{\hat{p}} \doteq 0.02924$, the margin of error is $1.960SE_{\hat{p}} \doteq 0.05731$, and the 95% confidence interval is 0.0913 to 0.2060. With the plus four method: $\tilde{p} = \frac{24}{152} \doteq 0.1579$, $SE_{\tilde{p}} \doteq 0.02958$, the margin of error is $1.960SE_{\tilde{p}} \doteq 0.05797$, and the 95% confidence interval is 0.0999 to 0.2159.
**(b)** $n = \left(\frac{1.96}{0.04}\right)^2 (0.1486)(0.8514) \doteq 303.7$—so use $n = 304$. (We should not use $p^* = 0.5$ here because we have evidence that the true value of $p$ is not in the range 0.3 to 0.7.)
**(c)** Aside from the 45% nonresponse rate, the sample comes from a limited area in Indiana, focuses on only one kind of business, and leaves out any businesses not in the Yellow Pages (there might be a few of these; perhaps they are more likely to fail). It is more realistic to believe that this describes businesses that match the above profile; it *might* generalize to food-and-drink establishments elsewhere, but probably not to hardware stores and other types of business.

**20.38. (a)** $n = \left(\frac{2.576}{0.015}\right)^2 (0.2)(0.8) \doteq 4718.8$—so use $n = 4719$. **(b)** $2.576\sqrt{\frac{(0.1)(0.9)}{4719}} \doteq 0.01125$.

**20.39.** **(a)** The margins of error are $1.96\sqrt{\hat{p}(1-\hat{p})/100} = 0.196\sqrt{\hat{p}(1-\hat{p})}$ (below). **(b)** With $n = 500$, the margins of error are $1.96\sqrt{\hat{p}(1-\hat{p})/500}$. The new margins of error are less than half their former size (in fact, they have decreased by a factor of $\frac{1}{\sqrt{5}} \doteq 0.447$).

| | $p$ | 0.1 | 0.2 | 0.3 | 0.4 | 0.5 | 0.6 | 0.7 | 0.8 | 0.9 |
|---|---|---|---|---|---|---|---|---|---|---|
| **(a)** | m.e. | .0588 | .0784 | .0898 | .0960 | .0980 | .0960 | .0898 | .0784 | .0588 |
| **(b)** | m.e. | .0263 | .0351 | .0402 | .0429 | .0438 | .0429 | .0402 | .0351 | .0263 |

**20.40.** **State:** What is the proportion $p$ of college students who support cracking down on underage drinking?
**Formulate:** We will give a 99% confidence interval for $p$.
**Solve:** We have an SRS with a very large sample size, so both large-sample and plus four methods can be used. Using the large-sample method: $\hat{p} = \frac{10010}{14941} \doteq 0.6700$, $\text{SE}_{\hat{p}} \doteq 0.00385$, the margin of error is $2.576\text{SE}_{\hat{p}} \doteq 0.00991$, and the 99% confidence interval is 0.6601 to 0.6799. With such a large sample, the plus four interval is nearly identical: $\tilde{p} = \frac{10012}{14945} \doteq 0.6699$, $\text{SE}_{\tilde{p}} \doteq 0.00385$, the margin of error is $2.576\text{SE}_{\tilde{p}} \doteq 0.00991$, and the 99% confidence interval is 0.6600 to 0.6798.
**Conclude:** Using either method, we are 99% confident that the proportion of college students who support cracking down on underage drinking is between about 0.66 and 0.68.

**20.41.** **State:** Does $\hat{p} = \frac{304}{803} \doteq 0.3786$ give significant evidence that more than one-third of heterosexuals in high-risk cities with multiple partners never use condoms?
**Formulate:** Let $p$ be this proportion. We will test $H_0$: $p = 1/3$ versus $H_a$: $p > 1/3$; we use a one-sided alternative because we are concerned that this proportion might be high.
**Solve:** We were told to consider this group to be an SRS, and the expected counts are easily large enough to make our inference methods safe. With $\hat{p} \doteq 0.3786$, the test statistic is $z = (0.3786 - 1/3)/\sqrt{\frac{(1/3)(2/3)}{803}} \doteq 2.72$, for which $P = 0.0033$.
**Conclude:** We have very strong evidence (significant at $\alpha = 0.01$) that more than one-third of this group never use condoms.

**20.42.** **State:** There are two questions: What proportion $p$ of *BMJ* authors would agree that the journal should continue its system? Is there evidence that $p$ is more than two-thirds?
**Formulate:** We will give a 95% confidence interval, and test $H_0$: $p = 2/3$ versus $H_a$: $p > 2/3$.
**Solve:** We have an SRS with a sufficiently large sample size, so both large-sample and plus four methods can be used. For the large-sample interval, $\hat{p} = \frac{72}{104} \doteq 0.6923$, $\text{SE}_{\hat{p}} \doteq 0.04526$, the margin of error is $1.960\text{SE}_{\hat{p}} \doteq 0.08870$, and the 95% confidence interval is 0.6036 to 0.7810. Using the plus four method: $\tilde{p} = \frac{74}{108} \doteq 0.6852$, $\text{SE}_{\tilde{p}} \doteq 0.04469$, the margin of error is $1.960\text{SE}_{\tilde{p}} \doteq 0.08759$, and the 95% confidence interval is 0.5976 to 0.7728. Meanwhile, the test statistic is $z = (0.6923 - 2/3)/\sqrt{\frac{(2/3)(1/3)}{104}} \doteq 0.55$, for which $P = 0.2912$ (using Table A) or 0.2895 (software).
**Conclude:** We are 95% confident that the proportion of authors who support continuing the current system is between 0.6036 and 0.7810 (or 0.5976 and 0.7728). This survey does not give us enough evidence to conclude that this proportion is over two-thirds.

**20.43. State:** There are two questions: What proportion $p$ of *BMJ* authors feel that abstract-only publishing is not acceptable? Is there evidence that $p$ is more than 0.5?
**Formulate:** We will give a 95% confidence interval, and test $H_0$: $p = 0.5$ versus $H_a$: $p > 0.5$.
**Solve:** We have an SRS with a sufficiently large sample size, so both large-sample and plus four methods can be used. For the large-sample interval, $\hat{p} = \frac{65}{104} \doteq 0.6250$, $\text{SE}_{\hat{p}} \doteq 0.04747$, the margin of error is $1.960\text{SE}_{\hat{p}} \doteq 0.09304$, and the 95% confidence interval is 0.5320 to 0.7180. Using the plus four method: $\tilde{p} = \frac{67}{108} \doteq 0.6204$, $\text{SE}_{\tilde{p}} \doteq 0.04670$, the margin of error is $1.960\text{SE}_{\tilde{p}} \doteq 0.09153$, and the 95% confidence interval is 0.5288 to 0.7119. Meanwhile, the test statistic is $z = (0.6250 - 0.5)/\sqrt{\frac{(0.5)(0.5)}{104}} \doteq 2.55$, for which $P = 0.0054$.
**Conclude:** We are 95% confident that the proportion of authors who feel that abstract-only publishing is not acceptable is between 0.5320 and 0.7180 (or 0.5288 and 0.7119). We have strong evidence—significant at $\alpha = 0.01$—that a majority feel this way.

# Chapter 21 Solutions

**21.1. State:** How large is the difference between the proportions of teenage and adult Internet users who use instant messaging?
**Formulate:** Let $p_1$ and $p_2$ be the proportions for teenage and adult populations who use instant messaging. We give a 95% confidence interval for $p_1 - p_2$.
**Solve:** Both of our samples satisfy the conditions for using large-sample methods. The sample proportions are $\hat{p}_1 = \frac{736}{981} \doteq 0.7503$ and $\hat{p}_2 = \frac{511}{1217} \doteq 0.4199$. The standard error is

$$\text{SE} = \sqrt{\frac{\hat{p}_1(1-\hat{p}_1)}{981} + \frac{\hat{p}_2(1-\hat{p}_2)}{1217}} \doteq 0.01978,$$

so the margin of error for 95% confidence is $1.96\,\text{SE} \doteq 0.03876$, and the 95% confidence interval is 0.2916 to 0.3691.
**Conclude:** We are 95% confident that the percent of teenage Internet users using instant messaging is higher than that of adults by between 29 and 37 percentage points.

**21.2. State:** How big is the difference between the proportion of smokers who quit with a nicotine patch and the proportion who quit with a patch combined with bupropion?
**Formulate:** Let $p_1$ be the proportion for the patch population, and $p_2$ be the proportion for the patch/bupropion population. We give a 99% confidence interval for $p_2 - p_1$ (treatment minus control).
**Solve:** Both of our samples satisfy the conditions for using large-sample methods. The sample proportions are $\hat{p}_1 = \frac{40}{244} \doteq 0.1639$ and $\hat{p}_2 = \frac{87}{245} \doteq 0.3551$. The standard error is

$$\text{SE} = \sqrt{\frac{\hat{p}_1(1-\hat{p}_1)}{244} + \frac{\hat{p}_2(1-\hat{p}_2)}{245}} \doteq 0.03868,$$

so the 99% confidence interval is $(\hat{p}_2 - \hat{p}_1) \pm 2.576\,\text{SE} \doteq 0.1912 \pm 0.0996 = 0.0915$ to 0.2908.
**Conclude:** We are 99% confident that the patch/bupropion combination increases the success rate by 9 to 29 percentage points over the patch alone.

**21.3. State:** How much does microwaving crackers reduce checking?
**Formulate:** Let $p_1$ be the proportion of checking in the control group, and $p_2$ be the proportion in the microwaved group. We give a 95% (plus four) confidence interval for $p_1 - p_2$. (An interval for $p_2 - p_1$ would give the same information, of course.)
**Solve:** To use plus four methods, we want samples of at least size 5; this condition is easily met here. The plus four estimates, adding two observations to each sample, are $\tilde{p}_1 = \frac{16+1}{65+2} \doteq 0.2537$ and $\tilde{p}_2 = \frac{0+1}{65+2} \doteq 0.0149$. The plus four confidence interval for $p_1 - p_2$ uses standard error

$$\text{SE} = \sqrt{\frac{\tilde{p}_1(1-\tilde{p}_1)}{n_1+2} + \frac{\tilde{p}_2(1-\tilde{p}_2)}{n_2+2}} \doteq \sqrt{\frac{(0.2537)(0.7463)}{67} + \frac{(0.0149)(0.9851)}{67}} \doteq 0.0552.$$

The 95% confidence interval is

$$(\tilde{p}_1 - \tilde{p}_2) \pm 1.960\,\text{SE} = 0.2388 \pm 0.1082 = 0.1306 \text{ to } 0.3470.$$

**Conclude:** We are 95% confident that microwaving reduces checking by between about 13% and 35%.

**21.4. (a)** One count is only 6, and the guidelines for using the large-sample method call for all counts to be at least 10. **(b)** We have $\tilde{p}_1 \doteq 0.1273$ and $\tilde{p}_2 \doteq 0.4182$, so $\text{SE} = \sqrt{\frac{\tilde{p}_1(1-\tilde{p}_1)}{53} + \frac{\tilde{p}_2(1-\tilde{p}_2)}{108}} \doteq 0.0650$. The plus four 95% confidence interval is $(\tilde{p}_2 - \tilde{p}_1) \pm 1.96\,\text{SE} \doteq 0.2909 \pm 0.1275 = 0.1634$ to $0.4184$. The two populations are injured skaters with (and without) wrist guards.

**21.5. State:** Is there good evidence that the proportion of African miners who died was higher than the proportion of European miners who died?
**Formulate:** Let $p_1$ be the proportion of deaths among African miners, and $p_2$ be the proportion among European miners. We test $H_0$: $p_1 = p_2$ versus $H_a$: $p_1 > p_2$; the one-sided alternative is suggested by the phrasing of the question. (Presumably, we suspected that the African death rate might be higher before seeing the data.)
**Solve:** The smallest success/failure count is 7, so the conditions for a significance test are met. The sample proportions are $\hat{p}_1 = \frac{223}{33809} \doteq 0.006596$ and $\hat{p}_2 = \frac{7}{1541} \doteq 0.004543$, and the pooled proportion is $\hat{p} = \frac{223+7}{33809+1541} \doteq 0.006506$. The standard error for a hypothesis test is

$$\text{SE} = \sqrt{\hat{p}(1-\hat{p})(\frac{1}{33809} + \frac{1}{1541})} \doteq 0.002094,$$

so $z = (\hat{p}_1 - \hat{p}_2)/\text{SE} \doteq 0.98$. This gives $P = P(Z > 0.98) = 0.1635$.
**Conclude:** We do not have enough evidence to conclude that the death rates are different.

**21.6. State:** How significant is the evidence that bupropion increases the success rate?

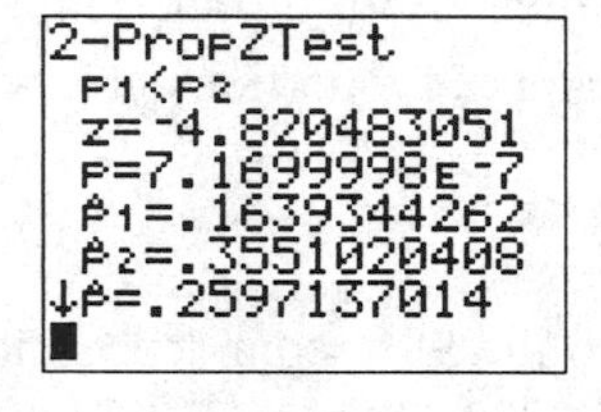


**Formulate:** With $p_1$ and $p_2$ as in Exercise 21.2, we test $H_0$: $p_1 = p_2$ versus $H_a$: $p_1 < p_2$. The alternative is one-sided because we are investigating whether the modified treatment (patch plus bupropion) increases the success rate.
**Solve:** The conditions for the test are easily satisfied. In Exercise 21.2, we computed $\hat{p}_1 \doteq 0.1639$ and $\hat{p}_2 \doteq 0.3551$; the pooled value is $\hat{p} = \frac{40+87}{244+245} \doteq 0.2597$. Then $\text{SE} = \sqrt{\hat{p}(1-\hat{p})(\frac{1}{244} + \frac{1}{245})} \doteq 0.03966$, so $z = (\hat{p}_1 - \hat{p}_2)/\text{SE} \doteq -4.82$. This gives a tiny $P$-value.
**Conclude:** We have very strong evidence that bupropion increases the success rate.

**21.7.** (b) Our conjecture determines the alternative hypothesis.

**21.8.** (a) $\hat{p}_M = \frac{484}{550} = 0.88$ and $\hat{p}_F = \frac{410}{500} = 0.82$.

**21.9.** (c) $\hat{p} = \frac{484+410}{550+500} = \frac{894}{1050} \doteq 0.8514$.

**21.10.** (b) The standard error for a hypothesis test is $\text{SE} = \sqrt{\hat{p}(1-\hat{p})(\frac{1}{550} + \frac{1}{500})} \doteq 0.02198$, so $z = (\hat{p}_1 - \hat{p}_2)/\text{SE} \doteq 2.73$.

**21.11.** (b) For a confidence interval, $\text{SE} = \sqrt{\frac{\hat{p}_1(1-\hat{p}_1)}{550} + \frac{\hat{p}_2(1-\hat{p}_2)}{500}} \doteq 0.02207$, so the margin of error is $1.96\,\text{SE} \doteq 0.04326$.

**21.12.** (a) $\hat{p} = \frac{7+2}{10+10} = 0.45$, $\text{SE} \doteq 0.2225$, $z = \left(\frac{7}{10} - \frac{2}{10}\right)/\text{SE} \doteq 2.25$. This is a one-sided test, so $P = 0.0122$.

**21.13.** (b) We would like all four counts (failures and successes) to be at least 5; one count is 2 and another is 3.

**21.14.** (b) $\tilde{p}_1 = \frac{8}{12} = 0.\overline{6}$, $\tilde{p}_2 = \frac{3}{12} = 0.25$, $\text{SE} \doteq 0.1848$, and the 90% confidence interval is $\tilde{p}_1 - \tilde{p}_2 \pm 1.645\,\text{SE} \doteq 0.4167 \pm 0.3039 = 0.1127$ to $0.7206$.

**21.15. (a)** One of the counts is 0; for large-sample intervals, we want all counts to be at least 10, and for significance testing, we want all counts to be at least 5. **(b)** Because large-sample methods are not safe, we find the plus four estimates: $\tilde{p}_1 = \frac{23+1}{33+2} \doteq 0.6857$ and $\tilde{p}_2 = \frac{0+1}{18+2} = 0.05$. The plus four confidence interval uses the standard error

$$\text{SE} = \sqrt{\frac{\tilde{p}_1(1-\tilde{p}_1)}{35} + \frac{\tilde{p}_2(1-\tilde{p}_2)}{20}} \doteq 0.09237,$$

so the 99% confidence interval is

$$(\tilde{p}_1 - \tilde{p}_2) \pm 2.576\,\text{SE} = 0.6357 \pm 0.2379 = 0.3978 \text{ to } 0.8736.$$

Lowering DNA methylation increases the incidence of tumors by between about 40% and 86%. **(c)** Because 0 is not in (or even close to) the 99% confidence interval for $p_1 - p_2$, we have very strong evidence—significant at $\alpha = 0.01$, and much smaller—that altered mice are more susceptible to tumors.

**21.16. (a)** One count is only 7, and the guidelines for using the large-sample method call for all counts to be at least 10. **(b)** For Wahtonka: 8 out of 137; for Warrenton: 28 out of 143. **(c)** We have $\tilde{p}_1 \doteq 0.0584$ and $\tilde{p}_2 \doteq 0.1958$, so $\text{SE} = \sqrt{\frac{\tilde{p}_1(1-\tilde{p}_1)}{137} + \frac{\tilde{p}_2(1-\tilde{p}_2)}{143}} \doteq 0.0388$. The plus four 95% confidence interval is $(\tilde{p}_2 - \tilde{p}_1) \pm 1.96\,\text{SE} \doteq 0.1374 \pm 0.0760 = 0.0614$ to $0.2134$.

**21.17. State:** Are unfair offers from a person more likely to be rejected than the same offers from a computer?
**Formulate:** Let $p_1$ be the proportion of people who will reject an unfair offer from another person, and $p_2$ be that proportion for offers from a computer. We test $H_0$: $p_1 = p_2$ versus $H_a$: $p_1 > p_2$, using a one-sided alternative because "we suspect that emotion will lead to offers from another person being rejected more often."
**Solve:** All counts are greater than 5, so significance testing is (fairly) safe. The test statistic uses the two sample proportions $\hat{p}_1 = \frac{18}{38} \doteq 0.4737$ and $\hat{p}_2 = \frac{6}{38} \doteq 0.1579$, and the pooled sample proportion $\hat{p} = \frac{18+6}{38+38} = \frac{24}{76} \doteq 0.3158$. The standard error for the test is

$$\text{SE} = \sqrt{\hat{p}(1-\hat{p})(\tfrac{1}{38} + \tfrac{1}{38})} \doteq 0.1066,$$

so $z = (\hat{p}_1 - \hat{p}_2)/\text{SE} \doteq 2.96$, and the $P$-value is $P(Z > 2.96) = 0.0015$.
**Conclude:** There is very strong evidence for the conclusion that people are more likely to

reject an unfair offer from another person than from a computer. This suggests that emotions play a strong role, because the economic conditions are the same for all offers.

**21.18.** To test $H_0$: $p_1 = p_2$ versus $H_a$: $p_1 < p_2$, we find $\hat{p}_1 = \frac{7}{135} \doteq 0.0519$, $\hat{p}_2 = \frac{27}{141} \doteq 0.1915$, and $\hat{p} = \frac{7+27}{135+141} \doteq 0.1232$. Then $\text{SE} = \sqrt{\hat{p}(1-\hat{p})(\frac{1}{135}+\frac{1}{141})} \doteq 0.0396$, so $z = (\hat{p}_1 - \hat{p}_2)/\text{SE} \doteq -3.53$. This gives $P = 0.0002$, so we have strong evidence that drug use is lower in schools with testing programs (if we can consider our samples as representative of similar schools).

**21.19.** To test $H_0$: $p_1 = p_2$ versus $H_a$: $p_1 \neq p_2$, we find $\hat{p}_1 = \frac{135}{190} \doteq 0.7105$, $\hat{p}_2 = \frac{293}{514} \doteq 0.5700$, and $\hat{p} = \frac{135+293}{190+514} \doteq 0.6080$. Then $\text{SE} \doteq 0.04145$ and $z = (0.7105 - 0.5700)/\text{SE} \doteq 3.39$, for which $P = 0.0006$.

**21.20.** (Use methods from Chapter 20.) We find $\hat{p} = \frac{514}{704} \doteq 0.7301$, $\text{SE} \doteq 0.01673$, and the 95% confidence interval is $\hat{p} \pm 1.96\,\text{SE} = 0.7301 \pm 0.0328 \doteq 0.6973$ to $0.7629$. Using the plus four method: $\tilde{p} = \frac{516}{708} \doteq 0.7288$, $\text{SE} \doteq 0.01671$, and the plus four interval is $\tilde{p} \pm 1.96\,\text{SE} = 0.7288 \pm 0.0327 \doteq 0.6961$ to $0.7616$.

**21.21.** As in Exercise 21.19, we find $\hat{p}_1 \doteq 0.7105$ and $\hat{p}_2 \doteq 0.5700$. For a confidence interval, the standard error is $\text{SE} \doteq 0.03949$, so the 95% confidence interval is $\hat{p}_1 - \hat{p}_2 \pm 1.96\,\text{SE} = 0.1405 \pm 0.0774 \doteq 0.0631$ to $0.2179$. Using the plus four method: $\tilde{p}_1 = \frac{135+1}{190+2} \doteq 0.7083$ and $\tilde{p}_2 = \frac{293+1}{514+2} \doteq 0.5698$, $\text{SE} \doteq 0.03939$, so the interval is $\tilde{p}_1 - \tilde{p}_2 \pm 1.96\,\text{SE} = 0.1386 \pm 0.0772 \doteq 0.0614$ to $0.2158$.

**21.22.** **(a)** The samples should be randomly chosen from a variety of schools. **(b)** $\hat{p} = \frac{34}{1679} \doteq 0.0203$ and $\text{SE} \doteq 0.00344$, so the 95% confidence interval is $\hat{p} \pm 1.960\,\text{SE} = 0.0203 \pm 0.00674 \doteq 0.0135$ to $0.0270$. Using the plus four method: $\tilde{p} = \frac{36}{1683} \doteq 0.0214$ and $\text{SE} \doteq 0.00353$, so the plus four interval is $\tilde{p} \pm 1.960\,\text{SE} = 0.0214 \pm 0.00691 \doteq 0.0145$ to $0.0283$. **(c)** For testing $H_0$: $p_1 = p_2$ versus $H_a$: $p_1 \neq p_2$, we have $\hat{p}_1 \doteq 0.02025$, $\hat{p}_2 = \frac{24}{1366} \doteq 0.01757$, and $\hat{p} = \frac{34+24}{1679+1366} \doteq 0.01905$. Then $\text{SE} = \sqrt{\hat{p}(1-\hat{p})(\frac{1}{1679}+\frac{1}{1366})} \doteq 0.004981$, so $z = (\hat{p}_1 - \hat{p}_2)/\text{SE} \doteq 0.54$, which gives $P = 0.5892$—no evidence of a difference in steroid usage rates.

**21.23.** The two samples are not independent, because the same 23 facilities were used for both. In particular, a facility that fails to detect the 1% GM beans almost certainly will not detect the 0.1% GM beans.

**21.24.** **(a)** To test $H_0$: $p_1 = p_2$ versus $H_a$: $p_1 \neq p_2$, we find $\hat{p}_1 = \frac{15}{106} \doteq 0.1415$, $\hat{p}_2 = \frac{7}{42} \doteq 0.1667$, and $\hat{p} = \frac{15+7}{106+42} \doteq 0.1486$. Then $\text{SE} = \sqrt{\hat{p}(1-\hat{p})(\frac{1}{106}+\frac{1}{42})} \doteq 0.06486$, so $z = (\hat{p}_1 - \hat{p}_2)/\text{SE} \doteq -0.39$. This gives $P = 0.6966$—little evidence of a difference in failure rates. **(b)** We still have $\hat{p}_1 \doteq 0.1415$, $\hat{p}_2 \doteq 0.1667$, and $\hat{p} \doteq 0.1486$; now $\text{SE} = \sqrt{\hat{p}(1-\hat{p})(\frac{1}{3180}+\frac{1}{1260})} \doteq 0.01184$, so $z = (\hat{p}_1 - \hat{p}_2)/\text{SE} \doteq -2.12$

and $P = 0.0340$. **(c)** For (a): SE $\doteq$ 0.06673; the 95% confidence interval is $(0.1415 - 0.1667) \pm 1.96\,\text{SE} = -0.1559$ to 0.1056. Using the plus four method: $\tilde{p}_1 \doteq 0.1481$ and $\tilde{p}_2 \doteq 0.1818$, SE $\doteq$ 0.06745, and the interval is $-0.0337 \pm 0.1322 \doteq -0.1659$ to 0.0985. For (b): SE $\doteq$ 0.01218; the 95% confidence interval is $-0.0252 \pm 0.0239 \doteq -0.04904$ to $-0.001278$. Using the plus four method: $\tilde{p}_1 \doteq 0.1417$ and $\tilde{p}_2 \doteq 0.1672$, SE $\doteq$ 0.01219, and the interval is $-0.0255 \pm 0.0239 \doteq -0.0493$ to $-0.0016$. The larger samples make the margin of error (and thus the length of the confidence interval) smaller.

**21.25. State:** Is the proportion $p_1$ of all black parents who think their state's high schools are good or excellent lower than the proportion $p_2$ of white parents with this opinion?

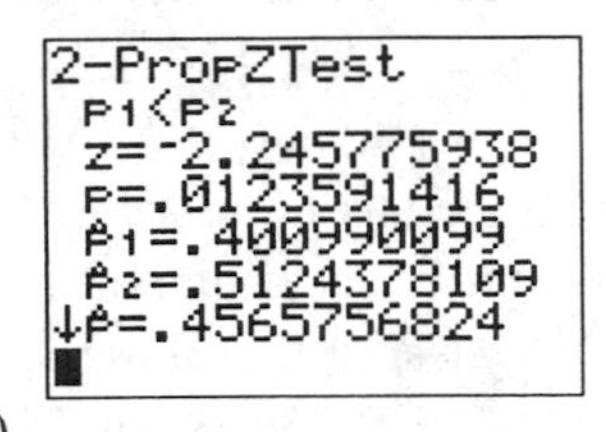


**Formulate:** We test $H_0$: $p_1 = p_2$ versus $H_a$: $p_1 < p_2$; the one-sided alternative is based on the question in the exercise. (We assume there was some reason to believe this before seeing the data.)
**Solve:** All counts are much greater than 5, so the significance test should be safe. We find $\hat{p}_1 = \frac{81}{202} \doteq 0.4010$, $\hat{p}_2 = \frac{103}{201} \doteq 0.5124$, and $\hat{p} = \frac{81+103}{202+201} \doteq 0.4566$. Then SE $= \sqrt{\hat{p}(1-\hat{p})(\frac{1}{202} + \frac{1}{201})} \doteq 0.04963$, $z = (\hat{p}_1 - \hat{p}_2)/\text{SE} \doteq -2.25$, and $P = 0.0122$. The TI-83 output on the right confirms these results (up to differences due to rounding).
**Conclude:** We have fairly strong evidence that black parents are less likely to rate schools favorably.

**21.26. State:** Is there evidence that different proportions of all black and white parents would strongly agree that a college education is now as important as a high school diploma used to be?

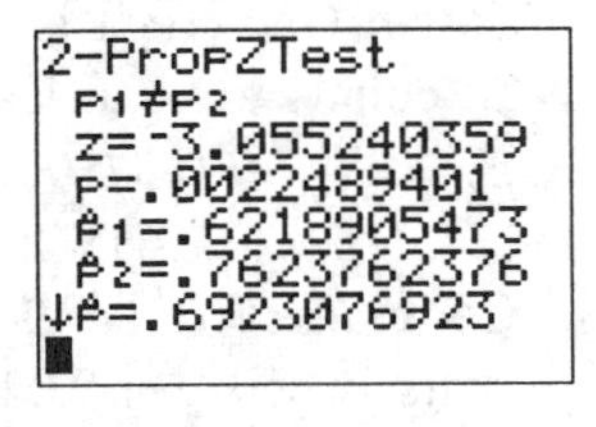


**Formulate:** Let $p_1$ be the white parent proportion, and $p_2$ the black parent proportion. Because we had no expectation that one proportion would be higher, we use a two-sided alternative: $H_0$: $p_1 = p_2$ versus $H_a$: $p_1 \neq p_2$.
**Solve:** All counts are much greater than 5, so the significance test should be safe. We find $\hat{p}_1 = \frac{125}{201} \doteq 0.6219$, $\hat{p}_2 = \frac{154}{202} \doteq 0.7624$, and the pooled value $\hat{p} = \frac{125+154}{201+202} \doteq 0.6923$. Then SE $= \sqrt{\hat{p}(1-\hat{p})(\frac{1}{201} + \frac{1}{202})} \doteq 0.04598$, $z = (\hat{p}_1 - \hat{p}_2)/\text{SE} \doteq -3.06$, and $P = 0.0022$.
**Conclude:** We conclude that these proportions differ; specifically, black parents are more likely to strongly agree.

**21.27. (a)** This is an observational study: No treatment was imposed; we simply observed drivers in the two cities. **(b) State:** Do we have evidence that female Hispanic drivers are more likely to wear seat belts in New York than in Boston?
**Formulate:** Let $p_1$ be the proportion of New York female Hispanic drivers who wear seat belts, and let $p_2$ be that proportion for Boston. The comparison of local laws suggests a one-sided alternative: $H_0$: $p_1 = p_2$ versus $H_a$: $p_1 > p_2$.
**Solve:** All counts are greater than 5, so the significance test should be safe. We find $\hat{p}_1 = \frac{183}{220} \doteq 0.8318$ and $\hat{p}_2 = \frac{68}{117} \doteq 0.5812$. The pooled proportion is $\hat{p} = \frac{183+68}{220+117} \doteq 0.7448$, and SE $\doteq$ 0.04988. The test statistic is therefore $z = (0.8318 - 0.5812)/\text{SE} \doteq 5.02$, for which $P$ is very small.
**Conclude:** We conclude that female Hispanic drivers in Boston are less likely to wear their seat belts.

**21.28. State:** Is there a significant difference in seat belt usage between Hispanic and white drivers in Chicago? How large is the difference?
**Formulate:** Let $p_1$ and $p_2$ be the proportions of (respectively) Hispanic and white drivers in Chicago who wear seat belts. For the first question, we test $H_0$: $p_1 = p_2$ versus $H_a$: $p_1 \neq p_2$. To answer the second question, we find a 95% confidence interval for $p_1 - p_2$. (Students might choose a different confidence level.)
**Solve:** All counts are large enough for both a significance test and a large-sample confidence interval. We find $\hat{p}_1 = \frac{286}{539} \doteq 0.5306$, $\hat{p}_2 = \frac{164}{292} \doteq 0.5616$, and pooled proportion $\hat{p} = \frac{286+164}{539+292} \doteq 0.5415$. The standard error for the significance test is SE $\doteq 0.03621$, so $z = (0.5306 - 0.5616)/\text{SE} \doteq -0.86$, which has $P = 0.3898$.

For a large-sample confidence interval, the standard error is SE $\doteq 0.03613$, so the 95% confidence interval is $-0.0310 \pm 0.0708 \doteq -0.1018$ to $0.0398$.

Using the plus four method: $\tilde{p}_1 = \frac{286+1}{539+2} \doteq 0.5305$ and $\tilde{p}_2 = \frac{164+1}{292+2} \doteq 0.5612$, SE $\doteq 0.03603$, and the interval is $-0.0307 \pm 0.0706 \doteq -0.1013$ to $0.0399$.
**Conclude:** The sample does not give evidence of a difference in seat belt usage, as we see from either the significance test ($P = 0.3898$) or the fact that the confidence interval contains 0.

**21.29. State:** How big is the difference in the proportions of mice ready to breed in good acorn years ($p_1$) and bad acorn years ($p_2$)?
**Formulate:** We give a 90% confidence interval for $p_1 - p_2$.
**Solve:** One count is only 7, and the guidelines for using the large-sample method call for all counts to be at least 10, so we use the plus four method. We have $\tilde{p}_1 = \frac{55}{74} \doteq 0.7432$, $\tilde{p}_2 = \frac{11}{19} \doteq 0.5789$, and SE $\doteq 0.1241$. The plus four 90% confidence interval is $(\tilde{p}_1 - \tilde{p}_2) \pm 1.645\,\text{SE} = 0.1643 \pm 0.2042 \doteq -0.0399$ to $0.3685$.
**Conclude:** We are 90% confident that the proportion of mice ready to breed in good acorn years is between 0.04 lower than and 0.37 higher than the proportion in bad acorn years.

**21.30. State:** Is there evidence that the proportion of students who succeed is different for urban/suburban backgrounds ($p_1$) versus rural/small-town backgrounds ($p_2$)? How large is the difference?
**Formulate:** For the first question, we test $H_0$: $p_1 = p_2$ versus $H_a$: $p_1 \neq p_2$, and for the second, we construct a 90% confidence interval.
**Solve:** The smallest count is 13, so both significance testing and large-sample confidence interval procedures are safe. We find $\hat{p}_1 = \frac{52}{65} = 0.8$, $\hat{p}_2 = \frac{30}{55} \doteq 0.5455$, and $\hat{p} = \frac{52+30}{65+55} \doteq 0.6833$. Then for the significance test, SE $= \sqrt{\hat{p}(1-\hat{p})(\frac{1}{65} + \frac{1}{55})} \doteq 0.08523$, so $z = (\hat{p}_1 - \hat{p}_2)/\text{SE} \doteq 2.99$ and $P = 0.0028$.

For a confidence interval, SE $= \sqrt{\frac{\hat{p}_1(1-\hat{p}_1)}{65} + \frac{\hat{p}_2(1-\hat{p}_2)}{55}} \doteq 0.08348$, so the 90% confidence interval for $p_1 - p_2$ is $(\hat{p}_1 - \hat{p}_2) \pm 1.645\,\text{SE} = 0.2545 \pm 0.1373 \doteq 0.1172$ to $0.3919$.

Using the plus four method: $\tilde{p}_1 = \frac{52+1}{65+2} \doteq 0.7910$ and $\tilde{p}_2 = \frac{30+1}{55+2} \doteq 0.5439$, SE $\doteq 0.08258$, and the interval is $0.2472 \pm 0.1358 \doteq 0.1114$ to $0.3830$.
**Conclude:** We have strong evidence (significant at $\alpha = 0.01$) that there is a difference in success rates. Specifically, we are 90% confident that the success rate for urban/suburban students is between about 12 and 39 (or 11 and 38) percentage points higher.

**21.31. State:** Do children who attend preschool have less need for social services as adults? How large is the difference between the proportions of the preschool ($p_1$) and non-preschool ($p_2$) populations that require social services?

**Formulate:** For the first question, we test $H_0$: $p_1 = p_2$ versus $H_a$: $p_1 < p_2$. To answer the second question, we find a 95% confidence interval for $p_1 - p_2$. (Students might choose a different confidence level.)

**Solve:** All counts are large enough for both a significance test and a large-sample confidence interval. We find $\hat{p}_1 = \frac{38}{62} \doteq 0.6129$ and $\hat{p}_2 = \frac{49}{61} \doteq 0.8033$, and pooled proportion $\hat{p} = \frac{38+49}{62+61} \doteq 0.7073$. The standard error for the significance test is $\text{SE} \doteq 0.08205$, so $z = (0.5306 - 0.5616)/\text{SE} \doteq -2.32$, which has $P = 0.0102$.

For a large-sample confidence interval, the standard error is $\text{SE} \doteq 0.08011$, so the 95% confidence interval is $-0.1904 \pm 0.1570 \doteq -0.3474$ to $-0.0334$.

Using the plus four method: $\tilde{p}_1 = \frac{38+1}{62+2} \doteq 0.6094$ and $\tilde{p}_2 = \frac{49+1}{61+2} \doteq 0.7937$, $\text{SE} \doteq 0.07949$, and the interval is $-0.1843 \pm 0.1558 \doteq -0.3401$ to $-0.0285$.

**Conclude:** The sample gives strong evidence that the preschool population has less need for social services than the non-preschool population. In fact, we are 95% confident that these proportions differ by between 0.03 and 0.35 (or 0.03 and 34).

**21.32. State:** Is there evidence of a difference between the proportions of women ($p_1$) and men ($p_2$) who succeed?

**Formulate:** We test $H_0$: $p_1 = p_2$ versus $H_a$: $p_1 \neq p_2$.

**Solve:** The smallest count is 11, so a large-sample significance test is safe. We find $\hat{p}_1 = \frac{23}{34} \doteq 0.6765$, $\hat{p}_2 = \frac{60}{89} \doteq 0.6742$, and $\hat{p} = \frac{23+60}{34+89} \doteq 0.6748$. Then $\text{SE} = \sqrt{\hat{p}(1-\hat{p})(\frac{1}{34} + \frac{1}{89})} \doteq 0.09445$, so $z = (\hat{p}_1 - \hat{p}_2)/\text{SE} \doteq 0.02$. This gives $P = 0.9840$.

**Conclude:** There is no reason to believe that women's and men's success rates are different.

**21.33.** The study used an experimental design; the other option described in this exercise is an observational study. It is possible that families in which the parents choose to enroll their children in preschool had different characteristics than non-preschool families. Those characteristics might have affected the childrens' use of social services as adults. With the experimental design, any systematic effect of those characteristics should be removed by the random assignment.

**21.34. State:** What proportion $p$ of customers at this store use a credit card? How do the proportions using a credit card differ for impulse ($p_1$) and planned ($p_2$) purchases?

**Formulate:** For the first question, we find a 95% confidence interval for $p$. (Note this is a *one-sample* problem.) For the second question, we test $H_0$: $p_1 = p_2$ versus $H_a$: $p_1 \neq p_2$.

**Solve:** All counts are large enough to use large-sample procedures. For the first question, we need the pooled proportion $\hat{p} = \frac{13+35}{31+66} \doteq 0.4948$. The standard error for this confidence interval is $\text{SE} = 0.05076$, and the interval is $\hat{p} \pm 1.96\,\text{SE} = 0.4948 \pm 0.0995 = 0.3953$ to $0.5943$. Using the plus four method: $\tilde{p} = \frac{48+2}{97+4} \doteq 0.4950$, the standard error is $\text{SE} = 0.04975$, and the interval is $\tilde{p} \pm 1.96\,\text{SE} = 0.4950 \pm 0.0975 = 0.3975$ to $0.5926$. For the significance test, we need the two sample proportions $\hat{p}_1 = \frac{13}{31} \doteq 0.4194$ and $\hat{p}_2 = \frac{35}{66} \doteq 0.5303$, as well as the pooled proportion $\hat{p}$ computed before. The standard error for the significance test is $\text{SE} \doteq 0.10886$, so $z = (\hat{p}_1 - \hat{p}_2)/\text{SE} \doteq -1.02$ and $P = 0.3078$.

**Conclude:** With either large-sample or plus four methods, we are 95% confident that between 40% and 59% of all customers pay by credit card. The data do not give good evidence that credit card use differs by type of purchase.

# Chapter 22 Solutions

**22.1.** **(a)** A two-sample $z$ for proportions: We are comparing proportions (percents) from two independent samples. **(b)** A two-sample $t$ for means: We are comparing means from two independent samples.

**Note:** *In both cases, we could perform a significance test and/or construct a confidence interval for the difference.*

**22.2.** A one-sample $t$ for means—specifically, construct a confidence interval for $\mu$.

**22.3.** No: We have information about all players, not just a sample. (Another consideration is that salary distributions, especially those of professional athletes, are often very sharply skewed, so $t$ procedures might not be safe even if we could justify treating these numbers as an SRS from some larger population.)

**22.4.** **(a)** Use a $t$ test for means (we want to examine the mean of responses to the attractiveness question). **(b)** A matched-pairs test would be appropriate, because we should keep each couple's responses together.

**22.5.** **(a)** Use a two-sample $z$ for proportions. **(b)** Two-sample $t$ for means. **(c)** Two-sample $z$ for proportions.

**22.6.** **(a)** Label the subjects from 01 to 44, and choose 22 subjects to eat regular chips first. From line 101 of Table B, we choose

19, 22, 39, 34, and 05.

**(b)** Use a matched-pairs test for means (that is, a one-sample $t$ test for differences).

**22.7.** A diagram of the design is shown below.

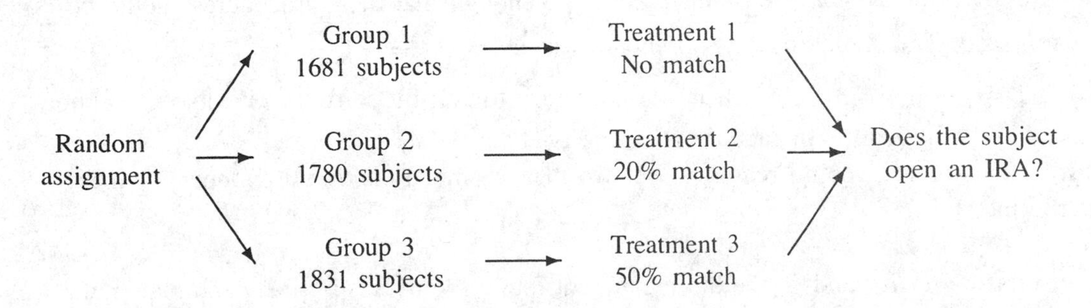

**22.8. Formulate:** We give 95% confidence intervals for the proportions $p_0$, $p_1$, and $p_2$ of taxpayers who would open an IRA if given each offer.
**Solve:** All counts are large enough to use large-sample procedures. In the table below are the sample proportions $\hat{p}$ (or plus four proportions $\tilde{p}$), the standard errors $\text{SE} = \sqrt{\hat{p}(1-\hat{p})/n}$ (or $\sqrt{\tilde{p}(1-\tilde{p})/n}$), the margin of error 1.96 SE, and the 95% confidence intervals. For example, $\hat{p}$ for the control group is $\hat{p} = \frac{49}{1681} \doteq 0.0291$.

| | Estimate | SE | m.e. | Interval |
|---|---|---|---|---|
| Control | $\hat{p} \doteq 0.0291$ | 0.00410 | 0.00804 | 0.0211 to 0.0372 |
| 20% match | $\hat{p} \doteq 0.1348$ | 0.00810 | 0.01587 | 0.1190 to 0.1507 |
| 50% match | $\hat{p} \doteq 0.2490$ | 0.01011 | 0.01981 | 0.2292 to 0.2689 |
| Control | $\tilde{p} \doteq 0.0303$ | 0.00417 | 0.00818 | 0.0221 to 0.0384 |
| 20% match | $\tilde{p} \doteq 0.1357$ | 0.00811 | 0.01589 | 0.1198 to 0.1515 |
| 50% match | $\tilde{p} \doteq 0.2496$ | 0.01010 | 0.01980 | 0.2298 to 0.2694 |

**Conclude:** Based on these intervals, it appears that matching the contribution has a noticeable impact on the proportion of families opening IRAs.

**22.9. Formulate:** With $p_1$ and $p_2$ as the proportions who open an IRA with (respectively) a 20% and a 50% match, we test $H_0$: $p_1 = p_2$ versus $H_a$: $p_1 < p_2$.
**Solve:** As we noted in the previous exercise, the counts are large enough to use the $z$ procedures. The sample proportions are $\hat{p}_1 = \frac{240}{1780} \doteq 0.1348$ and $\hat{p}_2 = \frac{456}{1831} \doteq 0.2490$, and the pooled proportion is $\hat{p} = \frac{240+456}{1780+1831} \doteq 0.1927$. The standard error for a significance test is $\text{SE} = \sqrt{\hat{p}(1-\hat{p})\left(\frac{1}{1780} + \frac{1}{1831}\right)} \doteq 0.01313$, and $z = (\hat{p}_1 - \hat{p}_2)/\text{SE} \doteq -8.70$. The $P$-value is $P(Z < -8.70)$, which is very small.
**Conclude:** The proportion opening an IRA is higher with a 50% match than with a 20% match.

**22.10. Formulate:** With $\mu_1$ and $\mu_2$ as the mean contribution with (respectively) a 20% and a 50% match, we test $H_0$: $\mu_1 = \mu_2$ versus $H_a$: $\mu_1 < \mu_2$.
**Solve:** We must assume that this data can be considered as having come from SRSs. We cannot assess Normality, but the samples are large enough that the $t$ procedures should be safe in any case. The standard error for this test is $\text{SE} = \sqrt{\frac{1332^2}{240} + \frac{1174^2}{456}} \doteq \$102.05$, so the $t$ statistic is $t = \dfrac{\bar{x}_1 - \bar{x}_2}{\text{SE}} \doteq -0.186$. It is not necessary to consult software or Table C to know that this is not significant. (In fact, the $P$-value is about 0.43.)
**Conclude:** This data gives no reason to believe that the mean contribution depends on the size of the match.

**22.11. Formulate:** Let $\mu_0$ and $\mu_1$ be the mean contribution with (respectively) no match and a 20% match. We give a 95% confidence interval for $\mu_1 - \mu_0$ (the added contribution due to the 20% match).
**Solve:** We must assume that this data can be considered as having come from SRSs. We cannot assess Normality, but the samples are large enough for the $t$ procedures to be safe in any case. The standard error for this interval is $\text{SE} = \sqrt{\frac{1652^2}{49} + \frac{1332^2}{240}} \doteq \$251.17$, and the confidence interval is $\bar{x}_1 - \bar{x}_0 \pm t^* \text{SE}$, where $t^* = 2.021$ (df = 40, from Table C) or

$t^* = 1.9993$ (df $= 61.37$, from software). This gives either $-\$333.62$ to $\$681.62$ (df $= 40$) or $-\$328.19$ to $\$676.19$ (df $= 61.37$).

**Conclude:** We are 95% confident that the added contribution due to offering a 20% match is between about $-\$330$ and $\$680$.

**22.12. Formulate:** Let $p_1$ be the proportion of students with a college graduate parent in 2004, and $p_2$ be that proportion in 1978. We find a 99% confidence interval for $p_1 - p_2$ (the increase in this proportion over time).

**Solve:** All counts are large enough to use large-sample (or plus four) procedures safely. The sample proportions are $\hat{p}_1 = \frac{1014}{2158} \doteq 0.4699$ and $\hat{p}_2 = \frac{5617}{17554} \doteq 0.3200$, so the standard error for a confidence interval is $\text{SE} \doteq 0.01131$, and the margin of error is $2.576\,\text{SE} \doteq 0.02912$. This gives the interval 0.1208 to 0.1790.

With such large sample sizes, the plus four interval is nearly identical: $\tilde{p}_1 = \frac{1014+1}{2158+2} \doteq 0.4699$, $\tilde{p}_2 = \frac{5617+1}{17554+2} \doteq 0.3200$, $\text{SE} \doteq 0.01130$, and the margin of error is 0.02911, and the interval is again 0.1208 to 0.1790.

**Conclude:** We are 95% confident that the proportion of students with a college-graduate parent increased between 0.12 and 0.18 from 1978 to 2004.

**22.13. Formulate:** We give a 99% confidence interval for $p$, the proportion of all students in 2004 who had at least one college-educated parent.

**Solve:** The counts of successes and failures are both much more than 10. The sample proportion (found in the previous solution) is $\hat{p} \doteq 0.4699$ and the standard error is $\text{SE} = \sqrt{\hat{p}(1-\hat{p})/2158} \doteq 0.01074$. The 99% confidence interval is therefore $\hat{p} \pm 2.576\,\text{SE} \doteq 0.4699 \pm 0.02767 = 0.4422$ to 0.4976. The plus four interval is nearly identical: $\tilde{p} = 0.4699$, $\text{SE} \doteq 0.01073$, and the interval is $0.4699 \pm 0.02765 = 0.4423$ to 0.4976.

**Conclude:** We are 99% confident that the proportion of students with at least one college-educated parent in 2004 was between 0.44 and 0.50.

**22.14. Formulate:** Let $\mu_1$ be the mean score for the population of students with at least one college-graduate parent, and $\mu_2$ be the mean score for other group of students. We wish to test $H_0$: $\mu_1 = \mu_2$ versus $H_a$: $\mu_1 \neq \mu_2$, and find a 95% confidence interval for $\mu_1 - \mu_2$.

**Solve:** We assume that we have SRSs from Normal populations (although the sample sizes are large, so Normality is not crucial). With the given means and standard deviations, we have $\text{SE} = \sqrt{\frac{28.6^2}{1014} + \frac{22.3^2}{410}} \doteq 1.4211$, so $t = \dfrac{\bar{x}_1 - \bar{x}_2}{\text{SE}} \doteq 15.48$. If is not necessary to consult software or Table C to know that this is significant at any reasonable level $\alpha$.

To find a 95% confidence interval for the difference, we take $\bar{x}_1 - \bar{x}_2 \pm t^*\,\text{SE}$, where $t^* = 1.984$ (df $= 100$, Table C) or 1.9624 (df $= 962.12$, software). The interval is therefore either 19.18 to 24.82 (df $= 100$) or 19.21 to 24.79 (df $= 962.12$).

**Conclude:** We have very strong evidence that students with at least one college-graduate parent score higher; specifically, we are 95% confident that they score between 19.2 and 24.8 points higher on average.

**22.15. Formulate:** We find a 95% confidence interval for $\mu_1$ (as defined in the previous solution).
**Solve:** We assume that we have an SRS from a Normal population (although the sample size is large, so Normality is not crucial). We find SE $= 28.6/\sqrt{1014} \doteq 0.8981$; the interval is $\bar{x}_1 \pm t^*$ SE; whether we use $t^* = 1.962$ (df $= 100$, Table C) or 1.9623 (df $= 1013$, software), the interval rounds to 315.24 to 318.76 points.
**Conclude:** We are 95% confident that the mean score for students with at least one college-graduate parent is between 315.2 and 318.8 points.

**22.16. Formulate:** We test $H_0$: $\mu_w = \mu_m$ versus $H_a$: $\mu_w \neq \mu_m$.
**Solve:** We assume that we have SRSs from Normal populations (although the sample sizes are large, so Normality is not crucial). Note that this exercise gives standard errors $(s/\sqrt{n})$ rather than standard deviations $(s)$. We find SE $= \sqrt{0.9^2 + 1.0^2} \doteq 1.3454$, so $t = (305 - 308)/\text{SE} \doteq -2.23$. The $P$-value from Table C (for df $= 1000$) is $0.02 < P < 0.04$. Software gives $P = 0.0259$ (df $= 2111.6$).
**Conclude:** Either way, we have evidence (significant at $\alpha = 0.05$) that the mean mathematics score is different—specifically, the men's mean is higher.

**22.17. Formulate:** We give a 99% confidence interval for $p$, the proportion of all Division I college athletes who believe that they have received preferential treatment.
**Solve:** The sample proportion is $\hat{p} = \frac{225}{757} \doteq 0.2972$, the standard error is SE $= \sqrt{\hat{p}(1-\hat{p})/757} \doteq 0.01661$, and the 99% confidence interval is

$$\hat{p} \pm 2.576\,\text{SE} \doteq 0.2972 \pm 0.04279 = 0.2544 \text{ to } 0.3400.$$

The plus four estimate is $\tilde{p} = \frac{227}{761} \doteq 0.2983$, the standard error is SE $= \sqrt{\tilde{p}(1-\tilde{p})/761} \doteq 0.01658$, and the plus four 99% confidence interval is

$$\tilde{p} \pm 2.576\,\text{SE} \doteq 0.2983 \pm 0.04272 = 0.2556 \text{ to } 0.3410.$$

**Conclude:** We are 99% confident that between 25% and 34% of Division I college athletes believe they have been given preferential treatment.

**22.18. (a)** The $t$ procedures are fairly safe with non-Normal data, provided we have large samples (as we do here).
**(b) Formulate:** We give a 95% confidence interval for $\mu_f$, the mean endurance for female mice swimming.
**Solve:** We assume that these data come from an SRS. We were given $\bar{x} = 11.4$ and $s = 26.09$ minutes, and for df $= 100$, we have $t^* = 1.984$ (software gives 1.9748 for df $= 161$). Therefore the 95% confidence interval is either $11.4 \pm 4.067 = 7.333$ to 15.467 minutes, or $11.4 \pm 4.048 = 7.352$ to 15.448 minutes.
**Conclude:** We are 95% confident that the mean endurance for female mice swimming is between 7.3 and 15.5 minutes.
**(c) Formulate:** We give a 95% confidence interval for $\mu_f - \mu_m$, the mean difference in endurance times.
**Solve:** Again, we assume that the conditions for $t$ procedures are met. The standard error of the difference $\bar{x}_f - \bar{x}_m$ is SE $\doteq 2.1292$. With either $t^* = 1.984$ (df $= 100$) or $t^* = 1.9728$ (df $= 186.02$), the interval is either 0.4758 to 8.9242 minutes, or 0.4996 to 8.9004 minutes.
**Conclude:** We are 95% confident that, on the average, female mice can endure between 0.5 and 8.9 minutes longer than males.

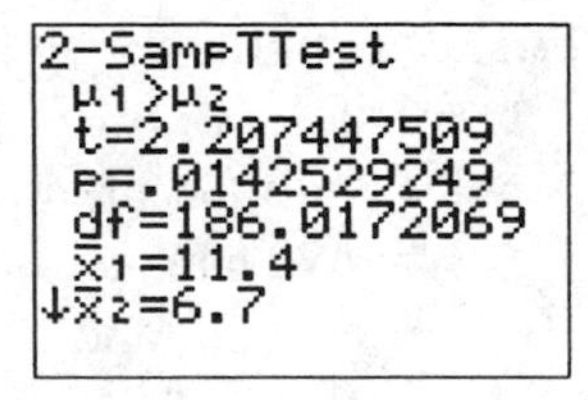


**22.19. Formulate:** We test $H_0$: $\mu_f = \mu_m$ versus $H_a$: $\mu_f > \mu_m$ (assuming we had some prior reason to suspect that females had higher endurance).
**Solve:** We assume that the conditions for inference are met. The standard error of the difference $\bar{x}_f - \bar{x}_m$ is SE $\doteq 2.1292$ (this was also found in the previous solution), and the test statistic is $t = (11.4 - 6.7)/\text{SE} \doteq 2.21$. With df $= 100$, Table C tells us that $0.01 < P < 0.02$; software gives $P = 0.0143$ (df $= 186.02$).
**Conclude:** This is fairly strong evidence (significant at the 5% level) that female mice have higher endurance.

**22.20. Formulate:** We give a 95% confidence interval for $p$, the proportion of all adults who favor registration.
**Solve:** We have an SRS, and large enough counts to use $z$ procedures. We find that $\hat{p} = \frac{904}{1176} \doteq 0.7687$, SE $\doteq 0.0123$, and the 95% confidence interval is $0.7687 \pm 0.0241 \doteq 0.7446$ to $0.7928$. Using the plus four method: $\tilde{p} = \frac{906}{1180} \doteq 0.7678$, SE $\doteq 0.0123$, and the plus four interval is $0.7678 \pm 0.0241 \doteq 0.7437$ to $0.7919$.
**Conclude:** We are 95% confident that between 74.5% and 79.3% (or 74.4% and 79.2%) of adults favor registration of handguns and pistols.

**22.21.** We have $\hat{p}_{2001} \doteq 0.7687 \doteq 76.9\%$ (as in the previous exercise) and $\hat{p}_{1998} \doteq 0.8526 \doteq 85.3\%$.
**Formulate:** We test $H_0$: $p_{1998} = p_{2001}$ versus $H_a$: $p_{1998} > p_{2001}$.
**Solve:** We assume both samples were SRSs; all counts are much more than 5. The pooled proportion is $\hat{p} = \frac{904+1024}{1176+1201} \doteq 0.8111$, so SE $\doteq 0.01606$ and $z = (0.8526 - 0.7687)/\text{SE} \doteq 5.23$, for which $P < 0.0001$.
**Conclude:** We have very strong evidence that the proportion favoring mandatory registration was lower in 2001.

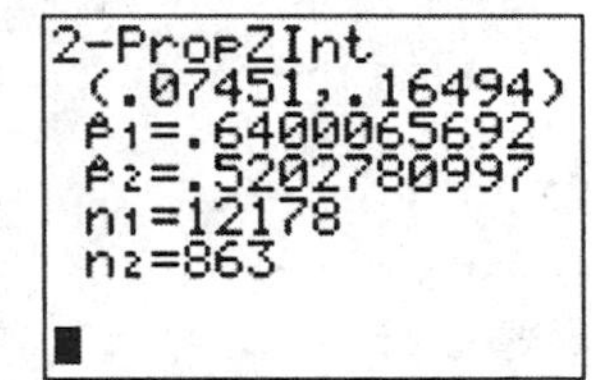


**22.22. (a)** The sample sizes (especially for Europeans) are so large that even a small difference between Americans and Europeans would be significant.
**(b) Formulate:** Let $p_1$ and $p_2$ be (respectively) the proportion of Americans and Europeans who believe that applying biotechnology to food production is risky. We give a 99% confidence interval for $p_2 - p_1$.
**Solve:** We assume that we have two SRSs; all counts are large enough for $z$ procedures. With $\hat{p}_1 = 0.52$ and $\hat{p}_2 = 0.64$, SE $= \sqrt{\frac{\hat{p}_1(1-\hat{p}_1)}{863} + \frac{\hat{p}_2(1-\hat{p}_2)}{12,178}} \doteq 0.01755$, so the 99% confidence interval is $(0.64 - 0.52) \pm (2.576)(0.01755) = 0.0748$ to $0.1652$. The TI-83 output on the right gives rough confirmation of this, with slight differences because 0.52 and 0.64 were entered as $\frac{449}{863}$ and $\frac{7794}{12,178}$. If we use those counts, we can apply the plus four method: $\tilde{p}_1 \doteq 0.5202$ and $\tilde{p}_2 \doteq 0.6400$, SE $\doteq 0.01753$, and the interval is $0.1198 \pm 0.0452 \doteq 0.0746$ to $0.1649$.
**Conclude:** We are 99% confident that the percent of Europeans who believe applying biotechnology to food production is risky is between 7.5 and 16.5 percentage points higher than that percent of Americans.

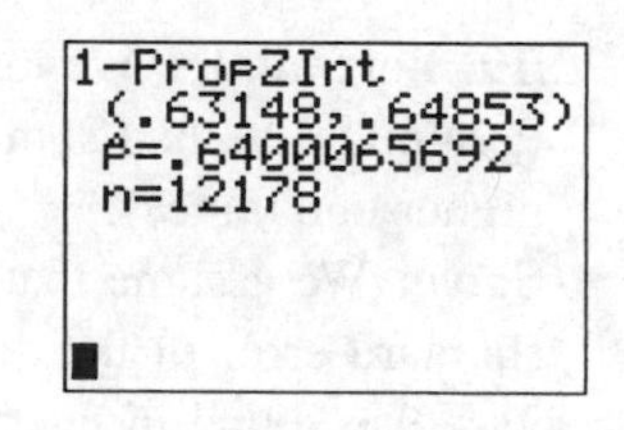


**22.23. Formulate:** We give a 95% confidence interval for $p$, the proportion of all European adults who consider the use of biotechnology in food production risky.
**Solve:** We have an SRS, and both counts are much more than 10. $\hat{p} = 0.64$, and SE $\doteq 0.00435$, so the 95% confidence interval is $0.64 \pm 1.96\,\text{SE} = 0.6315$ to $0.6485$. The TI-83 output on the right gives rough confirmation of this, with slight differences because 0.64 was entered as $\frac{7794}{12,178}$. Because the sample size is so large, the plus four method gives almost exactly the same interval: $\tilde{p} = \frac{7796}{12,182} \doteq 0.6400$, SE $\doteq 0.00435$, and the plus four interval is $0.6400 \pm 0.0085 \doteq 0.6314$ to $0.6485$.
**Conclude:** We are 95% confident that the the proportion of all European adults who believe the use of biotechnology in food production is risky is between 0.63 and 0.65.

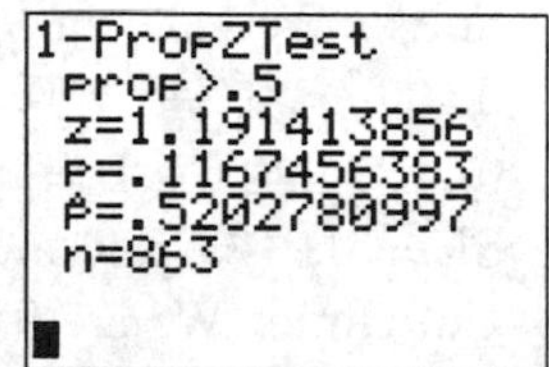


**22.24. Formulate:** Let $p$ be the proportion of all American adults who consider the use of biotechnology in food production risky. We test $H_0$: $p = 0.5$ versus $H_a$: $p > 0.5$.
**Solve:** We have an SRS, and both counts are greater than 5. With $\hat{p} = 0.52$, the test statistic is $z = (0.52 - 0.5)/\sqrt{\frac{(0.5)(0.5)}{863}} \doteq 1.175$, so $P = 0.1200$ (Table A gives 0.1190). The TI-83 output on the right gives rough confirmation of this, with slight differences because 0.52 was entered as $\frac{449}{863}$.
**Conclude:** We cannot conclude that more than half of Americans hold this opinion.

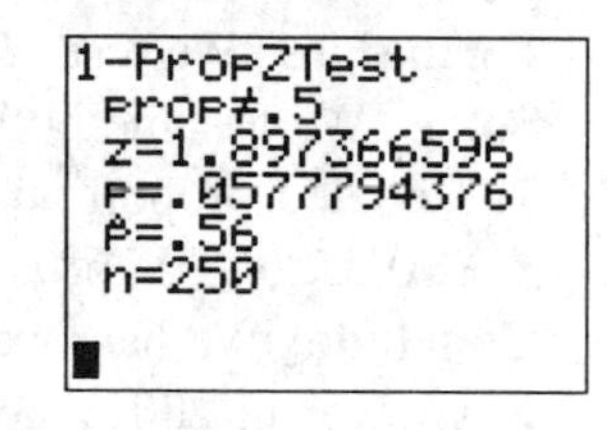


**22.25. Formulate:** Let $p$ be the proportion of times a Belgian Euro lands heads when spun. We test $H_0$: $p = 0.5$ versus $H_a$: $p \neq 0.5$.
**Solve:** We consider the 250 spins to be an SRS; both counts are much more than 5. We compute $\hat{p} = \frac{140}{250} = 0.56$ and $z = (0.56 - 0.5)/\sqrt{\frac{(0.5)(0.5)}{250}} \doteq 1.90$. The $P$-value is 0.0578 (0.0574 with Table A).
**Conclude:** We have some evidence that the Euro is not balanced, but it is not quite significant at the 5% level.

**22.26. Formulate:** We give a 95% confidence interval for $p$ (as defined in the previous exercise).
**Solve:** $\hat{p} = \frac{140}{250} = 0.56$, SE $\doteq 0.03139$, and the 95% confidence interval is $0.56 \pm 0.05164 \doteq 0.5084$ to $0.6116$. Using the plus four method, $\tilde{p} = \frac{142}{254} \doteq 0.5591$. SE $\doteq 0.03115$, and the plus four interval is $0.5591 \pm 0.05124 \doteq 0.5078$ to $0.6103$.
**Conclude:** We are 90% confident that a spun Euro lands heads between 50.8% and 61.2% (or 50.8% and 61.0%) of the time.

**22.27. Formulate:** We test $H_0$: $\mu_1 = \mu_2$ versus $H_a$: $\mu_1 > \mu_2$.
**Solve:** We assume that we have two SRSs from Normal populations. The standard error of the difference $\bar{x}_1 - \bar{x}_2$ is SE $\doteq 0.078716$, and the $t$ statistic is $t = (5.15 - 4.33)/\text{SE} \doteq 10.4$. Regardless of whether df $= 19$ or $32.39$, the $P$-value is tiny.
**Conclude:** We have strong evidence that the mean remating time is longer for large spermatophores.

**22.28. (a)** This is an observational study (one cannot "assign" a baby's birthweight).
**(b) Formulate:** We test $H_0$: $p_1 = p_2$ versus $H_a$: $p_1 < p_2$, where $p_1$ and $p_2$ are the high school graduation rates for (respectively) the VLBW male and control male populations.
**Solve:** We assume that our samples can be considered SRSs; all counts are large enough to use $z$ procedures. The graduation rates in our samples are $\hat{p}_1 \doteq 0.7397$ and $\hat{p}_2 \doteq 0.8283$, and the pooled graduation rate is $\hat{p} = \frac{179+193}{242+233} \doteq 0.7832$. Therefore $\text{SE} \doteq 0.03782$ and $z = (0.7397 - 0.8283)/\text{SE} \doteq -2.34$. The one-sided $P$-value is $P = 0.0096$.
**Conclude:** We have strong evidence (significant at $\alpha = 0.01$) that VLBW graduation rates are lower.

**22.29. Formulate:** Let $\mu_1$ be the mean IQ for the VLBW male population, and $\mu_2$ be the mean IQ for the control population. We test $H_0$: $\mu_1 = \mu_2$ versus $H_a$: $\mu_1 < \mu_2$.
**Solve:** We assume that we have SRSs; the samples are fairly large, so non-Normality should not be a concern. The standard error of the difference $\bar{x}_1 - \bar{x}_2$ is $\text{SE} \doteq 2.02786$, and the $t$ statistic is $t = (87.6 - 94.7)/\text{SE} \doteq -3.50$. Regardless of whether we take $\text{df} = 100$ or $216.4$, the $P$-value is less than 0.0005.
**Conclude:** We have very strong evidence that VLBW men have lower IQs.

**22.30. Formulate:** Let $p_1$ and $p_2$ be the proportions using drugs in (respectively) the female VLBW and female control populations, and let $\mu_1$ and $\mu_2$ be the mean IQs for those populations. We test $H_0$: $p_1 = p_2$ versus $H_a$: $p_1 \neq p_2$ and $H_0$: $\mu_1 = \mu_2$ versus $H_a$: $\mu_1 \neq \mu_2$.
**Solve:** We assume SRSs from both populations. The counts are large enough for $z$ procedures for the first significance test, and the sample sizes are large enough that we need not worry about non-Normality for the second. Compute $\hat{p}_1 \doteq 0.2937$, $\hat{p}_2 \doteq 0.4194$, and $\hat{p} = \frac{37+52}{126+124} \doteq 0.3560$. Then $\text{SE} \doteq 0.06057$, and the test statistic is $z = (0.2937 - 0.4194)/\text{SE} \doteq -2.08$. This has a two-sided $P$-value of $P = 0.0376$.

For comparing IQs, we compute $\text{SE} \doteq 1.7337$. The test statistic is $t = (86.2 - 89.8)/\text{SE} \doteq -2.08$. For any choice of df (100 or 247.1), this $t$ has a two-sided $P$-value of about 0.04.
**Conclude:** Both tests are significant at $\alpha = 0.05$; we have evidence that high school graduation rates and IQs are lower for the VLBW female population.

**22.31. Formulate:** Let $p_1$ be the proportion of walking flies responding to vibration, and $p_2$ be that proportion for resting flies. We test $H_0$: $p_1 = p_2$ versus $H_a$: $p_1 \neq p_2$.
**Solve:** One count is only 4; this makes the use of $z$ procedures potentially risky. Proceeding in spite of this, we find $\hat{p}_1 = \frac{54}{64} \doteq 0.8438$ and $\hat{p}_2 = \frac{4}{32} = 0.1250$, $\hat{p} = \frac{54+4}{64+32} \doteq 0.6042$, $\text{SE} \doteq 0.10588$, and $z = (0.8438 - 0.1250)/\text{SE} \doteq 6.79$. The $P$-value is tiny.
**Conclude:** We have strong evidence (significant at any reasonable choice of $\alpha$) that walking and resting flies respond differently. Although the conditions for inference were not quite met, the difference in the proportions was so great that the conclusion is almost certainly correct.

**22.32. Formulate:** Let $\mu_1$ be the mean cholesterol level for pets, and $\mu_2$ be the mean level for clinic dogs. We test $H_0$: $\mu_1 = \mu_2$ versus $H_a$: $\mu_1 > \mu_2$.
**Solve:** We find SE $\doteq$ 16.1870 mg/dl and $t \doteq 1.17$, so $0.10 < P < 0.15$ (df = 22) or $P = 0.1234$ (df = 43.3).
**Conclude:** This is not enough evidence to reject $H_0$; we cannot conclude that pet cholesterol levels are higher.

**22.33. Formulate:** With $\mu_1$ and $\mu_2$ as defined in the previous exercise, we give an 95% confidence interval for $\mu_1 - \mu_2$.
**Solve:** The interval is $(193 - 174) \pm t^*\text{SE}$. Using $t^* = 2.074$ (df = 22), this gives $-14.57$ to 52.57 mg/dl; using $t^* = 2.0164$ (df = 43.3), the interval is $-13.64$ to 51.64 mg/dl.
**Conclude:** We are 95% confident that the difference in mean cholesterol levels in pets and clinic dogs is between $-14.57$ and 52.57 mg/dl (or $-13.64$ and 51.64 mg/dl).

**22.34. Formulate:** We give a 95% confidence interval for $\mu_1$ (as defined in the previous two exercises).
**Solve:** With df = 25, the interval is $193 \pm (2.060)(68/\sqrt{26}) \doteq 165.53$ to 220.47 mg/dl.
**Conclude:** We are 95% confident that the mean cholesterol level in pets is between 165.5 and 220.5 mg/dl.

**22.35.** For all procedures, we are assuming that we have two SRSs from each population, and that underlying distributions are Normal. The chief threat to validity is that it is unlikely that we have random samples from either population, especially among pets.

**22.36. Formulate:** We test $H_0$: $\mu = 12$ versus $H_a$: $\mu > 12$, where $\mu$ is the mean age at first word (in months).
**Solve:** We regard the sample as an SRS; a stemplot (not shown) shows that the data are right-skewed with a high outlier (26 months). If we proceed with the $t$ procedures in spite of this, we find $\bar{x} = 13$ and $s \doteq 4.9311$ months. Therefore, $t = \frac{13-12}{4.9311/\sqrt{20}} \doteq 0.907$ with df = 19, so $0.15 < P < 0.20$ (software gives 0.1879).

We might choose to drop the additional outlier before proceeding (although it is difficult to justify that this child should not be considered a "normal" child). Not surprisingly, this gives us even less reason to reject $H_0$: $\bar{x} \doteq 12.3158$ and $s \doteq 3.9729$ months, so $t \doteq 0.346$ and $P = 0.3665$.
**Conclude:** We cannot conclude that the mean age at first word is greater than one year.

**22.37. Formulate:** We test $H_0$: $\mu = 0.604$ inch versus $H_a$: $\mu \neq 0.604$ inch.
**Solve:** Assuming that we have a random sample, and that the distribution is roughly Normal (a stemplot supports this), the $t$ procedures are safe. We find $\bar{x} = 0.60375$ and $s \doteq 0.001127$ inch. Therefore, $t = \frac{0.60375-0.604}{s/\sqrt{40}} \doteq -1.403$ with df = 39, so $0.10 < P < 0.20$ (software gives 0.1684).
**Conclude:** We do not have strong enough evidence to conclude that the mean distance differs from the specification.

**22.38. Formulate:** We give a 90% confidence interval for $\mu$, the mean age at first word (in months).

**Solve:** Using all 20 children, we find $\bar{x} = 13$ and $s \doteq 4.9311$ months. For df $= 19$, $t^* = 1.729$, so the interval is $13 \pm 1.9064 \doteq 11.09$ to $14.91$ months.

If we drop the late-speaking child (see the solution to Exercise 22.36), $\bar{x} \doteq 12.3158$ and $s \doteq 3.9729$ months, and $t^* = 1.734$ for df $= 18$, so the interval is $12.3158 \pm 1.5804 \doteq 10.74$ to $13.90$ months.

**Conclude:** We are 90% confident that the mean age at first word for normal children is between 11 and 15 (or 10.7 and 13.9) months.

**22.39. Formulate:** Do a two-sided test because we have no advance claim about the direction of the difference: $H_0$: $\mu_1 = \mu_2$ versus $H_a$: $\mu_1 \neq \mu_2$.

**Solve:** We view the data as coming for two SRSs; the distributions show no radical departures from Normality. The means and standard deviations of the lightness scores are $\bar{x}_1 \doteq 48.9513$ and $s_1 \doteq 0.2154$ (cotton) and $\bar{x}_2 \doteq 41.6488$ and $s_2 \doteq 0.3922$ (ramie). Ramie is darker (has a lower lightness score). The standard error for the significance test is SE $\doteq 0.1582$, and the test statistic is $t \doteq 46.16$. With either df $= 7$ or df $= 10.87$, the $P$-value is zero to many decimal places.

**Conclude:** There is overwhelming evidence that cotton is lighter than ramie.

**22.40. (a)** The design is shown below.

| | $n$ | $\bar{x}$ | $s$ |
|---|---|---|---|
| Method B | 8 | 41.2825 | 0.2550 |
| Method C | 8 | 42.4925 | 0.2939 |

**(b) Formulate:** We want to compare two means by testing $H_0$: $\mu_B = \mu_C$ versus $H_a$: $\mu_B \neq \mu_C$.

**Solve:** Stemplots (not shown) show that the distributions are somewhat irregular, as is common for small samples, but use of $t$ procedures appears justified. The summary statistics are given in the table on the right; method B gives a somewhat darker color (lower lightness score), but the difference between methods is small. The standard error is SE $\doteq 0.1376$ and the test statistic is $t = (\bar{x}_B - \bar{x}_C)/\text{SE} \doteq -8.79$. With df $= 7$, we see from Table C that $P < 0.001$; software (with df $= 13.73$) confirms that $P$ is very small.

**Conclude:** There is overwhelming evidence that method B gives darker color. However, the difference in mean lightness scores may be too small to be important in practice.

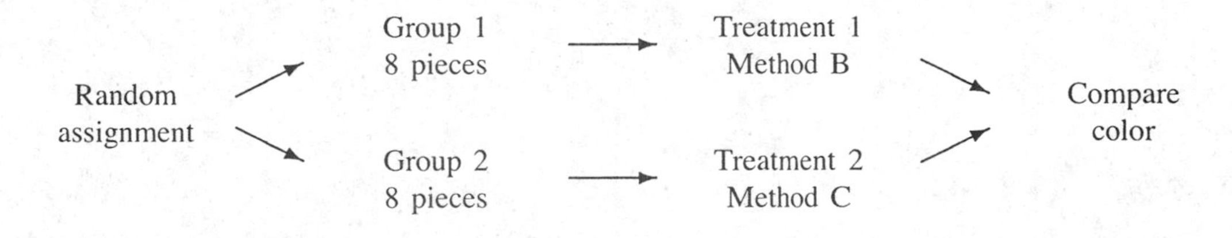

**22.41. Formulate:** We test $H_0$: $\mu_1 = \mu_2$ versus $H_a$: $\mu_1 \neq \mu_2$.

| Parent allows? | $n$ | $\bar{x}$ | $s$ |
|---|---|---|---|
| Yes | 65 | 4.1769 | 2.0261 |
| No | 29 | 4.5517 | 2.4251 |

| Parent allows drinking | | No parent allows drinking |
|---|---|---|
| 00000 | 1 | 000 |
| 55555550000 | 2 | 0 |
| 5500000000000 | 3 | 00000055 |
| 500000000000 | 4 | 000000 |
| 00000000 | 5 | 000 |
| 5000000 | 6 | 0 |
| 00000 | 7 | 000 |
| 00 | 8 | 0 |
| 0 | 9 | 00 |
| 0 | 10 | 0 |

**Solve:** The exercise states that we are willing to consider this an SRS. Back-to-back stemplots show that both distributions are slightly skewed, but $t$ procedures should be reasonably safe. (The stemplots also suggest that there is no significant difference in the means.) With the means and standard deviations in the table, we have SE $\doteq$ 0.5157 and $t = (\bar{x}_1 - \bar{x}_2)/\text{SE} \doteq -0.727$. This is so close to 0 that we know it is not significant even without consulting Table C or software. (Indeed, Table C tells us that $0.40 < P < 0.50$ for df $= 28$, and software gives $P = 0.47$ for df $= 46.19$.)
**Conclude:** There is no significant difference in the mean number of drinks between female students with a parent who allows drinking and those whose parents do not allow drinking.

**22.42. Formulate:** We give a 95% confidence interval for $p$, the proportion of female students who have at least one parent who allows drinking.
**Solve:** We have been told that we can consider this group to be an SRS, and the counts are 65 and 29, so large-sample methods can be used. We find $\hat{p} = \frac{65}{94} \doteq 0.6915$ and SE $\doteq 0.04764$, so the margin of error is $1.960\,\text{SE} \doteq 0.09337$, and the interval is 0.5981 to 0.7849.

The plus four estimate is $\tilde{p} = \frac{67}{98} \doteq 0.6837$, which gives SE $\doteq 0.04698$ and margin of error 0.09207, so the interval is 0.5916 to 0.7757.
**Conclude:** We are 95% confident that the proportion of female students who have at least one parent who allows drinking is between about 0.598 and 0.785 (or 0.592 and 0.776).

**22.43.** **(a)** Stemplots (back-to-back) are shown on the right. The diabetic potentials appear to be larger.

| | $n$ | $\bar{x}$ | $s$ |
|---|---|---|---|
| Diabetic | 24 | 13.0896 | 4.8391 |
| (no outlier) | 23 | 13.6130 | 4.1959 |
| Normal | 18 | 9.5222 | 2.5765 |

| Diabetic | | Normal |
|---|---|---|
| 1 | 0 | |
| | 0 | |
| | 0 | 4 |
| 7 | 0 | 6777 |
| 988 | 0 | 8888999 |
| 1000000 | 1 | 00 |
| 3 | 1 | 233 |
| 5444 | 1 | 4 |
| 76 | 1 | |
| 9988 | 1 | |
| | 2 | |
| 2 | 2 | |

**(b) Formulate:** We test $H_0$: $\mu_D = \mu_N$ versus $H_a$: $\mu_D \neq \mu_N$.

**Solve:** We assume we have two SRSs; the distributions appear to be safe for $t$ procedures. With the means and standard deviations in the table, the standard error is SE $\doteq$ 1.1595, so $t \doteq 3.077$. With df $= 17$, Table C tells use that $0.005 < P < 0.01$, while software gives $P = 0.0039$ (df $= 36.60$).

**Conclude:** We have very strong evidence that the electric potential in diabetic mice is greater than the potential in normal mice.

**(c) Solve:** With the outlier removed, the diabetic mean rises and the standard deviation decreases, so now SE $\doteq$ 1.0650 and $t \doteq 3.841$. This has a smaller $P$-value: either $0.001 < P < 0.002$ (df $= 16$, Table C) or $P = 0.0005$ (df $= 37.15$).

**Conclude:** With the outlier removed, the evidence that diabetic mice have a higher electric potential is stronger. (This makes sense, because the outlier was low; when it is removed, the diabetic numbers become higher overall.)

**22.44.** **(a) Formulate:** We want to compare the proportions $p_1$ (microwaved crackers that show checking) and $p_2$ (control crackers that show checking). This can be done either by testing $H_0$: $p_1 = p_2$ versus $H_a$: $p_1 < p_2$, or by constructing a confidence interval (95% or other) for $p_1 - p_2$. We do both in this exercise; students might choose one or the other, and might choose a different confidence level.

**Solve:** The "microwave checked" count is only 3, which means that the significance test is risky. We will give this result in any case; with such a large difference between the sample proportions, the result will clearly be significant: $\hat{p}_1 = \frac{3}{65} \doteq 0.0462$ and $\hat{p}_2 = \frac{57}{65} \doteq 0.8769$, the pooled proportion is $\hat{p} = \frac{3+57}{65+65} \doteq 0.4615$, SE $\doteq$ 0.08745, and $z \doteq -9.50$. (Because the significance test was not safe, we should not report a $P$-value; but again, we can be nearly certain that the two proportions are not equal.)

The large-sample interval should not be used either (we would like all counts to be 10 or more), but it is given here for any students who make a poor choice and do this computation: SE $\doteq$ 0.04835, and the 95% confidence interval is $\hat{p}_1 - \hat{p}_2 \pm 1.96\,\text{SE} \doteq -0.9255$ to $-0.7360$.

The plus four confidence interval is the only procedure that is really safe in this case (for 90% or higher confidence). The plus four estimates are $\tilde{p}_1 = \frac{3+1}{65+2} \doteq 0.0597$ and $\tilde{p}_2 = \frac{57+1}{65+2} \doteq 0.8657$. The plus four confidence interval uses the standard error

$$\text{SE} = \sqrt{\frac{\tilde{p}_1(1-\tilde{p}_1)}{67} + \frac{\tilde{p}_2(1-\tilde{p}_2)}{67}} \doteq 0.05073,$$

so the 95% plus four confidence interval is

$$\tilde{p}_1 - \tilde{p}_2 \pm 1.960\,\text{SE} \doteq -0.8060 \pm 0.0994 \doteq -0.9054 \text{ to } -0.7065.$$

**Conclude:** There is strong evidence that microwaved crackers are less likely to show checking. We are 95% confident that microwaving reduces the percent of checked crackers by between about 71% and 91%.

(b) **Formulate:** We want to compare the means $\mu_1$ and $\mu_2$, the breaking pressures of (respectively) microwaved and control crackers. We do this by testing $H_0$: $\mu_1 = \mu_2$ versus $H_a$: $\mu_1 > \mu_2$, and constructing a 95% confidence interval for $\mu_1 - \mu_2$ (students might choose different confidence levels).
**Solve:** We assume that the data can be considered SRSs from the two populations, and that the underlying distributions are (not too far from) Normal. The standard error is $\text{SE} \doteq \sqrt{\frac{33.6^2}{20} + \frac{22.6^2}{20}} \doteq 9.0546$, and the test statistic is $t = (\bar{x}_1 - \bar{x}_2)/\text{SE} \doteq 6.914$. The $P$-value is very small whether we use the conservative df $= 19$ or software df $= 33.27$.

For the confidence interval, take $\bar{x}_1 - \bar{x}_2 \pm t^*\text{SE}$, giving either 43.65 to 81.55 psi ($t^* = 2.093$, with df $= 19$) or 44.18 to 81.02 psi ($t^* = 2.0339$, with df $= 33.27$).
**Conclude:** There is very strong evidence that microwaving crackers increases their mean breaking strength. We are 95% confident that microwaved crackers withstand an additional 43.65 to 81.55 (or 44.18 to 81.02) psi before breaking.

**22.45. Formulate:** We give a 95% confidence interval for $\mu$, the mean date on which the tripod falls through the ice.
**Solve:** We assume that the data can be viewed as an SRS of fall-through times, and that the distribution is roughly Normal. (The stemplot in the solution of Exercise 7.39 supports this.) We find $n = 89$, $\bar{x} \doteq 15.4831$, and $s = 5.9888$ days. With df $= 88$ (or df $= 80$ from Table C), the 95% confidence interval is $\bar{x} \pm t^* s/\sqrt{n} = 14.22$ to $16.75$ days.
**Conclude:** We are 95% confident that, on the average, the tripod falls through the ice between 14 and 17 days from April 20—that is, May 3 through May 6.

**22.46.** Two of the counts are too small to perform a significance test safely (1 out of 11 blacks, 4 out of 31 whites).

**22.47. (a)** "SEM" stands for "standard error of the mean"; SEM $= s/\sqrt{n}$. **(b)** Two-sample $t$-tests were done, because wild-type and $aP2^{-/-}$ mice are separate (independent) groups. **(c)** The observed differences between the two groups of mice were so large that they would be unlikely to occur by chance if the two groups were not different. Specifically, if the groups were the same, and we took many samples, the difference in glucose levels would be so large less than 5% of the time, and the difference in insulin levels would be so large less than 0.5% of the time. We have stronger evidence of a difference in insulin levels.

**22.48.** The insulin means are $\bar{x}_1 = 5.9$ and $\bar{x}_2 = 0.75$ ng/ml, and the standard deviations are approximately $s_1 = 0.9\sqrt{10} \doteq 2.85$ and $s_2 = 0.2\sqrt{10} \doteq 0.632$ ng/ml.
**Formulate:** We test $H_0$: $\mu_I = \mu_G$ versus $H_a$: $\mu_I \neq \mu_G$.
**Solve:** The estimated standard error of the difference is $\text{SE} = \sqrt{0.9^2 + 0.2^2} \doteq 0.922$, so $t = (5.9 - 0.75)/\text{SE} \doteq 5.59$. With either df $= 9$ or df $= 9.89$, Table C allows us to say that $P < 0.001$.
**Conclude:** The evidence is even stronger than the paper claimed. (And with larger sample sizes, the evidence would be stronger still.)

Note that you do not actually need to compute $s_1$ and $s_2$ to find SE, but you do need them if you want to find the more accurate estimate for df. Doing so is overkill in this case because we do not know the correct sample sizes anyway.

**22.49. Formulate:** We want to compare the control standard deviation $\sigma_0$ to the 20% match standard deviation $\sigma_1$ by testing $H_0$: $\sigma_0 = \sigma_1$ versus $H_a$: $\sigma_0 \neq \sigma_1$.

**Solve:** The $F$ test statistic is $F = \frac{\text{larger } s^2}{\text{smaller } s^2} = \frac{1652^2}{1332^2} \doteq 1.54$.

Compare the calculated value $F = 1.54$ with critical values for the $F(48, 239)$ distribution. With Table D, refer to the $F(30, 200)$ distribution; there we see that 1.54 lies between the 0.025 and 0.05 critical values, so the two-sided $P$-value lies between 0.05 and 0.10. With software, we have $P = 0.0393$.

**Conclude:** With Table D, the evidence is not quite significant; using software, we have significant evidence at $\alpha = 0.05$ that the control group and the 20% match group variabilities are different. This conclusion cannot be trusted because the $F$ test depends heavily on Normality, and variables like these often have skewed distributions.

**22.50. Formulate:** We test $H_0$: $\sigma_1 = \sigma_2$ versus $H_a$: $\sigma_1 \neq \sigma_2$.

**Solve:** The test statistic is $F = \frac{68^2}{44^2} \doteq 2.388$ with df = 25 and 22. This $F$ value can be compared to Table D values for df = 20 and 20, where we find that $2.12 < F < 2.46$, so $0.05 < P < 0.10$ (software gives 0.043).

**Conclude:** With Table D, the evidence is not quite significant; using software, we have significant evidence at $\alpha = 0.05$ that the standard deviations differ.

**22.51. (a)** With df = 49, we take $t^* = 2.423$ (conservatively) or 2.403 (approximately) from Table C, or 2.405 (using software). The first and third of these are the best choices, but for a power computation, the second is acceptable. **(b)** Reject $H_0$ if $t \geq t^*$. Because $t = \bar{x}/(s/\sqrt{n})$, this means that we reject $H_0$ when $\bar{x} \geq t^*(108/\sqrt{50}) = 15.2735t^*$. For the three values of $t^*$ given above, this means that $\bar{x} \geq 37.01$, $\bar{x} \geq 36.70$, and $\bar{x} \geq 36.73$, respectively. **(c)** The power against $\mu = 100$ is $P(\bar{x} \geq 37) = P(Z \geq \frac{37-100}{108/\sqrt{50}}) \doteq P(Z \geq -4.12) > 0.9998$. A sample of size 50 will almost certainly detect a difference of \$100, so this should be quite adequate.

---

For solutions to the EESEE Case Studies (Exercises 52–58), see the instructor's version of EESEE.

# Chapter 23 Solutions

**23.1.** **(a)** The numbers in the first row sum to 187, so the desired percents are $\frac{56}{187} \doteq 29.9\%$, $\frac{54}{187} \doteq 28.9\%$, etc. These are given in the first row of the table below. **(b)** The second and third rows add to 139 and 133, so computations similar to those in (a) give the second and third rows of the table shown here. (Due to rounding, the numbers in the second row add to 99.9%.) **(c)** There is no substantial difference between the first two groups, but university-educated men seem to be more likely to be nonsmokers or moderate smokers.

| | *Smoking status* | | | | |
|---|---|---|---|---|---|
| Education | Nonsmoker | Former | Moderate | Heavy | TOTAL |
| Primary | 29.9% | 28.9% | 21.9% | 19.3% | 100% |
| Secondary | 26.6% | 30.9% | 19.4% | 23.0% | 100%* |
| University | 39.8% | 21.1% | 27.1% | 12.0% | 100% |

**Note:** *In this and similar problems, some students may not realize that they need to compute "marginal" totals first, and instead might take ratios of numbers that appear in the table. It may help to emphasize that proportions should take the form "part over whole," and that the "whole" sometimes needs to be found by putting all the "parts" together.*

*Furthermore, some might compute the* wrong *marginal totals—for example,* $\frac{56}{56+37+53}$. *To determine the proper ratios, a good practice is to identify—if possible—which variable is explanatory (as we did for scatterplots). In this case, education is explanatory, so we should compute percents for each level of that variable.*

**23.2.** **(a)** Compare the distributions of opinion among buyers and nonbuyers. That is, find each count as a percent of its row total; for example, $\frac{20}{20+7+9} = \frac{20}{36} \doteq 55.6\%$ of those who buy recycled filters believe the quality is higher. Buyers are more likely to say "higher" and less likely to say "lower." **(b)** It may be that actual use convinces people that the recycled filters are high quality. Or it may be that people use recycled filters because they think in advance that their quality is high.

| | *Think the quality is:* | | | |
|---|---|---|---|---|
| | Higher | The same | Lower | TOTAL |
| Buyers | 55.6% | 19.4% | 25.0% | 100% |
| Nonbuyers | 29.9% | 25.8% | 44.3% | 100% |

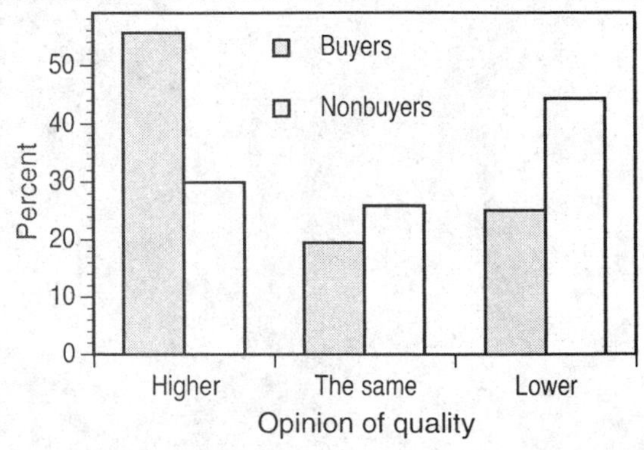

**23.3.** The sample proportions $\hat{p}_p$, $\hat{p}_s$, and $\hat{p}_u$ are given in the first column of the table in the solution to Exercise 23.1. Here are the other computations for the three tests:

| | $\hat{p} = \frac{x_1+x_2}{n_1+n_2}$ | $SE = \sqrt{\hat{p}(1-\hat{p})\left(\frac{1}{n_1}+\frac{1}{n_2}\right)}$ | $z = \frac{\hat{p}_1 - \hat{p}_2}{SE}$ | $P$-value |
|---|---|---|---|---|
| Primary/secondary | 0.2853 | 0.05057 | 0.66 | 0.5092 |
| Primary/university | 0.3406 | 0.05376 | −1.84 | 0.0658 |
| Secondary/university | 0.3309 | 0.05707 | −2.32 | 0.0204 |

**23.4. (a)** The confidence intervals are given in the table below. As usual, the standard error is $SE = \sqrt{\hat{p}(1-\hat{p})/n}$ or $\sqrt{\tilde{p}(1-\tilde{p})/n}$, and the margins of error equal 1.960 SE. Because the samples are large, the large-sample and plus four intervals are quite similar.

| Community type | $\hat{p}$ | SE | Confidence interval |
|---|---|---|---|
| Rural | $\frac{433}{896} \doteq 0.4833$ | 0.01669 | 0.4505 to 0.5160 |
| Suburban | $\frac{1072}{1699} \doteq 0.6310$ | 0.01171 | 0.6080 to 0.6539 |
| Urban | $\frac{536}{924} \doteq 0.5801$ | 0.01624 | 0.5483 to 0.6119 |

| Community type | $\tilde{p}$ | SE | Confidence interval |
|---|---|---|---|
| Rural | $\frac{433+2}{896+4} \doteq 0.4833$ | 0.01666 | 0.4507 to 0.5160 |
| Suburban | $\frac{1072+2}{1699+4} \doteq 0.6307$ | 0.01170 | 0.6077 to 0.6536 |
| Urban | $\frac{536+2}{924+4} \doteq 0.5797$ | 0.01620 | 0.5480 to 0.6115 |

**(b)** Every time we construct a 95% confidence interval, there is a 5% chance that it does not include the quantity we are attempting to estimate. We can be 95% confident in any *one* of these three (presumably independent) intervals, but only $(0.95)^3 \doteq 85.7\%$ confident in all three.

**23.5. (a)** We found the row totals in Exercise 23.1; the column totals are given in the table below. The expected values requested in this exercise are given in the table below: $\frac{(133)(146)}{459} \doteq 42.31$, $\frac{(133)(125)}{459} \doteq 36.22$, etc. The sum of these expected counts might differ slightly from the observed total as a result of rounding: the sum is 132 (if individual counts are rounded to the nearest whole number), 132.9 (rounded to the nearest tenth), 133.01 (rounded to the nearest hundredth), or 133 (rounded to the nearest thousandth). **(b)** The expected counts give mixed support for our conjecture: The nonsmoker count is higher than expected and the heavy-smoker count is less than expected—these are consistent with the conjecture—but the moderate-smoker count is slightly higher.

| | *Smoking status* | | | | |
|---|---|---|---|---|---|
| Education | Nonsmoker | Former | Moderate | Heavy | TOTAL |
| University | 53 | 28 | 36 | 16 | 133 |
| | 42.31 | 36.22 | 30.14 | 24.34 | |
| TOTAL | 146 | 125 | 104 | 84 | 459 |

**23.6.** **(a)** The expected counts are shown in the Minitab output on the right; for example, $\frac{(36)(49)}{133} \doteq 13.26$. It is easy to confirm that the expected counts and observed counts give the same row and column totals. **(b)** The largest differences between observed and expected counts are in the "higher" and "lower" columns. These differences are consistent with the observation made in Exercise 23.2: buyers are more likely to say "higher" and less likely to say "lower."

**Minitab output**

```
          Higher    Same   Lower   Total
Buyers        20       7       9      36
           13.26    8.66   14.08

Non           29      25      43      97
           35.74   23.34   37.92

Total         49      32      52     133

ChiSq = 3.422 + 0.319 + 1.830 +
        1.270 + 0.118 + 0.679 = 7.638
df = 2, p = 0.022
```

**23.7.** **(a)** Note that because of roundoff error, the first and third terms agree to only two decimal places. For example, Minitab gives the first term as 2.7038, while $\frac{(53-42.31)^2}{42.31} \doteq 2.7009$, because the first expected count $\frac{(133)(146)}{459} \doteq 42.3050$ was rounded to 42.31. **(b)** Minitab reports $X^2 = 13.305$ with df $= 6$, and a $P$-value of 0.038. **(c)** University-educated men contribute three of the four largest terms to $X^2$; that group contains more nonsmokers and fewer heavy smokers.

**23.8.** **(a)** The computed values of $X^2$ agree, up to roundoff error:

$$\frac{(20-13.26)^2}{13.26} + \frac{(7-8.662)^2}{8.662} + \frac{(9-14.08)^2}{14.08} + \frac{(29-35.74)^2}{35.74} + \frac{(25-23.34)^2}{23.34} + \frac{(43-37.92)^2}{37.92}$$

$$\doteq 3.4259 + 0.3189 + 1.8328 + 1.2711 + 0.1181 + 0.6805 = 7.6473.$$

*Note:* Minitab output for this same table is shown in the solution to Exercise 23.6. **(b)** The given $P$-value is 0.0219. Rejecting $H_0$ means that we have evidence that buyers and nonbuyers of recycled coffee filters have different opinions about the quality of those products. **(c)** The largest terms are the first, third, and fourth, which again confirms the relationship observed in Exercises 23.2 and 23.6: buyers are more likely to say "higher" and less likely to say "lower."

**23.9.** All expected cell counts are well over 5. (The smallest expected count is 24.34.)

**23.10.** All expected cell counts are over 5. (The smallest expected count is 8.662.)

**23.11.** **(a)** Graph and table below, left. The biggest difference between women and men is in administration: a higher percent of women chose this major. Meanwhile, greater proportions of men chose other fields, especially finance. **(b)** One expected count is less than 5, which is only one-eighth (12.5%) of the counts in the table, so the chi-square procedure is acceptable. **(c)** Minitab output below, right. We find $X^2 = 10.827$ with df $= 3$, and $P = 0.013$. We have fairly strong evidence that gender and choice of major are related. **(d)** The largest chi-square components are the two from the "Administration" row. Many more women than we expect (91 actual, 76.36 expected) chose this major, whereas only 40 men chose this (54.64 expected). These are consistent with the observations made in (a). **(e)** 386 responded, so $\frac{336}{722} \doteq 46.5\%$ did not respond. We do not know how those who did not respond might differ from those who did.

| | Female | Male |
|---|---|---|
| Accounting | 30.22% | 34.78% |
| Administration | 40.44% | 24.84% |
| Economics | 2.22% | 3.73% |
| Finance | 27.11% | 36.65% |

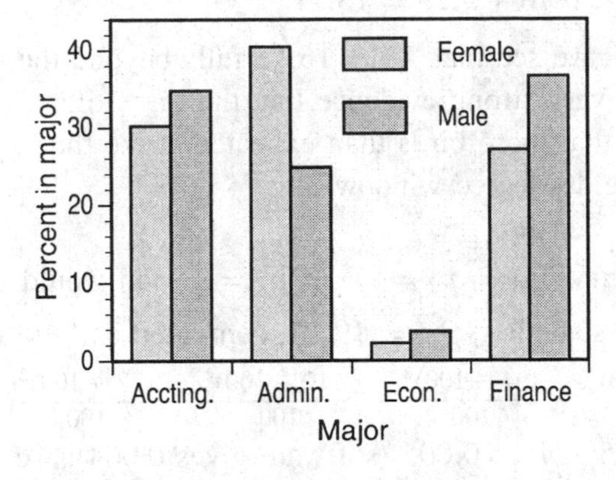


**Minitab output**

```
         Female     Male    Total
Acct.        68       56      124
          72.28    51.72

Admin.       91       40      131
          76.36    54.64

Econ.         5        6       11
           6.41     4.59

Finance      61       59      120
          69.95    50.05

Total       225      161      386

ChiSq =  0.253 +  0.354 +
         2.807 +  3.923 +
         0.311 +  0.434 +
         1.145 +  1.600 = 10.827
df = 3, p = 0.013
```

**23.12.** **(a)** df $= (r-1)(c-1) = (2-1)(3-1) = 2$. **(b)** On the df $= 2$ row of Table E, we find that $7.38 < X^2 < 7.82$, so $0.02 < P < 0.025$. **(c)** If $H_0$ is true, the mean value of $X^2$ would be 2 (the degrees of freedom). The observed value is quite a bit larger than this.

**23.13.** **(a)** df $= (r-1)(c-1) = (3-1)(4-1) = 6$. **(b)** On the df $= 6$ row of Table E, we find that $12.59 < X^2 < 14.45$, so $0.025 < P < 0.05$.

**23.14.** **(a)** The actual counts of successes and failures are all greater than 5, so the $z$ test is safe, and the expected cell counts arc all greater than 5, so the $X^2$ test is safe. **(b)** To test $H_0$: $p_1 = p_2$ versus $H_a$: $p_1 \neq p_2$, we find $\hat{p}_1 = \frac{28}{82} = 0.3415$, $\hat{p}_2 = \frac{30}{78} \doteq 0.3846$, and $\hat{p} = \frac{28+30}{82+78} = 0.3625$. Then SE $= \sqrt{\hat{p}(1-\hat{p})(\frac{1}{82}+\frac{1}{78})} \doteq 0.07603$, $z = (\hat{p}_1 - \hat{p}_2)/\text{SE} \doteq -0.57$, and $P = 0.5686$. **(c)** See Minitab output on the right. $X^2 = 0.322$, which equals $z^2$ (up to rounding; it is even closer if we carry out to more decimals in the computation of $z$). With df $= 1$, Table E tells us that $P > 0.25$; Minitab reports $P = 0.570$. **(d)** Gastric freezing is not significantly more (or less) effective than a placebo treatment.

**Minitab output**

```
          Freezing  Placebo   Total
Improved        28       30      58
             29.73    28.27

No              54       48     102
             52.28    49.72

Total           82       78     160

ChiSq =      0.100 +  0.105 +
             0.057 +  0.060 = 0.322
df = 1, p = 0.570
```

**23.15.** We test $H_0$: $p_1 = p_2 = p_3 = \frac{1}{3}$ versus $H_a$: not all three are equally likely. There were 53 bird strikes in all, so the expected counts are each $53 \times \frac{1}{3} = 17.67$. The chi-square statistic is

$$X^2 = \sum \frac{(\text{observed count} - 17.67)^2}{17.67} = \frac{(31-17.67)^2}{17.67} + \frac{(14-17.67)^2}{17.67} + \frac{(8-17.67)^2}{17.67}$$
$$= 10.06 + 0.76 + 5.29 = 16.11.$$

The degrees of freedom are df = 2. From Table E, we see that $X^2 = 16.11$ falls beyond the 0.0005 critical value. So $P < 0.0005$ and there is very strong evidence that the three tilts differ. The data and the terms of chi-square show that more birds than expected strike the vertical window and fewer than expected strike the 40 degree window.

**23.16.** **(a)** If all days were equally likely, we would have $p_1 = p_2 = \cdots = p_7 = \frac{1}{7}$, and would expect 100 births on each day. **(b)** The chi-square statistic is $X^2 = 19.12$, computed as

$$\frac{(84-100)^2}{100} + \frac{(110-100)^2}{100} + \frac{(124-100)^2}{100} + \frac{(104-100)^2}{100} + \frac{(94-100)^2}{100} + \frac{(112-100)^2}{100} + \frac{(72-100)^2}{100}.$$

**(c)** We have df = 7 − 1 = 6, so we see that $0.0025 < P < 0.005$ (software gives 0.004); we have strong evidence that births are not spread evenly across the week.

**23.17.** **(a)** See the table on the right; for example, $\frac{22}{91} \doteq 24.2\%$ received A's. (There were 91 students in the class.) **(b)** Expected counts are also given in the table; for example, (91)(0.32) = 29.12. **(c)** We test $H_0$: $p_1 = 0.32$, $p_2 = 0.41$, $p_3 = 0.20$, $p_4 = 0.07$ versus $H_a$: at least one of these probabilities is different. (Of course, if one value of $p_i$ is different, then at least one more must be different!) The guideline for using chi-square is satisfied: All the expected counts are greater than 5. The chi-square statistic is

| | A | B | C | D/F |
|---|---|---|---|---|
| Percent | 24.2% | 41.8% | 22.0% | 12.1% |
| Exp. count | 29.12 | 37.31 | 18.20 | 6.37 |

$$\frac{(22-29.12)^2}{29.12} + \frac{(38-37.31)^2}{37.31} + \frac{(20-18.20)^2}{18.20} + \frac{(11-6.37)^2}{6.37} \doteq 5.297.$$

We have df = 4 − 1 = 3, so we see that $0.15 < P < 0.20$ (software gives 0.1513); there is not enough evidence to conclude that the professor's grade distribution was different from the TA grade distribution.

**23.18.** **State:** Does the GSS data suggest that births are not spread uniformly across the year? **Formulate:** We test $H_0$: $p_1 = p_2 = \cdots = p_{12} = \frac{1}{12}$ versus $H_a$: at least one $p_i$ is not $\frac{1}{12}$. **Solve:** There were 2779 responses, so we would expect $\frac{2779}{12} \doteq 231.58$ in each group. The $X^2$ statistic is

$$\frac{(225-231.58)^2}{231.58} + \frac{(222-231.58)^2}{231.58} + \frac{(241-231.58)^2}{231.58} + \cdots \frac{(244-231.58)^2}{231.58} \doteq 14.39.$$

With df = 11, we see from Table E that $0.20 < P < 0.25$ (software gives 0.212). **Conclude:** There is not enough evidence to conclude that births are not uniformly spread through the year.

**23.19.** (b) The numbers in the first (female) column add to 2625.

**23.20.** (a) This fraction is $\frac{1174}{2625} \doteq 44.7\%$.

**23.21.** (a) The corresponding fraction of males is $\frac{756}{2252} \doteq 33.6\%$.

**23.22.** (c) The expected count is $\frac{(1930)(2625)}{4877} \doteq 1038.8$.

**23.23.** (a) This term in the chi-square statistic is $\frac{(1174-1038.8)^2}{1038.8} \doteq 17.6$.

**23.24.** (a) The degrees of freedom are df $= (r-1)(c-1) = (5-1)(2-1) = 4$.

**23.25.** (b) The null hypothesis of this chi-square test says that gender is not related to opinions about marriage.

**23.26.** (a) Alternatives for such tests are "many-sided"; they do not specify any direction for the difference in the distributions.

**23.27.** (c) $X^2 = 69.8$ is larger than the last critical value on the df = 4 line (20.00, for $p = 0.0005$).

**23.28.** (b) While a large sample and large cell counts are nice to have, the most important issue is that we have an SRS (or something close to it).

**23.29.** **(a)** The sample proportions are $\hat{p}_r = \frac{433}{896} \doteq 0.4833$ and $\hat{p}_s = \frac{1072}{1699} \doteq 0.6310$. The standard error is SE $\doteq 0.02039$, so the large-sample 95% confidence interval for $p_r - p_u$ is

$$\hat{p}_r - \hat{p}_s \pm 1.96\,\text{SE} \doteq -0.1477 \pm 0.03996 \doteq -0.1877 \text{ to } -0.1077.$$

Alternatively, use the plus four method: $\tilde{p}_r = \frac{433+1}{896+2} \doteq 0.4833$ and $\tilde{p}_s = \frac{1072+1}{1699+2} \doteq 0.6308$, the standard error is SE $\doteq 0.02037$, and the interval is

$$\tilde{p}_r - \tilde{p}_s \pm 1.96\,\text{SE} \doteq -0.1475 \pm 0.03993 \doteq -0.1874 \text{ to } -0.1076.$$

**(b)** Overall, the proportion is highest in suburban communities and lowest in rural communities. To determine whether the relationship is significant, we test $H_0$: $p_r = p_s = p_u$ versus $H_a$: some proportion is different. All expected counts are much more than 5, so the guidelines for the chi-square test are satisfied. We find $X^2 = 52.5$, df $= 2$, and $P < 0.0005$, so the evidence for the observed relationship is very strong.

**Minitab output**

```
         Rural   Suburb    Urban    Total
User       433     1072      536     2041
        519.67   985.41   535.91

Non        463      627      388     1478
        376.33   713.59   388.09

Total      896     1699      924     3519

ChiSq = 14.456 +  7.609 +  0.000 +
        19.963 + 10.507 +  0.000 = 52.535
df = 2, p = 0.000
```

**23.30.** **(a)** The percents are, respectively, 7.01%, 14.02%, and 13.05%. (Watch out for students who do not notice that the table in the text was not given in the usual way; it gives the total and the number of blacks within each group, so it is not necessary to compute marginal totals. For example, $7.01\% \doteq \frac{172}{2455}$.) **(b)** Table at right (actual counts above, expected counts below). **(c)** Expected counts are all much bigger than 5, so the chi-square test is safe. We test $H_0$: there is no relationship between worker class and race, versus $H_a$: there is some relationship. **(d)** For a 2 × 3 table, df = 2; this is the mean of $X^2$ if $H_0$ is true. From Table E, we have $P < 0.0005$ (basically 0). **(e)** Black female child-care workers are more likely to work in nonhousehold or preschool positions.

| | Black | Other |
|---|---|---|
| Household | 172 | 2283 |
| | 242.36 | 2212.64 |
| Nonhousehold | 167 | 1024 |
| | 117.58 | 1073.42 |
| Teachers | 86 | 573 |
| | 65.06 | 593.94 |

**23.31.** **(a)** Out of 900 adults, 578 would allow a racist to speak, so the sample proportion is $\hat{p} = \frac{578}{900} \doteq 0.6422$, the standard error is SE $\doteq 0.01598$, and the large-sample 99% confidence interval is

$$\hat{p} \pm 2.576\,\text{SE} \doteq 0.6422 \pm 0.04116 \doteq 0.6011 \text{ to } 0.6834.$$

With the plus four method: $\tilde{p} = \frac{578+2}{900+4} \doteq 0.6416$, SE $\doteq 0.01595$, and the interval is

$$\tilde{p} \pm 2.576\,\text{SE} \doteq 0.6416 \pm 0.04108 \doteq 0.6005 \text{ to } 0.6827.$$

**(b)** These percents are $\hat{p}_b = \frac{67}{120} \doteq 0.5583 \doteq 55.8\%$, $\hat{p}_w = \frac{476}{728} \doteq 0.6538 \doteq 65.4\%$, and $\hat{p}_o = \frac{35}{+.2052} \doteq 0.6731 \doteq 67.3\%$. The proportion of blacks is noticeably lower than the white and other proportions (which are quite similar). We test $H_0$: $p_b = p_w = p_o$ versus $H_a$: some proportion is different; all expected counts are large enough to use the chi-square test. We find $X^2 \doteq 4.319$, df = 2, and $0.10 < P < 0.15$; there is not enough evidence to conclude that attitudes differ.

Note that if we form a 2 × 2 table by combining the "white" and "other" counts, the chi-square test is significant ($X^2 = 4.241$, df = 1, $P = 0.040$). In some situations, there may be good justification for this kind of aggregation, but we should be cautious about doing so.

**Minitab output**

```
         Black    White    Other    Total
Allow       67      476       35      578
         77.07   467.54    33.40

Not         53      252       17      322
         42.93   260.46    18.60

Total      120      728       52      900

ChiSq =  1.315 +  0.153 +  0.077 +
         2.360 +  0.275 +  0.138 =  4.319
df = 2, p = 0.116
```

**23.32.** We test $H_0$: all proportions are equal, versus $H_a$: some proportions are different. To find the entries in the table (right), take (0.21)(800), (0.25)(800), and (0.28)(800). We find $X^2 = 10.619$ with df = 2, so $P < 0.005$—strong evidence that the contact method makes a difference in response.

| | Yes | No |
|---|---|---|
| Phone | 168 | 632 |
| One-on-one | 200 | 600 |
| Anonymous | 224 | 576 |

**23.33.** **(a)** The Minitab output (below on the left) includes the two-way table. **(b)** We find $X^2 = 4.513$ with df $= 2$, for which $0.10 < P < 0.15$—not significant evidence of a difference in seat belt use.

**Minitab output for Exercise 23.33**

```
         Belted   NoBelt    Total
Black       273       96      369
         265.20   103.80

Hisp        372      168      540
         388.10   151.90

White       193       64      257
         184.70    72.30

Total       838      328     1166

ChiSq =  0.229 +  0.586 +
         0.668 +  1.706 +
         0.373 +  0.952 =  4.513
df = 2, p = 0.105
```

**Minitab output for Exercise 23.34**

```
           Female     Male    Total
PBM            11        9       20
            11.05     8.95

NLCP           11        8       19
            10.50     8.50

PL-LCP         11        8       19
            10.50     8.50

TG-LCP          9       10       19
            10.36     8.64

Total          42       35       77

ChiSq =  0.001 +  0.001 +
         0.039 +  0.047 +
         0.039 +  0.047 +
         0.179 +  0.215 =  0.568
df = 3, p = 0.904
```

**23.34.** **(a)** The diagram is shown below. To perform the randomization, label the infants 01 to 77, and choose pairs of random digits. **(b)** See the Minitab output (above on the right) for the two-way table. We find $X^2 = 0.568$, df $= 3$, and $P = 0.904$. There is no reason to doubt that the randomization "worked."

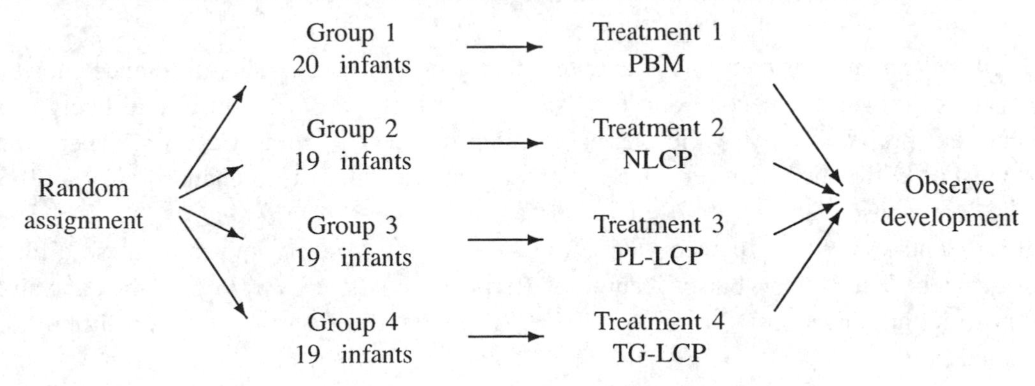

**23.35.** **(a)** To test $H_0$: $p_b = p_g$ versus $H_a$: $p_b \neq p_g$, we find sample proportions $\hat{p}_b = \frac{135}{206} \doteq 0.6553$ and $\hat{p}_g = \frac{64}{114} \doteq 0.5614$, pooled proportion $\hat{p} = \frac{135+64}{206+114} \doteq 0.6219$, standard error SE $\doteq 0.05661$, and test statistic $z = (\hat{p}_b - \hat{p}_g)/\text{SE} \doteq 1.66$. The two-sided $P$-value is $2P(Z > 1.66) \doteq 0.0970$. We cannot conclude that there is a difference in the proportions favoring the death penalty. **(b)** The chi-square statistic is $X^2 = 2.754$, which agrees (up to rounding) with $z^2 = 1.66^2$. For df $= 1$, Table E tells us that $0.05 < P < 0.10$, while software gives $P = 0.097$, which again agrees with the result from (a).

**Minitab output**

```
        Favor   Oppose   Total
Bach      135       71     206
       128.11    77.89

Grad       64       50     114
        70.89    43.11

Total     199      121     320

ChiSq =  0.371 +  0.610 +
         0.670 +  1.102 = 2.754
df = 1, p = 0.097
```

**23.36.** **(a)** We test $H_0$: $p_1 = p_2$ versus $H_a$: $p_1 < p_2$. The $z$ test must be used because the chi-square procedure will not work for a one-sided alternative. **(b)** The sample proportions are $\hat{p}_1 = \frac{11}{30} \doteq 0.3667$ and $\hat{p}_2 = \frac{22}{30} \doteq 0.7333$, and the pooled proportion is $\hat{p} = \frac{33}{60} = 0.55$. Then SE $\doteq 0.12845$, so $z = (\hat{p}_1 - \hat{p}_2)/\text{SE} \doteq -2.85$. This gives $P = 0.0022$, so we reject $H_0$; there is strong evidence that attitude influences tumor growth.

**23.37.** **(a)** "Less than high school" had the highest support (50%); "some college" was lowest (36.5%). The "less than high school" terms contribute the most to $X^2$; they account for over half of the total. ("Some college" accounts for a little over a third). Support is highest with the least and the most educated, and lowest in the middle. **(b)** The degrees of freedom are df $= (2-1)(5-1) = 4$. $X^2 = 8.525$ is larger than 4, the mean under $H_0$; $P = 0.074$ tells us that the evidence is not significant at $\alpha = 0.05$.

**23.38.** Overall, men give themselves a better chance of being rich. This difference shows up most noticeably in the second and fifth rows of the table: Women were more likely to say, "some, but probably not," while men more often responded, "almost certain." There was virtually no difference between men and women in the "almost no chance" and "a 50-50 chance" responses, and little difference in "a good chance."

If students compute expected values and chi-square terms, the impact of these differences can be seen: The "some, but probably not" terms account for over 75% of the $X^2$ value, and "almost certain" accounts for another 17%. The first and third rows add very little (0.021) to the total.

**23.39. Formulate:** To describe the differences, we compare the percents of American and of Asian students who cite each reason. Then we test $H_0$: there is no difference between American and Asian students (all proportions are the same) versus $H_a$: at least one American/Asian proportion is different.
**Solve:** We compute the percents of each group of students who gave each response by taking each count divided by its column total; for example, $\frac{29}{115} \doteq 25.2\%$:

| | American | Asian |
|---|---|---|
| Save time | 25.2% | 14.5% |
| Easy | 24.3% | 15.9% |
| Low price | 14.8% | 49.3% |
| Live far from stores | 9.6% | 5.8% |
| No pressure to buy | 8.7% | 4.3% |
| Other reason | 17.4% | 10.1% |

Minitab output for the chi-square test is shown on the right; one expected count is less than 5, but this is within our guidelines for using the chi-square test. Note that the chi-square terms for low price account for 18.511 of the total chi-square 25.737. With df = 5, Table E tells us that $P < 0.0005$.

**Minitab output**

```
             Amer    Asian    Total
Save time      29       10       39
            24.37    14.63

Easy           28       11       39
            24.37    14.63

Low price      17       34       51
            31.87    19.13

Live far       11        4       15
             9.37     5.63

No press       10        3       13
             8.12     4.87

Other          20        7       27
            16.88    10.12

Total         115       69      184

ChiSq =     0.878 +  1.463 +
            0.539 +  0.899 +
            6.942 + 11.569 +
            0.282 +  0.469 +
            0.433 +  0.721 +
            0.579 +  0.965 = 25.737
df = 5, p = 0.000
```

**Conclude:** There is very strong evidence that Asian and American students buy from catalogs for different reasons; specifically, Asian students place much more emphasis on "low price" and less emphasis on "easy" and "save time."

**23.40. Formulate:** To describe the differences, we compare the percents of men and women in each situation. Then we test $H_0$: there is no difference between males and females (all proportions are the same) versus $H_a$: at least one male/female proportion is different.
**Solve:** We compute the percents of each group who gave each response by taking each count divided by its column total; for example, $\frac{923}{2488} \doteq 37.1\%$:

| | Female | Male |
|---|---|---|
| Parents' home | 37.1% | 41.7% |
| Another person's home | 5.8% | 5.6% |
| Own place | 52.0% | 47.7% |
| Group quarters | 5.1% | 5.0% |

**Minitab output**

```
          Female     Male    Total
Parents      923      986     1909
          978.49   930.51

Another      144      132      276
          141.47   134.53

Own         1294     1129     2423
         1241.95  1181.05

Group        127      119      246
          126.09   119.91

Total       2488     2366     4854

ChiSq =    3.147 +  3.309 +
           0.045 +  0.048 +
           2.181 +  2.294 +
           0.007 +  0.007 = 11.038
df = 3, p = 0.012
```

Minitab output for the chi-square test is shown on the right; all expected cell counts are much greater than 5. Note that the chi-square terms for "parents' home" account for 6.456 of the total $X^2 = 11.038$, and "own place" accounts for most of the remainder (4.475). With df $= 3$, Table E tells us that $0.01 < P < 0.02$.
**Conclude:** There is strong evidence that young men and young women have different living situations. Specifically, women are less likely to live with their parents and more likely to have their own place.

**23.41. Formulate:** We test the null hypothesis "there is no relationship between race and opinions about schools."
**Solve:** We find $X^2 = 22.426$ (df $= 8$) and $P = 0.004$ (Minitab output at right; all expected cell counts are greater than 5). Nearly half of the total chi-square comes from the first two terms; most of the rest comes from the second and fifth rows.
**Conclude:** We have strong evidence that there is a relationship; specifically, blacks are less likely and Hispanics are more likely to consider schools excellent, while Hispanics and whites differ in the percent considering schools good (whites are higher) and the percent who "don't know" (Hispanics are higher). Also, a higher percent of blacks rated schools as "fair."

**Minitab output**

```
           Black     Hisp    White    Total
Excelnt       12       34       22       68
           22.70    22.70    22.59

Good          69       55       81      205
           68.45    68.45    68.11

Fair          75       61       60      196
           65.44    65.44    65.12

Poor          24       24       24       72
           24.04    24.04    23.92

DontKnow      22       28       14       64
           21.37    21.37    21.26

Total        202      202      201      605

ChiSq =  5.047 + 5.620 + 0.015 +
         0.004 + 2.642 + 2.441 +
         1.396 + 0.301 + 0.402 +
         0.000 + 0.000 + 0.000 +
         0.019 + 2.058 + 2.481 = 22.426
df = 8, p = 0.004
```

**23.42.** **(a)** This is not an experiment; no treatment was assigned to the subjects. **(b)** A high nonresponse rate might mean that our attempt to get a random sample was thwarted because of those who did not participate; this nonresponse rate is extraordinarily low. **(c)** **Formulate:** We perform a chi-square test of the null hypothesis "there is no relationship between olive oil consumption and cancer."

**Minitab output**

```
             Low    Medium      High     Total
Colon        398       397       430      1225
          404.39    404.19    416.42

Rectal       250       241       237       728
          240.32    240.20    247.47

Ctrl        1368      1377      1409      4154
         1371.29   1370.61   1412.10

Total       2016      2015      2076      6107

ChiSq = 0.101 +  0.128 +  0.443 +
        0.390 +  0.003 +  0.443 +
        0.008 +  0.030 +  0.007 =   1.552
df = 4, p = 0.817
```

**Solve:** All expected counts are much more than 5, so the chi-square test should be safe. The chi-square statistic is $X^2 = 1.552$ (df $= 4$); if $H_0$ were true, the mean of $X^2$ would be 4. This value is smaller than the mean, suggesting that we have little reason to doubt $H_0$. The $P$-value (0.817) confirms this.

**Conclude:** High olive oil consumption is *not* more common among those without cancer; in fact, when looking at the conditional distributions of olive oil consumption, all percents are between 32.4% and 35.1%—that is, within each group (colon cancer, rectal cancer, control) roughly one-third fall in each olive oil consumption category.

**23.43.** **Formulate:** We compare how detergent preferences vary by laundry habits, and test the null hypothesis that there is no relationship between laundry habits and preference.

**Solve:** To compare people with different laundry habits, we just compare the percent in each class who prefer the new product.

| | Soft water, warm wash | Soft water, hot wash | Hard water, warm wash | Hard water, hot wash |
|---|---|---|---|---|
| Prefer new product | 54.3% | 51.8% | 61.8% | 58.3% |

The differences are not large, but the "hard water, warm wash" group is most likely to prefer the new detergent. A chi-square test gives $X^2 = 2.058$, df $= 3$, and $P = 0.560$.

**Conclude:** The data give no reason to think that laundry habits influence preference.

**Minitab output**

```
            S/W      S/H      H/W      H/H   Total
Standard     53       27       42       30     152
          49.81    24.05    47.23    30.92

New          63       29       68       42     202
          66.19    31.95    62.77    41.08

Total       116       56      110       72     354

ChiSq =   0.205 + 0.363 + 0.579 + 0.027
          0.154 + 0.273 + 0.436 + 0.020 = 2.058
df = 3, p = 0.560
```

**23.44. Formulate:** We give a 95% confidence interval for $p$, the proportion of American adults who support "other parties."
**Solve:** There are 2718 responses represented in the table; adding the numbers in the bottom row, we find that 48 supported other parties. The counts are large enough to safely use large-sample methods: $\hat{p} = \frac{48}{2718} \doteq 0.0177$, so SE $\doteq 0.00253$ and the 95% confidence interval is

$$\hat{p} \pm 0.00495 \doteq 0.0127 \text{ to } 0.0226.$$

The plus four method is (of course) also safe to use: $\tilde{p} = \frac{48+2}{2718+4} \doteq 0.0184$, SE $\doteq 0.00257$ and the 95% confidence interval is

$$\tilde{p} \pm 0.00504 \doteq 0.0133 \text{ to } 0.0234.$$

**Conclude:** We are 95% confident that the percent of Americans who support other parties is between about 1.3% and 2.3%.

**23.45. Formulate:** We will form a 2 × 4 table of political party and age-group, and compute the percents of each age-group leaning each direction.

| | 18–30 | 31–40 | 41–55 | 56–89 |
|---|---|---|---|---|
| Democrat | 231 | 265 | 328 | 361 |
| | 55.5% | 59.3% | 54.7% | 53.1% |
| Republican | 185 | 182 | 272 | 319 |
| | 44.5% | 40.7% | 45.3% | 46.9% |

**Solve:** Adding up the three "Democrat" rows and the three "Republican" rows gives the counts shown in the accompanying table. Also shown are the percents of each age-group leaning each direction; for example, $\frac{231}{231+185} \doteq 55.5\%$. (It would suffice to compute only one of these percents for each age-group.)
**Conclude:** Of adults who align themselves with either Democrats or Republicans, Democrats are favored by a majority at all ages. Support for the Democrats is highest in the 31–40 age-group, and drops for older groups.

**23.46. Formulate:** We will perform a chi-square test on the full table, testing the null hypothesis that there is no relationship between age and political preference.
**Solve:** The Minitab output (below) confirms that the data are highly significant ($X^2 = 92.114$, df $= 21$, $P < 0.0005$). We also note that the expected counts are all greater than 5, so the test is safe to use. By examining the largest contributions to the chi-square statistic, we note the most important differences among the age-groups. Nearly one-third of the value of $X^2$ comes from "Independents" among the youngest and oldest age-groups. The next four large contributions arise from the youngest and oldest groups in the "Strong Democrat" and "Strong Republican" classifications.
**Conclude:** Young adults are more likely—and senior citizens less likely—to consider themselves to be independent than what we would expect if there were no relationship between age and political preference. Another observation—probably related to the first—is that young adults are less likely to describe themselves as having "strong" affiliation with either party, while senior citizens are more likely to have a strong preference.

**Minitab output**

```
          18--30   31--40   41--55   56--89    Total
StrongDem     60       83      113      151      407
           86.40    87.30   114.25   119.05

Democrat      99      126      138      148      511
          108.48   109.61   143.45   149.46

NearDem       72       56       77       62      267
           56.68    57.27    74.95    78.10

Indpndnt     152      124      149      102      527
          111.88   113.04   147.94   154.14

NearRep       53       41       50       54      198
           42.03    42.47    55.58    57.91

Repub         90       85      133      138      446
           94.68    95.67   125.20   130.45

StrongRep     42       56       89      127      314
           66.66    67.35    88.15    91.84

Other          9       12       14       13       48
           10.19    10.30    13.47    14.04

Total        577      583      763      795     2718

ChiSq =    8.067 +  0.212 +  0.014 +  8.577 +
           0.828 +  2.452 +  0.207 +  0.014 +
           4.140 +  0.028 +  0.056 +  3.317 +
          14.390 +  1.063 +  0.008 + 17.640 +
           2.861 +  0.051 +  0.561 +  0.265 +
           0.231 +  1.189 +  0.486 +  0.437 +
           9.122 +  1.913 +  0.008 + 13.458 +
           0.139 +  0.282 +  0.020 +  0.077 = 92.114
df = 21, p = 0.000
```

---

For solutions to the EESEE Case Studies (Exercises 47–48), see the instructor's version of EESEE.

# Chapter 24 Solutions

**24.1.** **(a)** Price is explanatory (and so is on the horizontal axis). The plot shows a positive linear association. The correlation is $r = 0.955$, and the regression equation is $\hat{y} = -0.9764 + 0.05429x$. The appearance of the plot and the size of the correlation suggest that this line should give good predictions. **(b)** The slope $\beta$ is the rate at which deforestation changes with increases in the price of coffee. The estimates of $\beta$ and $\alpha$ are the two coefficients in the regression equation: slope $b = 0.05429$ and intercept $a = -0.9764$. **(c)** The computation of the residuals is shown in the table below; they do add up to zero (except for roundoff error). To estimate $\sigma$, square the residuals, add them up (the total is 0.3019), divide by $n - 2 = 3$ (leaving 0.1006), then take the square root, which gives $s \doteq 0.3172$. This agrees with the value shown in the Minitab output below.

| | | | Residual | |
|---|---|---|---|---|
| $x$ | $y$ | $\hat{y}$ | $y - \hat{y}$ | $(y - \hat{y})^2$ |
| 29 | 0.49 | 0.5980 | −0.1080 | 0.0117 |
| 40 | 1.59 | 1.1951 | 0.3949 | 0.1559 |
| 54 | 1.69 | 1.9551 | −0.2651 | 0.0703 |
| 55 | 1.82 | 2.0094 | −0.1894 | 0.0358 |
| 72 | 3.10 | 2.9323 | 0.1677 | 0.0281 |

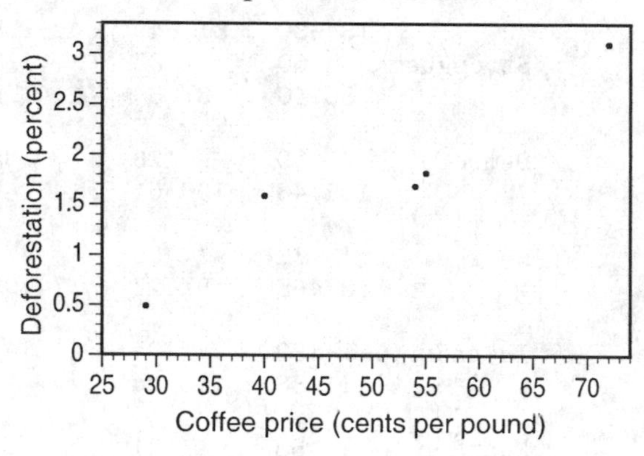


**Minitab output**

```
The regression equation is deforest = - 0.976 + 0.0543 price

Predictor       Coef       Stdev     t-ratio       p
Constant     -0.9764      0.5061       -1.93    0.149
price       0.054287    0.009716        5.59    0.011

s = 0.3172      R-sq = 91.2%      R-sq(adj) = 88.3%
```

**24.2.** See also the solution to Exercise 4.7. **(a)** The scatterplot is shown on the right. The Minitab output shown in the text (Figure 24.4) gives $r^2 = 99.2\%$. **(b)** The estimates of $\alpha$, $\beta$, and $\sigma$ are $a = -2.3948$ cm, $b = 0.158483$ cm/min, and $s = 0.8059$ cm. **(c)** The regression equation is $\hat{y} = -2.39 + 0.158x$.

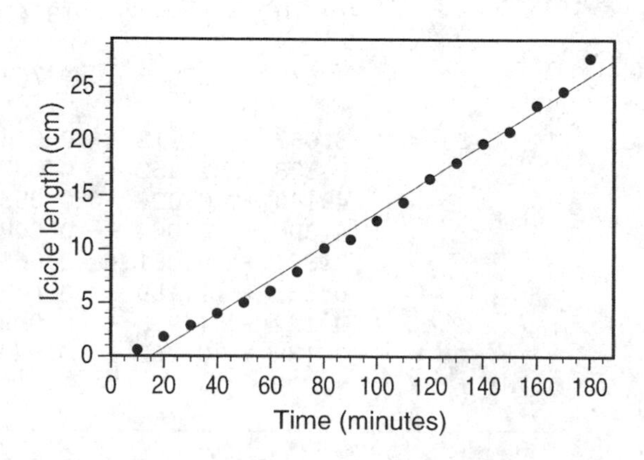

**24.3.** **(a)** The scatterplot on the right shows a weak increasing trend. The straight-line relationship explains only $r^2 = 11.2\%$ of the variation in discharge. **(b)** (See the Minitab output below.) The regression line is $\hat{y} = -2057 + 1.97x$, and the regression standard error is $s = 104.0$ km$^3$ of water.

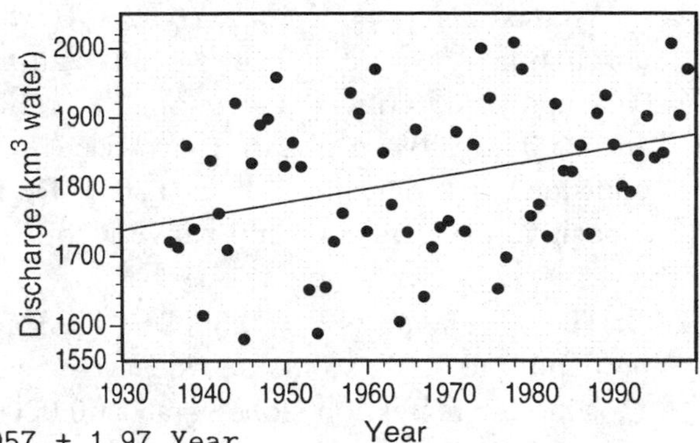


**Minitab output**

```
The regression equation is Dischg = - 2057 + 1.97 Year

Predictor        Coef        Stdev     t-ratio        p
Constant        -2057         1385       -1.49    0.143
Year           1.9662       0.7037        2.79    0.007

s = 104.0        R-sq = 11.2%      R-sq(adj) = 9.7%
```

**24.4.** See also the Minitab output in the solution to Exercise 24.1. **(a)** The $t$ statistic is $t = b/\text{SE}_b = 0.0543/0.0097 \doteq 5.60$. (This is slightly different from the Minitab value due to rounding.) **(b)** The degrees of freedom are df $= n - 2 = 3$, so the one-sided $P$-value is $0.005 < P < 0.01$. We have strong evidence that the population slope $\beta$ is positive.

**24.5.** Using software (see the Minitab output in the solution to Exercise 24.3), we find $b = 1.9662$ and $\text{SE}_b = 0.7037$. The $t$ statistic for testing $H_0$: $\beta = 0$ is therefore $t = b/\text{SE}_b = 1.9662/0.7037 \doteq 2.79$. This has df $= n - 2 = 62$; Table C allows us to conclude that $0.005 < P < 0.01$, while software gives $P = 0.007$. This is significant evidence at $\alpha = 0.01$ that $\beta$ is nonzero.

**24.6.** Regression of fuel consumption on speed gives $b = -0.01466$, $\text{SE}_b = 0.02334$, and $t = -0.63$. With df $= 13$, we see that $P > 2(0.25) = 0.50$ (software reports 0.541), so we have no evidence to suggest a straight-line relationship. While the relationship between these two variables is quite strong, it is definitely not linear. See also the solution to Exercise 4.6.

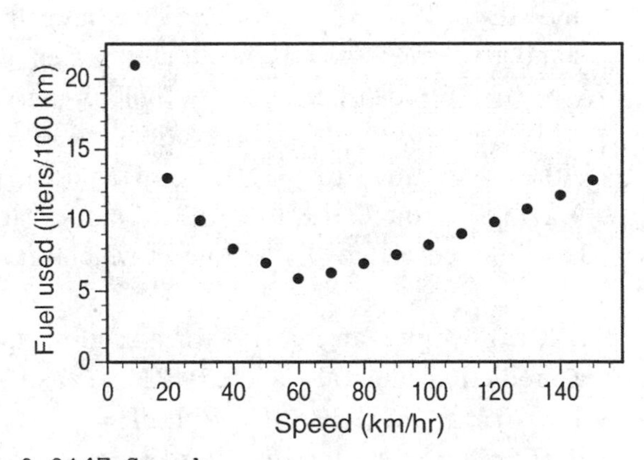


**Minitab output**

```
The regression equation is Fuel = 11.1 - 0.0147 Speed

Predictor        Coef        Stdev     t-ratio        p
Constant       11.058        2.122        5.21    0.000
Speed        -0.01466      0.02334       -0.63    0.541
```

**24.7.** We test $H_0$: $\rho = 0$ versus $H_a$: $\rho > 0$, where $\rho$ is the population correlation. The sample correlation is $r = 0.9552$; in Table F with $n = 5$ we see that 0.9552 falls between the upper 0.01 and 0.005 critical values for the correlation, so the one-sided $P$-value is between 0.01 and 0.005. Software gives the two-sided $P$-value for regression slope as 0.01132, or the one-sided $P$ as half this, about 0.0057. Despite the small sample, there is strong evidence of a positive linear relationship between coffee price and deforestation.

**24.8.** The correlation is $r = 0.8782$. Table F for $n = 13$ gives critical value 0.8010 for tail probability 0.0005, so the one-sided $P$-value is $P < 0.0005$. Software gives the two-sided $P$-value for regression slope as about 0.000078; this is also the $P$-value for testing the correlation. The one-sided $P$-value (for slope or correlation) is half this, about 0.00004. There is a strong ($r^2 = 0.7713$) and highly significant linear relationship between social distress and brain activity.

**24.9.** The degrees of freedom are df $= n - 2 = 3$, so the appropriate critical value is $t^* = 3.182$, and the 95% confidence interval is

$$b \pm t^* \mathrm{SE}_b = 0.0543 \pm (3.182)(0.0097) \doteq 0.0543 \pm 0.0309 = 0.0234 \text{ to } 0.0852.$$

**24.10.** The Minitab output gives $b = 0.158483$ and $\mathrm{SE}_b = 0.003661$. There were $n = 18$ observations, so df $= 16$. For a 95% confidence interval, we use $t^* = 2.120$:

$$0.158483 \pm 2.120\,\mathrm{SE}_b = 0.1507 \text{ to } 0.1662 \text{ cm/min}.$$

The slope $\beta$ represents the average rate (in cm/min) at which icicles grow under the conditions of this experiment.

**24.11.** The Minitab output (shown in the solution to Exercise 24.3) gives $b = 1.9662$ and $\mathrm{SE}_b = 0.7037$; to compute the latter by hand, note that the estimated regression standard error is $s = 104.0$ km$^3$ of water (given in the solution to Exercise 24.3), and that $\sqrt{\sum(x - \bar{x})^2}$ can be found by multiplying the standard deviation of $x$ (year) by $\sqrt{63}$.

There were $n = 64$ observations, so df $= 62$. For a 90% confidence interval, we use either $t^* = 1.671$ (df $= 60$, from Table C) or $t^* = 1.6698$ (for df $= 62$); with either choice, $b \pm t^*\,\mathrm{SE}_b$ rounds to 0.79 to 3.14 km$^3$/year. Because this interval does not contain 0, we have evidence that $\beta$ (the rate at which discharge is increasing) is positive.

**24.12.** **(a)** To give an interval for a single response (like next year's forest loss), we use a prediction interval (labeled "P.I." in the CrunchIt! output), so the interval we want is 1.1326% to 3.4292%. **(b)** With df $= 3$, the critical value for a 90% confidence interval is $t^* = 2.353$, so the margin of error is $t^*\mathrm{SE}_{\hat{\mu}} \doteq (2.353)(0.17195) \doteq 0.4046$, and the confidence interval is 1.8763% to 2.6855%.

**24.13.** **(a)** The regression equation was $\hat{y} = -2.3948 + 0.158483x$; with $x = 200$, we have $\hat{y} = -2.3948 + 0.158483(200) = 29.3018$ cm. **(b)** We want the 95% confidence interval (labeled "CI" in the Minitab output): 28.393 to 30.211 cm. ("PI" is the prediction interval, the range of numbers which we expect will include new individual observations 95% of the time.)

**24.14.** **(a)** One residual (51.32) may be a high outlier, but the stemplot does not show any other deviations from Normality. **(b)** Other than the high outlier, there are no striking features in the scatterplot.

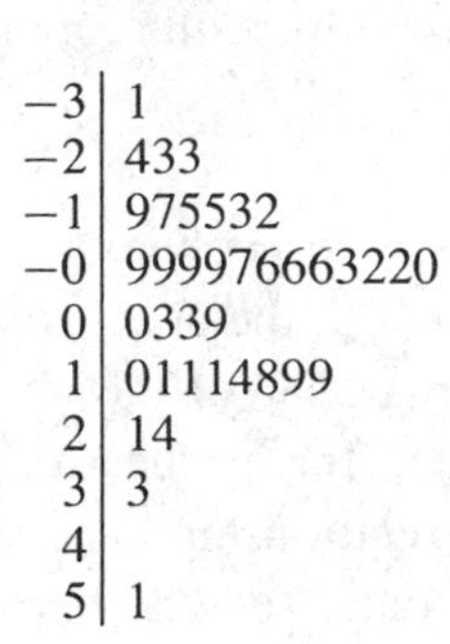

−3 | 1
−2 | 433
−1 | 975532
−0 | 999976663220
0 | 0339
1 | 01114899
2 | 14
3 | 3
4 |
5 | 1


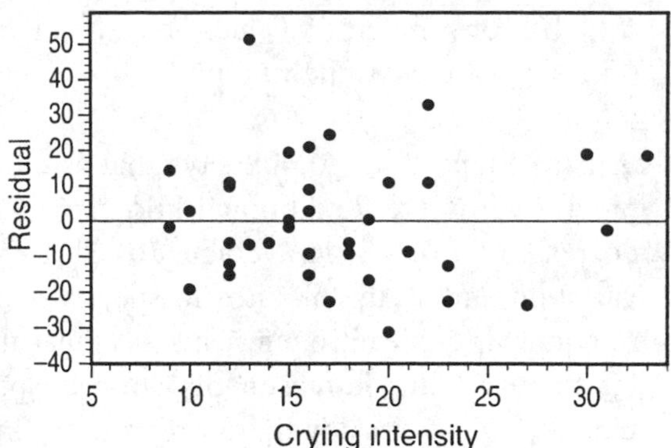


**24.15.** **(a)** A child who is, say, above average in height at one age is likely to be tall at other ages as well, so repeated measurements on the same child could not be considered independent. **(b)** and **(c)** Scatterplot shown below on the right. Roughly, the residuals are first positive, then negative, then positive again. **(d)** A stemplot (equivalent to a histogram) is shown below; it reveals slight right-skewness, but no clear deviations from Normality.

−1 | 0
−0 | 97765
−0 | 3110
0 | 0114
0 | 5
1 | 04
1 | 6

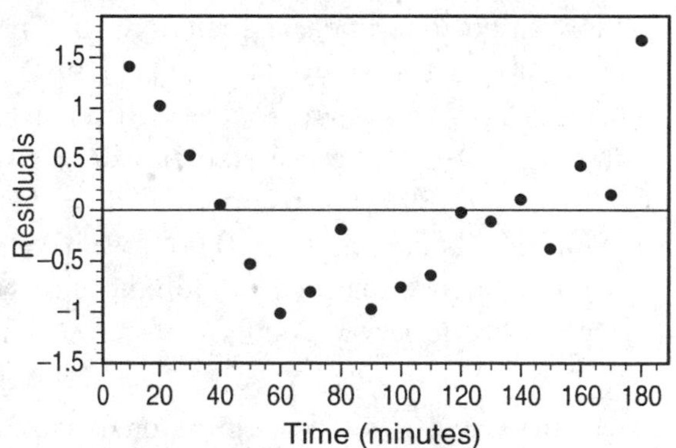


**24.16.** (b) These numbers are given in the "Coef" column of the Minitab output.

**24.17.** (c) $r$ is the square root of the value of "R-sq" ($r^2$) given in the Minitab output. (We take the positive square root because the sign of $r$ must be the same as the sign of the slope, 1.0466.)

**24.18.** (b) $\beta$ is the *average* rate of increase; it is not exact (unless there is no variation in the data; that is, unless $r^2 = 1$).

**24.19.** (a) "Selling price increases as appraised value increases" if the slope is positive.

**24.20.** (b) The $P$-value reported on the "appraisal" line is "0.000."

**24.21.** (b) This is "S" in the Minitab output.

**24.22.** (a) There are $n = 16$ data pairs, so $\text{df} = n - 2 = 14$.

**24.23.** (a) With df = 14, $t^* = 2.145$, so the margin of error is $t^*\ \text{SE}_b \doteq (2.145)(0.1126) \doteq 0.2415$.

**24.24.** (b) For a range of values for an individual unit, we should use the prediction interval ("PI") from the Minitab output.

**24.25.** **(a)** Slope $b = -0.408$ says that as nitrogen goes up, species richness goes down. More precisely, for every additional kilogram of nitrogen per hectare, the species richness measure decreases by 0.408 on average. **(b)** That $r^2 = 0.55$ says that 55% of the total observed variation among the 68 sites in species richness is accounted for by the straight-line relationship with nitrogen. This says that the straight-line relationship described by the least-squares line is reasonably strong, especially for field data. **(c)** The hypotheses concern the slope $\beta$ of the population regression line. It is not clear whether the alternative was one- or two-sided: $H_0$: $\beta = 0$ versus $H_a$: $\beta \neq 0$ (or $\beta < 0$). The small $P$ says that there is very strong evidence that the population slope is negative, that is, that species richness does decrease as nitrogen deposited increases.

**24.26.** **(a)** Stumps (the explanatory variable) should be on the horizontal axis; the plot shows a positive linear association. **(b)** The regression line is $\hat{y} = -1.286 + 11.894x$. **(c)** Our hypotheses are $H_0$: $\beta = 0$ versus $H_a$: $\beta \neq 0$, and the test statistic is $t = b/\text{SE}_b = 11.894/1.136 = 10.47$ (df = 21). Table C tells us that $P < 0.001$; we have strong evidence that beaver stump counts help explain beetle larvae counts.

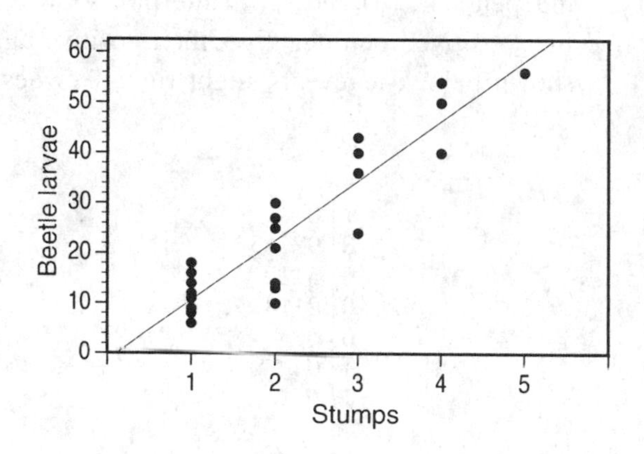


**24.27.** **(a)** Excel gives the regression equation as $\hat{y} = 0.1205 + 0.0086x$. That the slope is positive tells us that as the number of perch increases, the proportion being killed by bass also increases. **(b)** The regression standard error is $s = 0.1886$ (given in cell B7 of the Excel output).

**24.28.** **(a)** See also the solution to Exercise 7.44. The scatterplot is shown with the regression line $\hat{y} = 70.44 + 274.78x$. The squared correlation is $r^2 \doteq 49.3\%$ ("R-sq" in the CrunchIt! output). **(b)** The $t$ statistic for testing $H_0$: $\beta = 0$ is $t = b/\text{SE}_b = 274.7821/88.17712 \doteq 3.12$ with df = $n - 2 = 10$. The two-sided $P$-value is between 0.01 and 0.02, so we conclude that $\beta \neq 0$.

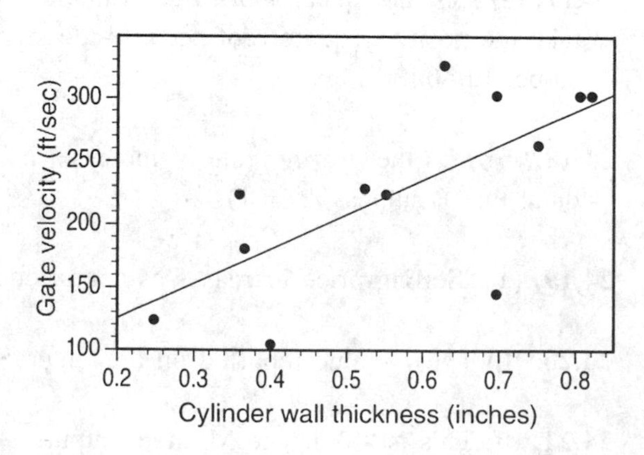

**24.29.** **(a)** Excel's 95% confidence interval for $\beta$ is 0.0033 to 0.0138; this can be verified (except for roundoff error) as $b \pm t^*\text{SE}_b = 0.0086 \pm (2.145)(0.0025)$, using critical value $t^* = 2.145$ from a $t$ distribution with df $= 14$. **(b)** With df $= 14$, we have $t^* = 1.761$, so the 90% confidence interval is $0.0086 \pm (1.761)(0.0025) = 0.0042$ to 0.0130.

**24.30.** For 90% intervals with df $= 10$, use $t^* = 1.812$. **(a)** The confidence interval for $\beta$ is

$$\begin{aligned} b \pm t^*\text{SE}_b &= 274.7821 \pm (1.812)(88.17712) \\ &= 274.78 \pm 159.78 = 115.0 \text{ to } 434.6 \text{ fps/inch.} \end{aligned}$$

**(b)** Use $\hat{y} = 207.82793$ and $\text{SE}_{\hat{\mu}} = 17.428537$, labeled "Pred. Y" and "s.e.(Pred. Y)" in the output:

$$\hat{y} \pm t^*\text{SE}_{\hat{\mu}} \doteq 207.83 \pm (1.812)(17.43) \doteq 176.3 \text{ to } 239.3 \text{ fps.}$$

**24.31.** In Table F with $n = 16$, we find that $0.6643 < r < 0.7114$, so the one-sided $P$-value is $0.001 < P < 0.0025$. Excel's $P$-value (0.0036) for testing $\beta = 0$ is for a two-sided test, so the one-sided $P$-value would be 0.0018.

**24.32.** **(a)** The residuals add up to 0 (as they should). **(b)** The scatterplot shows no obvious nonlinearity or change in spread. **(c)** A stemplot (equivalent to a histogram) is quite spread out, but not strikingly non-Normal.

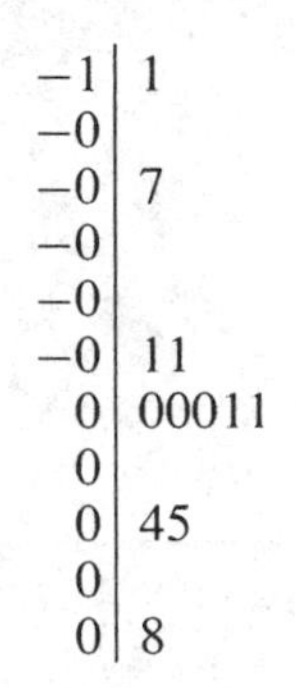

```
−1 | 1
−0 |
−0 | 7
−0 |
−0 |
−0 | 11
 0 | 00011
 0 |
 0 | 45
 0 |
 0 | 8
```

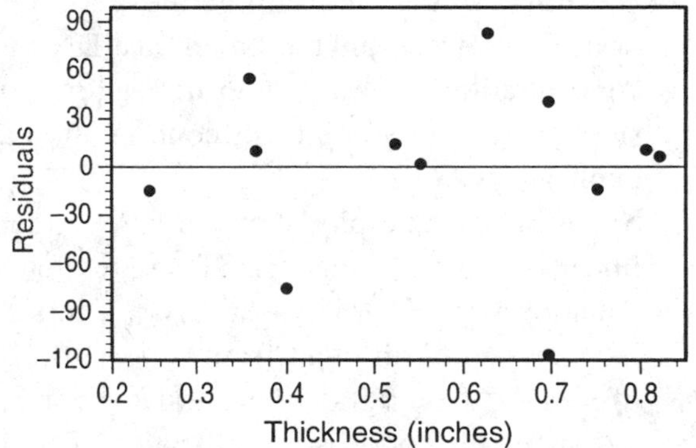


**24.33.** The distribution is skewed to the right, but the sample is large, so $t$ procedures should be safe. We find that $\bar{x} \doteq 0.2781$ g/m$^2$ and $s \doteq 0.1803$ g/m$^2$. Table C gives $t^* = 1.984$ for df $= 100$, while software gives $t^* = 1.9808$ for df $= 115$. Therefore, the the 95% confidence interval for $\mu$ is 0.2449 to 0.3113 g/m$^2$. (The lower limit rounds to 0.2450 using the software value.)

```
 0 | 0067778999
 1 | 00001111222333455555566677778889
 2 | 0000011112233344466666777888889
 3 | 00000111222333456667788999
 4 | 01456667
 5 | 3589
 6 | 04
 7 |
 8 | 29
 9 | 0
10 | 5
```

**24.34.** See also the solution to Exercise 5.3. **(a)** Table F for $n = 16$ gives critical value 0.7419 for tail probability 0.0005, so the one-sided $P$-value for $r = -0.7786$ is $P < 0.0005$. There is strong evidence that the correlation is negative. **(b)** To find this interval, we need $\text{SE}_b$; this is given in the Minitab output below as 0.0007414. With df $= 14$, $t^* = 1.761$ for 90% confidence, so the 90% confidence interval for $\beta$ is

$$b \pm t^*\text{SE}_b \doteq -0.00344 \pm 0.0013 \doteq -0.00475 \text{ to } -0.00214.$$

**(c)** This question calls for a prediction interval. The Minitab output below gives the interval as 0.488 to 3.789 kg.

If software is not readily available, this can also be done by hand starting from the regression standard error $s = 0.7399$, and the mean and standard deviation of $x$: $\bar{x} = 324.8$ and $s_x = 257.7$ calories. With these, we can find $\sum(x - \bar{x})^2 = 15s_x^2 \doteq 996,140$, so

$$\mathrm{SE}_{\hat{y}} = 0.7399\sqrt{1 + \frac{1}{16} + \frac{(400 - 324.8)^2}{996,140}} \doteq 0.7647.$$

Then the margin of error for the prediction interval is $2.145\,\mathrm{SE}_{\hat{y}} \doteq 1.6403$, so the interval is $2.13 \pm 1.64 \doteq 0.49$ to $3.77$ kg.

**Minitab output**

```
The regression equation is fat = 3.51 - 0.00344 nea

Predictor        Coef       Stdev     t-ratio        p
Constant       3.5051      0.3036       11.54    0.000
nea        -0.0034415   0.0007414       -4.64    0.000

s = 0.7399      R-sq = 60.6%      R-sq(adj) = 57.8%

    Fit  Stdev.Fit          95.0% C.I.            95.0% P.I.
  2.129      0.193    (  1.714,   2.543)  (   0.488,    3.769)
```

**24.35. Formulate:** We examine the relationship between phytopigment and DNA concentrations with a scatterplot and regression, treating phytopigment concentration as explanatory.

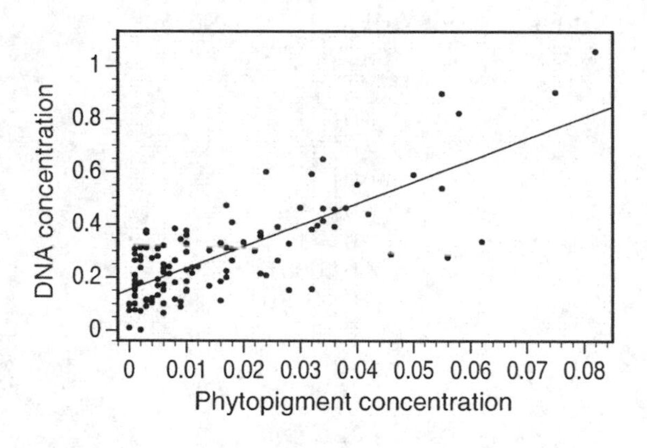


**Solve:** The scatterplot shows a fairly strong linear positive association. The regression equation is $\hat{y} = 0.1523 + 8.1676x$. The slope is significantly different from 0 ($t = 13.25$, df $= 114$, $P < 0.001$). The squared correlation ($r^2 = 0.606$) is an indication of the strength of the relationship.

**Conclude:** The significant linear relationship between phytopigment and DNA concentrations is consistent with the belief that organic matter settling is a primary source of DNA. Starting from a measurement of phytopigment concentration, we could give a fairly accurate prediction of DNA concentration, because the relationship explains about 60% of the variation in DNA concentration.

**Minitab output**

```
The regression equation is dna = 0.152 + 8.17 phyto

Predictor        Coef       Stdev     t-ratio        p
Constant      0.15231     0.01419       10.73    0.000
phyto          8.1676      0.6163       13.25    0.000

s = 0.1136      R-sq = 60.6%      R-sq(adj) = 60.3%
```

**24.36. (a)** The Minitab output gives the regression equation as $\hat{y} = 31.9 - 0.304x$; with $x = 60$, we predict $\hat{y} = 13.66$; this differs from the given `Fit` value (13.69) due to roundoff error. (If we use the values listed in the "`Coef`" column, we get 13.6928.) **(b)** Use the confidence interval (CI): 11.43 to 15.95 returning birds.

**24.37. (a)** There is considerably greater scatter for larger values of the explanatory variable, especially when one considers the small number of observations we have for high phytopigment concentrations. **(b)** A stemplot (equivalent to a histogram) is shown below. The distribution of residuals looks reasonably Normal.

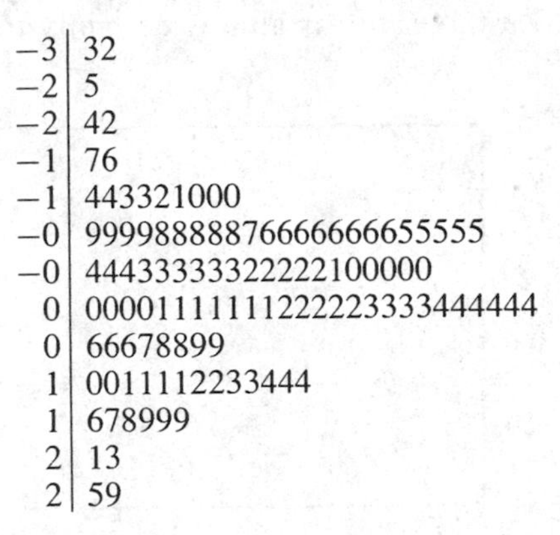


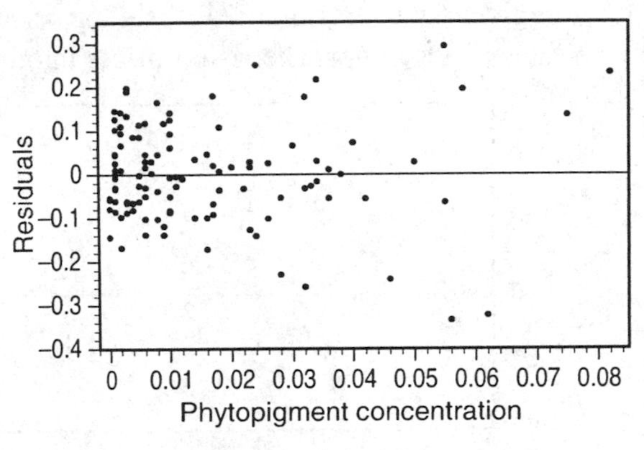


**24.38. (a)** The observations are independent because they come from 13 unrelated colonies. **(b)** The scatterplot of the residuals against the percent returning (below) shows no obvious pattern. **(c)** The spread may be slightly wider in the middle, but not markedly so. **(d)** A stemplot (equivalent to a histogram) shows no clear deviation from Normality.

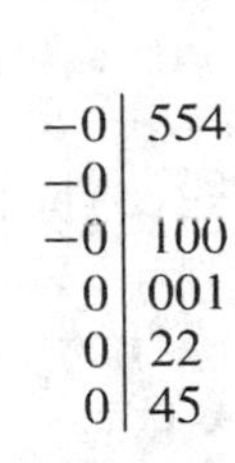


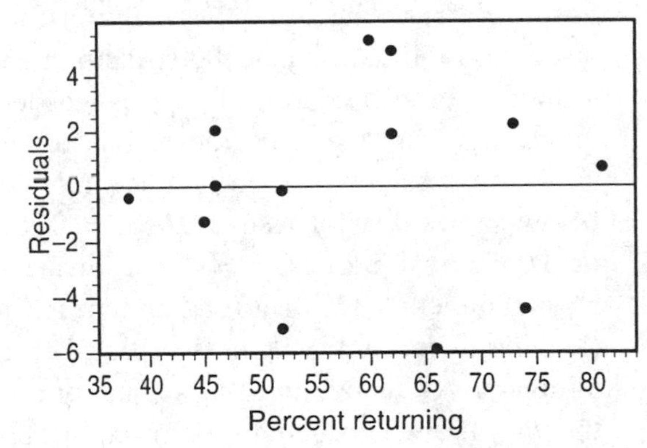

**24.39.** **(a)** This plot is below on the left; as usual, we add a horizontal line at residual zero, the mean of the residuals. This line corresponds to the regression line in the plot of selling price against appraised value. The residuals show a random scatter about the line, with roughly equal vertical spread across their range. This is what we expect when the conditions for regression inference hold. **(b)** The stemplot is shown on the right. **(c)** The plot of residuals against the month of the sale is below on the right. The pattern of steadily rising residuals shows that predicted prices are too high for early sales and too low for later sales. This is what we expect if selling prices are rising and appraised values aren't updated quickly enough to keep up. The prediction given in Exercise 24.24 (a selling price of \$967.3 thousand) is almost certainly too low, because it does not take rising prices into account.

| | |
|---|---|
| −0 | 87765 |
| −0 | 4222 |
| 0 | 233 |
| 0 | 68 |
| 1 | 01 |

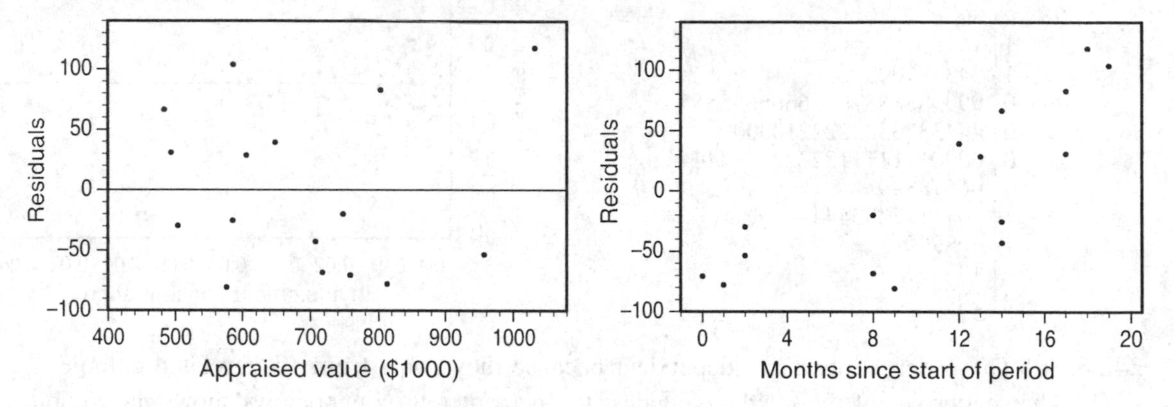


**24.40.** **Formulate:** We examine the relationship between HAV angle and MA angle using a scatterplot and regression.

**Solve:** Refer to the solutions to Exercises 7.19, 7.21 and 7.22 for a scatterplot and other discussions. In particular, the scatterplot shows a roughly linear relationship, with one point standing out as a clear outlier. It is reasonable to view the observations as independent, as they came from (we presume) unrelated children.

The regression equation for the entire data set is $\hat{y} = 19.7 + 0.339x$. The Minitab output below shows that for testing $H_0$: $\beta = 0$ versus $H_a$: $\beta \neq 0$, we find $t = 1.90$ and a $P$-value of 0.065. As we know, $\beta \neq 0$ is equivalent to a nonzero correlation. This means that we have some evidence of a relationship, but not what would usually be considered significant. (It is possible the researchers expected that severe MA deformity would be associated with a larger HAV angle, and so used the one-sided alternative $H_a$: $\beta > 0$. If that is the case, the $P$-value would be half as much, or about 0.033.) An analysis of the residuals, in both a stemplot and a plot against MA angle, shows the same outlier visible in the original scatterplot; this might make us hesitate to use inference procedures. Other than the outlier, there are no great causes of concern: the rest of the stemplot appears to be roughly Normal, and the scatterplot has no clear pattern, although there is some suggestion that the spread about the line is slightly greater for small MA angle.

There may be some justification for removing the outlier. Repeating the regression analysis with the outlier omitted gives the equation $\hat{y} = 17.7 + 0.419x$. In the absence of the outlier, there is strong evidence of a significant correlation ($t = 2.93$, $P = 0.006$). Residual analysis shows little reason for concern: the stemplot has a roughly Normal shape, and the scatterplot appears to be fine (although there is again a slight suggestion that the spread is slightly greater for small MA angle).

**Conclude:** The correlation is significantly positive with the full data set, and significantly different from 0 with the outlier removed. In neither case is the relationship very useful for prediction ($r^2 = 9.1\%$ with all data, $r^2 = 19.6\%$ with the outlier omitted).

**Minitab output (full data set):**

```
The regression equation is HAV = 19.7 + 0.339 MA

Predictor       Coef        Stdev     t-ratio       p
Constant      19.723        3.217        6.13   0.000
MA            0.3388       0.1782        1.90   0.065

s = 7.224       R-sq = 9.1%       R-sq(adj) = 6.6%
```

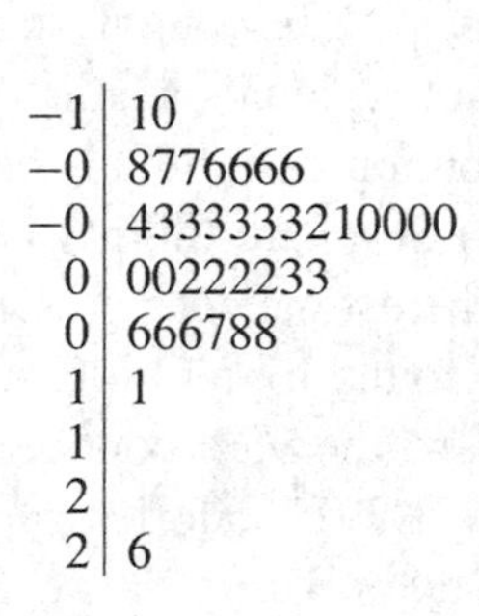


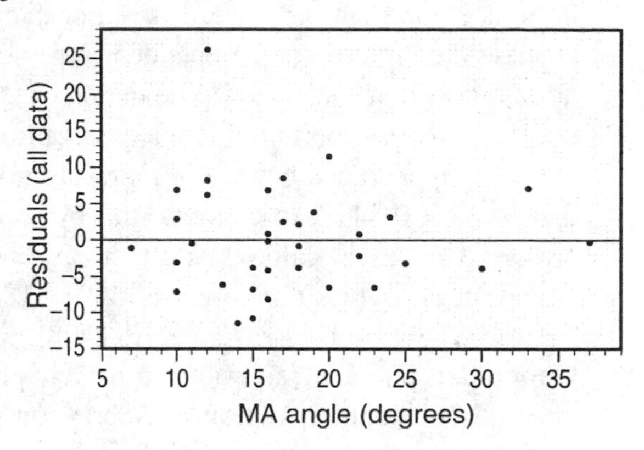


**Minitab output (outlier omitted):**

```
The regression equation is HAV = 17.7 + 0.419 MA

Predictor       Coef        Stdev     t-ratio       p
Constant      17.659        2.605        6.78   0.000
MA            0.4189       0.1432        2.93   0.006

s = 5.763       R-sq = 19.6%      R-sq(adj) = 17.3%
```

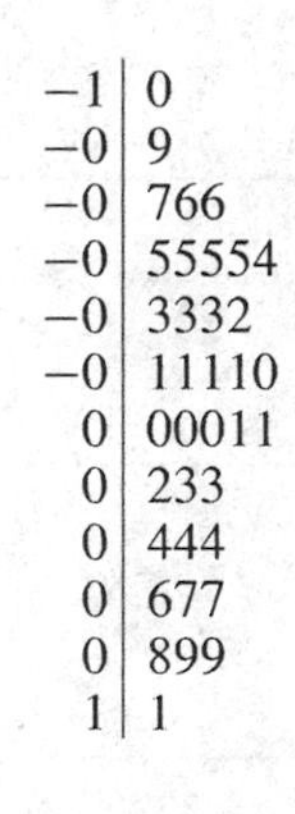


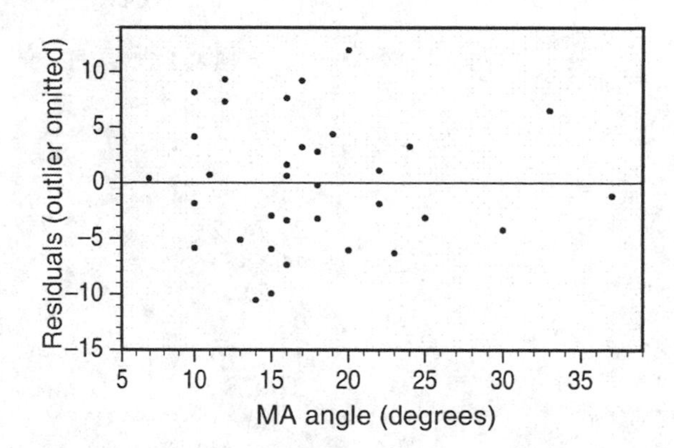

**24.41. Formulate:** We examine the relationship using a scatterplot and regression, and find a 95% confidence interval for the slope.

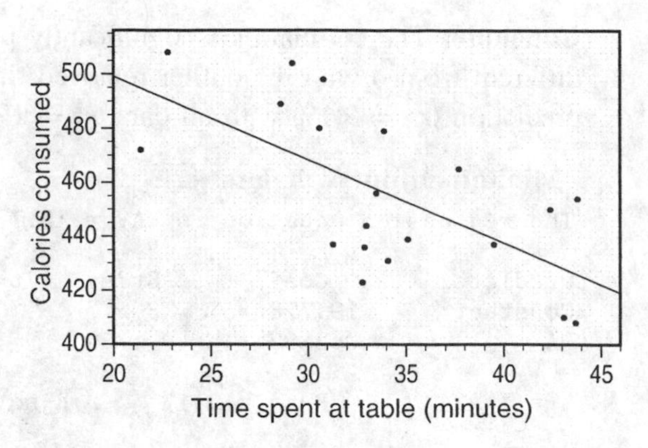


**Solve: (a)** The scatterplot is shown on the right. The regression equation is $\hat{y} = 560.65 - 3.0771x$; this and the plot show that, generally, the longer a child remains at the table, the fewer calories he or she will consume. **(b)** All the conditions for inference appear to be met: it is reasonable to view the children as independent. The scatterplot appears to be roughly linear, and does not suggest that the standard deviation changes (the plot of residuals against time spent at the table also supports the latter observation). The distribution of residuals has a slightly irregular appearance but is not markedly non-Normal. **(c)** Software (output below) reports that $\text{SE}_b = 0.8498$; to compute this by hand, note that the estimated regression standard error is $s = 23.40$ calories and that $\sqrt{\sum(x - \bar{x})^2}$ can be found by multiplying the standard deviation of $x$ (time) by $\sqrt{19}$. For df $= 18$, $t^* = 2.101$, so the 95% confidence interval is $b \pm t^*\text{SE}_b = -3.0771 \pm (2.101)(0.8498) = -4.8625$ to $-1.2917$ calories per minute.
**Conclude:** The analysis shows a moderately strong negative relationship, which explains $r^2 = 42.1\%$ of the variation in calorie consumption. We are 95% confident that, on the average, calorie consumption drops by between 1.3 and 4.9 calories for each additional minute at the table.

**Minitab output**

```
The regression equation is Calories = 561 - 3.08 Time

Predictor        Coef       Stdev    t-ratio        p
Constant       560.65       29.37      19.09    0.000
Time          -3.0771      0.8498      -3.62    0.002

s = 23.40        R-sq = 42.1%     R-sq(adj) = 38.9%
```

| Stem | Leaves |
|---|---|
| −3 | 6 |
| −2 | 7432 |
| −1 | 8853 |
| −0 | 21 |
| 0 | |
| 1 | 3679 |
| 2 | 028 |
| 3 | 23 |

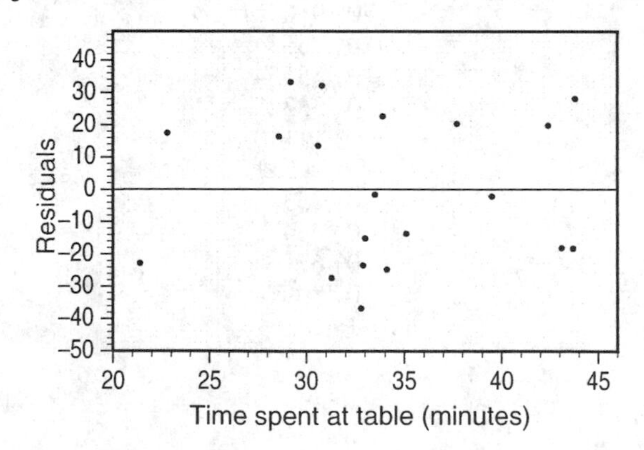

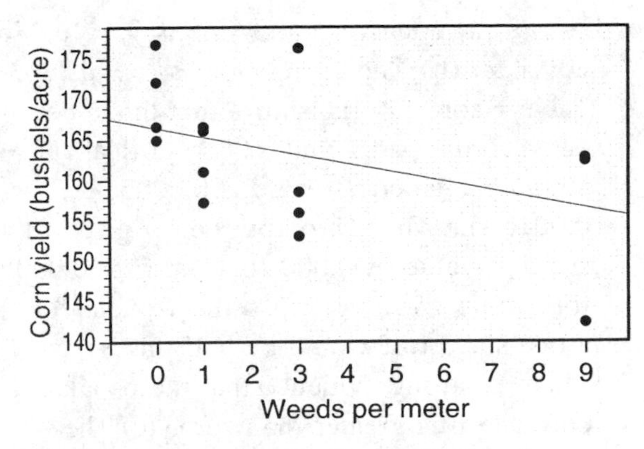


**24.42.** **(a)** Scatterplot at right. Regression gives $\hat{y} = 166.5 - 1.099x$; the linear relationship explains about $r^2 = 20.9\%$ of the variation in yield. **(b)** The $t$ statistic for testing $\beta = 0$ is $t = -1.92$; with df $= 14$, the $P$-value is 0.075 (Table C tells us that $0.05 < P < 0.10$). We have some evidence that weeds influence corn yields, but it is not strong enough to meet the usual standards of statistical significance. **(c)** The small value of $r^2$ and the lack of significance of the $t$ test indicate that this regression has little predictive use. When $x = 6$, $\hat{y} = 159.9$ bu/acre; the 95% confidence interval (given by Minitab, below) is 154.4 to 165.3 bu/acre. [Up to rounding error, this agrees with the hand-computed value, with $t^* = 2.145$ and $\text{SE}_{\hat{\mu}} = 2.54$: $159.9 \pm (2.145)(2.54)$.] The width of this interval is another indication that the model has little practical use.

**Minitab output**

```
The regression equation is Corn = 166 - 1.10 Weeds

Predictor         Coef        Stdev    t-ratio        p
Constant       166.483        2.725      61.11    0.000
Weeds          -1.0987       0.5712      -1.92    0.075

s = 7.977         R-sq = 20.9%        R-sq(adj) = 15.3%
```

**(output continues)**

```
     Fit   Stdev.Fit         95.0% C.I.             95.0% P.I.
  159.89        2.54   (  154.44,   165.34)   (  141.93,   177.85)
```

**24.43.** This question calls for a prediction interval, rather than for a confidence interval. Shown below is Minitab output that gives the interval as 386 to 489 calories.

If software is not readily available, this can also be done by hand starting from the regression standard error $s = 23.4$, and the mean and standard deviation of $x$: $\bar{x} = 34.01$ and $s_x = 6.3165$ minutes. With these, we can find $\sum(x - \bar{x})^2 = 19s_x^2 \doteq 758.07$, so $\text{SE}_{\hat{y}} = 23.4\sqrt{1 + \frac{1}{20} + \frac{(40 - 34.01)^2}{758.07}} \doteq 24.51$. Then the margin of error for the prediction interval is $2.101\,\text{SE}_{\hat{y}} \doteq 51.5$, so the interval is $437.57 \pm 51.5 \doteq 386$ to 489 calories.

**Minitab output**

```
     Fit   Stdev.Fit         95.0% C.I.             95.0% P.I.
  437.57        7.30   (  422.23,   452.91)   (  386.06,   489.08)
```

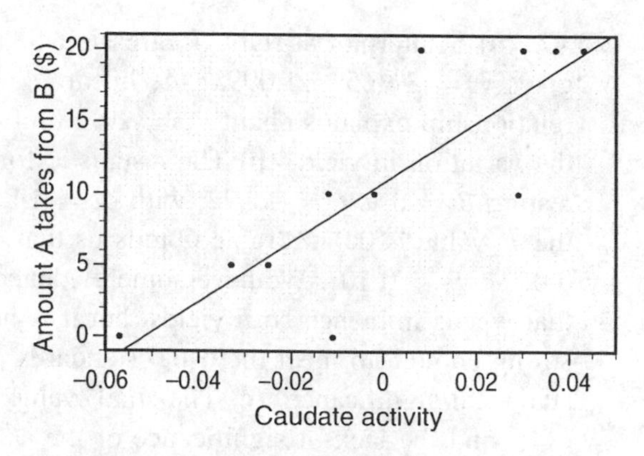


**24.44. (a)** The least-squares line is $\hat{y} = 10.776 + 209.12x$. **(b)** The correlation is $r = 0.8363$. Table F for $n = 11$ shows that this $r$ lies between the 0.001 and 0.0005 critical values, so the one-sided $P$-value is $0.0005 < P < 0.001$. The Minitab output below gives a two-sided $P$-value of 0.000 (that is, $P < 0.0005$) for testing $H_0$: $\beta = 0$, so the $P$-value for a one-sided test would be half this large. There is strong evidence that the population correlation is greater than zero. **(c)** The response variable takes only values 0, 5, 10, and 20 (these were the only options allowed to player A). The statistical model for regression inference states that the response varies Normally about the true regression line. While it is fine for the *explanatory* variable to take only a small set of values, the response variable must vary continuously.

**Minitab output**

```
The regression equation is takes = 10.8 + 209 caudate

Predictor       Coef       Stdev    t-ratio       p
Constant      10.776       1.395       7.72   0.000
caudate       209.12       45.69       4.58   0.000

s = 4.626         R-sq = 69.9%      R-sq(adj) = 66.6%
```

**24.45. (a)** The mean is $\bar{x} \doteq 0.00174$, and the standard deviation is $s \doteq 1.0137$. For a standardized set of values, we expect the mean and standard deviation to be (up to rounding error) 0 and 1, respectively. (See note below.) **(b)** The stemplot (below, left) does not look particularly symmetric, but it is not strikingly non-Normal (for such a small sample). In a set of 23 observations from a standard Normal distribution, we expect most (95%) to be between −2 and 2, so −1.99 is quite reasonable. **(c)** The plot of residuals versus stump counts (below, right) gives no cause for concern.

| | |
|---|---|
| −1 | 965 |
| −1 | 30 |
| −0 | 7 |
| −0 | 4422 |
| 0 | 0224 |
| 0 | 56789 |
| 1 | 2233 |

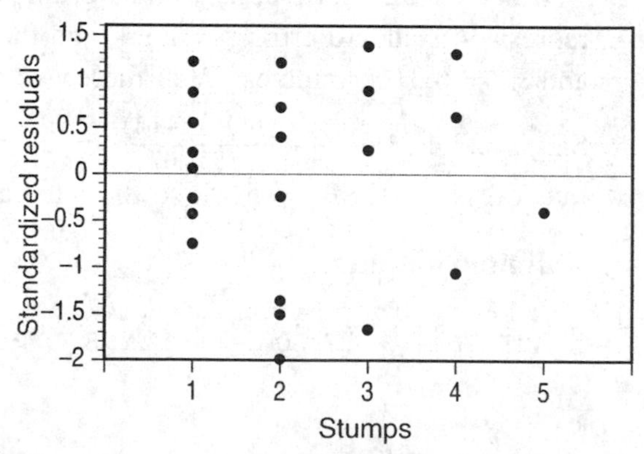


**Note:** *The process for finding standardized residuals is more complicated than simply finding the standard deviation of the set of residuals, and then dividing each residual by that standard deviation. (The mean of the residuals will necessarily be 0.) Standardized residuals will generally have mean and standard deviation* close to, *but not exactly equal to, 0 and 1 (respectively). For this data set, for example, even if we take unrounded standardized residuals, the mean is 0.0015107 (not 0) and the standard deviation is 1.0140*

*(not 1). A simpler example is the data set (1, 1), (2, 1), (3, 2), for which the standardized residuals are 1, −1, 1, with mean 1/3 and standard deviation* $\sqrt{4/3} \doteq 1.1547$.

**24.46.** The $t$ statistic given in Figure 24.7 (rounded to a more reasonable number of decimal places) is $-1.0050 \doteq a/\text{SE}_a = \frac{-0.01270}{0.01264}$. The given $P$-value is 0.332, so we do not have enough evidence to conclude that the intercept $\alpha$ is different from 0.

**24.47.** For df $= 14$ and a 95% confidence interval, we use $t^* = 2.145$, so the interval is

$$-0.01270 \pm (2.145)(0.01264) = -0.0398 \text{ to } 0.0144.$$

This interval does contain 0.

---

For solutions to the EESEE Case Studies (Exercises 48–50), see the instructor's version of EESEE.

# Chapter 25 Solutions

**25.1.** **(a)** Diagram below. **(b)** The null hypothesis is "all groups have the same mean rest period," and the alternative is "at least one group has a different mean rest period." The $P$-value shows significant evidence against $H_0$, and the graph leads us to conclude that caffeine has the effect of reducing the length of the rest period.

**Note:** *Students might be tempted to think that the alternative hypothesis is "mean rest period decreases with increasing caffeine dosage" or something similar, but ANOVA alternatives are nondirectional.*

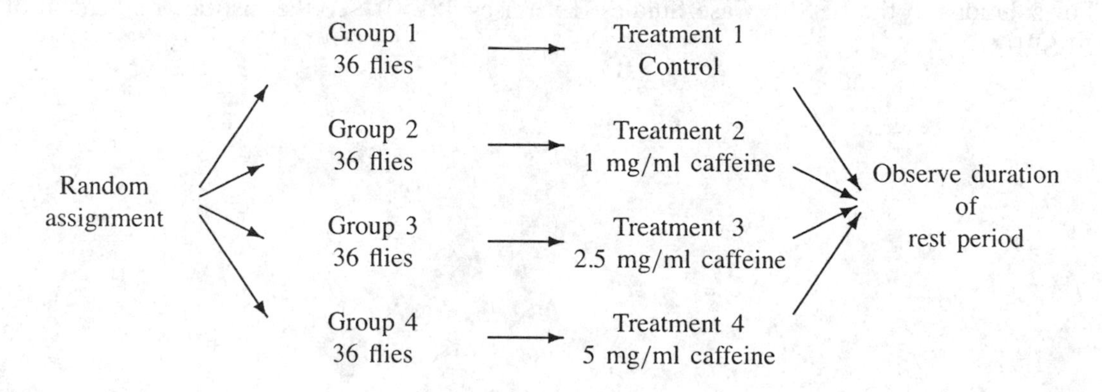


**25.2.** **(a)** The null hypothesis is "all age groups have the same (population) mean road-rage measurement," and the alternative is "at least one group has a different mean." **(b)** The $F$ test is quite significant, giving strong evidence that the means are different. The sample means suggest that the degree of road rage decreases with age. (We assume that higher numbers indicate *more* road rage.)

**25.3.** **(a)** The stemplots (right) appear to suggest that logging reduces the number of trees per plot and that recovery is slow (the 1-year-after and 8-years-after stemplots are similar). **(b)** The means lead one to the same conclusion as in (a): the first mean is much larger than the other two. **(c)** In testing $H_0$: $\mu_1 = \mu_2 = \mu_3$ versus $H_a$: not all means are the same, we find that $F = 11.43$ with df $= 2$ and $30$, which has $P = 0.000205$, so we conclude that these differences are significant: The number of trees per plot really is lower in logged areas.

| Never logged | | 1 year ago | | 8 years ago | |
|---|---|---|---|---|---|
| 0 | | 0 | 2 | 0 | 4 |
| 0 | | 0 | 9 | 0 | |
| 1 | | 1 | 2244 | 1 | 22 |
| 1 | 699 | 1 | 57789 | 1 | 5889 |
| 2 | 0124 | 2 | 0 | 2 | 22 |
| 2 | 7789 | 2 | | 2 | |
| 3 | 3 | 3 | | 3 | |

**25.4.** **(a)** The stemplots (right) show no extreme outliers or skewness. **(b)** The means suggest that a dog reduces heart rate, but being with a friend appears to raise it. **(c)** $F = 14.08$ and $P = 0.000$ (meaning $P < 0.0005$), which means that we reject $H_0$: $\mu_P = \mu_F = \mu_C$ in favor of $H_a$: at least one mean is different. Based on the confidence intervals, it appears that the mean heart rate is lowest when a pet is present (although this interval overlaps the control interval) and is highest when a friend is present (although again, this interval overlaps the control interval).

| Dog | | Friend | | Alone | |
|---|---|---|---|---|---|
| 5 | 9 | 5 | | 5 | |
| 6 | 4 | 6 | | 6 | 3 |
| 6 | 5999 | 6 | | 6 | |
| 7 | 0002 | 7 | | 7 | 13 |
| 7 | 6 | 7 | 7 | 7 | 58 |
| 8 | 0 | 8 | 023 | 8 | 0 |
| 8 | 56 | 8 | 78 | 8 | 555778 |
| 9 | | 9 | 012 | 9 | 02 |
| 9 | 8 | 9 | 78 | 9 | 9 |
| 10 | | 10 | 0112 | 10 | |

**25.5.** **(a)** By moving the middle mean to the same level as the other two, it is possible to reduce $F$ to 0.0236, which has a $P$-value very close to the left end of the scale (near 1). **(b)** By moving any mean about 1 centimeter up or down (or any two means about 0.5 cm in opposite directions), the value of $F$ increases (and $P$ decreases) until it appears at the right end of the scale.

**25.6.** **(a)** $F$ can be made as small as 0.3174, while $P > 0.5$. **(b)** $F$ can be made quite large (and $P$ small) by separating the means.

**25.7.** **(a)** Yes: $\frac{\text{largest } s}{\text{smallest } s} = \sqrt{\frac{33.1944}{24.8106}} = \frac{5.761}{4.981} \doteq 1.16$. **(b)** Yes: $\frac{\text{largest } s}{\text{smallest } s} = \frac{9.970}{8.341} \doteq 1.20$.

**25.8.** The standard deviations (0.1201, 0.1472, 0.1134) do not violate our rule of thumb. However, the distributions appear to be skewed and have outliers, especially the 1-year-ago group.

| Never logged | | 1 year ago | | 8 years ago | |
|---|---|---|---|---|---|
| 4 | | 4 | 2 | 4 | |
| 4 | 8 | 4 | | 4 | |
| 5 | | 5 | | 5 | |
| 5 | | 5 | | 5 | |
| 6 | 3 | 6 | | 6 | |
| 6 | 57 | 6 | | 6 | 8 |
| 7 | | 7 | | 7 | |
| 7 | 5889 | 7 | 7 | 7 | 8 |
| 8 | 111 | 8 | 3 | 8 | 13 |
| 8 | | 8 | 588 | 8 | |
| 9 | | 9 | 01123 | 9 | 34 |
| 9 | 5 | 9 | | 9 | |
| 10 | | 10 | 0 | 10 | 000 |

**25.9. (a)** Compressed soil has the lowest penetrability, intermediate is next, and loose is highest. **(b)** With a ratio of $\frac{0.3190}{0.1390} \doteq 2.3$, the standard deviations do not satisfy the rule of thumb. In the stemplots below, we see two outliers in the loose data and one in the intermediate data; use of ANOVA would be risky. **(c)** Without the outliers, the "intermediate" and "loose" standard deviations would be much smaller. (These are given in the table on the lines marked with asterisks.) The standard deviation ratio would be $\frac{0.2397}{0.1390} \doteq 1.7$, so ANOVA would be safe.

| | $\bar{x}$ | $s$ |
|---|---|---|
| Compressed | 2.9075 | 0.1390 |
| Intermediate | 3.3360 | 0.3190 |
| Loose | 4.2315 | 0.2713 |
| Intermediate* | 3.2874 | 0.2397 |
| Loose* | 4.1572 | 0.1545 |

| Compressed | | Intermediate | | Loose | |
|---|---|---|---|---|---|
| 26 | 8 | 2 | 99 | 39 | 4689 |
| 27 | | 3 | 0111111 | 40 | 03 |
| 27 | 6888 | 3 | 2333 | 41 | 12369 |
| 28 | 122 | 3 | 4445 | 42 | 079 |
| 28 | 66 | 3 | 6 | 43 | 04 |
| 29 | 024 | 3 | 8 | 44 | 11 |
| 29 | 68 | 4 | | 45 | |
| 30 | 0 | 4 | 2 | 46 | |
| 30 | 88 | | | 47 | |
| 31 | | | | 48 | 9 |
| 31 | 68 | | | 49 | 1 |

**25.10. (a)** $I$, the number of populations, is 3; the sample sizes from each population are $n_1 = n_2 = 12$ and $n_3 = 9$; the total sample size is $N = 33$. **(b)** Numerator ("Between Groups"): $I - 1 = 2$, denominator ("Within Groups"): $N - I = 30$. **(c)** Because $F > 9.22$, the largest critical value for an $F(2, 25)$ distribution in Table D, we conclude that $P < 0.001$.

**25.11. (a)** $I = 3$ and $N = 96$, so df = 2 and 93. From Table D, we compare with $F(2, 50)$ critical values, from which we conclude that $P < 0.001$, so there is very strong evidence that racial mix affects music choice for white hosts. **(b)** $I = 3$ and $N = 90$, so df = 2 and 87. From Table D, we compare with $F(2, 50)$ critical values, from which we conclude that $0.05 < P < 0.10$. (Software gives $P = 0.0905$.) There is some evidence that racial mix affects music choice for black hosts, but it is not significant at $\alpha = 0.05$.

**25.12. (a)** The sample sizes are quite large, and the $F$ test is robust against non-Normality with large samples. **(b)** Yes (barely): the ratio is $\frac{3.11}{1.60} \doteq 1.94$. **(c)** We have $I = 3$ and $N = 1342$. The details of the computations are given here; the Minitab output below confirms the computed values.

$$\begin{aligned}
\bar{x} &\doteq 1.31 & &\doteq \frac{244 \times 2.22 + 734 \times 1.33 + 364 \times 0.66}{1342} \\
\text{SSG} &\doteq 356.14 & &\doteq 244(2.22 - 1.31)^2 + 734(1.33 - 1.31)^2 + 364(0.66 - 1.31)^2 \\
\text{MSG} &\doteq 178.07 & &\doteq \frac{356.14}{3 - 1} \\
\text{SSE} &\doteq 6859.65 & &\doteq 243 \times 3.11^2 + 733 \times 2.21^2 + 363 \times 1.60^2 \\
\text{MSE} &\doteq 5.12 & &\doteq \frac{6859.65}{1342 - 3} \\
F &\doteq 34.76 & &\doteq \frac{178.07}{5.12}
\end{aligned}$$

**(d)** With df = 2 and 1339, we find that $P < 0.001$; this is strong evidence that the means differ among the age-groups.

**Minitab output**

| Source | DF | SS | MS | F | p |
|---|---|---|---|---|---|
| Factor | 2 | 356.14 | 178.07 | 34.76 | 0.000 |
| Error | 1339 | 6859.65 | 5.12 | | |
| Total | 1341 | 7215.79 | | | |

**25.13. (a)** Yes: the rule-of-thumb ratio is $\frac{5.2}{4.2} \doteq 1.24$. **(b)** $\bar{x} \doteq 9.92$, and MSG $\doteq 10.0$ (details below). **(c)** MSE $\doteq 21.9$ (details below). **(d)** $F \doteq 0.46$ (details below). With df = 2 and 112 (use 2 and 100 in the table), we find $P > 0.100$ (software gives 0.634), so we have no reason to doubt the null hypothesis; that is, there is not enough evidence to conclude that mean weight loss differs between these exercise programs.

In the details of the computations, we have $I = 3$ and $N = 115$:

$$\begin{aligned}
\bar{x} &\doteq 9.92 & &\doteq \frac{37 \times 10.2 + 36 \times 9.3 + 42 \times 10.2}{115} \\
\text{SSG} &\doteq 20.03 & &\doteq 37(10.2 - 9.92)^2 + 36(9.3 - 9.92)^2 + 42(10.2 - 9.92)^2 \\
\text{MSG} &\doteq 10.0 & &\doteq \frac{20.03}{3 - 1} \\
\text{SSE} &\doteq 2452.4 & &\doteq 36 \times 4.2^2 + 35 \times 4.5^2 + 41 \times 5.2^2 \\
\text{MSE} &\doteq 21.9 & &\doteq \frac{2452.4}{115 - 3} \\
F &\doteq 0.46 & &\doteq \frac{10.0}{21.9}
\end{aligned}$$

**Minitab output**

| Source | DF | SS | MS | F | p |
|---|---|---|---|---|---|
| Factor | 2 | 20.0 | 10.0 | 0.46 | 0.634 |
| Error | 112 | 2452.4 | 21.9 | | |
| Total | 114 | 2472.5 | | | |

**25.14.** The details of the computations, with $I = 5$ and $N = 4413$, are:

$$\begin{aligned}
\bar{x} \doteq 2.459 &\doteq \frac{809 \times 2.57 + 1860 \times 2.32 + 654 \times 2.63 + 883 \times 2.51 + 207 \times 2.51}{4413} \\
\text{SSG} \doteq 67.86 &\doteq 809(2.57 - \bar{x})^2 + 1860(2.32 - \bar{x})^2 + 654(2.63 - \bar{x})^2 \\
&\qquad + 883(2.51 - \bar{x})^2 + 207(2.51 - \bar{x})^2 \\
\text{MSG} \doteq 16.97 &\doteq \frac{67.86}{5 - 1} \\
\text{SSE} \doteq 8010.98 &\doteq 808 \times 1.40^2 + 1859 \times 1.36^2 + 653 \times 1.32^2 + 882 \times 1.31^2 + 206 \times 1.28^2 \\
\text{MSE} \doteq 1.82 &\doteq \frac{8010.98}{4413 - 5} \\
F \doteq 9.34 &\doteq \frac{16.97}{1.82}
\end{aligned}$$

The ANOVA is very significant ($P < 0.0005$), but this is not surprising because the sample sizes were very large. The differences might not have practical importance. (The largest difference is 0.31, which is relatively small on a 5-point scale.)

**Minitab output**

| Source | DF | SS | MS | F | p |
|---|---|---|---|---|---|
| Factor | 4 | 67.86 | 16.97 | 9.34 | 0.000 |
| Error | 4408 | 8010.98 | 1.82 | | |
| Total | 4412 | 8078.85 | | | |

**25.15.** (c) ANOVA is used for comparing means in two or more populations.

**25.16.** (b) There are $I = 3$ groups, and the total sample size is $N = 600$, so the degrees of freedom are $I - 1 = 2$ and $N - I = 597$.

**25.17.** (c) In ANOVA, $H_0$ says all the means are the same, and $H_a$ says that at least one mean is different.

**25.18.** (b) The winter mean is much smaller than the other three means. (We cannot determine that "the air ... is clearly unhealthy" unless we know how to interpret a measurement of, for example, 209 CFUs.)

**25.19.** (b) The conservative interval uses df $= 3$, so $t^* = 2.353$. The standard error is $\text{SE} \doteq \sqrt{\frac{906.4^2}{4} + \frac{136.6^2}{4}} \doteq 458.3$, and the margin of error is $t^*\text{SE} \doteq 1078.4$.

**25.20.** (a) This is "the problem of multiple comparisons" discussed in the text.

**25.21.** (a) The $P$-value from the ANOVA table is 0.014, which is strong evidence against $H_0$, and allows us to conclude that the means are not all the same. (It does not tell us that the winter mean is smaller than *all* other seasonal means.)

**25.22.** (b) By comparing to $F(3, 12)$ critical values, we see that $4.47 < F < 5.95$, so the $P$-value is between 0.01 and 0.025.

**25.23.** (a) ANOVA assumes that all standard deviations are equal. Our rule of thumb says that ANOVA is not reliable if the ratio of the largest-to-smallest standard deviations is more than 2; in this case, that ratio is 7.84. (An examination of the data does *not* show any extreme outliers.)

**25.24.** The populations are students at four different types of colleges (public/private doctorate/nondoctorate). The response variable is the amount of money borrowed. There are $I = 4$ populations; the sample sizes are $n_1 = 137$, $n_2 = 313$, $n_3 = 148$, and $n_4 = 95$, so the total sample size is $N = 693$. The degrees of freedom are therefore $I - 1 = 3$ and $N - I = 689$.

**25.25.** The populations are morning people, evening people, and people who are neither. The response variable is the difference in memorization scores. There are $I = 3$ populations; the sample sizes are $n_1 = 16$, $n_2 = 30$, and $n_3 = 54$, so the total sample size is $N = 100$. The degrees of freedom are therefore $I - 1 = 2$ and $N - I = 97$.

**25.26.** The populations are students with no additional instruction, those required to prepare a written outline, those who were given 15 relevant ideas, and those given the ideas and required to prepare an outline. The response variable is the quality scores for their essays. There are $I = 4$ populations; the sample sizes are $n_1 = n_2 = n_3 = n_4 = 20$, so the total sample size is $N = 80$. The degrees of freedom are therefore $I - 1 = 3$ and $N - I = 76$.

**25.27.** The populations are normal-weight men, overweight men, and obese men. The response variable is the triglyceride level. There are $I = 3$ populations; the sample sizes are $n_1 = 719$, $n_2 = 885$, and $n_3 = 220$, so the total sample size is $N = 1824$. The degrees of freedom are therefore $I - 1 = 2$ and $N - I = 1821$.

**25.28.** We have $I = 3$ populations. **(a)** For this test, we consider all the mating pairs, so $N = 13 + 9 + 8 = 30$. The degrees of freedom are $I - 1 = 2$ and $N - I = 27$. With $F = 0.07$, the $P$-value is very large (Table D tells us that $P > 0.10$; software gives $P = 0.9326$). We conclude that there was no difference among the groups in the number of young in the first brood. (In other words, the random allocation to the three groups "worked": No group produced a significantly different number of offspring in the first brood.) **(b)** For this test, we consider only the 27 mating pairs which produced broods both times, so $N = 27$. (We don't know the three sample sizes $n_1$, $n_2$, or $n_3$, but we do not need those for the ANOVA test.) The degrees of freedom are $I - 1 = 2$ and $N - I = 24$. With $F = 5.45$, Table D tells us that $0.01 < P < 0.025$; software gives $P = 0.0112$. We have fairly strong evidence that at least one mean second-minus-first count is different.

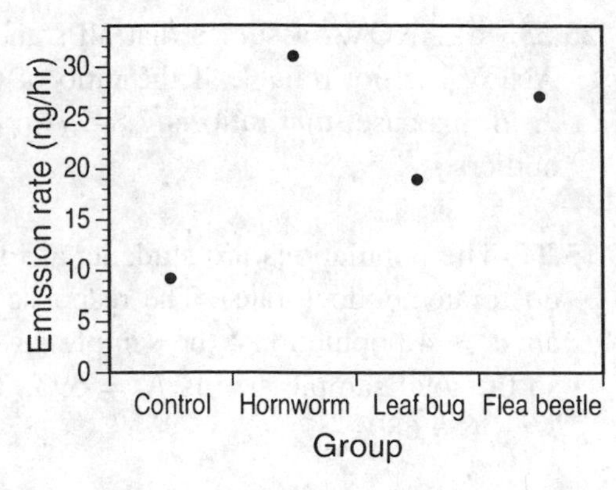


**25.29.** **(a)** The graph does suggest that emissions rise when a plant is attacked, because the mean control emission rate is half the smallest of the other rates. **(b)** The null hypothesis is "all groups have the same mean emission rate." The alternative is "at least one group has a different mean emission rate." **(c)** The most important piece of additional information would be whether the data are sufficiently close to Normally distributed. (From the description, it seems reasonably safe to assume that these are more-or-less random samples.) **(d)** The SEM equals $s/\sqrt{8}$, so we can find the standard deviations by multiplying by $\sqrt{8}$—however, this factor of $\sqrt{8}$ would cancel out in the process of finding the ratio of the largest and smallest standard deviations, so we can simply find this ratio directly from the SEMs: $\frac{8.75}{5.93} \doteq 1.4755$, which satisfies our rule of thumb.

**25.30.** Only Design A would allow use of one-way ANOVA, because it produces four independent sets of numbers. The data resulting from Design B would be dependent (a subject's responses to the first list would be related to that same subject's responses to the other lists), so that ANOVA would not be appropriate for comparison.

**25.31.** **(a)** Table below (part of Minitab output); stemplots at right. The data suggest that the presence of too many nematodes reduces growth. ANOVA seems to be safe, because the standard deviations satisfy our rule of thumb, and there are no clear outliers in the stemplots. **(b)** $H_0$: $\mu_1 = \cdots = \mu_4$ (all mean heights are the same) versus $H_a$: not all means are the same. This ANOVA tests whether nematodes affect mean plant growth. **(c)** Minitab output is shown below: $F = 12.08$, df $= 3$ and 12, and $P = 0.001$, so the differences are significant. The first two levels (0 and 1000 nematodes) do not appear to be significantly different, nor do the last two. However, it does appear that somewhere between 1000 and 5000 nematodes, the tomato plants begin to feel the effects of the worms and are hurt by their presence.

| 0 | | 1000 | | 5000 | | 10,000 | |
|---|---|---|---|---|---|---|---|
| 3 | | 3 | | 3 | | 3 | 2 |
| 4 | | 4 | | 4 | 6 | 4 | |
| 5 | | 5 | | 5 | 04 | 5 | 38 |
| 6 | | 6 | | 6 | | 6 | |
| 7 | | 7 | | 7 | 4 | 7 | 5 |
| 8 | | 8 | 2 | 8 | | 8 | |
| 9 | 12 | 9 | | 9 | | 9 | |
| 10 | 8 | 10 | | 10 | | 10 | |
| 11 | | 11 | 113 | 11 | | 11 | |
| 12 | | 12 | | 12 | | 12 | |
| 13 | 5 | 13 | | 13 | | 13 | |

**Minitab output**

```
Source     DF       SS       MS       F       p
Nematode    3   100.65    33.55   12.08   0.001
Error      12    33.33     2.78
Total      15   133.97
                                  Individual 95% CIs For Mean
                                  Based on Pooled StDev
  Level     N     Mean    StDev   ------+---------+---------+---------+
      0     4   10.650    2.053                        (-------*------)
   1000     4   10.425    1.486                       (-------*------)
   5000     4    5.600    1.244    (------*-------)
  10000     4    5.450    1.771    (------*------)
                                  ------+---------+---------+---------+
Pooled StDev =   1.667                  5.0       7.5      10.0      12.5
```

**25.32.** The ANOVA test statistic is $F = 4.92$ (df $= 3$ and 92), which has $P = 0.003$, so there is strong evidence that the means are not all the same. In particular, list 1 seems to be the easiest, and lists 3 and 4 are the most difficult.

**25.33. (a)** The design, with four treatments, is shown below. **(b) Formulate:** We compare the mean lightness of the four methods using a plot of the means and ANOVA.

**Solve:** ANOVA should be safe: it is reasonable to view the samples as SRSs from the four populations, the distributions do not show drastic deviations from Normality, and the standard deviations satisfy our rule of thumb ($\frac{0.392}{0.250} \doteq 1.568$).

The Minitab output below includes a table of the means, and a display that is equivalent to a plot of the means. The means show rather small differences in lightness score; Method C is lightest and Method B is darkest. The differences in mean lightness are nonetheless highly significant ($F = 22.77$, $P < 0.001$).

**Conclude:** The manufacturer will prefer Method B. Whether these differences are large enough to be important in practice requires more information about the scale of lightness scores.

**Minitab output**

```
Source     DF        SS        MS        F       p
Method      3    6.2815    2.0938    22.77   0.000
Error      28    2.5752    0.0920
Total      31    8.8567
                                   Individual 95% CIs For Mean
                                   Based on Pooled StDev
 Level      N      Mean     StDev  ---------+---------+---------+-------
     A      8    41.649     0.392              (---*---)
     B      8    41.283     0.255  (----*---)
     C      8    42.493     0.294                           (----*---)
     D      8    41.950     0.250                    (---*---)
                                   ---------+---------+---------+-------
Pooled StDev =    0.303                 41.50     42.00     42.50
```

```
Method A      Method B      Method C      Method D

40 |          40 | 89       40 |          40 |
41 | 1        41 |          41 |          41 |
41 | 2        41 | 2233     41 |          41 |
41 | 44       41 | 5        41 |          41 |
41 | 7        41 | 6        41 |          41 | 667
41 | 8                      41 |          41 | 99
42 | 0                      42 |          42 | 0
42 | 2                      42 | 223      42 | 23
                            42 | 445
                            42 | 6
                            42 |
                            43 | 1
```

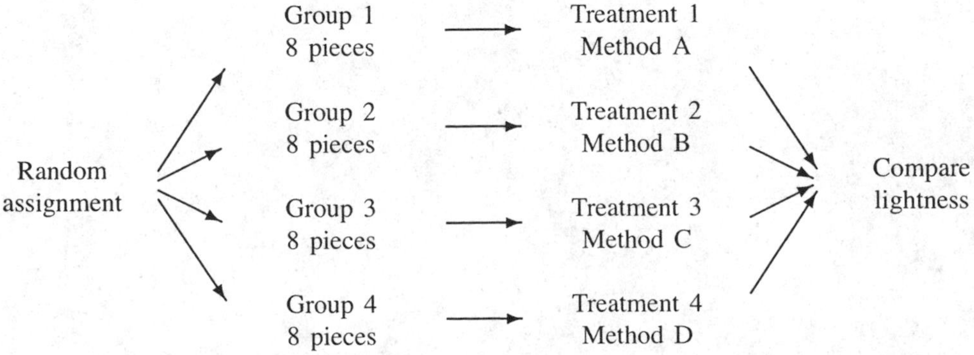

Random assignment → Group 1, 8 pieces → Treatment 1, Method A → Compare lightness

Random assignment → Group 2, 8 pieces → Treatment 2, Method B → Compare lightness

Random assignment → Group 3, 8 pieces → Treatment 3, Method C → Compare lightness

Random assignment → Group 4, 8 pieces → Treatment 4, Method D → Compare lightness

**25.34. Formulate:** We compare the mean healing rates in the five groups using a plot of the means and ANOVA.

**Solve:** It is reasonable to view the samples as SRSs from the five populations. The distributions are somewhat irregular; in particular, the "0 times" group includes a possible outlier. However, these deviations from Normality are not too severe. The standard deviations barely satisfy our rule of thumb ($\frac{17.39}{8.86} \doteq 1.963$).

The Minitab output below includes a table of the means, and a display that is equivalent to a plot of the means. The natural electrical field had the second highest mean, but the 1.25-times field did slightly better in the sample. The differences in mean healing rate are significant ($F = 4.04$, $P = 0.005$).

**Conclude:** Electrical field has an effect on healing rate. The natural group and the 1.25-times groups showed the fastest healing, the 0- and 0.5-times groups were slower, and the 1.5-times group had the slowest healing.

**Minitab output**

```
Source     DF       SS         MS         F        p
Field       4     2232        558      4.04    0.005
Error      69     9528        138
Total      73    11761
                                     Individual 95% CIs For Mean
                                     Based on Pooled StDev
  Level     N     Mean      StDev   -----+---------+---------+---------+-
      0    12    -6.42      10.71             (-------*-------)
    0.5    14    -5.71      10.56              (-------*-------)
      1    18    -0.17       9.34                     (------*------)
   1.25    15     1.47       8.86                      (-------*------)
    1.5    15   -13.80      17.39   (-------*------)
                                    -----+---------+---------+---------+-
Pooled StDev =   11.75                 -16.0      -8.0       0.0       8.0
```

| 0 times | | 0.5 times | | 1 times | | 1.25 times | | 1.5 times | |
|---|---|---|---|---|---|---|---|---|---|
| −4 | | −4 | | −4 | | −4 | | −4 | 96 |
| −4 | | −4 | | −4 | | −4 | | −4 | |
| −3 | | −3 | | −3 | | −3 | | −3 | 5 |
| −3 | 1 | −3 | 1 | −3 | | −3 | | −3 | |
| −2 | | −2 | | −2 | | −2 | | −2 | |
| −2 | | −2 | 2 | −2 | | −2 | | −2 | 2 |
| −1 | | −1 | | −1 | 6 | −1 | 5 | −1 | 6 |
| −1 | 210 | −1 | 20 | −1 | 43 | −1 | 4 | −1 | 310 |
| −0 | 9875 | −0 | 7 | −0 | 87 | −0 | 7 | −0 | 85 |
| −0 | 21 | −0 | 433311 | −0 | 44221 | −0 | 421 | −0 | 42 |
| 0 | | 0 | 34 | 0 | 3 | 0 | 01 | 0 | 22 |
| 0 | 6 | 0 | | 0 | 556 | 0 | 5788 | 0 | |
| 1 | 3 | 1 | 0 | 1 | 013 | 1 | 114 | 1 | 0 |
| | | | | 1 | 5 | | | | |

**25.35. Formulate:** We compare the mean strength in the three groups using a plot of the means and ANOVA.

**Solve:** It is reasonable to view the samples as SRSs from the three populations. The distributions show no severe deviations from Normality. (Stemplots are not shown; with only five observations in each group, they are not very informative.) The standard deviations do *not* satisfy our rule of thumb; the largest-to-smallest ratio is $\frac{9.53}{4.60} \doteq 2.07$. Because this is more than 2, ANOVA is somewhat risky.

The Minitab output below includes a table of the means, and a display that is equivalent to a plot of the means. The means vary over time but do not consistently decrease; in fact, the 8-week mean is highest. If we do ANOVA in spite of the rule-of-thumb violation, we find $F = 3.70$ and $P = 0.056$.
**Conclude:** The differences in breaking strength are not quite significant, and even if they were, the data do not support the investigator's conjecture. These data suggest that breaking strength *variability* increases over time.

**Minitab output**

```
Source     DF       SS        MS        F        p
Weeks       2    381.7     190.9     3.70    0.056
Error      12    619.2      51.6
Total      14   1000.9
                                   Individual 95% CIs For Mean
                                   Based on Pooled StDev
 Level      N     Mean     StDev   ----+---------+---------+---------+--
     2      5   123.80      4.60   (---------*---------)
     4      5   123.60      6.54   (---------*---------)
     8      5   134.40      9.53                (---------*---------)
                                   ----+---------+---------+---------+--
Pooled StDev =     7.18              119.0     126.0     133.0     140.0
```

**25.36.** First, we note that ANOVA with all four groups shows large differences, as expected. The untreated mean is 58.56, roughly double the means for the other groups; the differences are highly significant ($F = 236.68$, $P < 0.001$).
**Formulate:** We compare the mean strengths of the three durable press treatments using a plot of the means and ANOVA.
**Solve:** It is reasonable to view the samples as SRSs from the three populations. The distributions show no severe deviations from Normality. (Stemplots are not shown; with only five observations in each group, they are not very informative.) The standard deviations do *not* satisfy our rule of thumb; the largest-to-smallest ratio is $\frac{2.669}{1.167} \doteq 2.29$. Because this is more than 2, ANOVA is somewhat risky, but we proceed anyway.

The Minitab output below includes a table of the means, and a display that is equivalent to a plot of the means. There is a highly significant ($F = 5.02$, $P = 0.026$) difference among the mean breaking strengths for the three durable press treatments.
**Conclude:** Fabrics treated with Permafresh 55 have considerably higher strength than fabrics treated with Permafresh 48 or Hylite.

**Note:** *See also the solution to Exercise 19.47, where we used two-sample* t *procedures to compare Permafresh 55 to Hylite LF.*

**Minitab output**

```
Source     DF       SS        MS        F        p
treat       2    47.50     23.75     5.02    0.026
Error      12    56.74      4.73
Total      14   104.24
                                   Individual 95% CIs For Mean
                                   Based on Pooled StDev
 Level      N     Mean     StDev   --------+---------+---------+--------
P55         5   29.540     1.167                    (-------*--------)
P48         5   27.020     2.387           (-------*--------)
HY          5   25.200     2.669   (--------*-------)
                                   --------+---------+---------+--------
Pooled StDev =   2.174                   25.0      27.5      30.0
```

**25.37.** First, we note that the mean angle for untreated fabric is 79 degrees, showing much less wrinkle resistance than any of the treated fabrics. ANOVA on four groups gives $F = 153.76$ and $P < 0.001$.

A comparison of wrinkle recovery angle for the three durable press treatments is more interesting. The ANOVA results are shown in the Minitab output below. Hylite LF, which in Exercise 25.36 was seen to have the lowest breaking strength, has the highest wrinkle resistance. There is almost no difference between the means for two versions of Permafresh, even though we saw in Exercise 25.36 that Permafresh 55 is stronger than Permafresh 48.

The ANOVA $F$-test cannot be trusted because the standard deviations violate our rule of thumb: $\frac{10.16}{1.92} \doteq 5.29$. In particular, Permafresh 48 shows much more variability from piece to piece than either of the other treatments. Large variability in performance is a serious defect in a commercial product, so it appears that Permafresh 48 is unsuited for use on these grounds. The data are very helpful to a maker of durable press fabrics despite the fact that the formal test is not valid.

**Note:** *See also the solution to Exercise 19.48, where we used two-sample* t *procedures to compare Permafresh 55 to Hylite LF.*

**Minitab output**

```
Source    DF       SS       MS       F       p
treat      2    253.2    126.6    3.39   0.068
Error     12    448.4     37.4
Total     14    701.6
                                   Individual 95% CIs For Mean
                                   Based on Pooled StDev
 Level     N     Mean    StDev   -------+---------+---------+---------
P55        5   134.80     1.92     (---------*---------)
P48        5   134.20    10.16    (---------*---------)
HY         5   143.20     2.28                (---------*---------)
                                 -------+---------+---------+---------
Pooled StDev =   6.11                 132.0     138.0     144.0
```

**25.38.** **(a)** The table is given in the Minitab output below; because $\frac{4.500}{3.529} \doteq 1.28$, ANOVA should be safe. The means appear to suggest that logging reduces the number of species per plot and that recovery takes more than 8 years. **(b)** ANOVA gives $F = 6.02$ with df $= 2$ and 30, so $P < 0.010$ (software gives 0.006). We conclude that these differences are significant; the number of species per plot really is lower in logged areas.

**Minitab output**

```
Source    DF       SS       MS       F       p
Code       2    204.4    102.2    6.02   0.006
Error     30    509.2     17.0
Total     32    713.6
                                   Individual 95% CIs For Mean
                                   Based on Pooled StDev
 Level     N     Mean    StDev   ---------+---------+---------+-------
     1    12   17.500    3.529                   (-------*-------)
     2    12   11.750    4.372   (-------*-------)
     3     9   13.667    4.500        (---------*--------)
                                 ---------+---------+---------+-------
Pooled StDev =  4.120                  12.0      15.0      18.0
```

**25.39.** We have $I = 4$ and $N = 32$. Also, all SEMs must be squared and multiplied by 8 to find the variances. The details of the computations are given below, along with Minitab output that confirms the computed values. With df = 3 and 28, we find $P > 0.100$, so we have no reason to doubt the null hypothesis; that is, there is not enough evidence to conclude that mean emission rates are different.

$$\bar{x} \doteq 21.585 = \frac{8 \times (9.22 + 31.03 + 18.97 + 27.12)}{32}$$

$$\text{SSG} \doteq 2236.6 = 8(9.22 - \bar{x})^2 + 8(31.03 - \bar{x})^2 + 8(18.97 - \bar{x})^2 + 8(27.12 - \bar{x})^2$$

$$\text{MSG} \doteq 745.5 = \frac{2236.6}{4 - 1}$$

$$\text{SSE} \doteq 12,886.8 = 7 \times 8 \times (5.93^2 + 8.75^2 + 6.64^2 + 8.62^2)$$

$$\text{MSE} \doteq 460.2 = \frac{12,886.8}{32 - 4}$$

$$F \doteq 1.62 = \frac{745.5}{460.2}$$

**Minitab output**

```
Source     DF        SS        MS        F        p
Factor      3      2237       746     1.62    0.207
Error      28     12887       460
Total      31     15123
```

**25.40.** **(a)** The standard error is $\text{SE} = \sqrt{0.38^2/13 + 0.58^2/17} \doteq 0.1758$, so the $t$ statistic is $t = \frac{2.31-2.37}{0.1758} \doteq -0.34$, which is obviously not significant. The conservative method gives df = 12, and software reports $P = 0.74$. (Table C tells us that $P > 0.5$.) **(b)** The details of the computations are given below, along with Minitab output that confirms the computed values. With df = 1 and 28, software reports that $P = 0.749$. (Table F tells us that $P > 0.1$.) **(c)** The two $P$-values (given by software) are very close.

$$\bar{x} \doteq 2.344 = \frac{13 \times 2.31 + 17 \times 2.37}{30}$$

$$\text{MSG} \doteq 0.02652 = \frac{13(2.31 - \bar{x})^2 + 17(2.37 - \bar{x})^2}{2 - 1}$$

$$\text{MSE} \doteq 0.2541 \doteq \frac{12 \times 0.38^2 + 16 \times 0.58^2}{30 - 2} = \frac{7.1152}{30 - 2}$$

$$F \doteq 0.1044 \doteq \frac{0.02652}{0.2541}$$

**Minitab output (t-test)**

```
95% C.I. for mu Stock - mu Mutual: ( -0.42,  0.30)
T-Test mu Stock = mu Mutual (vs not =): T= -0.34  P=0.74  DF=  27
```

**Minitab output (ANOVA)**

```
Source     DF        SS        MS        F        p
Factor      1     0.027     0.027     0.10    0.749
Error      28     7.115     0.254
Total      29     7.142
```

**25.41.** **(a)** A chi-square test is appropriate, because we are comparing three proportions (attrition rates in each of three groups). **(b)** ANOVA is appropriate, because we are comparing three means (weight loss in each of three groups). **(c)** ANOVA is appropriate, because we are comparing three means (duration of exercise in each of three groups).

---

For solutions to the EESEE Case Studies (Exercises 42–44), see the instructor's version of EESEE.

# Chapter 26 Solutions

**26.1. (a)** See the table on the right.

| Count | Color | Rank | Count | Color | Rank |
|---|---|---|---|---|---|
| 7 | blue | 1 | 21 | blue | 7 |
| 11 | blue | 2 | 25 | green | 8 |
| 14 | blue | 3 | 32 | green | 9 |
| 15 | green | 4 | 37 | green | 10 |
| 16 | blue | 5 | 39 | green | 11 |
| 20 | blue | 6 | 41 | green | 12 |

**(b)** $W = 4 + 8 + 9 + 10 + 11 + 12 = 54$.
**(c)** If $H_0$ is true, then

$$\mu_W = \frac{(6)(13)}{2} = 39, \text{ and}$$

$$\sigma_W = \sqrt{\frac{(6)(6)(13)}{12}} \doteq 6.245.$$

Our computed value of $W$ is about $2.4\sigma_W$ away from $\mu_W$, giving us some reason to believe that $H_0$ is not true.

**26.2. (a)** Shown is a back-to-back stemplot; a pair of histograms could also be used. We see that the DDT group generally had higher nerve response than the control group. **(b)** We test $H_0$: nerve response is unaffected by DDT, versus $H_a$: nerve response is systematically higher with DDT. The lowest DDT group measurement ranked 3rd, and the other 5 measurements were the highest among the 12 (ranks 8, 9, 10, 11, 12), so $W = 53$. Under $H_0$, the mean and standard deviation would be

| DDT | | Control |
|---|---|---|
| | 0 | 6 |
| 8 | 0 | 899 |
| | 1 | 1 |
| 2 | 1 | 2 |
| | 1 | |
| 6 | 1 | |
| | 1 | |
| 0 | 2 | |
| 2 | 2 | |
| 5 | 2 | |

$$\mu_W = \frac{(6)(13)}{2} = 39 \quad \text{and} \quad \sigma_W = \sqrt{\frac{(6)(6)(13)}{12}} \doteq 6.245.$$

**(c)** The observed value of $W$ is about 2.24 standard deviations above the mean (that is, $\frac{53-39}{6.245} \doteq 2.24$), giving us some reason to believe that $H_0$ is not true.

**26.3. (a)** We observed $W = 54$, so with the continuity correction, we compute $P(W \geq 53.5)$. **(b)** $P(W \geq 53.5) \doteq P(Z \geq 2.32) = 0.0102$. This is significant at $\alpha = 0.05$ (and nearly significant at the 1% level), so we have strong evidence that green boards attract more beetles than blue boards.

**26.4. (a)** We observed $W = 53$, so with the continuity correction, we compute $2P(W \geq 52.5)$. **(b)** $2P(W \geq 52.5) \doteq 2P(Z \geq 2.16) = 0.0308$. This is significant at $\alpha = 0.05$, so we have strong evidence that DDT affects nerve response; specifically, the "second spike" described in Exercise 19.13 is higher for the DDT group.

**26.5. Formulate:** We compare scores using a graph and a test of $H_0$: there is no difference, versus $H_a$: high-progress readers score higher.
**Solve:** The back-to-back stemplot supports the suspicion that high-progress readers have higher scores. The low outlier in the high-progress group should make us hesitant to use $t$ procedures, so the Wilcoxon test is a better choice.

| High | | Low |
|---:|:---:|:---|
| | 2 | 8 |
| | 3 | |
| | 3 | 8 |
| | 4 | |
| | 4 | 9 |
| 4 | 5 | |
| | 5 | |
| | 6 | |
| | 6 | 6 |
| | 7 | |
| 9 | 7 | 7 |
| 20 | 8 | |
| 9 | 8 | |

The stemplot makes it easy to determine the rankings for the high-progress scores: $W = 4 + 7 + 8 + 9 + 10 = 38$. Under $H_0$,

$$\mu_W = \frac{(5)(11)}{2} = 27.5 \quad \text{and} \quad \sigma_W = \sqrt{\frac{(5)(5)(11)}{12}} \doteq 4.787.$$

The $P$-value is $P(W \geq 37.5) \doteq P(Z > 2.09) = 0.0183$.
**Conclude:** There is significant evidence that high-progress readers score higher on Story 2.

**Minitab output**

```
Mann-Whitney Confidence Interval and Test

high       N =   5    Median =        0.8000
low        N =   5    Median =        0.4900
W = 38.0
Test of ETA1 = ETA2  vs.  ETA1 > ETA2 is significant at 0.0184
```

**26.6.** Minitab output agrees (up to rounding) with the $P$-value found in Exercise 26.3. (The version of Minitab used to prepare these solutions uses the Normal approximation with continuity correction.)

**Minitab output**

```
green       N =    6      Median =        34.50
blue        N =    6      Median =        15.00
W = 54.0
Test of ETA1 = ETA2  vs.  ETA1 > ETA2
                 is significant at 0.0101
```

**26.7.** Minitab output agrees (up to rounding) with the $P$-value found in Exercise 26.4. (The version of Minitab used to prepare these solutions uses the Normal approximation with continuity correction.)

**Minitab output**

```
DDT         N =    6      Median =       18.729
Control     N =    6      Median =        9.518
W = 53.0
Test of ETA1 = ETA2  vs.  ETA1 ~= ETA2
                 is significant at 0.0306
```

**26.8. (a)** We find $W = 26$ and $P \doteq 0.0152$. We have strong evidence against the hypothesis of identical distributions; we conclude that the weed-free yield is higher. **(b)** For testing $H_0$: $\mu_0 = \mu_9$ versus $H_a$: $\mu_0 > \mu_9$, we find $\bar{x}_0 = 170.2$, $s_0 \doteq 5.4216$, $\bar{x}_9 = 157.575$, $s_9 \doteq 10.1181$, and $t = 2.20$, which gives $P = 0.0423$ (df $= 4.6$). We have fairly strong evidence that the mean yield is higher with no weeds—but the evidence is not quite as strong as in (a). **(c)** Both tests still reach the same conclusion, so there is no "practically important impact" on our conclusions. The Wilcoxon evidence is slightly weaker: $W = 22$ and $P \doteq 0.0259$. The $t$-test evidence is slightly stronger: $t = 2.79$, df $= 3$, and $P = 0.0341$. The new statistics for the 9-weeds-per-meter group are $\bar{x}_9 = 162.633$ and $s_9 \doteq 0.2082$; these are substantial changes for each value.

**Minitab output: All points**

```
Weed0        N =   4      Median =        169.45
Weed9        N =   4      Median =        162.55
W = 26.0
Test of ETA1 = ETA2  vs.  ETA1 > ETA2 is significant at 0.0152
```

**With outlier removed**

```
Weed0        N =   4      Median =        169.45
Weed9        N =   3      Median =        162.70
W = 22.0
Test of ETA1 = ETA2  vs.  ETA1 > ETA2 is significant at 0.0259
```

**26.9.** For a $t$ test, our hypotheses are $H_0$: $\mu_b = \mu_g$ versus $H_a$: $\mu_b < \mu_g$. For a Wilcoxon test, $H_0$: the distribution of the trapped-insect count is the same for green and blue boards, versus $H_a$: insects trapped is systematically higher for green boards.

**26.10. (a)** To compare means, test $H_0$: $\mu_D = \mu_C$ versus $H_a$: $\mu_D \neq \mu_C$. This is typically done with a two-sample $t$ test, which requires SRSs from (approximately) Normal populations. In particular, because these sample sizes are small, we want no sharp skewness and no outliers. **(b)** To compare medians, test $H_0$: $\text{median}_D = \text{median}_C$ versus $H_a$: $\text{median}_D \neq \text{median}_C$. For this, we use a Wilcoxon test, which requires only two independent SRSs.

**26.11. (a)** For the Wilcoxon test, we test $H_0$: breaking strength is unaffected by burial time, versus $H_a$: breaking strength is lower for the 16-week strips, or equivalently, $H_0$: $\text{median}_2 = \text{median}_{16}$ versus $H_a$: $\text{median}_2 > \text{median}_{16}$. For the $t$ test, we test $H_0$: $\mu_2 = \mu_{16}$ versus $H_a$: $\mu_2 > \mu_{16}$. **(b)** The two 110s are tied for second, so they receive the rank 2.5. The 126s are seventh and eighth, so they receive the rank 7.5. **(c)** The Wilcoxon rank-sum test gives $W = 33$ and $P \doteq 0.1481$ (0.1467, adjusted for ties). This is slightly stronger evidence than the $t$ test gave, but still not significant.

**Minitab output**

```
2weeks       N =   5      Median =        126.00
16weeks      N =   5      Median =        110.00
W = 33.0
Test of ETA1 = ETA2  vs.  ETA1 > ETA2 is significant at 0.1481
The test is significant at 0.1467 (adjusted for ties)
```

**26.12. (a)** The ranks are given in the table on the right. Because there are ties, the ranks for 125, 141, and 145 are "averaged" across those ranks. (In fact, the only important tie is the three 145s, because two of those are in the Permafresh group and one is in the Hylite group. The other two ties fall in one group or the other.) **(b)** For the Permafresh group, $W = 22$. **(c)** The $P$-value is 0.2963 (or 0.2873 "adjusted for ties"—see the Minitab output below). The difference is not significant.

| Treatment | WRA | Rank |
|---|---|---|
| PF | 125 | 1.5 |
| PF | 125 | 1.5 |
| PF | 131 | 3 |
| HY | 141 | 4.5 |
| HY | 141 | 4.5 |
| HY | 143 | 6 |
| PF | 145 | 8 |
| PF | 145 | 8 |
| HY | 145 | 8 |
| HY | 146 | 10 |

**Minitab output**

```
PF           N =   5      Median =        131.00
HY           N =   5      Median =        143.00
W = 22.0
Test of ETA1 = ETA2  vs.  ETA1 ~= ETA2 is significant at 0.2963
The test is significant at 0.2873 (adjusted for ties)
```

**26.13.** **(a)** The two observations 4.6 are the third and fourth numbers in the sorted list, so they have the rank 3.5. Similarly, the two 7.7s are assigned the rank of 7.5, and the two 11.3s are ranked 9.5. (In fact, the only important tie is the two 7.7s, because one of those is in the control group and one is in the supplemented group. The other two ties fall in one group or the other.) **(b)** For the supplemented group, $W = 67.5$. **(c)** The $P$-value is 0.0051 (or 0.0049 "adjusted for ties"—see the Minitab output below). The difference is significant; the supplemented group misses the peak by more days than the control group does.

| Group | Days | Rank |
|---|---|---|
| Ctrl | −1.2 | 1 |
| Ctrl | 2.3 | 2 |
| Ctrl | 4.6 | 3.5 |
| Ctrl | 4.6 | 3.5 |
| Supp | 5.4 | 5 |
| Ctrl | 6.0 | 6 |
| Ctrl | 7.7 | 7.5 |
| Supp | 7.7 | 7.5 |
| Supp | 11.3 | 9.5 |
| Supp | 11.3 | 9.5 |
| Supp | 11.4 | 11 |
| Supp | 15.5 | 12 |
| Supp | 16.5 | 13 |

**Minitab output**

```
Supplemt    N =    7      Median =         11.300
Control     N =    6      Median =          4.600
W = 67.5
Test of ETA1 = ETA2  vs.   ETA1 > ETA2 is significant at 0.0051
The test is significant at 0.0049 (adjusted for ties)
```

**26.14.** **(a)** At right. Deviations from Normality are hard to spot with such a small sample; no deviations are apparent here (although 0.00 may be a low outlier). **(b)** To test $H_0$: $\mu_1 = \mu_2$ versus $H_a$: $\mu_1 > \mu_2$, we find $\bar{x}_1 = 0.676$, $\bar{x}_2 = 0.406$, and $t = 2.059$, which gives $P = 0.0446$ (df $= 5.5$). We have fairly strong evidence that high-progress readers have higher mean scores. **(c)** We test $H_0$: scores for both groups are identically distributed, versus $H_a$: high-progress children systematically score higher. We find that $W = 36$ and $P \doteq 0.0473$ (or 0.0463 "adjusted for ties"; Minitab output below); we have strong evidence against the hypothesis of identical distributions. This is equivalent to the conclusion reached in (b).

| High | | Low |
|---|---|---|
| | 0 | 0 |
| | 1 | |
| | 2 | |
| | 3 | 6 |
| | 4 | 0 |
| 75 | 5 | 5 |
| | 6 | |
| 20 | 7 | 2 |
| 4 | 8 | |

**Minitab output**

```
HiProg1     N =    5      Median =        0.7000
LoProg1     N =    5      Median =        0.4000
W = 36.0
Test of ETA1 = ETA2  vs.   ETA1 > ETA2 is significant at 0.0473
The test is significant at 0.0463 (adjusted for ties)
```

**26.15. Formulate:** Compare the seed masses for the two groups of plants (with and without cicadas), graphically and numerically, and using an appropriate test.

**Solve:** See the solution to Exercise 7.9 for back-to-back stemplots and summary statistics. Both stemplots suggest that the two-sample $t$ test might not be safe: The cicada stemplot has two possible outliers, and the control stemplot suggests possible non-Normality (it appears to have two peaks).

We test $H_0$: seed masses for both groups are identically distributed, versus $H_a$: cicada-group seed masses are systematically higher. We find that $W = 1567$ and $P \doteq 0.0530$.

**Conclude:** We have fairly strong evidence that dead cicadas increase seed mass, although it is not quite significant at $\alpha = 0.05$.

**Minitab output**

```
cicada     N =  39      Median =       0.23800
control    N =  33      Median =       0.24100
W = 1567.0
Test of ETA1 = ETA2  vs.  ETA1 > ETA2 is significant at 0.0530
The test is significant at 0.0530 (adjusted for ties)
```

**26.16. Formulate:** We wish to test the alternative hypothesis that women rate restaurant food as less safe than men so (that is, women tend to give higher ratings). We compare men's and women's ratings of restaurant-food safety using summary statistics and an appropriate test.

| | Women | | Men | |
|---|---|---|---|---|
| Rating | Count | % | Count | % |
| 1 | 48 | 24.49 | 52 | 48.60 |
| 2 | 123 | 62.76 | 45 | 42.06 |
| 3 | 19 | 9.69 | 8 | 7.48 |
| 4 | 5 | 2.55 | 0 | 0 |
| 5 | 1 | 0.51 | 2 | 1.87 |

**Solve:** A table of counts and percents suggests that this is true. One could do a chi-square test (which yields $X^2 = 21.940$ and $P$ tiny), but this is not advisable because there are so many small counts. The Wilcoxon test is better; it gives $W = 32{,}267.5$ and $P = 0.0003$ (or $P = 0.0001$ adjusted for ties).

**Conclude:** We have strong evidence that women really do rate restaurant food as less safe than men do.

**Minitab output**

```
women      N = 196      Median =       2.0000
men        N = 107      Median =       2.0000
W = 32267.5
Test of ETA1 = ETA2  vs.  ETA1 > ETA2 is significant at 0.0003
The test is significant at 0.0001 (adjusted for ties)
```

**26.17.** We do not have independent samples from two populations; rather, we have dependent samples (each person answered both questions).

**26.18. (a)** Depending on the order of subtraction (control minus treated, or vice versa), either all differences are negative or all are positive. This means that either $W^+ = 0$ or $W^+ = 6$. **(b)** Under $H_0$, $\mu_{W^+} = \frac{(3)(4)}{4} = 3$ and $\sigma_{W^+} = \sqrt{\frac{(3)(4)(6)}{24}} \doteq 1.732$. While our value of $W^+$ differs from $\mu_{W^+}$ by the greatest possible amount (for a sample of this size), any conclusion we draw must be *very* tentative because the difference is less than 2 standard deviations (and because we had such a small sample).

**26.19. (a)** The table on the right shows the ranks (by absolute value); the value of $W^+$ is 125. **(b)** Under $H_0$,

$$\mu_{W^+} = \frac{(21)(22)}{4} = 115.5$$

and

$$\sigma_{W^+} = \sqrt{\frac{(21)(22)(43)}{24}} \doteq 28.771.$$

Our observed $W^+$ is barely 0.33 standard deviations above this mean, so we expect that we will not reject $H_0$.

| Diff | Rank | Diff | Rank |
|---|---|---|---|
| −7.37 | 9 | −24.57 | 20 |
| −3.14 | 3 | 16.17 | 17 |
| 4.10 | 4 | −7.84 | 10 |
| −4.4 | 5 | 8.6 | 11 |
| 19.47 | 19 | −10.77 | 13 |
| −10.8 | 14 | 24.97 | 21 |
| −0.87 | 1 | −4.47 | 6 |
| 8.70 | 12 | 11.9 | 15 |
| 2.94 | 2 | −6.26 | 7 |
| −17.24 | 18 | 6.67 | 8 |
| 14.3 | 16 | | |

**26.20.** Taking $W^+ = 0$, the $P$-value is $P(W^+ \leq 0.5) \doteq P(Z \leq -1.44) = 0.0749$. This evidence is not strong enough to reject the null hypothesis.

**26.21.** In the solution to Exercise 18.34, we found $P = 0.044$.

**26.22.** The $P$-value is $P(W^+ \geq 124.5) \doteq P(Z \geq 0.31) = 0.3783$; the $t$ test carried out in Example 18.4 gave $P = 0.3652$.

**26.23.** **(a)** A stemplot (right) shows some left-skewness; there are no outliers. (A histogram could also be used to show the distribution.) **(b)** Because all differences (observed value minus 78.1) are negative, the statistic value is $W^+ = 0$. This gives $P \doteq 0.009$, so we reject $H_0$; we have strong evidence that the median is not 78.1%. (Specifically, we have evidence that it is lower.)

```
4 | 9
5 | 1
5 |
5 | 4
5 |
5 |
6 | 0
6 | 33
6 | 445
```

**Minitab output**

```
TEST OF MEDIAN = 78.10 VERSUS MEDIAN N.E. 78.10

                  N FOR   WILCOXON              ESTIMATED
            N     TEST   STATISTIC   P-VALUE      MEDIAN
Nitrogen    9       9          0.0     0.009       59.65
```

**Note:** *Observe that the "estimated median" in the Minitab output (59.65) is not the same as the median of the nine observations (63.3). The process of computing this point estimate is not discussed in the text, but we will illustrate it for a simple case, using the first three observations in this data set: 63.4, 65.0, and 64.4. The Wilcoxon estimated median is the median of the set of* Walsh averages *of these numbers. This set consists of every possible pairwise average $(x_i + x_j)/2$ for $i \leq j$; note that this includes $i = j$, in which case the average is $x_i$. In general, there are $n(n+1)/2$ such averages, so with $n = 3$ observations, we have 6 Walsh averages: the three observations (63.4, 65.0, and 64.4), and the averages of each pair (64.2, 63.9, and 64.7). The median of these 6 numbers is 64.3. The full set of 9 observations yields 45 Walsh averages, for which the median is 59.65.*

**26.24.** **(a)** The ranks are shown in the table on the right; the Wilcoxon statistic is $W^+ = 22.5$. **(b)** Software gives $P \doteq 0.032$—fairly strong evidence that the natural electric field is best. It is also worth noting that some of the negative differences are quite large. (See the note in the solution to Exercise 26.23 for an explanation of the estimated median reported by Minitab.)

| Diff | Rank | Diff | Rank |
|---|---|---|---|
| −1 | 10.5 | −3 | 8 |
| 10 | 14 | −7 | 5 |
| 3 | 12 | −10 | 4 |
| −3 | 8 | −22 | 2 |
| −31 | 1 | −4 | 6 |
| 4 | 13 | −1 | 10.5 |
| −12 | 3 | −3 | 8 |

**Minitab output**

```
TEST OF MEDIAN = 0.000000 VERSUS MEDIAN L.T. 0.000000

                  N FOR   WILCOXON              ESTIMATED
            N     TEST   STATISTIC   P-VALUE      MEDIAN
Diffs      14      14         22.5     0.032      -4.000
```

**26.25.** **(a)** Considering sweetness rating changes, we test $H_0$: median $= 0$ versus $H_a$: median $> 0$. We find $W^+ = 47.5$ and $P \doteq 0.023$, so we conclude that the cola does lose sweetness in storage. (See the note in the solution to Exercise 26.23 for an explanation of the estimated median reported by Minitab.) **(b)** The conclusions are the same, and the

$P$-values are quite similar. The $t$ test hypotheses are $H_0$: $\mu_1 = \mu_2$ versus $H_a$: $\mu_1 > \mu_2$. Both tests assume that the tasters are an SRS of all tasters; the $t$ test also assumes that the before-minus-after sweetness differences are Normally distributed.

**Minitab output**

```
TEST OF MEDIAN = 0.000000 VERSUS MEDIAN G.T. 0.000000

                    N FOR   WILCOXON             ESTIMATED
             N      TEST   STATISTIC   P-VALUE      MEDIAN
Loss        10        10        47.5     0.023       1.150
```

**26.26.** See also the solution to Exercise 18.42.

**Formulate:** Considering the difference in performance (fund minus EAFE), we test $H_0$: median $= 0$ versus $H_a$: median $\neq 0$, taking a two-sided alternative because the VIG Fund could outperform or underperform the benchmark.

**Solve:** The Wilcoxon signed rank test gives $W^+ = 166$ and $P = 0.658$. (See the note in the solution to Exercise 26.23 for an explanation of the estimated median reported by Minitab.)

**Conclude:** We have very little reason to doubt that the median difference is 0; VIG Fund performance is not significantly different from its benchmark. (We reached essentially the same conclusion in Exercise 18.42, where we found that $t = 0.46$ and $P = 0.65$ for testing $H_0$: $\mu = 0$ versus $H_a$: $\mu \neq 0$.)

**Minitab output**

```
TEST OF MEDIAN = 0.000000 VERSUS MEDIAN N.E. 0.000000

                    N FOR   WILCOXON             ESTIMATED
             N      TEST   STATISTIC   P-VALUE      MEDIAN
diff        24        24       166.0     0.658      0.8250
```

**26.27.** See also the solution to Exercise 18.35.

**Formulate:** Consider the differences, kill-room count minus processing count. Because it is not clear that we would have expected the kill-room count to be higher prior to seeing the data, a two-sided alternative seems best, so we test $H_0$: median $= 0$ versus $H_a$: median $\neq 0$.

**Solve:** The Wilcoxon signed rank test gives $W^+ = 10$ and $P = 0.100$. If students chose the one-sided alternative hypothesis, median $> 0$, then $P = 0.05$. (See the note in the solution to Exercise 26.23 for an explanation of the estimated median reported by Minitab.)

**Conclude:** We have some evidence that the median difference is different from 0, but it is not significant at $\alpha = 0.05$—or it is barely significant, if we use a one-sided alternative.

**Minitab output**

```
TEST OF MEDIAN = 0.000000 VERSUS MEDIAN N.E. 0.000000

                    N FOR   WILCOXON             ESTIMATED
             N      TEST   STATISTIC   P-VALUE      MEDIAN
diff         4         4        10.0     0.100        1825
```

**Note:** *All four differences were positive, so the test statistic was as large as it could possibly be. With only four pairs, the Wilcoxon signed rank test can* never *give a $P$-value smaller than 0.10 for a two-sided alternative This is one difference between some nonparametric tests and parametric tests like the* t *test: With the* t *test, the power improves when we consider alternatives that are farther from the null hypothesis; for example, if $H_0$ says $\mu = 0$, we have higher power for the alternative $\mu = 10$ than for $\mu = 5$. With the Wilcoxon* *signed rank test, all alternatives look the same; the values of $W^+$ and $P$ would be the same for* any *set of four positive differences.*

**26.28. (a)** In the order given, the medians are 46.5, 15.5, 34.5, and 15 insects; it appears that yellow is most effective, green is in the middle, and white and blue are least effective. **(b)** For ANOVA, we test $H_0$: $\mu_1 = \cdots = \mu_4$ versus $H_a$: Not all $\mu_i$ are equal. For Kruskal-Wallis, $H_0$: the distribution of trapped insect counts is the same for all board colors, versus $H_a$: insects trapped is systematically higher for some colors. **(c)** $I = 4$ populations (board colors); $n_1 = \cdots = n_4 = 6$ and $N = 24$. After ranking, we find that $R_1 = 129$ (yellow), $R_2 = 43$ (white), $R_3 = 90$ (green), and $R_4 = 38$ (blue). **(d)** The test statistic is

$$H = \frac{12}{(24)(25)}\left(\frac{129^2 + 43^2 + 90^2 + 38^2}{6}\right) - 3(25) = 18.45,$$

with df $= 3$; the $P$-value is 0.000, so we have strong evidence that color affects the insect count (that is, the difference we observed is statistically significant).

**Minitab output**

```
 LEVEL    NOBS     MEDIAN  AVE. RANK   Z VALUE
  Blue       6      15.00        6.3     -2.47
 Green       6      32.00       15.0      1.00
 White       6      15.50        7.2     -2.13
Yellow       6      46.50       21.5      3.60
OVERALL     24                  12.5

H = 18.45  d.f. = 3  p = 0.000
H = 18.51  d.f. = 3  p = 0.000 (adjusted for ties)
```

**26.29. (a)** Stemplots are shown on the right; histograms would also work. The medians are

| Never logged | 1 year ago | 8 years ago |
|---|---|---|
| 0.7895 | 0.8912 | 0.9333 |

| Never logged | | 1 year ago | | 8 years ago | |
|---|---|---|---|---|---|
| 4 | | 4 | 2 | 4 | |
| 4 | 8 | 4 | | 4 | |
| 5 | | 5 | | 5 | |
| 5 | | 5 | | 5 | |
| 6 | 3 | 6 | | 6 | |
| 6 | 57 | 6 | | 6 | 8 |
| 7 | | 7 | | 7 | |
| 7 | 5889 | 7 | 7 | 7 | 8 |
| 8 | 111 | 8 | 3 | 8 | 13 |
| 8 | | 8 | 588 | 8 | |
| 9 | | 9 | 01123 | 9 | 34 |
| 9 | 5 | 9 | | 9 | |
| 10 | | 10 | 0 | 10 | 000 |

The graphs and the medians suggest that richness is greater in logged plots. **(b)** We test the hypotheses $H_0$: the three richness distributions are the same, versus $H_a$: richness is systematically higher in some group(s). Output from Minitab (below) gives $H = 9.10$ (df $= 2$) and $P = 0.011$. (If done by hand, note that there are quite a few ties. The rank sums for the three groups are 124.5, 238.5, and 198.) The differences are significant; logged plots are richer.

**Minitab output**

```
LEVEL     NOBS    MEDIAN  AVE. RANK   Z VALUE
    1       12    0.7895       10.4     -2.98
    2       12    0.8912       19.9      1.29
    3        9    0.9333       22.0      1.82
OVERALL     33                 17.0

H = 9.10  d.f. = 2  p = 0.011
H = 9.13  d.f. = 2  p = 0.011 (adjusted for ties)
```

**26.30. Formulate:** We use the Kruskal-Wallis procedure to test the hypotheses $H_0$: all medians are equal, versus $H_a$: at least one median is different.
**Solve:** The four medians are 126, 126, 131, and 110 pounds. The Kruskal-Wallis test gives $H = 5.35$, df $= 3$, and $P \doteq 0.149$.
**Conclude:** We do not have enough evidence to conclude that breaking strength differs for varying lengths of burial.

**Note:** *In Exercise 25.35, we compared the 2-, 4-, and 8-week data using analysis of variance. ANOVA is not appropriate for comparing these four groups because of the large differences in the standard deviations (which range from 4.6043 lbs for the 2-week sample to 16.0873 lbs for the 16-week sample).*

**Minitab output**

```
LEVEL      NOBS     MEDIAN  AVE. RANK    Z VALUE
  2          5       126.0        9.7      -0.35
  4          5       126.0       10.2      -0.13
  8          5       131.0       15.3       2.09
 16          5       110.0        6.8      -1.61
OVERALL     20                   10.5

H = 5.35  d.f. = 3  p = 0.149
H = 5.38  d.f. = 3  p = 0.147 (adjusted for ties)
```

**26.31. Formulate:** We compare soil penetrability for the three compression levels, and test $H_0$: the three distributions are the same, versus $H_a$: penetrability is systematically higher in some group(s).
**Solve:** Side-by-side stemplots and summary statistics are found in the solution to Exercise 2.37. The Kruskal-Wallis test gives $H = 47.41$, df $= 2$, and $P < 0.0005$.
**Conclude:** We have very strong evidence that penetrability is different; specifically, loose soil appears to be have the highest penetrability, while compressed soil is the least penetrable.

**Note:** *In Exercise 25.9, we concluded that ANOVA would be risky for these data.*

**Minitab output**

```
LEVEL      NOBS     MEDIAN  AVE. RANK    Z VALUE
  1         20       2.880       11.9      -5.83
  2         20       3.310       29.7      -0.25
  3         20       4.175       49.9       6.08
OVERALL     60                   30.5

H = 47.41  d.f. = 2  p = 0.000
H = 47.43  d.f. = 2  p = 0.000 (adjusted for ties)
```

**26.32.** For the Kruskal-Wallis test, we need two or more independent samples. Because these data come from different questions being asked of the same people, the responses are not independent. (We have several variables measured from a single group, rather than a single variable measured for several different groups.)

**26.33.** (c) We want to compare the scores of three groups, which requires Kruskal-Wallis.

**26.34.** (a) We have two independent samples, so the Wilcoxon rank sum test is appropriate. (We could also use the Kruskal-Wallis test, but we typically reserve it for three or more populations.)

**26.35.** (b) For a matched-pairs situation like this, use the Wilcoxon signed rank test.

**26.36.** (b) The control group emissions are ranked 6, 8, 5, 4, 1, and 2, so $W = 26$.

**26.37.** (a) The mean is $\mu_W = \frac{6(12+1)}{2} = 39$.

**26.38.** (b) The altered data creates two ties; the new ranks for the control group are now 6.5, 8, 4.5, 3, 1, and 2.

**26.39.** (b) Except for couple #8, all differences are positive. That difference $(-1)$ is tied with couple #4 for smallest in absolute value, so the positive differences have ranks 1.5 and 3 through 10. Therefore, $W^+ = 1.5 + 3 + 4 + 5 + 6 + 7 + 8 + 9 + 10 = 53.5$.

**26.40.** (a) The mean is $\mu_{W^+} = \frac{10(10+1)}{4} = 27.5$.

**26.41.** (a) Two couples (#4 and #10) now have difference 0, so we ignore them. Couple #8 is again the only negative difference, and is the smallest in absolute value, so $W^+ = 2 + 3 + 4 + 5 + 6 + 7 + 8$.

**26.42.** (a) The Kruskal-Wallis test statistic has df $= I - 1 = 4 - 1 = 3$.

**26.43. Formulate:** We compare improvements for the two groups of students by testing $H_0$: improvements are identically distributed, versus $H_a$: treatment group improvements are systematically higher.
**Solve:** See the solution to Exercise 19.45 for back-to-back stemplots and summary statistics. The Wilcoxon test statistic is $W = 114$, for which $P = 0.0501$ (or 0.0494, adjusted for ties).
**Conclude:** We have fairly strong evidence—nearly (or barely) significant at the 5% level—that the encouraging subliminal message led to an greater improvement in math scores.

**Minitab output**

```
trtmt      N =  10     Median =        11.500
ctrl       N =   8     Median =         7.500
W = 114.0
Test of ETA1 = ETA2  vs.  ETA1 > ETA2 is significant at 0.0501
The test is significant at 0.0494 (adjusted for ties)
```

**26.44. Formulate:** We use the Kruskal-Wallis procedure to test $H_0$: all four lightness distributions are the same, versus $H_a$: some distribution is different.
**Solve:** See the solution to Exercise 25.33 for side-by-side stemplots; medians are listed in the Minitab output below. The Kruskal-Wallis test statistic is $H = 22.35$ with df $= 3$, for which $P < 0.0005$.
**Conclude:** The observed differences are significant. In particular, it appears that Method B typically yields the darkest results, and Method C yields the lightest results.

**Note:** *This agrees with the conclusion of Exercise 25.33, where this question was answered using ANOVA.*

**Minitab output**

```
LEVEL      NOBS     MEDIAN  AVE. RANK   Z VALUE
    A         8      41.61       13.0     -1.22
    B         8      41.29        6.6     -3.46
    C         8      42.44       27.9      3.98
    D         8      41.98       18.5      0.70
OVERALL      32                  16.5

H = 22.35  d.f. = 3  p = 0.000
H = 22.36  d.f. = 3  p = 0.000 (adjusted for ties)
```

**26.45.** See also the solution to Exercise 18.43.
**Formulate:** Considering the right-threaded minus left-threaded differences, we test $H_0$: median $= 0$ (that is, times have the same distribution for both directions) against $H_a$: median $< 0$ (that is, clockwise times are systematically lower).
**Solve:** The mean and median differences are $-13.32$ and $-12$ seconds; the stemplot (optional) shows many negative differences. The Wilcoxon signed rank test statistic is $W^+ = 56.5$, which has $P = 0.004$. (See the note in the solution to Exercise 26.23 for an explanation of the estimated median reported by Minitab.)
**Conclude:** Clockwise times are lower.

```
−5 | 2
−4 | 853
−3 | 511
−2 | 94
−1 | 66621
−0 | 74331
 0 | 02
 1 | 1
 2 | 03
 3 | 8
```

**Minitab output**

```
TEST OF MEDIAN = 0.000000 VERSUS MEDIAN L.T. 0.000000

              N FOR   WILCOXON             ESTIMATED
         N     TEST  STATISTIC   P-VALUE      MEDIAN
RH-LH   25       24       56.5     0.004      -14.00
```

**26.46. Formulate:** We compare the number of species on the two groups of plots, including a test of the hypotheses $H_0$: there is no difference in the number of species on logged and unlogged plots, versus $H_a$: unlogged plots have a greater number of species.
**Solve:** Back-to-back stemplots suggest that the unlogged plots have more species. The Wilcoxon test gives $W = 159$ and $P \doteq 0.0298$ (0.0290, adjusted for ties).
**Conclude:** The observed difference is significant; unlogged plots really do have a greater number of species.

| Unlogged | | Logged |
|---|---|---|
| | 0 | 4 |
| | 0 | |
| | 0 | |
| | 1 | 0 |
| 333 | 1 | 2 |
| 55 | 1 | 455 |
| | 1 | 7 |
| 998 | 1 | 88 |
| 10 | 2 | |
| 22 | 2 | |

**Note:** *In Exercise 25.38, ANOVA was used to compare these two groups, along with a sample of plots that had been logged one year earlier.*

**Minitab output**

```
Unlogged    N =  12      Median =         18.500
Logged      N =   9      Median =         15.000
W = 159.0
Test of ETA1 = ETA2  vs.  ETA1 > ETA2 is significant at 0.0298
The test is significant at 0.0290 (adjusted for ties)
```

**26.47. Formulate:** Consider the differences sfair – srest. We test the hypotheses $H_0$: median $= 0$ versus $H_a$: median $> 0$; the one-sided alternative means "food at fairs is systematically rated higher (less safe) than restaurant food."
**Solve:** We find $\bar{x} = 0.5149$ and $M = 0.5$. Applying the Wilcoxon signed rank test to these differences, we find $W^+ = 10{,}850.5$ and $P < 0.0005$. (See the note in the solution to Exercise 26.23 for an explanation of the estimated median reported by Minitab.)
**Conclude:** Restaurant food is viewed as being safer than food at fairs. However, there were 146 ties; the text cautions us that when there are many ties, the test may be biased in favor of $H_a$, so we must be cautious about our conclusion.

**Minitab output**

```
TEST OF MEDIAN = 0.000000 VERSUS MEDIAN G.T. 0.000000

                 N FOR   WILCOXON              ESTIMATED
            N    TEST   STATISTIC  P-VALUE       MEDIAN
Diffs     303     157     10850.5    0.000       0.5000
```

**26.48. Formulate:** Consider the differences sfair – sfast. We test the hypotheses $H_0$: median $= 0$ versus $H_a$: median $\neq 0$; the two-sided alternative means "ratings for fairs and fast food restaurants are systematically different in some way."
**Solve:** We find $\bar{x} = 0.0693$ and $M = 0$. Applying the Wilcoxon signed rank test to these differences, we find $W^+ = 4730.5$ and $P = 0.206$.
**Conclude:** The difference in safety ratings is not significant. (The large number of ties is not a cause for concern in this case. Ties can lead to a bias in favor of $H_a$, but even with this advantage for the alternative, the evidence was not convincing.)

**Minitab output**

```
TEST OF MEDIAN = 0.000000 VERSUS MEDIAN N.E. 0.000000

                 N FOR   WILCOXON              ESTIMATED
            N    TEST   STATISTIC  P-VALUE       MEDIAN
Diffs     303     129      4730.5    0.206    0.000E+00
```

**26.49.** See also the solution to Exercise 25.31.
**Formulate:** For Kruskal-Wallis, we test $H_0$: the distribution of growth is the same for all nematode counts, versus $H_a$: growth is systematically larger for some counts.
**Solve: (b)** The medians are 10, 11.1, 5.2, and 5.55 cm—noticeably lower for the latter two, suggesting that nematodes retard growth (after a point). The Kruskal-Wallis test statistic is $H = 11.34$, with df $= 3$; the $P$-value is 0.01.
**Conclude:** We have strong evidence that growth is not the same for all nematode counts (that is, the difference that we observed is statistically significant).

**Minitab output**

```
LEVEL     NOBS     MEDIAN  AVE. RANK   Z VALUE
    0        4     10.000       12.3      1.82
 1000        4     11.100       12.8      2.06
 5000        4      5.200        4.2     -2.06
10000        4      5.550        4.7     -1.82
OVERALL     16                   8.5

H = 11.34  d.f. = 3  p = 0.010
H = 11.35  d.f. = 3  p = 0.010 (adjusted for ties)
```

**26.50. Formulate:** We examine the downstream minus upstream differences for the 13 tributaries, and test $H_0$: same richness distribution for both locations, versus $H_a$: richness is systematically higher downstream.
**Solve:** We ignore the one difference of 0. There are only two negative differences in the data (ranks 7 and 8.5); the sum of the ranks of the positive differences is $W^+ = 62.5$, for which $P = 0.036$.
**Conclude:** This matches the paper's claim: there is good evidence that species richness is higher downstream from tributaries.

```
−0 | 4
−0 | 3
−0 |
 0 | 0111
 0 | 222
 0 | 45
 0 | 67
```

**Note:** *The researchers actually used the binomial sign test, which is appropriate for matched pairs situations like this. This test is not presented in* BPS.

**Minitab output**

```
TEST OF MEDIAN = 0.000000 VERSUS MEDIAN G.T. 0.000000

                 N FOR   WILCOXON            ESTIMATED
            N    TEST   STATISTIC  P-VALUE     MEDIAN
diff       13     12         62.5    0.036      1.500
```

**26.51. Formulate:** We examine the within-stream minus upstream differences for the 13 tributaries, and test $H_0$: same richness distribution for both locations, versus $H_a$: richness is systematically higher within tributaries.
**Solve:** There are three negative differences (ranks 1.5, 8.5, and 12); the sum of the ranks of the positive differences is $W^+ = 69$, for which $P = 0.054$.
**Conclude:** There is evidence that richness is higher within tributaries than upstream from them, but the evidence is not very strong. In particular, it falls just short of being significant at the 5% level.

```
−1 | 1
−0 | 5
−0 | 1
 0 | 122334
 0 | 579
 1 | 3
```

**Note:** *The researchers actually used the binomial sign test.*

**Minitab output**

```
TEST OF MEDIAN = 0.000000 VERSUS MEDIAN G.T. 0.000000

                 N FOR   WILCOXON            ESTIMATED
            N    TEST   STATISTIC  P-VALUE     MEDIAN
diff       13     13         69.0    0.054      3.000
```

**26.52. Formulate:** We examine the within-stream minus downstream differences for the 13 tributaries, and test $H_0$: same richness distribution for both locations, versus $H_a$: different richness distributions.
**Solve:** We ignore the two differences of 0. There are three negative differences (ranks 3.5, 9, and 11); the sum of the ranks of the positive differences is $W^+ = 42.5$, for which $P = 0.424$.
**Conclude:** We do not have compelling evidence of a difference in species richness in a tributary and in the main stream just below the tributary.

```
−1 | 5
−1 |
−0 | 6
−0 | 30
 0 | 022344
 0 | 557
```

**Note:** *The researchers actually used the binomial sign test.*

**Minitab output**

```
TEST OF MEDIAN = 0.000000 VERSUS MEDIAN N.E. 0.000000

                 N FOR   WILCOXON            ESTIMATED
            N    TEST   STATISTIC  P-VALUE     MEDIAN
diff       13     11         42.5    0.424      2.000
```

# Chapter 27 Solutions

**27.4.** These DRGs account for a total of 80.5% of all losses. Certainly the first two (209 and 116) should be among those that are studied first; some students may also include 107, 462, and so on.

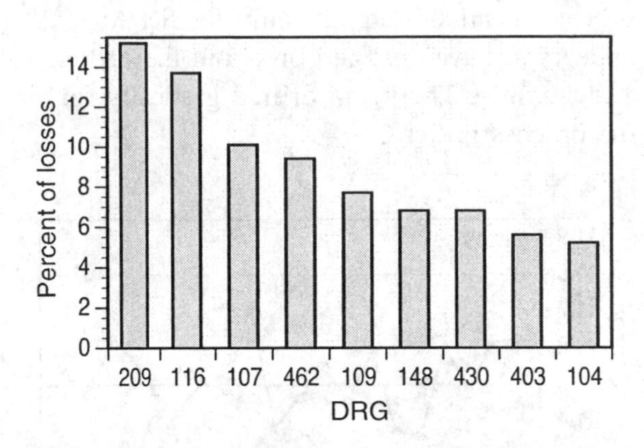


**27.5.** Possible causes could include alarm not set, had to wait for a train (or traffic), flat tire, spent too much time eating breakfast, and so forth.

**27.6.** Possible examples of special causes might include wind speed and direction, traffic, temperature, Jeannine's health, or mechanical problems with the bicycle (a flat tire or a broken brake cable).

**27.8.** Common causes of variation might include time spent showering, getting dressed, or preparing and eating breakfast. Examples of special causes might include forgetting to set the alarm, encountering (or being in) a traffic accident, waiting for a train, or getting an unexpected phone call before leaving. (These special causes would result in late arrival; it is harder to imagine special causes that might result in early arrival.)

**27.9.** The center line is at $\mu = 75^\circ$ F; the control limits should be at $\mu \pm 3\sigma/\sqrt{4}$, which means $74.25^\circ$ F and $75.75^\circ$ F.

**27.10.** **(a)** Center: 11.5 kg; control limits: $\mu \pm 3\sigma/\sqrt{4} = 11.5 \pm 0.3 = 11.2$ and 11.8 kg.
**(b)** Graphs at right and below. Points outside control limits are marked with an "X."
**(c)** Set B is from the in-control process. The process mean shifted suddenly for Set A; it appears to have changed on about the 11th or 12th sample. The mean drifted gradually for the process in Set C.

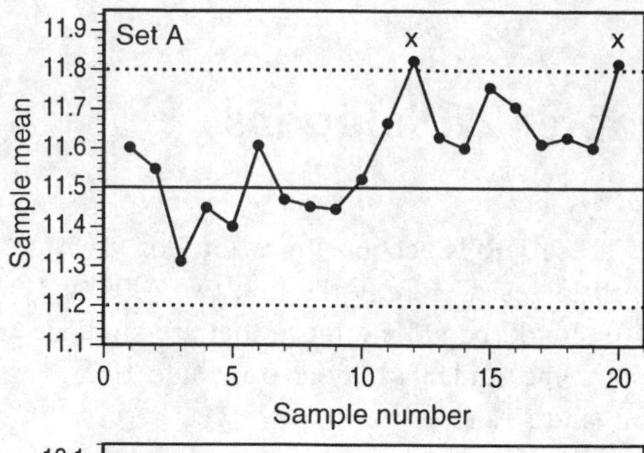


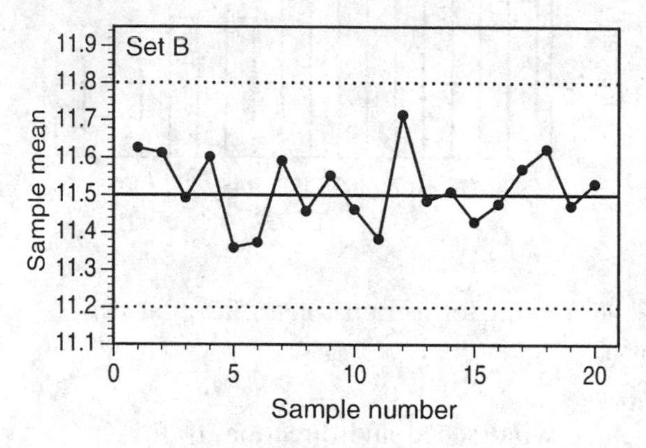


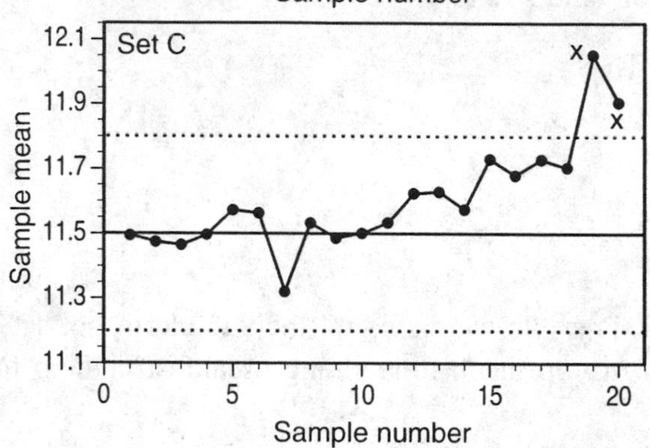


**27.11.** **(a)** Common causes might include processing time, normal workload fluctuation, or postal delivery time. **(b)** $s$-type special causes might include a new employee working in the personnel department. **(c)** Special causes affecting $\bar{x}$ might include a sudden large influx of applications, or perhaps introducing a new filing system for applications.

**27.12.** For $n = 4$, $c_4 = 0.9213$, so the center line is $(0.9213)(0.5) = 0.46065°$ F. $B_5$ is not given, so the lower control limit is 0° F, and $B_6 = 2.088$, so the upper control limit is 1.044° F.

**27.13.** **(a)** For the $\bar{x}$ chart, the center line is 11.5 kg and the control limits are 11.2 and 11.8 kg (as in Exercise 27.10). For $n = 4$, $c_4 = 0.9213$ and $B_6 = 2.088$, so the center line for the $s$ chart is $(0.9213)(0.2) = 0.18426$ kg, and the control limits are 0 and 0.4176 kg. **(b)** The $s$ chart is certainly out of control at sample 11; the increase might have happened slightly before that point. The $s$ chart is consistently above the center line (and often above the UCL) after that; the $\bar{x}$ chart is noticeably out of control shortly after that sample. **(c)** A change in the mean does not affect the $s$ chart; the effect on the $\bar{x}$ chart is masked by the change in $\sigma$: because of the increased variability, the sample means are sometimes below the center line even after the process mean shifts.

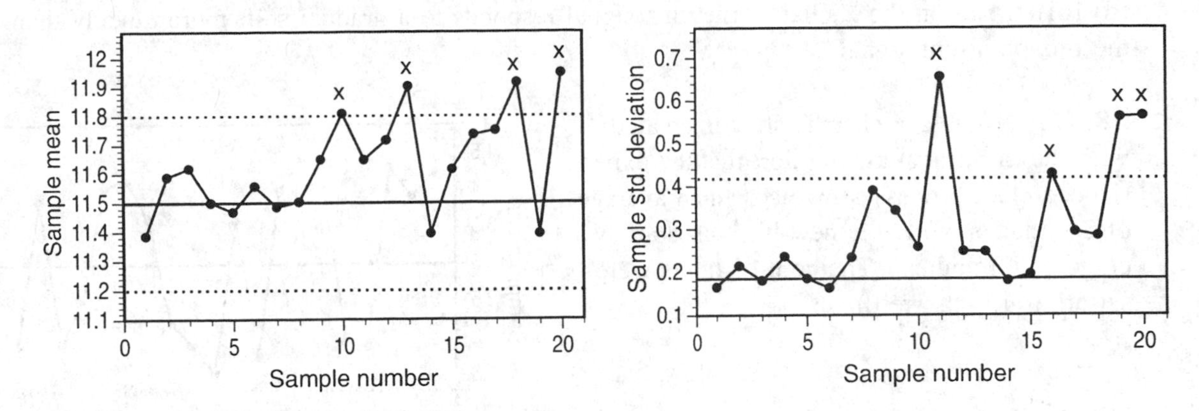


**27.14.** **(a)** For $n = 5$, we have $c_4 = 0.94$, $B_5 = 0$, and $B_6 = 1.964$, so the center line is 0.11938 and the control limits are 0 and 0.249428. **(b)** The center line is $\mu = 4.22$, and the control limits are $\mu \pm 3\sigma/\sqrt{5} \doteq 4.0496$ to 4.3904.

**27.15.** The first two means and standard deviations are $\bar{x}_1 = 48$, $s_1 = 8.9$, $\bar{x}_2 = 46$, and $s_2 = 13.0$. For the $\bar{x}$ chart, the center line is 43 and the control limits are 25.91 and 60.09. For $n = 5$, $c_4 = 0.9400$ and $B_6 = 1.964$, so the center line for the $s$ chart is $(0.9400)(12.74) = 11.9756$, and the control limits are 0 and 25.02. The control charts (below) show that sample 5 was above the UCL on the $s$ chart, but it appears to have been special cause variation, because there is no indication that the samples that followed it were out of control.

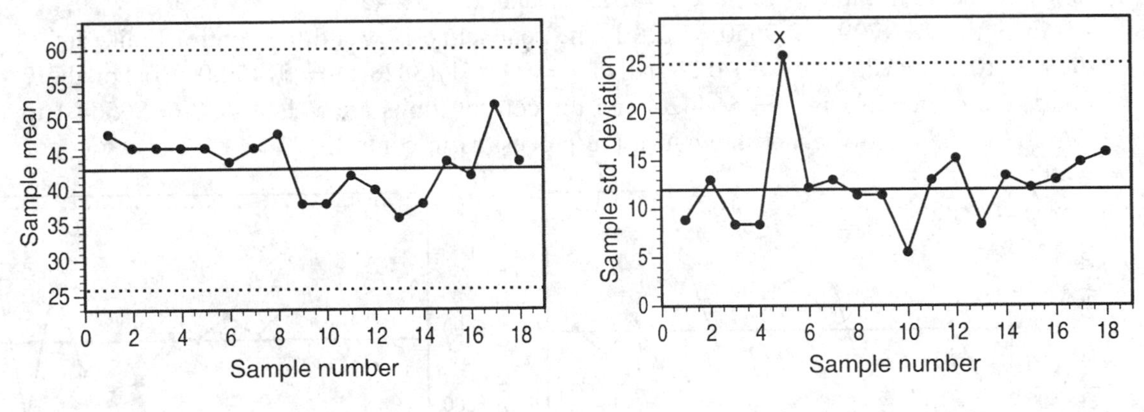


**27.16.** The new type of yarn would appear on the $\bar{x}$ chart because it would cause a shift in the mean pH. (It might also affect the process variability, and therefore show up on the $s$ chart.) Additional water in the kettle would change the pH for that kettle, which would change the mean pH and also change the process variability, so we would expect that special cause to show up on both the $\bar{x}$ and $s$ charts.

**27.17.** **(a)** Either (ii) or (iii), depending on whether the deterioration happens quickly or gradually. We would not necessarily expect that this deterioration would result in a change in variability ($s$ or $R$). **(b)** (i) $s$ or $R$ chart: a change in precision suggests altered variability ($s$ or $R$), but not necessarily a change in center ($\bar{x}$). **(c)** (i) $s$ or $R$ chart: assuming there are other (fluent) customer service representatives answering the phones, this new person would have unusually long times, which should most quickly show up as an increase in variability.

**(d)** (iii) A run on the $\bar{x}$ chart: "the runs signal responds to a gradual shift more quickly than the one-point-out signal."

**27.18.** One possible $\bar{x}$ chart is shown, created with the (arbitrary) assumption that the experienced clerk processes invoices in an average of 2 minutes, while the new hire takes an average of 4 minutes. (The control limits were set arbitrarily as well.)

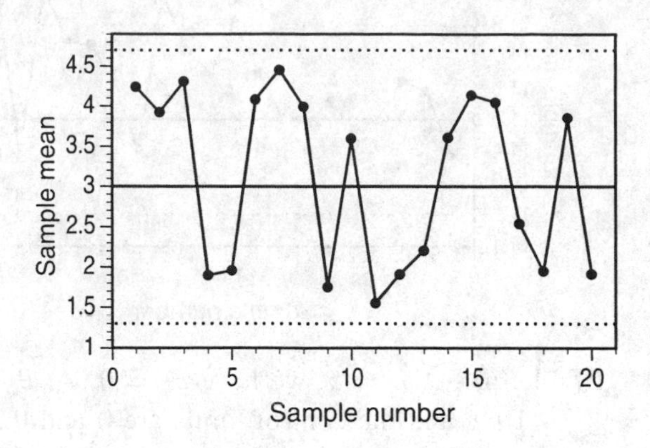


**27.19.** We estimate $\hat{\sigma}$ to be $\bar{s}/0.9213 \doteq 0.9986$, so the $\bar{x}$ chart has center line $\bar{\bar{x}} = 48.7$ and control limits $\bar{\bar{x}} \pm 3\hat{\sigma}/\sqrt{4} = 47.2$ to $50.2$. The $s$ chart has center line $\bar{s} = 0.92$ and control limits 0 and $2.088\hat{\sigma} = 2.085$.

**27.20. (a)** Average the 20 sample means and standard deviations, and estimate $\mu$ to be $\hat{\mu} = \bar{\bar{x}} = 275.07$ mV and $\sigma$ to be $\hat{\sigma} = \bar{s}/c_4 = 34.55/0.9213 \doteq 37.50$ mV. **(b)** In the $s$ chart shown in Figure 27.7, most of the points fall below the center line.

**27.21.** For the 15 samples, we have $\bar{s} = \$799.1$ and $\bar{\bar{x}} = \$6442.4$.
**(a)** $\hat{\sigma} = \bar{s}/c_4 = 799.1/0.9650 = 828.1$; the center line is $\bar{s}$, and the control limits are $B_5\hat{\sigma} = (0.179)(\$828.1) = \$148.2$ and $B_6\hat{\sigma} = (1.751)(\$828.1) = \$1450.0$. **(b)** For the $\bar{x}$ chart, the center line is $\bar{\bar{x}} = \$6442.4$ and the control limits are $\bar{\bar{x}} \pm 3\hat{\sigma}/\sqrt{8} = \$5564.1$ to $\$7320.7$. The control chart shows that the process is in control.

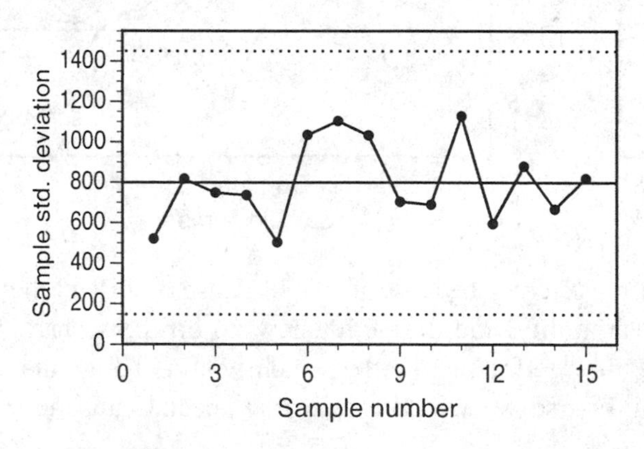


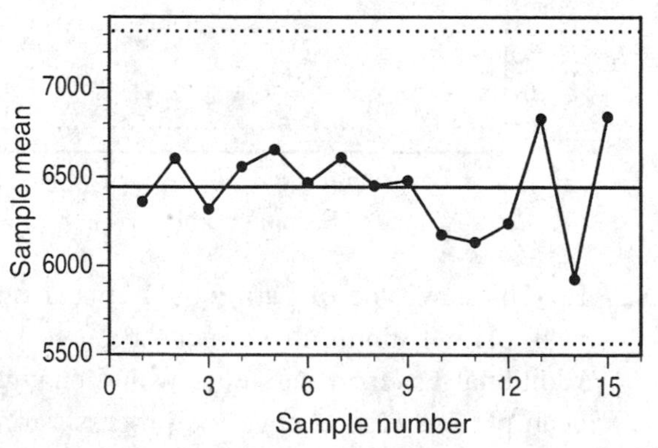


**27.22. (a)** For the 21 samples, we have $\bar{s} \doteq 0.2786$, so $\hat{\sigma} = \bar{s}/c_4 = 0.2786/0.9213 \doteq 0.3024$; the center line is $\bar{s}$, and the control limits are $B_5\hat{\sigma} = 0$ and $B_6\hat{\sigma} = (2.088)(0.3024) \doteq 0.6313$. Short-term variation seems to be in control. **(b)** For the $\bar{x}$ chart, the center line is 0 and the control limits are $\pm 3\hat{\sigma}/\sqrt{4} = \pm 0.4536$. The $\bar{x}$ chart suggests that the process mean has drifted. (Only the first four out-of-control points are marked.) One possible cause for the increase in the mean is that the cutting blade is getting dull.

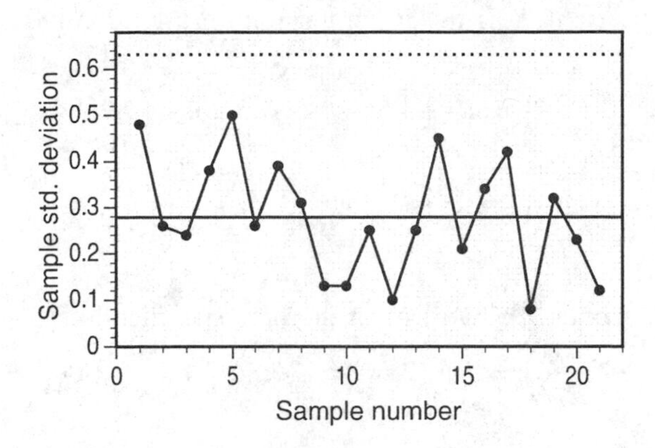


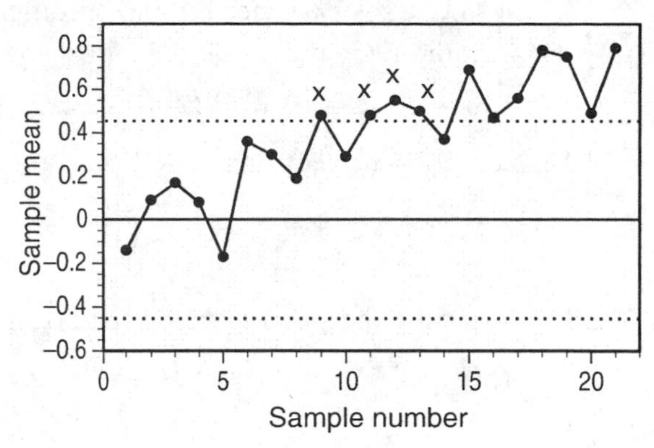


**27.23.** The process is no longer the same as it was during the downward trend (from the 1950s into the 1980s). In particular, including those years in the data used to establish the control limits results in a mean that is too high to use for current winning times, and a standard deviation that includes variation attributable to the "special cause" of the changing conditioning and professional status of the best runners. Such special cause variation should not be included in a control chart.

**27.24.** If the manufacturer practices SPC, that provides some assurance that the monitors are roughly uniform in quality—as the text says, "We know what to expect in the finished product." So, assuming that uniform quality is sufficiently high, the purchaser does not need to inspect the monitors as they arrive because SPC has already achieved the goal of that inspection: to avoid buying many faulty monitors. (Of course, a few unacceptable monitors may be produced and sold even when SPC is practiced—but inspection would not catch all such monitors, anyway.)

**27.25.** The standard deviation of all 120 measurements is $s \doteq \$811.53$, and the mean is $\bar{x} \doteq \$6442.4$ (the same as $\bar{\bar{x}}$—as it must be, provided all the individual samples were the same size). The natural tolerances are $\bar{x} \pm 3s = \$4007.8$ to $\$8877.0$.

**27.26.** A histogram (right) or stemplot shows that the number of losses between \$6000 and \$6500 is noticeably higher than we might expect from a Normal distribution, but otherwise the shape of the graph suggests that the natural tolerances should be fairly trustworthy.

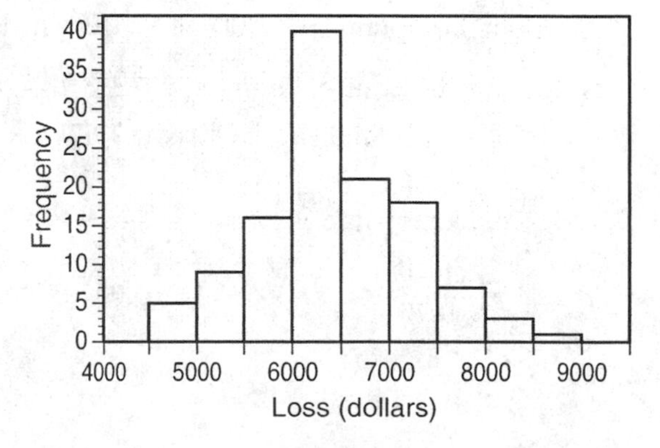


**Note:** *In fact, the smallest and largest losses were \$4727 and \$8794; these are both within the tolerances, but note that the minimum is quite a bit above the lower limit of the tolerances (\$4008). The large number of losses between \$6000 and \$6500 makes the mean slightly lower, and therefore lowers both of the tolerance limits.*

**27.27. (a)** About 99.9% meet the old specifications: if $X$ is the mesh tension on a randomly chosen monitor, then

$$P(100 < X < 400) = P\left(\frac{100-275}{38.4} < Z < \frac{400-275}{38.4}\right) = P(-4.56 < Z < 3.26) \doteq 0.9994.$$

**(b)** About 97.4% meet the new specifications:

$$P(150 < X < 350) = P\left(\frac{150-275}{38.4} < Z < \frac{350-275}{38.4}\right) = P(-3.26 < Z < 1.95) \doteq 0.9738.$$

**27.28.** If we shift the process mean to 250 mV, about 99% will meet the new specifications:

$$P(150 < X < 350) = P\left(\frac{150-250}{38.4} < Z < \frac{350-250}{38.4}\right) = P(-2.60 < Z < 2.60) \doteq 0.9906.$$

**27.29.** The mean of the 17 in-control samples is $\bar{\bar{x}} = 43.4118$, and the standard deviation is 11.5833, so the natural tolerances are $\bar{\bar{x}} \pm 3s = 8.66$ to 78.16.

**27.30.** Only about 44% of meters meet the specifications: using the mean (43.4118) and standard deviation (11.5833) found in the solution to Exercise 27.29,

$$P(44 < X < 64) = P\left(\frac{44-43.4118}{11.5833} < Z < \frac{64-43.4118}{11.5833}\right) = P(0.05 < Z < 1.78) \doteq 0.4426.$$

**27.31.** For those 10 days, there were 961 absences, and $10 \cdot 987 = 9870$ person-days available for work, so $\bar{p} = \frac{961}{9870} \doteq 0.09737$, and

$$\text{CL} = \bar{p} = 0.09737, \text{control limits: } \bar{p} \pm 3\sqrt{\frac{\bar{p}(1-\bar{p})}{987}} = 0.06906 \text{ and } 0.12567.$$

**27.32. (a)** For those 10 months, there were 960 overdue invoices out of 28,750 total invoices, so $\bar{p} = \frac{960}{28{,}750} \doteq 0.03339$. **(b)** The center line and control limits are

$$\text{CL} = \bar{p} = 0.03339, \text{control limits: } \bar{p} \pm 3\sqrt{\frac{\bar{p}(1-\bar{p})}{2875}} = 0.02334 \text{ and } 0.04344.$$

**27.33.** One complaint per 200 passengers means that the center line is $\bar{p} = 0.005$ (one-half of 1%), and the control limits are $\bar{p} \pm 3\sqrt{\frac{\bar{p}(1-\bar{p})}{1000}} = 0.005 \pm 0.0067$. As the problem says, we take LCL = 0, and the UCL is 0.0117.

**27.34.** The center line is $\bar{p} = \frac{208}{34{,}700} \doteq 0.005994$, and the control limits are $\bar{p} \pm 3\sqrt{\frac{\bar{p}(1-\bar{p})}{1070}} = 0.005994 \pm 0.007079$. Take the lower limit to be 0; the upper limit is 0.01307.

**27.35.** **(a)** The student counts sum to 9218, while the absentee total is 3277, so $\bar{p} = \frac{3277}{9218} = 0.3555$ and $\bar{n} = 921.8$. **(b)** The center line is $\bar{p} = 0.3555$, and the control limits are

$$\bar{p} \pm 3\sqrt{\frac{\bar{p}(1-\bar{p})}{921.8}} = 0.3082 \text{ and } 0.4028.$$

The $p$ chart suggests that absentee rates are in control. **(c)** For October, the limits are 0.3088 and 0.4022; for June, they are 0.3072 and 0.4038. These limits appear as solid lines on the $p$ chart, but they are not substantially different from the control limits found in (b). Unless $n$ varies *a lot* from sample to sample, it is sufficient to use $\bar{n}$.

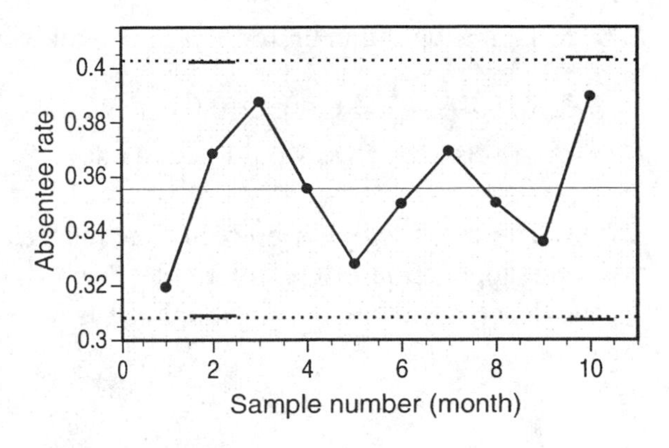


**27.36.** Control charts focus on ensuring that the *process* is consistent, not that the *product* is good. An in-control process may consistently produce some percent of low-quality products. Keeping a process in control allows one to detect shifts in the distribution of the output (which may have been caused by some correctable error); it does not help in fixing problems that are inherent to the process.

**27.37.** **(a)** (ii) A sudden change in the $\bar{x}$ chart: this would immediately increase the amount of time required to complete the checks. **(b)** (i) A sudden change (decrease) in $s$ or $R$, because the new measurement system will remove (or decrease) the variability introduced by human error. **(c)** (iii) A gradual drift in the $\bar{x}$ chart (presumably a drift up, if the variable being tracked is the length of time to complete a set of invoices).

**27.39.** **(a)** The percents do not add to 100% because one customer might have several complaints; that is, he or she could be counted in several categories. **(b)** Clearly, the process of creating, correcting, and adjusting invoices should be given top priority, because the three most common complaints involved invoices.

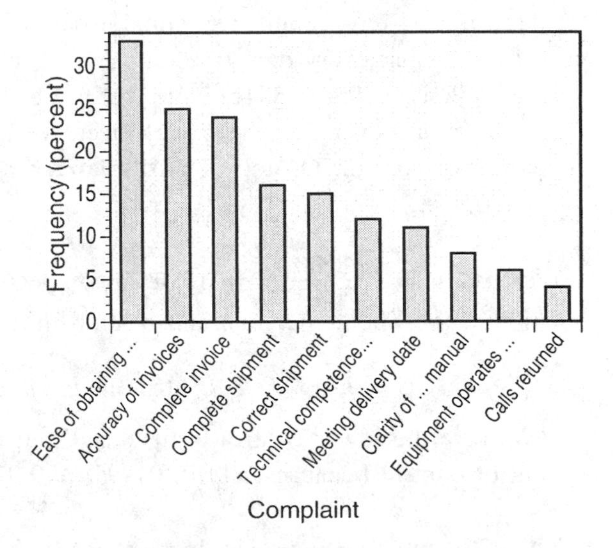


**27.40.** **(a)** Use $\bar{x}$ and $s$ charts to track the time required. **(b)** Use a $p$ chart to track the acceptance percent. **(c)** Use a $p$ chart to track the proportion of employees participating.

**27.41.** **(a)** Depending on how one interprets "availability," either $\bar{x}$ and $s$ charts or a $p$ chart is appropriate. **(b)** Use $\bar{x}$ and $s$ (or $R$) charts to control response time. **(c)** Use a $p$ chart for undocumented programming changes.

**27.42.** This situation calls for a $p$ chart with center line $\bar{p} = \frac{5}{1000} = 0.005$ and control limits $\bar{p} \pm 3\sqrt{\frac{\bar{p}(1-\bar{p})}{300}} = 0.005 \pm 0.0122$. We take LCL = 0, and the UCL is 0.0172. (In order to exceed this UCL, we would need to have 6 rejected lots out of 300.)

**27.43.** The most common problems are related to the application of the color coat; that should be the focus of our initial efforts.

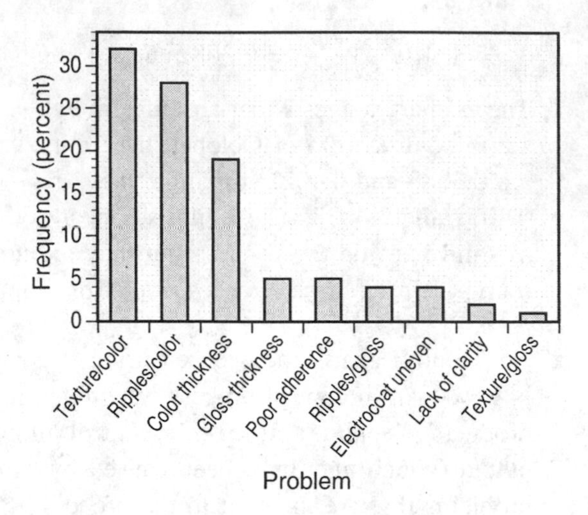


**27.44.** For the $s$ chart with $n = 5$, we have $c_4 = 0.94$, $B_5 = 0$, and $B_6 = 1.964$, so the center line is 0.001128 and the control limits are 0 and 0.0023568. For the $\bar{x}$ chart, the center line is $\mu = 0.8750$ inch, and the control limits are $\mu \pm 3\sigma/\sqrt{5} \doteq 0.8750 \pm 0.0016 = 0.8734$ and 0.8766 inches.

**27.45. (a)** $\bar{p} = \frac{3.5}{1{,}000{,}000} = 0.0000035$. At 5000 pieces per day, we expect 0.0175 defects per day; in a 24-day month, we would expect 0.42 defects. **(b)** The center line is 0.0000035; assuming that every day we examine all 5000 pieces, the LCL is negative (so we use 0), and the UCL is 0.0000083. **(c)** Note that most of the time, we will find 0 defects, so that $\hat{p} = 0$. If we should ever find even one defect, we would have $\hat{p} = 0.0002$, and the process would be out of control. On top of this, it takes an absurd amount of testing in order to catch the rare defect.

**27.46. (a)** $\bar{p} = \frac{8000}{1{,}000{,}000} = 0.008$. We expect about $4 = (500)(0.008)$ defective orders per month. **(b)** The center line and control limits are

$$\text{CL} = \bar{p} = 0.008, \text{ control limits: } \bar{p} \pm 3\sqrt{\frac{\bar{p}(1-\bar{p})}{500}} = -0.00395 \text{ and } 0.01995.$$

(We take the lower control limit to be 0.) It takes at least ten bad orders in a month to be out of control because $(500)(0.01995) = 9.975$.

**27.47.** Students will have varying justifications for the sampling choice. Choosing six calls per shift gives an idea of the variability and mean for the shift as a whole. If we took six consecutive calls (at a randomly chosen time), we might see additional variability in $\bar{x}$, because sometimes those six calls might be observed at particularly busy times (when a customer has to wait for a long time until a representative is available, or when a representative is using the restroom).

**27.48. (a)** For $n = 6$, we have $c_4 = 0.9515$, $B_5 = 0.029$, and $B_6 = 1.874$. With $\bar{s} = 29.985$ seconds, we compute $\hat{\sigma} = \bar{s}/c_4 \doteq 31.5134$ seconds, so the initial $s$ chart has centerline $\bar{s}$ and control limits $B_5\hat{\sigma} \doteq 0.9139$ and $B_6\hat{\sigma} \doteq 59.0561$ seconds. There are four out-of-control points, from samples 28, 39, 42, and 46. **(b)** With the remaining 46 samples, $\bar{s} = 24.3015$, so $\hat{\sigma} = \bar{s}/c_4 = 25.54$ seconds, and the control limits are $B_5\hat{\sigma} = 0.741$ and $B_6\hat{\sigma} = 47.86$ seconds. There are no more out-of-control points. (The second $s$ chart is not shown.) **(c)** We have center line $\bar{\bar{x}} = 29.2087$ seconds, and control limits $\bar{\bar{x}} \pm 3\hat{\sigma}/\sqrt{6} = -2.072$ and $60.489$ seconds. (The lower control limit should be ignored or changed to 0.) The $\bar{x}$ chart has no out-of-control points.

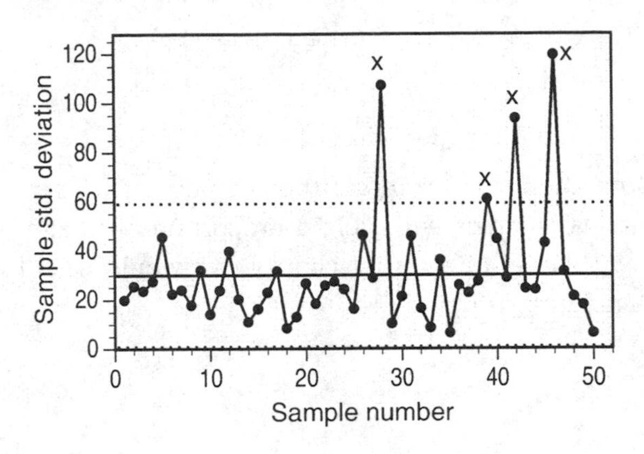


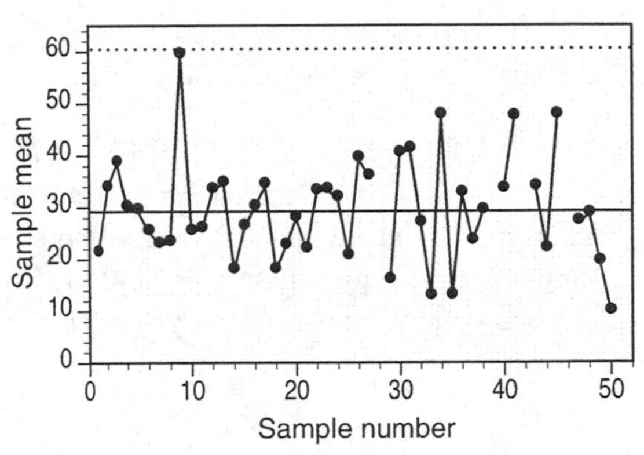


**27.49.** The outliers are 276 seconds (sample 28), 244 seconds (sample 42), and 333 seconds (sample 46). After dropping those outliers, the standard deviations drop to 9.284, 6.708, and 31.011 seconds. (Sample #39, the other out-of-control point, has two moderately large times, 144 and 109 seconds; if they are removed, $s$ drops to 3.416.)

**27.50.** The initial center line and control limits are

$$\text{CL} = p = 0.01, \text{ control limits: } p \pm 3\sqrt{\frac{p(1-p)}{75{,}000}} = 0.008910 \text{ and } 0.011090.$$

On a day when only 50,000 prescriptions are filled, the center line is unchanged, while the control limits change to

$$p \pm 3\sqrt{\frac{p(1-p)}{50{,}000}} = 0.008665 \text{ and } 0.011335.$$

**27.51.** We find that $\bar{s} = 7.65$, so with $c_4 = 0.8862$ and $B_6 = 2.276$, we compute $\hat{\sigma} = 8.63$ and UCL $= 19.65$. One point (from sample #1) is out of control. (And, if that cause were determined and the point removed, a new chart would have $s$ for sample #10 out of control.) The second (lower) UCL line on the control chart is the final UCL, after removing both of those samples (per the instructions in Exercise 27.52).

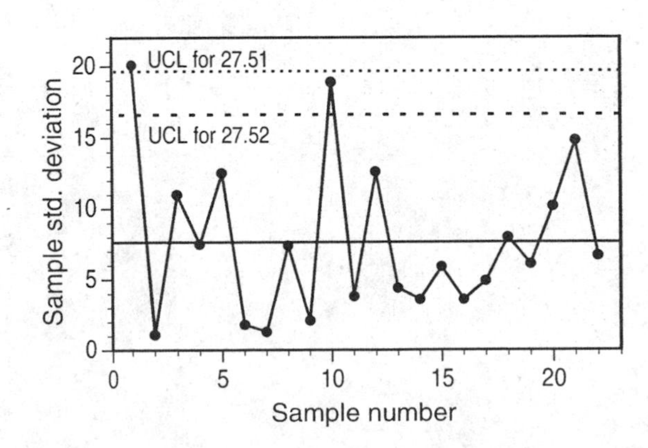

**27.52.** Without samples 1 and 10, $\bar{s} = 6.465$, $\hat{\sigma} = \bar{s}/c_4 \doteq 7.295$, and the new UCL is $2.276\hat{\sigma} = 16.60$; this line is shown on the control chart in the solution to the previous problem. Meanwhile, $\bar{\bar{x}} = 834.5$, and the control limits are $\bar{\bar{x}} \pm 3\hat{\sigma}/\sqrt{3} = 821.86$ to $847.14$. The $\bar{x}$ chart gives no indication of trouble—the process seems to be in control.

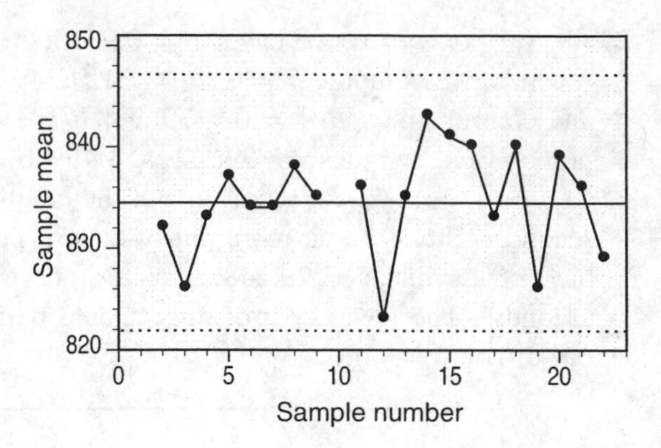


**27.53.** **(a)** Use a $p$ chart, with center line $\bar{p} = \frac{15}{5000} = 0.003$ and control limits $\bar{p} \pm 3\sqrt{\frac{\bar{p}(1-\bar{p})}{100}}$, or 0 to 0.0194. **(b)** There is little useful information to be gained from keeping a $p$ chart: if the proportion remains at 0.003, about 74% of samples will yield a proportion of 0, and about 22% of proportions will be 0.01. To call the process out of control, we would need to see two or more unsatisfactory films in a sample of 100.

# Chapter 28 Solutions

**28.1.** The model would be $\mu_y = \beta_0 + \beta_1 x_1 + \beta_2 x_2$, where:

- $\beta_0$ is the intercept (the number of new birds for the first species when there are no returning birds),
- $\beta_2$ is the amount that the intercept differs for the second species (that is, $\beta_0 + \beta_2$ is the number of new birds for the second species when there are no returning birds), and
- $\beta_1$ is the slope—the rate at which the number of new birds changes in response to changes in the percent of returning birds.

**28.2.** The simplest interpretation of this exercise is that $x_2$ is equal to either 10 or 20 cm, in which case the model would be

$$\mu_y = 0.15x_1 + x_2.$$

Some students might treat $x_2$ as an indicator variable (0 for 10-cm icicles, 1 for 20-cm icicles), so their model would be

$$\mu_y = 10 + 0.15x_1 + 10x_2.$$

**28.3.** With $x$ representing the reporting date and $y$ representing the percent reporting for jury duty, the slope and intercept for the simple regression model $\mu_y = \beta_0 + \beta_1 x$ are

$$b_1 = r \cdot \frac{s_y}{s_x} \quad \text{and} \quad b_0 = \bar{y} - b_1\bar{x}.$$

**(a)** For 1985, $b_1 = 0.399 \cdot \frac{4.537}{7.65} \doteq 0.2366$ and $b_0 = 22.135 - b_1 \cdot 13.50 \doteq 18.94$.

**(b)** For 1997, $b_1 = 0.707 \cdot \frac{17.94}{7.65} \doteq 1.6580$ and $b_0 = 48.10 - b_1 \cdot 13.50 \doteq 25.72$.

**(c)** For 1985 reporting dates, the slope tells us that as coded reporting date increases, the percent reporting for jury duty increases; specifically, that percent increases by 0.2366 for each unit increase in reporting date (a two-week period). For 1997 reporting dates, the rate of increase is much greater: 1.6580 percentage points for each unit change in reporting date. **(d)** The slopes are quite different. (This is also evident from the scatterplot.) **(e)** Considering the difference in the computed slopes and the appearance of the scatterplot, a multiple regression model with equal slopes seems inappropriate for this setting.

**28.4.** **(a)** For 1998 ($x_3 = 1$), the equation is $\hat{y} = (94.9 - 17.8) - 0.717x_1 = 77.1 - 0.717x_1$. For 2000 ($x_3 = 0$), the equation is $\hat{y} = 94.9 - 0.717x_1$. **(b)** These equations are identical to those found in Example 28.3. **(c)** The regression standard error will be unchanged ($s = 6.709$) with the new indicator variable, because the scatter about the two regression lines remains the same.

**28.5.** With $x$ representing the reporting date and $y$ representing the percent reporting for jury duty, the slope and intercept for the simple regression model $\mu_y = \beta_0 + \beta_1 x$ are

$$b_1 = r \cdot \frac{s_y}{s_x} \quad \text{and} \quad b_0 = \bar{y} - b_1\bar{x}.$$

**(a)** For 2003, $b_1 = -0.068 \cdot \frac{7.00}{7.65} \doteq -0.0622$ and $b_0 = 89.06 - b_1 \cdot 13.50 \doteq 89.90$.

**(b)** For 2004, $b_1 = 0.094 \cdot \frac{4.772}{7.65} \doteq 0.0586$ and $b_0 = 86.761 - b_1 \cdot 13.50 \doteq 85.97$.

**(c)** For 2003 reporting dates, the percent reporting for jury duty *decreases* by 0.0622 for each unit increase in reporting date. For 2004 reporting dates, the percent reporting *increases* by 0.0586 for each unit increase in reporting date. **(d)** The slopes are fairly similar—one is negative and one is positive, but both are rather close to 0. Over 26 two-week periods, the percent reporting changes by −1.6% (2003 slope) or +1.5% (2004 slope); both of those changes are small relative to the intercept. **(e)** Because the slopes are similar, a multiple regression model with equal slopes would appear to be acceptable in this case. (Note, however, that there is some suggestion in the scatterplot that the 2003 scatter might be greater than the 2004 scatter.) **(f)** The slopes in 1998 and 2000 (−0.668 and −0.766) are substantially greater (more negative) than the 2003 slope. **(g)** The commissioner should be quite happy. His modifications appear to have had two positive results: more potential jurors are reporting (all percents in 2003 and 2004 are greater than 75%), and there is less variation over the course of the year (the slopes are close to 0).

**28.6.** **(a)** The model is $\mu_y = \beta_0 + \beta_1 x_1 + \beta_2 x_2$, where $y$ is height, $x_1$ is weight, and $x_2$ is an indicator variable for gender—either 0 for boys and 1 for girls, or vice versa. In this model, $\beta_1$ is the slope (the rate at which height changes in response to changes in weight), $\beta_0$ is the intercept for boys (or girls), and $\beta_0 + \beta_2$ is the intercept for girls (or boys). **(b)** Three columns would be needed, containing height, weight, and the gender indicator variable.

**28.7.** **(a)** The regression formula is $\hat{y} = 18.1 - 5.41x_1 + 0.848x_2$. **(b)** Because $b_2 = 0.848$ is positive, we can conclude that nestling mass was higher for exposed nests. (This might not have been true for for all nests, but it holds on average.) **(c)** The regression standard error is $s = 1.01583$; this is our estimate of the degree of scatter about the regression formula. **(d)** The squared multiple correlation coefficient is "R-sq" in the Minitab output: $R^2 = 47.7\% = 0.477$. This tells us that the regression formula explains about 47.7% of the variation in nestling mass.

**28.8.** **(a)** The slope $b \doteq 0.82179$ is our estimate of $\beta$. The intercept 1.28071 estimates the log of $\alpha$, so our estimate of $\alpha$ is $10^{1.28071} \doteq 19.0858$. **(b)** Student opinions may vary. The primary cause for concern is that the histogram of residuals appears to be left-skewed. **(c)** The model explains $R^2 = 93.7\%$ of the variation in log(MR). **(d)** Note that there were $n = 209$ observations. The 95% confidence interval is $b \pm t^*\text{SE}_b$, where $b \doteq 0.82179$, $\text{SE}_b \doteq 0.01477$, and $t^* = 1.984$ (from Table C with df = 100), 1.9715 (from software with df = 207), or 1.96 (for students who use a Normal distribution). This gives 0.7925 to 0.8511, 0.7927 to 0.8509, or 0.7928 to 0.8507. **(e)** Neither $\frac{2}{3}$ nor $\frac{3}{4}$ is contained in this interval. **(f)** To test this hypothesis against a two-sided alternative, we take $t = \frac{b - 2/3}{\text{SE}_b} = \frac{0.82179 - 2/3}{0.01477} \doteq 10.5$. This value of $t$ is so large that we know the $P$-value is tiny even without consulting software or Table C, so we have very strong evidence against $\beta$

being different from $\frac{2}{3}$. **(g)** Now $t = \frac{b - 3/4}{\text{SE}_b} = \frac{0.82179 - 3/4}{0.01477} \doteq 4.86$. Again, this value of $t$ is quite large, and the $P$-value is quite small (software gives $P \doteq 0.0000023$), so we have very strong evidence against $\beta$ being different from $\frac{3}{4}$.

**Note:** *Of course, our interval from part (d)—and specifically, the observation made in part (e)—told us that the tests in (f) and (g) would be significant.*

**28.9.** **(a)** The 95% confidence interval is $b_1 \pm t^*\text{SE}_{b_1}$, where $b_1 \doteq 0.69828$, $\text{SE}_{b_1} \doteq 0.02628$, and $t^* = 1.984$ (from Table C with df $= 100$), 1.9715 (from software with df $= 206$), or 1.96 (for students who use a Normal distribution). This gives 0.6461 to 0.7504, 0.6465 to 0.7501, or 0.6468 to 0.7498. **(b)** Use the same interval: under this model, the lines are parallel, so the slope is the same. **(c)** Both $\frac{2}{3}$ and $\frac{3}{4}$ should be in both intervals. (For students who used $t^* = 1.96$, $\frac{3}{4}$ is barely outside the interval.) **(d)** Compared to the interval in the previous exercise, this interval has a larger margin of error, and is lower (the upper limit of this interval is less than the lower limit of the previous interval). **(e)** To test this hypothesis against a two-sided alternative, we take $t = \frac{b - 2/3}{\text{SE}_b} = \frac{0.69828 - 2/3}{0.02628} \doteq 1.20$. This value of $t$ is clearly too small to be significant (software tells us that $P \doteq 0.2304$, so we have little reason to doubt that $\beta = \frac{2}{3}$). **(f)** Now $t = \frac{b - 3/4}{\text{SE}_b} = \frac{0.69828 - 3/4}{0.02628} \doteq -1.97$, and $P \doteq 0.0504$. This is fairly strong evidence that $\beta$ is different from $\frac{3}{4}$, although it is not quite significant at the 5% level.

**Note:** *Of course, our interval from part (a)—and specifically, the observation made in part (c)—told us that the tests in (e) and (f) would not be significant.*

**28.10.** **(a)** Except for the number of reported digits, the two values agree: Minitab reports 6.70905, and CrunchIt! reports 6.7090526. This is our estimate of the degree of scatter about the regression formula. **(b)** The regression model explains about 71.9% of the variation in reporting percent. **(c)** In either output, the answer to this question is found in the $P$-value on the line labeled "Group": 0.000 (Minitab) or $P < 0.0001$ (CrunchIt!). We have strong evidence that $\beta_1$ is different from 0. **(d)** The 98% confidence interval is $b_1 \pm t^*\text{SE}_{b_1}$, where $b_1 = -0.7168$, $\text{SE}_{b_1} \doteq 0.1241$, and $t^* = 2.423$ (from Table C with df $= 40$) or 2.4049 (from software with df $= 49$). This gives either $-1.0174$ to $-0.4162$ or $-1.0151$ to $-0.4185$. (These come from the more accurate value of $\text{SE}_{b_1}$ given by CrunchIt!; using the Minitab standard error, the intervals are slightly different: $-1.0175$ to $-0.4161$ or $-1.0152$ to $-0.4184$.) **(e)** The $P$-value for "Ind2000" is very small, indicating strong evidence that $\beta_2$ is not zero. Because $\beta_2$ is the difference between the two intercepts, we conclude that the intercepts are different.

**28.11.** The model is $\mu_y = \beta_0 + \beta_1 x_1 + \beta_2 x_2 + \beta_3 x_1 x_2$. $\beta_0$ and $\beta_1$ are the intercept and slope for the first species (when $x_2 = 0$), and $(\beta_0 + \beta_2)$ and $(\beta_1 + \beta_3)$ are the intercept and slope for the other species (when $x_2 = 1$).

**28.12.** This is the same question as was asked in Exercise 28.2. The simplest interpretation of this exercise is that $x_2$ is equal to either 10 or 20 cm, in which case the model would be

$$\mu_y = 0.15x_1 + x_2.$$

Some students might treat $x_2$ as an indicator variable (0 for 10-cm icicles, 1 for 20-cm icicles), so their model would be

$$\mu_y = 10 + 0.15x_1 + 10x_2.$$

**28.13.** The realistic restriction (time $= y = 0$ when $x_1 = 0$) means that the intercept $\beta_0$ of our model should be 0. Recalling the algebra formula *distance* $=$ *rate* $\cdot$ *time*, we note that a trip of $x_1$ miles at speed $s$ mph takes $x_1/s$ hours. Therefore, we need a line with slope $\frac{1}{20}$ for buses, and a line with slope $\frac{1}{28}$ for autos. If $x_2$ is the indicator of transportation type (0 for bus, 1 for auto), then the model is

$$\mu_y = \frac{1}{20}x_1 + \left(\frac{1}{28} - \frac{1}{20}\right)x_1x_2 = \frac{1}{20}x_1 - \frac{1}{70}x_1x_2.$$

If $x_2$ is the other way around (1 for bus, 0 for auto), then the model is

$$\mu_y = \frac{1}{28}x_1 - \left(\frac{1}{20} - \frac{1}{28}\right)x_1x_2 = \frac{1}{28}x_1 + \frac{1}{70}x_1x_2.$$

**28.14. (a)** When more than half take the SAT (ind_half = 0), the model is

$$\widehat{\text{SATV}} = 513.7567 - 0.1161\ \text{PCT}.$$

**(b)** When at most half take the SAT (ind_half = 1), the model is

$$\widehat{\text{SATV}} = (513.7567 + 74.6677) - (0.1161 + 1.7953)\ \text{PCT}$$
$$= 588.4244 - 1.9114\ \text{PCT}.$$

**(c)** ANOVA ($F = 110.96$, $P < 0.0001$) gives strong evidence that the model is useful; that is, at least one of the coefficients (apart from the intercept) is nonzero. **(d)** The model explains $R^2 = 87.63\%$ of the variation in mean SATV scores. **(e)** The $t$ distribution has df $= 47$ (from the "Error" row of the ANOVA table, or using the formula df $= n - 4$, because the model had 4 parameters to estimate). **(f)** The estimate of $\sigma$ is given in the CrunchIt! output as "Root MSE": $s = 12.279312$. **(g)** The scatterplot is shown below on the left. **(h)** The plot of residuals against fitted values (below, right) shows no particular reason for concern. **(i)** A stemplot of residuals is shown; a histogram could also be used. The distribution looks reasonably Normal.

| Stem | Leaves |
|---|---|
| −2 | 8 |
| −2 | |
| −1 | 9655 |
| −1 | 44100 |
| −0 | 99776666655 |
| −0 | 4444432 |
| 0 | 0334 |
| 0 | 56999 |
| 1 | 0112344 |
| 1 | 557779 |
| 2 | 0 |

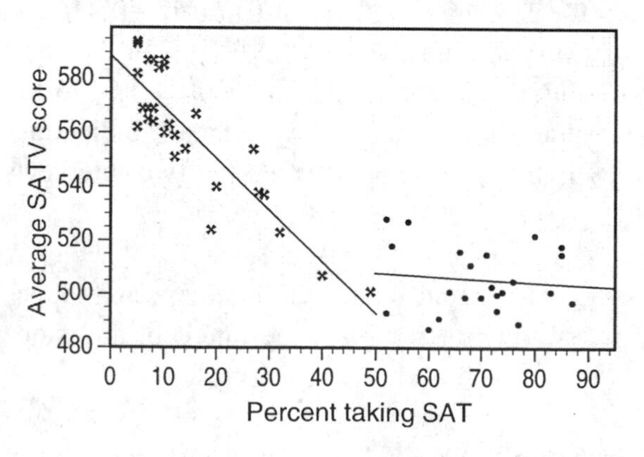


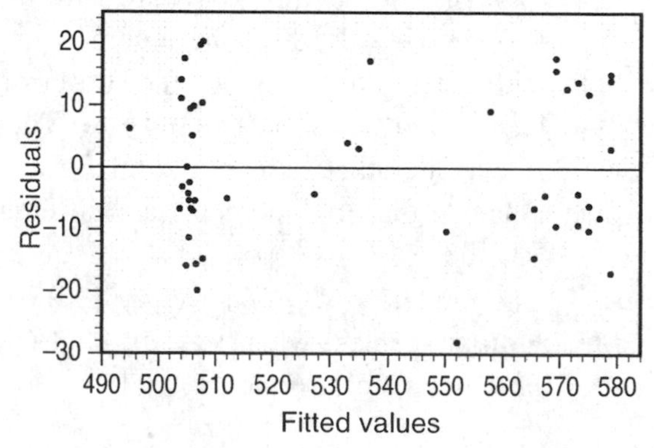

**28.15.** Note that this data set also appears in Exercise 4.25. **(a)** Both men (filled circles) and women (open circles) show fairly steady improvement. Women have made more rapid progress, but their progress seems to have slowed, while men's records may be dropping more rapidly in recent years. **(b)** The two regression formulas are

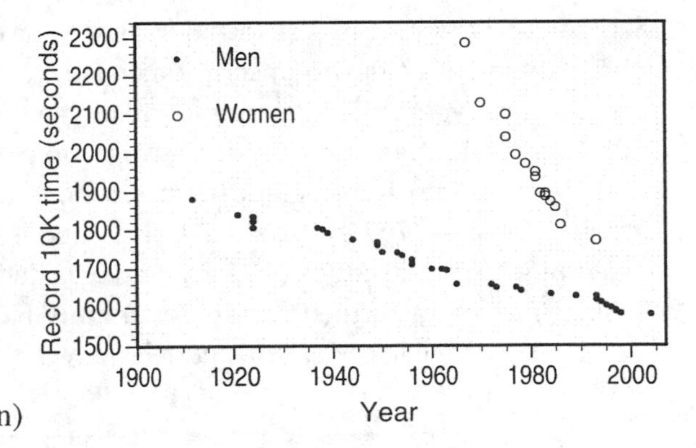


$\widehat{\text{RECORD}} = 8126.6 - 3.2720 \text{ YEAR}$ (men)

$\widehat{\text{RECORD}} = 41373 - 19.905 \text{ YEAR}$ (women)

These can be found as two separate regressions (one for men and one for women), or as a multiple regression model with an indicator variable for gender and an interaction term. **(c)** The data support the first claim (the women's line is much steeper), but do not seem to support the second.

**Note:** *Some software—like the version of Minitab used to prepare these solutions—is reluctant to perform the multiple regression because gender and gender*year are highly correlated (see the output below, in which gender* = 0 *for men and 1 for women). Exercise 28.26 calls for the ANOVA table for the multiple regression; check whether your software will perform this computation before assigning this exercise.*

**Minitab output**

```
* NOTE *   gender is highly correlated with other  predictor variables
* NOTE *   gen*yr is highly correlated with other  predictor variables

The regression equation is
   record = 8127 - 3.27 year + 33247 gender - 16.6 gen*yr

Predictor        Coef       Stdev    t-ratio       p
Constant       8126.6       268.2      30.30   0.000
year          -3.2720      0.1366     -23.95   0.000
gender          33247        1734      19.17   0.000
gen*yr       -16.6326      0.8759     -18.99   0.000

s = 21.17         R-sq = 98.3%      R-sq(adj) = 98.2%
```

**28.16.** The model is $\mu_y = \beta_0 + \beta_1 x_1 + \beta_2 x_2 + \beta_3 x_1 x_2$, where $y$ is height, $x_1$ is weight, and $x_2$ is an indicator variable for gender—either 0 for boys and 1 for girls, or vice versa. In this model, $\beta_1$ is the slope (the rate at which height changes in response to changes in weight), $\beta_0$ is the intercept for boys (or girls), and $\beta_0 + \beta_2$ is the intercept for girls (or boys). $\beta_0$ and $\beta_1$ are the intercept and slope for the boys (or girls), and $(\beta_0 + \beta_2)$ and $(\beta_1 + \beta_3)$ are the intercept and slope for girls (or boys).

**28.17.** Based on the description, the model is $\mu_{\sqrt{y}} = \beta_0 + \beta_1 x + \beta_2 x^2$. (Students might try to express the model in terms of $y$ rather than $\sqrt{y}$, but that overcomplicates the model: it means squaring the quadratic expression to obtain a fourth-degree polynomial, in which the five coefficients are derived from the three coefficients in the model above.)

**28.18.** $\mu_{\text{Price}} = \beta_0 + \beta_1 \text{ CARAT} + \beta_2 \text{ CUT} + \beta_3 \text{ CARAT} * \text{CUT}$.

**28.19.** **(a)** Scatterplot is shown below on the left. **(b)** The quadratic regression equation gives the estimated mean response at time $t$: $\mu_{\text{count}} = 2002.9 - 5.2725t + 0.003180t^2$ (Minitab output below). **(c)** The quadratic model does a poor job of approximating the points of the scatterplot, and is therefore a poor choice for prediction. **(d)** This scatterplot is below on the right. **(e)** Regressing the natural logarithm of the counts on time gives the line $\widehat{\text{LogCount}} = 7.3767 - 0.004521t$. This line is shown on the second scatterplot below. A stemplot of the residuals and a plot of residuals versus fitted values are also shown. **(f)** The linear fit to transformed counts is certainly better than the quadratic model, but the residual plots show that it is far from perfect.

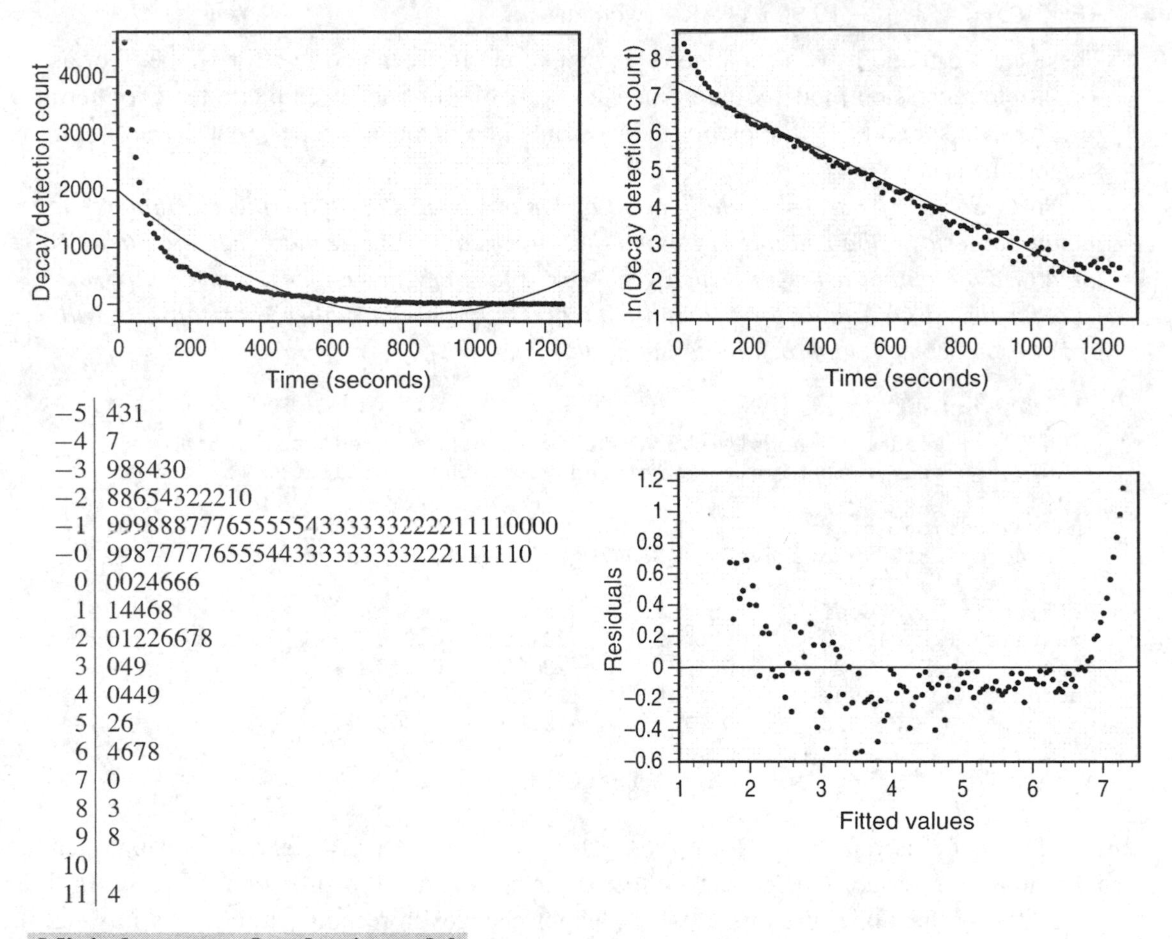


| Stem | Leaves |
|---|---|
| −5 | 431 |
| −4 | 7 |
| −3 | 988430 |
| −2 | 88654322210 |
| −1 | 9998887776555554333333222211110000 |
| −0 | 99877777655544333333333222111110 |
| 0 | 0024666 |
| 1 | 14468 |
| 2 | 01226678 |
| 3 | 049 |
| 4 | 0449 |
| 5 | 26 |
| 6 | 4678 |
| 7 | 0 |
| 8 | 3 |
| 9 | 8 |
| 10 | |
| 11 | 4 |

**Minitab output: Quadratic model**

```
The regression equation is count = 2003 - 5.27 seconds + 0.00318 secsqd

Predictor        Coef        Stdev    t-ratio       p
Constant       2002.9        115.6      17.33   0.000
seconds       -5.2725       0.4196     -12.57   0.000
secsqd      0.0031798    0.0003204       9.92   0.000
```

**Linear model on transformed data**

```
The regression equation is logcnt = 7.38 - 0.00452 seconds

Predictor        Coef        Stdev    t-ratio       p
Constant      7.37666      0.05482     134.56   0.000
seconds   -0.00452103   0.00007520     -60.12   0.000
```

**28.20. (a)** The regression equation is

$$\widehat{\text{SATV}} = 575.625 - 1.0133\ \text{PCT}$$

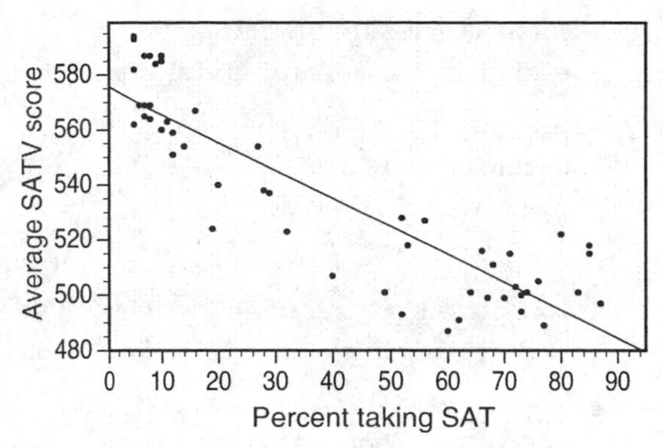


(Minitab output below). **(b)** The scatterplot on the right shows this line. **(c)** $R^2 = 79.0\%$ is reasonably large, but the line does not fit the points very well. Residual plots are not shown, but from the scatterplot on the right we see that the points generally lie above the line on the left and right, and they lie below the line in the middle. (In other words, the residuals are first positive, then negative, then positive again.) **(d)** The equations (as given in the CrunchIt! output shown in Exercise 28.14) are

$$\widehat{\text{SATV}} = 513.7567 - 0.1161\ \text{PCT} \quad \text{when more than half take the SAT, and}$$

$$\widehat{\text{SATV}} = (513.7567 + 74.6677) - (0.1161 + 1.7953)\ \text{PCT}$$

$$= 588.4244 - 1.9114\ \text{PCT} \quad \text{when at most half take the SAT.}$$

The solution to Exercise 28.14 includes a scatterplot showing both lines. The parameter estimates, $t$-statistics, and $P$-values (as given in the CrunchIt! output) are:

| Variable | Estimate | Std. Err. | $t$ | $P$-value |
|---|---|---|---|---|
| Intercept | 513.7567 | 17.361177 | 29.592272 | < 0.0001 |
| Pct | −0.11606738 | 0.24591577 | −0.4719802 | 0.6391 |
| ind_half | 74.66769 | 17.782257 | 4.1989994 | 0.0001 |
| ind_half*pct | −1.7953479 | 0.32017267 | −5.6074367 | < 0.0001 |

**(e)** The tests on the model from part (d) suggest that the coefficient of "Pct" is not significantly different from 0. Dropping that term from the model leaves $\mu_y = \beta_0 + \beta_2 x_2 + \beta_3 x_1 x_2$, for which regression gives the equations

$$\widehat{\text{SATV}} = 505.652 \quad \text{when more than half take the SAT, and}$$

$$\widehat{\text{SATV}} = (505.652 + 82.772) - 1.9114\ \text{PCT}$$

$$= 588.424 - 1.9114\ \text{PCT} \quad \text{when at most half take the SAT.}$$

This model seems to be the best: all coefficients are significantly different from 0 (see the Minitab output below), and $R^2 = 87.6\%$ is nearly identical to the model in (d). Residual plots (not shown) show no particular cause for concern.

**Linear regression model**

```
The regression equation is satv = 576 - 1.01 Pct

Predictor       Coef       Stdev    t-ratio       p
Constant     575.625       3.684     156.24   0.000
Pct         -1.01328     0.07457     -13.59   0.000

s = 15.66         R-sq = 79.0%      R-sq(adj) = 78.6%
```

**Multiple regression model without "Pct"**

```
The regression equation is satv = 506 + 82.8 ind_half - 1.91 half*pct

Predictor       Coef       Stdev    t-ratio       p
Constant     505.652       2.540     199.11   0.000
ind_half      82.772       4.583      18.06   0.000
half*pct     -1.9114      0.2034      -9.40   0.000

s = 12.18         R-sq = 87.6%      R-sq(adj) = 87.1%
```

**28.21. (a)** Body fat $y$ and waist size $x_1$ should be positively correlated, because large (small) values of one variable tend to go with large (small) values of the other; that is, people with high (low) body fat will typically have larger (smaller) waists. **(b)** In general, among men with the same waist size but different amounts of body fat, we would expect taller men to have lower body fat. (For example, we expect a 6-foot 6-inch man with a 40-inch waist to be carrying less fat than a 5-foot 6-inch man with the same waist size.) **(c)** With both variables in the model, we would expect the coefficient of height ($x_2$) to be negative, because the presence of waist size ($x_1$) would allow the model to give separate predictions for men of varying heights with a fixed waist size, as was discussed in part (b).

**28.22. (a)** Solve the first equation for $x_2$: $x_1 + 4 = 2x_2$, so $x_2 = \frac{1}{2}x_1 + 2$. Therefore,

$$y = 3x_2 + 4 = 3\left(\frac{1}{2}x_1 + 2\right) + 4 = \frac{3}{2}x_1 + 10,$$

so $y$ and $x_1$ are positively correlated. **(b)** Adding the equations gives $x_1 + y = 5x_2$, so $y = -x_1 + 5x_2$. The coefficient of $x_1$ is negative.

**28.23. (a)** The regression equation is $\widehat{\text{PRICE}} = -28408 + 766\,\text{DEPTH} - 3.23\,\text{DEPTH}^2$.

**(b)** For this model, $R^2 = 4.7\%$—much smaller than the 92.6% for the quadratic model based on the carat weight of the diamond. While this exercise did not ask for a scatterplot, the one on the right clearly illustrates that there is little association between these variables; no model using only depth could predict price well.

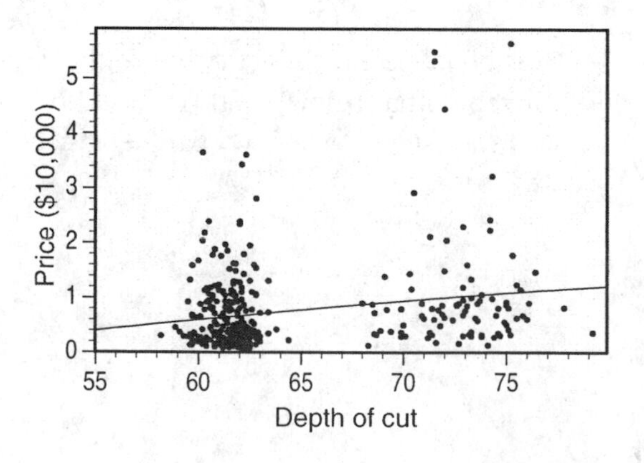

**Minitab output**

```
The regression equation is price = - 28408 + 766 depth - 3.2 depthsqd

Predictor      Coef     Stdev   t-ratio      p
Constant     -28408    112212     -0.25  0.800
depth           766      3353      0.23  0.819
depthsqd      -3.23     24.87     -0.13  0.897

s = 7616       R-sq = 4.7%      R-sq(adj) = 4.2%
```

**28.24. (a)** The regression equation is given in the first Minitab output below. **(b)** With this formula, we estimate tuition and fees in 1961 to have been \$505. **(c)** This estimate is clearly too low—it is unreasonable to believe that the tuition and fees in 1961 were lower than in any other year, and only one-fourth of the 1960 tuition and fees. **(d)** The residual plot (right) shows that the linear fit is inadequate: The residuals are negative from 1964 to 1992 and positive elsewhere. **(e)** This model underestimates actual tuition and fees starting in 1992. (A positive residual means that the actual value is greater than the predicted value.) **(f)** The quadratic regression formula is given in the second Minitab output below. **(g)** The quadratic model fits much better ($R^2 = 99.6\%$ and $s = 722.2$ instead of $R^2 = 85.8\%$ and $s = 4390$). The smaller standard deviation means that the fitted values for this model are generally closer to the actual values (most differ by less than \$1000). **(h)** An examination of the residuals suggests that the conditions for inference are not met—especially Normality (the distribution is bimodal) and independence (the residuals still show a pattern of rising and falling over time).

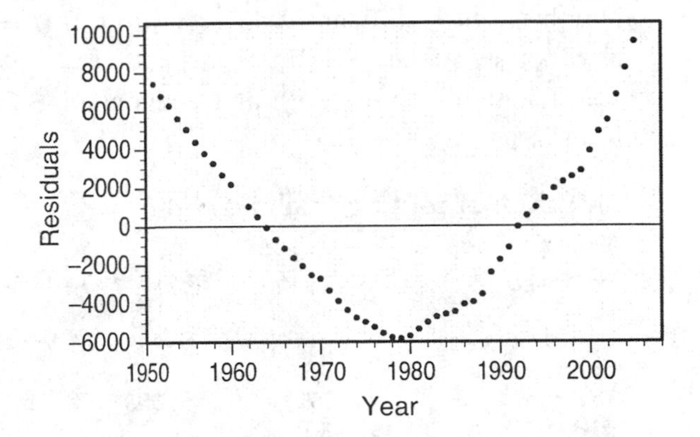


**Minitab output: Linear model**

```
The regression equation is tuition = - 1308548 + 668 year

Predictor       Coef     Stdev   t-ratio      p
Constant    -1308548     74567    -17.55  0.000
year          667.54     37.69     17.71  0.000

s = 4390       R-sq = 85.8%      R-sq(adj) = 85.5%
```

**Quadratic model**

```
The regression equation is tuition =71847488 - 73306 year + 18.7 yearsqd

Predictor       Coef     Stdev   t-ratio      p
Constant    71847488   1691656     42.47  0.000
year          -73306      1711    -42.86  0.000
yearsqd      18.6989    0.4324     43.25  0.000

s = 722.2      R-sq = 99.6%      R-sq(adj) = 99.6%
```

**28.25. (a)** The regression equation is in the first Minitab output below. **(b)** This model explains $R^2 = 93.7\%$ of the variation in weight. **(c)** The ANOVA table ($F = 396.10$, $P < 0.0005$) gives strong evidence that at least one of $\beta_1$ and $\beta_2$ is not zero. **(d)** The $t$ tests ($t = 2.53$ and $P = 0.014$ for length, $t = 3.75$ and $P < 0.0005$ for width) suggest that both coefficients are not zero. **(e)** The new regression equation is in the second Minitab output below. **(f)** This model explains $R^2 = 98.5\%$ of the variation in weight. **(g)** The ANOVA table ($F = 1114.68$, $P < 0.0005$) gives strong evidence that at least one of the three coefficients is not zero. **(h)** With the addition of an interaction term to the model, the coefficient of length is not significantly different from 0 ($t = -1.10$, $P = 0.274$). In fact, the intercept is also not significantly different from 0 ($t = 1.94$, $P = 0.058$). Furthermore, the estimated coefficients of both length and width change from positive to negative when the interaction term is added.

**Minitab output: length and width**

```
The regression equation is
  weight = - 579 + 14.3 length + 113 width

Predictor       Coef       Stdev    t-ratio       p
Constant     -578.76       43.67     -13.25   0.000
length        14.307       5.659       2.53   0.014
width         113.50       30.26       3.75   0.000

s = 88.68         R-sq = 93.7%     R-sq(adj) = 93.5%

Analysis of Variance

SOURCE       DF          SS          MS         F        p
Regression    2     6229333     3114666    396.10    0.000
Error        53      416762        7863
Total        55     6646094
```

**length, width, and length*width**

```
The regression equation is
  weight = 114 - 3.48 length - 94.6 width + 5.24 interact

Predictor       Coef       Stdev    t-ratio       p
Constant      113.93       58.78       1.94   0.058
length        -3.483       3.152      -1.10   0.274
width         -94.63       22.30      -4.24   0.000
interact      5.2412      0.4131      12.69   0.000

s = 44.24         R-sq = 98.5%     R-sq(adj) = 98.4%

Analysis of Variance

SOURCE       DF          SS          MS         F        p
Regression    3     6544329     2181443   1114.68    0.000
Error        52      101765        1957
Total        55     6646094
```

**28.26.** **(a)** The ANOVA table is below. Some software—like the version of Minitab used to prepare these solutions—is reluctant to perform the multiple regression because gender and gender*year are highly correlated. Check whether your software will perform this computation before assigning this exercise. **(b)** All coefficients are significantly different from zero (see the test statistics and $P$-values in the Minitab output below). As given in the solution to Exercise 28.15, the two lines are

$$\widehat{\text{RECORD}} = 8126.6 - 3.2720\ \text{YEAR} \quad \text{(men)}$$
$$\widehat{\text{RECORD}} = 41373 - 19.905\ \text{YEAR} \quad \text{(women)}$$

In the context of this problem, we see that the men's record is decreasing at an average rate of about 3.3 seconds per year, and women's record is decreasing at an average rate of about 19.9 seconds per year.

**Minitab output**

```
The regression equation is
   record = 8127 - 3.27 year + 33247 gender - 16.6 gen*yr

Predictor        Coef       Stdev    t-ratio       p
Constant       8126.6       268.2      30.30   0.000
year          -3.2720      0.1366     -23.95   0.000
gender          33247        1734      19.17   0.000
gen*yr       -16.6326      0.8759     -18.99   0.000

s = 21.17       R-sq = 98.3%     R-sq(adj) = 98.2%

Analysis of Variance

SOURCE       DF        SS          MS         F        p
Regression    3    1194832     398277    888.37    0.000
Error        47      21071        448
Total        50    1215903
```

**28.27.** Shown below are the Minitab fits, confidence intervals, and prediction intervals for the first 10 fish, using the second model found in Exercise 28.25. (The Minitab command used to produce these intervals also produced results for the other 46 fish, but they are not shown here.) These intervals were created using a $t$ distribution with df $= 52$.

In particular, for the tenth fish, the fitted value is 84.02 g. We are 95% confident that the mean weight of all such fish (length 21 cm, width 2.8 cm) is between 63.12 and 104.91 g, and we are 95% confident that an individual fish would weigh between $-7.20$ and 175.23 g. (The lower limit of the prediction interval is nonsense, so we should report it as 0 g.)

**Minitab output**

```
    Fit  Stdev.Fit        95.0% C.I.            95.0% P.I.
  15.38      29.05   ( -42.94,    73.69)  (  -90.85,   121.60) XX
  27.57      17.30   (  -7.15,    62.29)  (  -67.77,   122.91)
  32.36      13.64   (   4.97,    59.75)  (  -60.56,   125.28)
  42.38      11.74   (  18.83,    65.93)  (  -49.48,   134.24)
  56.27      10.04   (  36.11,    76.42)  (  -34.78,   147.32)
  66.87      11.12   (  44.55,    89.19)  (  -24.68,   158.42)
  68.22       9.38   (  49.40,    87.05)  (  -22.54,   158.99)
  78.44       8.49   (  61.39,    95.48)  (  -11.98,   168.85)
  84.66       8.58   (  67.44,   101.87)  (   -5.79,   175.10)
  84.02      10.41   (  63.12,   104.91)  (   -7.20,   175.23)
 ...
XX denotes a row with very extreme X values
```

**28.28. (a)** Minitab output for both models is shown below for comparison. The new model has $R^2 = 94.0\%$, the same (up to rounding) as the final model developed in the text. **(b)** The new variable has $t = 0.15$ ($P = 0.881$). The other $t$ statistics (and the coefficients) changed very little from the previous model. **(c)** The new variable adds almost nothing to the accuracy of the prediction; the final model from the text is better.

**Final model from Example 28.24**

```
The regression equation is
   amount = 32.3 + 0.563 Purch12 + 0.00253 Pur12sq - 0.0181 IntRec12

Predictor        Coef        Stdev     t-ratio       p
Constant       32.302        9.851        3.28   0.002
Purch12        0.5633       0.1698        3.32   0.002
Pur12sq     0.0025257    0.0004205        6.01   0.000
IntRec12    -0.018137     0.006603       -2.75   0.008

s = 28.33          R-sq = 94.0%      R-sq(adj) = 93.6%
```

**Model with Purchase12b added**

```
The regression equation is
   amount = 31.4 + 0.565 Purch12 + 0.00252 Pur12sq - 0.0180 IntRec12
           + 0.0090 Purch12b

Predictor        Coef        Stdev     t-ratio       p
Constant        31.40        11.63        2.70   0.009
Purch12        0.5649       0.1717        3.29   0.002
Pur12sq     0.0025162    0.0004292        5.86   0.000
IntRec12    -0.017995     0.006733       -2.67   0.010
Purch12b      0.00902      0.06007        0.15   0.881

s = 28.60          R-sq = 94.0%      R-sq(adj) = 93.5%
```

**28.29.** Both scatterplots suggest nonconstant standard deviation: the residuals are more widely scattered for large values of Purchase12 and for small values of Recency.

**28.30.** The scatterplot suggests greater variation for lower predicted values, so the constant standard deviation condition might not hold. The histogram reveals one very high residual, and suggests a right skew—possible indicators of non-Normality.

**28.31.** (a) There are four parameters (a constant term, and the coefficients of MPH, Ind_slow, and Incline).

**28.32.** (a) Use the numbers in the "Coef" column.

**28.33.** (b) This is "S = 33.9422" in the Minitab output.

**28.34.** (b) Use the regression formula with Ind_slow = 1 and Incline = 0.

**28.35.** (a) Use the regression formula with Ind_slow = 0 and Incline = 0.

**28.36.** (c) Use the regression formula with Ind_slow = 0 and Incline = 2.

**28.37.** (b) $\beta_1$ is the coefficient of MPH in the model (estimated to be 145.84). "More calories are burned for higher speeds" means that this coefficient is positive.

**28.38.** (b) This is the "Error" degrees of freedom in the ANOVA table. Alternatively, there were $n = 54$ data points and 4 parameters, so df $= 54 - 4 = 50$.

**28.39.** (a) Use the prediction interval (labeled "PI") given in the Minitab output, because we are estimating calories burned for one particular run on the treadmill.

**28.40.** (b) We now have five parameters: a constant, and four coefficients (one for each explanatory variable).

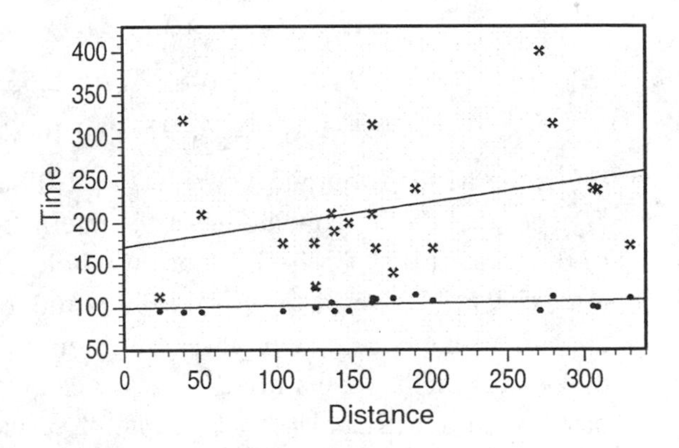


**28.41. (a)** The model is $\mu_y = \beta_0 + \beta_1$ DIST $+ \beta_2$ HAND $+ \beta_3$ DIST $*$ HAND, where HAND is an indicator variable for which hand is being used (either 1 for right and 0 for left, or vice versa). In this model, $\beta_0$ and $\beta_1$ are the intercept and slope for one hand (when HAND $=$ 0), while $\beta_0 + \beta_2$ and $\beta_1 + \beta_3$ are the intercept and slope for the other hand (when HAND $=$ 1). **(b)** The equation is given in the Minitab output below (where hand $=$ 1 for right hand); this model explains $R^2 = 59.8\%$ of the variation in time. **(c)** The two equations are

$$\widehat{\text{TIME}} = 171.55 + 0.2619\text{ DIST} \qquad \text{for the left hand, and}$$

$$\widehat{\text{TIME}} = (171.55 - 72.18) + (0.2619 - 0.2336)\text{ DIST}$$
$$= 99.37 + 0.0283\text{ DIST} \qquad \text{for the right hand.}$$

(To find these, replace "hand" in the equation with 0 and then with 1.) In the scatterplot, right-hand points are shown as dots, while left-hand points are shown as crosses.

**Minitab output**

```
The regression equation is
   time = 172 + 0.262 distance - 72.2 hand - 0.234 dist*hand

Predictor        Coef        Stdev    t-ratio        p
Constant       171.55        25.25       6.79    0.000
distance       0.2619       0.1308       2.00    0.053
hand           -72.18        35.71      -2.02    0.051
dist*hand     -0.2336       0.1850      -1.26    0.215

s = 50.61        R-sq = 59.8%       R-sq(adj) = 56.4%

Analysis of Variance

SOURCE        DF         SS          MS          F        p
Regression     3     136949       45650      17.82    0.000
Error         36      92198        2561
Total         39     229146
```

**28.42. (a)** In the scatterplot, large banks are dots and small banks are crosses. **(b)** It does appear that a parallel-lines model might be reasonable, because both groups of points seem to have about the same slope. **(c)** To test for parallel slopes, we fit a multiple regression model with interaction, then test the coefficient of the interaction term. (If it is zero, then the two lines have the same slope.) The Minitab output below gives the fitted model (where IndSmall = 1 for small banks); it leads to the two equations

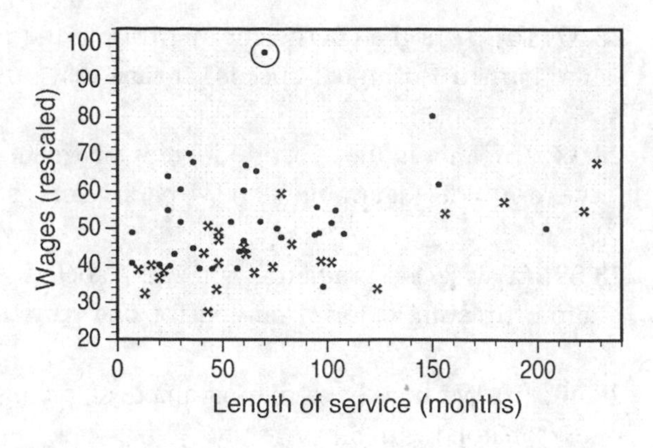


$$\widehat{\text{WAGES}} = 48.447 + 0.05286\ \text{LOS} \qquad \text{for large banks, and}$$
$$\widehat{\text{WAGES}} = (48.447 - 12.533) + (0.05286 + 0.05138)\ \text{LOS}$$
$$= 35.914 + 0.10424\ \text{LOS} \qquad \text{for small banks.}$$

From the Minitab output, we read $t = 1.08$ and $P = 0.285$ for testing $H_0$: $\beta_3 = 0$ versus $H_a$: $\beta_3 \neq 0$, so we conclude that the interaction term does not make a significant contribution to the model; that is, the lines are parallel. (According to these $t$ tests, LOS could also be removed, but if we fit the parallel lines model, this coefficient is significant.) **(d)** Inference appears to be safe: a stemplot (or histogram) of the residuals appears to be Normal, and a plot of residuals versus fitted values does not reveal any major problems. (Other residual plots, such as residuals versus length of service, also appear to be fine.)

| Stem | Leaves |
|---|---|
| −1 | 95 |
| −1 | 2211 |
| −0 | 99987765555 |
| −0 | 4444444322100 |
| 0 | 00001111122223 |
| 0 | 555888 |
| 1 | 0034 |
| 1 | 557 |
| 2 | 04 |

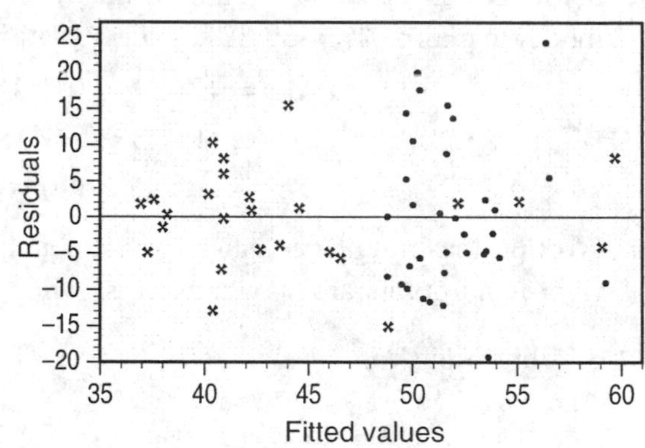


**Minitab output**

```
The regression equation is
   wages = 48.4 + 0.0529 los - 12.5 IndSmall + 0.0514 Small*los

Predictor         Coef        Stdev    t-ratio        p
Constant        48.447        2.863      16.92    0.000
los            0.05286      0.03639       1.45    0.152
IndSmall       -12.533        4.154      -3.02    0.004
Small*los      0.05138      0.04759       1.08    0.285

s = 9.259         R-sq = 30.6%     R-sq(adj) = 26.8%
```

**28.43.** **(a)** In the scatterplot, Pasadena temperatures are dots and Redding temperatures are crosses. **(b)** A parallel-lines model does not appear to be appropriate, because Pasadena temperatures rise more than Redding temperatures. **(c)** To test for parallel slopes, we fit a multiple regression model with interaction, then test the coefficient of the interaction term. (If it is zero, then the two lines have the same slope.) The Minitab output below gives the fitted model (where IndRedd = 1 for Redding); it leads to the two equations

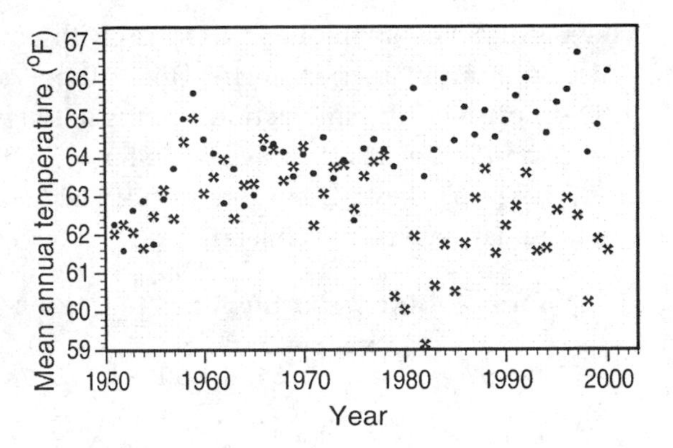


$$\widehat{\text{TEMP}} = -48.86 + 0.05726 \text{ YEAR} \quad \text{for Pasadena and}$$

$$\widehat{\text{TEMP}} = (-48.86 + 175.16) + (0.05726 - 0.08950) \text{ YEAR}$$

$$= 126.3 - 0.03224 \text{ YEAR} \quad \text{for Redding.}$$

From the Minitab output, we read $t = -6.21$ and $P < 0.0005$ for testing $H_0$: $\beta_3 = 0$ versus $H_a$: $\beta_3 \neq 0$, so we conclude that the interaction term is important to the model; that is, the lines are not parallel. **(d)** Inference appears to be safe: a stemplot (or histogram) of the residuals appears to be Normal (apart from a moderate low outlier), and a plot of residuals versus fitted values does not reveal any major problems. (Other residual plots, such as residuals versus year, also appear to be fine.)

```
-3 | 2
-2 |
-2 | 41
-1 | 87666
-1 | 4333210
-0 | 877766666665555
-0 | 44444333332221110000
 0 | 00001112333334444
 0 | 5555555667789999
 1 | 011222333
 1 | 5555679
 2 | 3
```

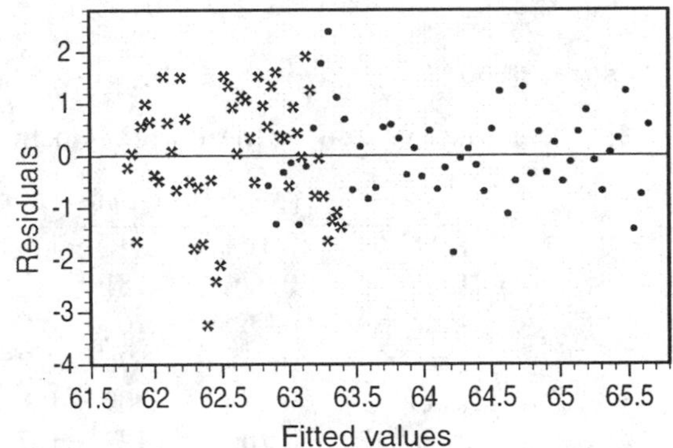


**Minitab output**

```
The regression equation is
   temp = - 48.9 + 0.0573 year + 175 IndRedd - 0.0895 Redd*temp

Predictor        Coef       Stdev    t-ratio       p
Constant       -48.86       20.12      -2.43   0.017
year          0.05726     0.01019       5.62   0.000
IndRedd        175.16       28.46       6.16   0.000
Redd*temp    -0.08950     0.01441      -6.21   0.000

s = 1.039        R-sq = 52.2%      R-sq(adj) = 50.7%
```

**28.44.** **(a)** Students might fit a model with parallel lines, or one with different slopes (that is, with an interaction term). Both Minitab outputs are shown below; we note that the coefficient of the interaction term is not significantly different from 0, and neither model fits the data well ($R^2 = 8.3\%$ and $s = 76.55$ or $s = 76.60$). The distribution of residuals is slightly left-skewed, but the plot of residuals against fitted values (not shown) reveals no particular causes for concern.

**Minitab output: Parallel lines model for Hgt90 and Fert**

```
The regression equation is
   Hgt97 = 321 + 2.54 Hgt90 - 37.8 Fert

Predictor        Coef        Stdev     t-ratio        p
Constant      321.116        9.759       32.90    0.000
Hgt90          2.5373       0.4790        5.30    0.000
Fert          -37.802        5.403       -7.00    0.000

s = 76.55        R-sq = 8.3%        R-sq(adj) = 8.0%
```

**Hgt90 and Fert interaction model (separate lines)**

```
The regression equation is
   Hgt97 = 322 + 2.51 Hgt90 - 38.8 Fert + 0.050 H90*Fert

Predictor        Coef        Stdev     t-ratio        p
Constant       321.56        13.02       24.70    0.000
Hgt90          2.5137       0.6618        3.80    0.000
Fert           -38.76        19.23       -2.02    0.044
H90*Fert       0.0496       0.9597        0.05    0.959

s = 76.60        R-sq = 8.3%        R-sq(adj) = 7.9%
```

**(b)** The first column of the correlation matrix contains the information we need:

| | Hgt97 | Hgt90 | Hgt96 | Diam96 | Grow96 | Diam97 | Spread97 |
|---|---|---|---|---|---|---|---|
| Hgt90 | 0.164 | | | | | | |
| Hgt96 | 0.974 | 0.181 | | | | | |
| Diam96 | 0.865 | 0.167 | 0.902 | | | | |
| Grow96 | 0.755 | 0.075 | 0.759 | 0.562 | | | |
| Diam97 | 0.870 | 0.209 | 0.886 | 0.930 | 0.612 | | |
| Spread97 | 0.760 | 0.177 | 0.769 | 0.757 | 0.570 | 0.779 | |
| Needles97 | 0.116 | 0.130 | 0.116 | 0.115 | 0.053 | 0.153 | 0.198 |

We see that Hgt97 is most strongly related to Hgt96, which makes sense because that measurement is the one we wish to predict, taken one year earlier. **(c)** Shown below is the Minitab output for predicting Hgt97 from Hgt90, Hgt96, and Fert (with no interaction). It does a much better job of fitting the data ($R^2 = 94.4\%$, $s = 18.63$).

**Model with Hgt90, Hgt96, Fert**

```
The regression equation is Hgt97 = 45.0 - 0.159 Hgt90 - 2.39 Fert + 1.09 Hgt96

Predictor        Coef        Stdev     t-ratio        p
Constant       44.964        3.470       12.96    0.000
Hgt90         -0.1590       0.1195       -1.33    0.183
Fert           -2.390        1.361       -1.76    0.079
Hgt96         1.09409      0.00992      110.24    0.000

s = 18.63        R-sq = 94.4%        R-sq(adj) = 94.3%
```

**(d)** With Hgt96 present in the model, the coefficient of Hgt90 is not significantly different from 0 ($t = -1.33$, compared to $t = 5.30$ without Hgt96). The information supplied by using Hgt96 makes Hgt90 redundant (no longer useful). **(e)** The $t$ tests (output below) indicate that all coefficients are significantly different from 0. This model is marginally better than the previous model ($R^2 = 94.8\%$, $s = 18.29$), but these differences are likely not big enough to make this model preferable. (In fact, the linear regression model using only Hgt96 is quite adequate; it has nearly the same $R^2$ and $s$ values.)

**Model with Hgt96, Diam97, Fert**

```
The regression equation is Hgt97 = 45.7 + 1.04 Hgt96 + 2.14 Diam97 - 2.68 Fert

Predictor        Coef       Stdev     t-ratio        p
Constant       45.680       2.876       15.88    0.000
Hgt96         1.03756     0.01909       54.36    0.000
Diam97         2.1432      0.7203        2.98    0.003
Fert           -2.678       1.297       -2.07    0.039

s = 18.29         R-sq = 94.8%       R-sq(adj) = 94.8%
```

**(f)** We would expect that the presence of fertilizer (Fert = 1) would be associated with increased growth, so that this coefficient would be positive. In fact, the estimated coefficient is $-2.68$, meaning that on average, fertilized trees are about 2.7 cm shorter in 1997 than unfertilized trees. **(g)** As in (a), the residuals are somewhat skewed, but there are no majors causes for concern. There are other issues regarding the use of this model for other seedlings: Does it apply to seedlings planted in other locations, or in other years? Is it practically useful to have to measure the diameter in order to predict height? (That is, the model might be more helpful if we used Diam96 rather than Diam97 to predict Hgt97.) As was noted earlier, Hgt96 alone does a good job of predicting Hgt97, but the questions about location and year still apply to this simpler model.

**Note:** *The linear regression model with Hgt96 has $R^2 = 94.9\%$, which is slightly higher than the multiple regression model that includes Hgt96, Diam97, and Fert. Generally speaking, adding additional explanatory variables to a model will* increase *$R^2$. In this case, the value of $R^2$ drops slightly because of missing values for Diam97: 854 data points are used for the Hgt96 model, but only 849 are used for the Hgt96/Diam97/Fert model.*

**28.45.** **(a)** The scatterplot is shown on the right. **(b)** The fitted model is in the Minitab output below; the two regression lines are

$$\widehat{\text{GAS}} = 1.1755 + 0.16768 \text{ DegDay}$$

for nonwinter months, and

$$\widehat{\text{GAS}} = (1.1755 + 0.3023) + (0.16768 + 0.01293) \text{ DegDay} = 1.4778 + 0.18061 \text{ DegDay}$$

for winter months.

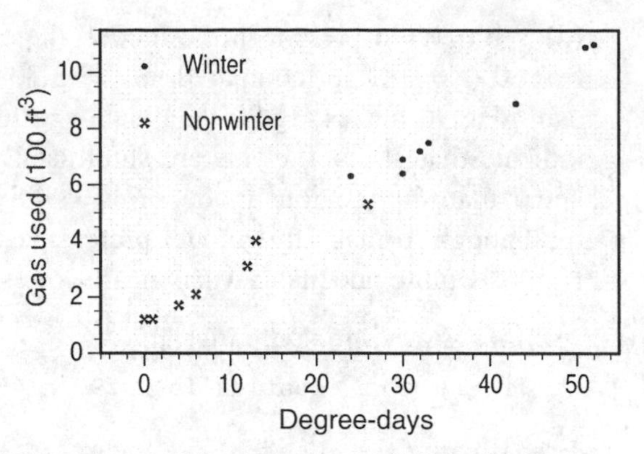


**(c)** Based on the appearance of the scatterplot (both sets of points appear to fall in the same linear pattern) and the final two coefficients in the Minitab output (which are not significantly different from 0), one regression line would be sufficient. (Indeed, regression with DegDay as the only explanatory variable gives $R^2 = 99.1\%$ and $s = 0.3389$, which are similar to the results for this multiple regression model. See also the solution to Exercise 4.27.)

**Minitab output**

```
The regression equation is
   gas = 1.18 + 0.168 DegDay + 0.302 IndWinter + 0.0129 dd*winter

Predictor        Coef       Stdev    t-ratio       p
Constant       1.1755      0.1523       7.72   0.000
DegDay        0.16768     0.01334      12.57   0.000
IndWinter      0.3023      0.4619       0.65   0.525
dd*winter     0.01293     0.01757       0.74   0.476

s = 0.3161         R-sq = 99.3%      R-sq(adj) = 99.1%
```

**28.46.** **(a)** The model is

$$\mu_{\text{cal}} = \beta_0 + \beta_1 \text{ MPH} + \beta_2 \text{ Ind\_slow} + \beta_3 \text{ NoIncline} + \beta_4 \text{ 2\%Incline},$$

and the parameter estimates are

$$b_0 \doteq 64.75, \; b_1 \doteq 145.841, \; b_2 \doteq -50.01, \; b_3 \doteq -145.06, \; b_4 \doteq -72.83, \text{ and } s \doteq 34.2865.$$

**(b)** There are six separate lines; all have the same slope (145.841), but different intercepts. The intercepts are determined by the pace (walking or running) and the incline according to the formula 64.75 − 50.01(Ind_slow) − 145.06(NoIncline) − 72.83(2%Incline):

| | Ind_slow | NoIncline | 2%Incline | Intercept |
|---|---|---|---|---|
| Walking, no incline | 1 | 1 | 0 | −130.32 |
| Walking, 2% incline | 1 | 0 | 1 | −58.09 |
| Walking, 4% incline | 1 | 0 | 0 | 14.74 |
| Running, no incline | 0 | 1 | 0 | −80.31 |
| Running, 2% incline | 0 | 0 | 1 | −8.08 |
| Running, 4% incline | 0 | 0 | 0 | 64.75 |

Note that the indicator variables NoIncline and 2%Incline cannot both equal 1. **(c)** Based on the value of $R^2$ (99.3%), the model fits the data well. **(d)** "More calories are burned for higher speeds" is equivalent to testing $H_0$: $\beta_1 = 0$ versus $H_a$: $\beta_1 > 0$; the $t$ statistic for that test is $t = 56.17$, which has a very small $P$-value. A 175-pound man burns about 149 cal/hr for each additional MPH of speed. (The fact that $b_2$ is significantly negative further supports the conclusion that more calories are burned for higher speeds; it means that when the man makes the transition from walking to running, calories burned increases by about 50 cal/hr.)

**28.47.** **(a)** The points in this scatterplot are so close together that it is difficult to distinguish between them in the lower left. **(b)** The coefficients for this model are given in the Minitab output below. **(c)** The model fits the data well ($R^2 = 98.6\%$, $s = 49.98$). We note that the coefficient of Ind_slow is not significantly different from 0, so it might be dropped from the model. **(d)** The coefficient of the Treadmill indicator variable is significantly different from 0, so there is a difference between the two treadmills. Specifically, we estimate that users of the Cybex treadmill burn about 26.2 fewer calories per hour, on the average.

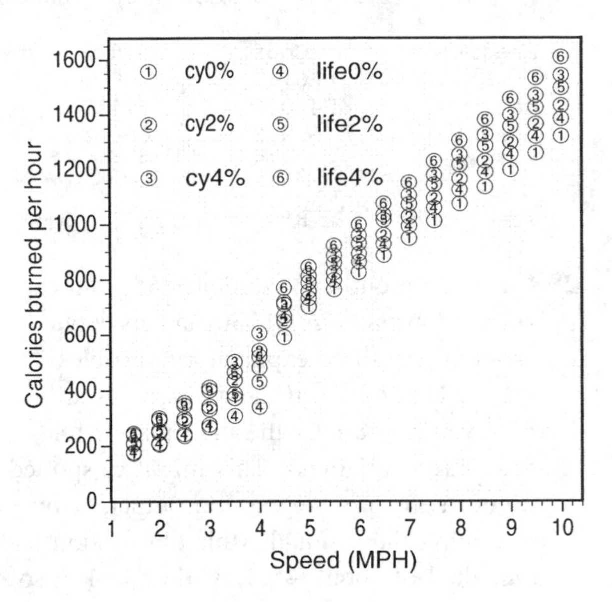


**Minitab output**

```
The regression equation is
   calories = 42.7 + 154 mph - 27.3 Ind_slow - 148 NoIncline - 73.7 2%Incline
            - 26.2 Treadmill

Predictor        Coef       Stdev    t-ratio       p
Constant        42.72       20.63       2.07   0.041
mph           153.566       2.676      57.38   0.000
Ind_slow       -27.33       16.70      -1.64   0.105
NoIncline     -147.89       11.78     -12.55   0.000
2%Incline      -73.69       11.78      -6.26   0.000
Treadmill     -26.204       9.619      -2.72   0.008

s = 49.98         R-sq = 98.6%      R-sq(adj) = 98.6%
```

**28.48.** **(a)** The association is linear and positive; the women's points show a stronger association. As a group, males typically have larger values for both variables.
**(b)** The Minitab output below gives the full equation (where the variable IndMale = 1 for males). From this we obtain the equations of the two lines (which are graphed in the scatterplot):

$\widehat{\text{RATE}} = 201.2 + 24.026\,\text{MASS}$ for women, and

$\widehat{\text{RATE}} = (201.2 + 509.3) + (24.026 - 7.275)\,\text{MASS}$

$= 710.5 + 16.751\,\text{MASS}$ for men.

**(c)** The coefficient of the interaction term is not significantly different from 0 ($t = -0.78$, $P = 0.447$), so we would be willing to fit a parallel-lines model. In fact, we can model metabolic rate reasonably well using only body mass (ignoring gender); for this model, $R^2 = 74.8\%$.

**Minitab output**

```
The regression equation is
   rate = 201 + 24.0 mass + 509 IndMale - 7.27 Male*mass

Predictor        Coef        Stdev     t-ratio        p
Constant        201.2        236.6        0.85    0.409
mass           24.026        5.435        4.42    0.000
IndMale         509.3        468.2        1.09    0.294
Male*mass      -7.275        9.309       -0.78    0.447

s = 123.8       R-sq = 80.7%      R-sq(adj) = 76.9%
```

**28.49. (a)** The outlier is student #55, who had the lowest GPA (0.530) but moderate values of the three explanatory variables (IQ $=$ 103, c2 $=$ 10, and c5 $=$ 5—all three values are near the first quartile for these three variables). This might be spotted in your software's regression output, or by examining the residuals (this observation had a residual of about $-5.8$, while $s \doteq 1.5$, so it was nearly 4 standard deviations below 0).

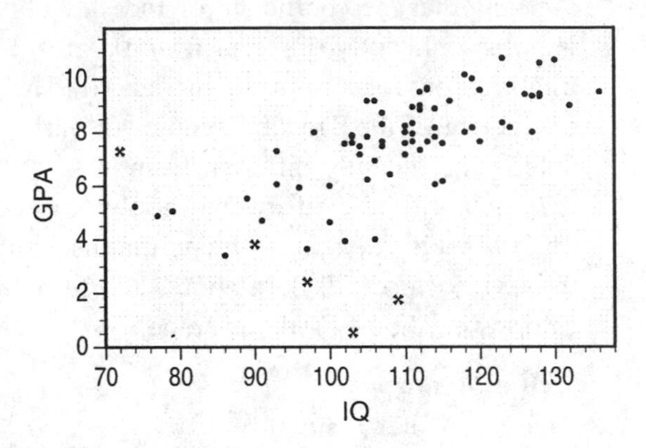


**(b)** Point identified as influential might vary among software packages; the version of Minitab used for these solutions produced the list below, and these points are marked with crosses in the scatterplot.

**Minitab output: Regression diagnostics**

```
Unusual Observations
Obs.      iq        gpa        Fit   Stdev.Fit    Residual     St.Resid
  8       97      2.412      6.205       0.313      -3.793       -2.59R
 22      109      1.760      5.220       0.595      -3.460       -2.51RX
 51      103      0.530      6.326       0.244      -5.796       -3.92R
 54       72      7.295      4.703       0.696       2.592        1.95 X
 72       90      3.820      4.834       0.723      -1.014       -0.77 X
```

**(c)** Regression using only the variable c2 explains $r^2 = 36.1\%$ of the variation in GPA.

**Model using c2 only**

```
The regression equation is gpa = 3.31 + 0.330 c2

Predictor       Coef        Stdev     t-ratio        p
Constant      3.3060       0.6603        5.01    0.000
c2           0.33023      0.05041        6.55    0.000

s = 1.689       R-sq = 36.1%      R-sq(adj) = 35.3%
```

**(d)** Regression using both c2 and IQ is a better fit for the data ($R^2 = 49.4\%$), and the coefficient of c2 is still significantly nonzero ($t = 3.70$, $P < 0.0005$), indicating that the predictive value of c2 does not completely overlap with that of IQ.

**Model using c2 and IQ**

```
The regression equation is gpa = - 2.61 + 0.199 c2 + 0.0694 iq

Predictor        Coef       Stdev    t-ratio       p
Constant       -2.613       1.459      -1.79   0.077
c2            0.19935     0.05394       3.70   0.000
iq            0.06941     0.01564       4.44   0.000

s = 1.514       R-sq = 49.4%      R-sq(adj) = 48.0%
```

**(e)** Using the IQ and c2 model, the predicted GPA is $\widehat{\text{GPA}} = -2.61 + 0.199(14) + 0.0694(115) \doteq 8.16$.

**28.50.** **(a)** The multiple regression model to fit two lines to the data (Minitab output below) reveals that gender is not significant: neither IndMale nor the interaction term for gender and estimated ability has a coefficient that is significantly different from 0.

**Separate lines for each gender**

```
The regression equation is
   read = 23.3 + 12.8 est + 7.0 IndMale - 3.91 male*est

Predictor        Coef       Stdev    t-ratio       p
Constant        23.29       12.12       1.92   0.060
est            12.778       3.209       3.98   0.000
IndMale          7.03       15.98       0.44   0.661
male*est       -3.907       4.297      -0.91   0.367

s = 19.87       R-sq = 33.3%      R-sq(adj) = 29.7%
```

**(b)** This model does not give very accurate estimates; it only explains about one-third ($R^2 = 35.1\%$) of the variation in IQ.

**Predicting IQ from LSS, Read, and EST**

```
The regression equation is iq = 85.2 + 0.51 lss + 0.229 read + 3.47 est

Predictor        Coef       Stdev    t-ratio       p
Constant       85.179       7.908      10.77   0.000
lss             0.513       1.390       0.37   0.713
read          0.22869     0.08181       2.80   0.007
est             3.472       1.606       2.16   0.035

s = 12.24       R-sq = 35.1%      R-sq(adj) = 31.6%
```

**(c)** A stemplot of the residuals and a plot of residuals against fitted values are shown; they reveal a moderately low outlier (−30.25), but no other causes for concern. Plots of residuals against the explanatory variables (not shown) likewise show no obvious problems.

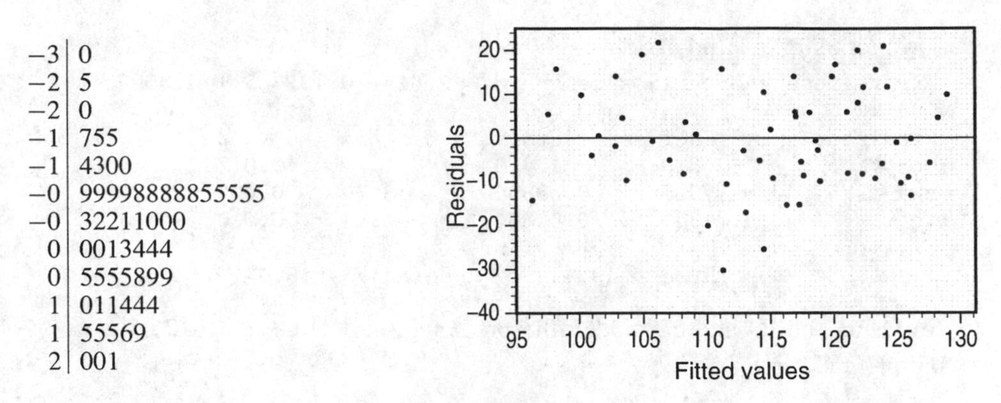


**(d)** The coefficient of LSS is not significantly different from 0. Removing it and adding an interaction term gives the following result:

**Predicting IQ from Read and EST (with interaction)**

```
The regression equation is
   iq = 88.0 + 0.222 read + 3.40 est + 0.0033 read*est

Predictor        Coef        Stdev    t-ratio        p
Constant        87.97        13.31       6.61    0.000
read           0.2225       0.2394       0.93    0.357
est             3.402        4.060       0.84    0.406
read*est      0.00327      0.06394       0.05    0.959

s = 12.26         R-sq = 34.9%      R-sq(adj) = 31.4%
```

The value of $R^2$ dropped only slightly, but all three $t$ tests now indicate that the coefficients are not significantly different from 0. Even though LSS was not statistically significant, it has a noticeable impact when removed from the model. (As an illustration of how seemingly contradictory regression results can be, we note that the ANOVA test for this model yields $F = 10.01$ and $P < 0.0005$, leading us to conclude that at least one of $\beta_1$, $\beta_2$, and $\beta_3$ should be nonzero—but the three $t$ tests do not support this conclusion.)

**28.51.** **(a)** Students might fit a model with or without interaction; both are shown below.

**Predicting selling price from appraised value and month (no interaction)**

```
The regression equation is
   sell = - 6.1 + 1.11 appraise + 8.62 month

Predictor        Coef        Stdev     t-ratio        p
Constant        -6.11        55.52       -0.11    0.914
appraise      1.10879      0.06991       15.86    0.000
month           8.625        1.742        4.95    0.000

s = 42.59        R-sq = 95.2%      R-sq(adj) = 94.4%
```

**... and with interaction**

```
The regression equation is
   sell = 56 + 1.03 appraise + 3.44 month + 0.0070 app*month

Predictor        Coef        Stdev     t-ratio        p
Constant         56.2        109.4        0.51    0.617
appraise       1.0258       0.1436        7.14    0.000
month           3.438        7.985        0.43    0.674
app*month     0.00698      0.01048        0.67    0.518

s = 43.53        R-sq = 95.3%      R-sq(adj) = 94.2%
```

**(b)** The coefficient of multiple determination is $R^2$—either 95.2% or 95.3%, depending on which model was used. Either model explains over 95% of the variation in selling price. **(c)** The regression standard error is either 42.59 or 43.53. **(d)** Assuming that month $= 0$, these models predict a selling price of either \$883,800 or \$879,500. For example, the first of these is $-6.11 + 1.10879(802.6) = 883.8049$.

**Minitab's reported fit for the no-interaction model**

```
     Fit  Stdev.Fit        95.0% C.I.             95.0% P.I.
   883.8       21.4   (   837.5,    930.1)  (   780.8,    986.8)
```

**Reported fit for the interaction model**

```
     Fit  Stdev.Fit        95.0% C.I.             95.0% P.I.
   879.5       22.8   (   829.8,    929.2)  (   772.4,    986.6)
```

**(e)** Shown are the residuals for only the no-interaction model; we see no particular causes for concern, except for the observation that the two units with high appraised values may have been influential. (The residuals for the other model look similar.)

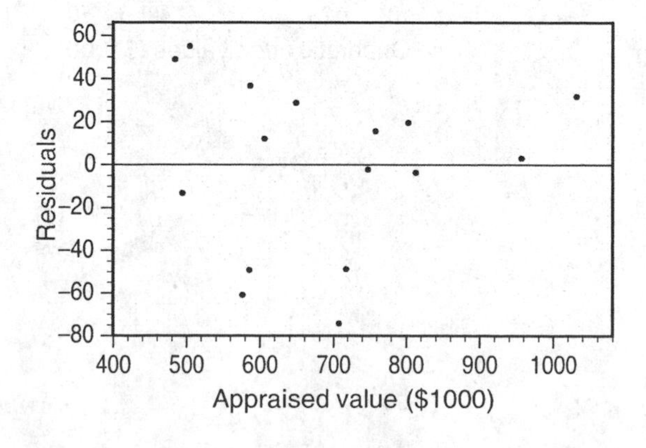


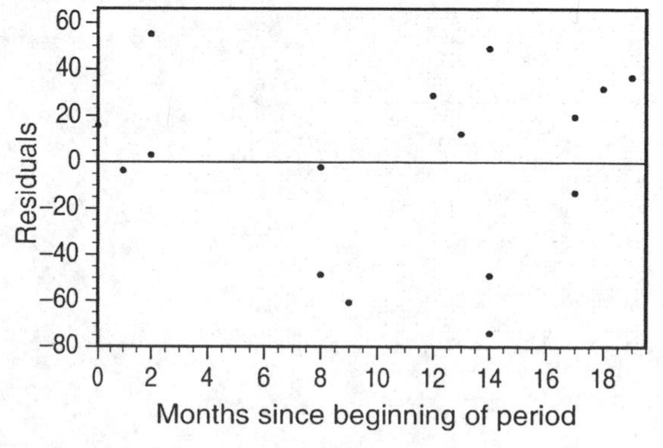

**28.52.** **(a)** Here is the Minitab output:

**Simple linear regression**

```
The regression equation is price = - 7181 + 14638 carat

Predictor        Coef        Stdev    t-ratio        p
Constant      -7181.3        347.5     -20.66    0.000
carat         14638.4        311.8      46.95    0.000

s = 2881        R-sq = 86.3%      R-sq(adj) = 86.3%
```

**(b)** The model explains $R^2 = 86.3\%$ of the variation in price, which is fairly good. However, the residuals do not look very good: the distribution (not shown) is right-skewed, and a plot of residuals against fitted values (below, left) shows a curved pattern. **(c)** Here is the quadratic fitted model (which agrees with that in Example 28.15):

**Quadratic regression**

```
The regression equation is price = - 523 + 2386 carat + 4498 caratsq

Predictor        Coef        Stdev    t-ratio        p
Constant       -522.7        466.3      -1.12    0.263
carat          2386.0        752.5       3.17    0.002
caratsq        4498.2        263.0      17.10    0.000

s = 2127        R-sq = 92.6%      R-sq(adj) = 92.5%
```

**(d)** The new model explains $R^2 = 92.6\%$ of the variation in price (up from 86.3%), and the residuals are more satisfactory (histogram not shown, scatterplot versus fitted values below, right). **(e)** We wish to test $H_0$: $\beta_2 = 0$ versus $H_a$: $\beta_2 \neq 0$, for which the Minitab output gives $t = 17.10$ and $P < 0.0005$, so we conclude that this coefficient is different from 0.

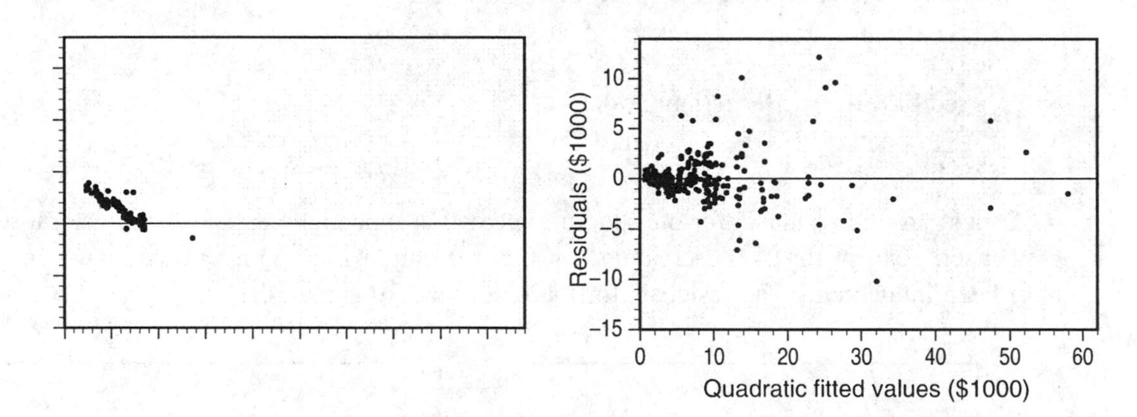

**28.53.** **(a)** The estimated equation is given in the Minitab output below. **(b)** To test $H_0$: $\beta_1 = \beta_2 = \beta_3 = 0$ versus $H_a$: at least one $\beta_i$ is not zero, we have $F = 935.67$ and $P < 0.0005$ (ANOVA table below), so we conclude that something in the model is useful. **(c)** The estimated regression parameters, standard errors, $t$ statistics, and $P$-values are found (in that order) in the Minitab output. **(d)** The distribution of residuals (histogram not shown) is somewhat right-skewed, and the plot of residuals versus fitted values shows a curved pattern (similar to that observed in the previous exercise). **(e)** The model explains $R^2 = 89.0\%$ of the variation in price. **(f)** The estimate of $\sigma$ is $s \doteq 2592$; this is our estimate of the degree of scatter about the regression formula.

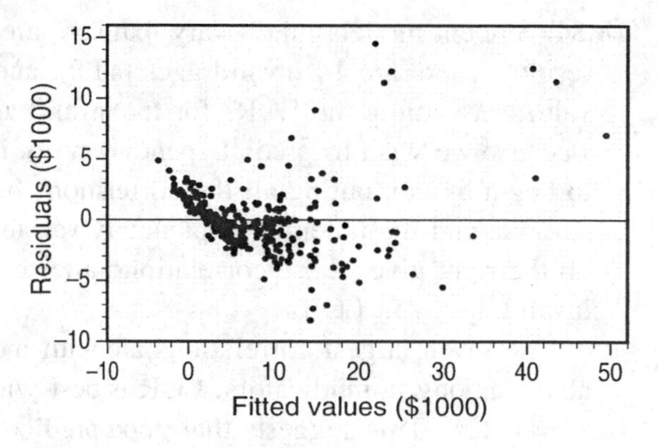


**Minitab output**

```
The regression equation is
   price = 31171 - 11828 carat - 598 depth + 408 carat*depth

Predictor        Coef       Stdev    t-ratio       p
Constant        31171        4220       7.39   0.000
carat          -11828        3436      -3.44   0.001
depth         -598.18       65.47      -9.14   0.000
carat*depth    408.45       51.96       7.86   0.000

s = 2592         R-sq = 89.0%      R-sq(adj) = 88.9%

Analysis of Variance

SOURCE         DF          SS          MS          F        p
Regression      3 18858539008  6286179840     935.67    0.000
Error         347  2331269632     6718356
Total         350 21189808128
```

**28.54.** Student models might vary, but here are some basic results. There are 14 invalid ages (all 0), and 2 invalid LOR values (assuming the LORs for the invalid ages are valid). Because we wish to predict spending ratio, it makes sense to begin by computing all the correlations between that variable and the potential explanatory variables. The table on the right gives these correlations, after excluding the invalid ages and LORs.

| | |
|---|---|
| Age | 0.039 |
| LOR | 0.128 |
| Income | 0.071 |
| Total assets | 0.062 |
| Security assets | 0.012 |
| Short-term liquidity | 0.109 |
| Long-term liquidity | 0.058 |
| Wealth index | 0.119 |
| Spending volume | 0.025 |
| Spending velocity | −0.037 |
| Collectible Gifts | 0.320 |
| Brick and Mortar | 0.308 |
| Martha's Home | 0.345 |
| Sunday Ads | 0.151 |
| Theme Collections | 0.248 |
| Custom Decorating | 0.208 |
| Retail Kids | 0.095 |
| Teen Wear | 0.222 |
| Car Lovers | 0.104 |
| Country Collections | 0.260 |

The seven largest correlations are with indicator variables; among nonindicators, LOR is best with a mere $r = 0.128$. This suggests that good predictions will be hard to produce, and this is indeed the case: even a model with all 20 variables explains only 30.8% of the variation in spending ratio! Exploration of other models reveals comparable performance with simpler formulas. Shown below are the results of two Minitab tools for choosing a model: "stepwise regression" and "best subset selection." Neither of these commands considered interaction terms, which further complicates model selection.

Residual analysis is not shown here, but make sure that students include this analysis for whatever models they choose.

**Minitab's "Stepwise Regression" attempts to choose the best model:**

```
 F-to-Enter:        4.00    F-to-Remove:        4.00

 Response is SpendRat on 20 predictors, with N =  184
 N(cases with missing obs.) =  16 N(all cases) =  200

    Step         1        2        3        4        5
Constant    27.131   12.757    4.522   -2.287  -15.743

MarthaHm      45.8     38.2     27.5     28.3     28.7
T-Ratio       4.78     4.05     2.87     2.99     3.06

CollGift               35.0     38.7     29.8     30.3
T-Ratio                3.86     4.37     3.20     3.28

BrkMortr                        35.9     39.2     39.3
T-Ratio                         3.59     3.95     4.00

ThemeCol                                 25.0     25.6
T-Ratio                                  2.67     2.75

LOR                                               0.88
T-Ratio                                           2.07

S             62.5     60.2     58.3     57.4     56.8
R-Sq         11.16    17.91    23.39    26.32    28.06
```

**Minitab's Breg ("best regression") output:**

| Vars | R-sq | Adj. R-sq | C-p | s | Age | LOR | Income | TotAsset | SecAsset | ShTrmLiq | LgTrmLiq | WlthIndx | SpendVol | SpendVel | CollGift | BrkMortr | MarthaHm | SunAds | ThemeCol | CustDeco | RetlKids | TeenWear | CarLover | CntryCol |
|---|---|---|---|---|---|---|---|---|---|---|---|---|---|---|---|---|---|---|---|---|---|---|---|---|
| 1 | 11.2 | 10.7 | 29.2 | 62.474 | | | | | | | | | | | | | X | | | | | | | |
| 1 | 10.5 | 10.0 | 30.8 | 62.710 | | | | | | | | | | | X | | | | | | | | | |
| 2 | 19.9 | 19.0 | 10.6 | 59.486 | | | | | | | | | | | X | X | | | | | | | | |
| 2 | 17.9 | 17.0 | 15.3 | 60.218 | | | | | | | | | | | X | | X | | | | | | | |
| 3 | 23.4 | 22.1 | 4.4 | 58.335 | | | | | | | | | | | X | X | X | | | | | | | |
| 3 | 22.6 | 21.3 | 6.2 | 58.624 | | | | | | | | | | | X | X | | | X | | | | | |
| 4 | 26.3 | 24.7 | -0.5 | 57.368 | | | | | | | | | | | X | X | X | | X | | | | | |
| 4 | 25.0 | 23.3 | 2.6 | 57.883 | | X | | | | | | | | | X | X | X | | | | | | | |
| 5 | 28.1 | 26.0 | -2.6 | 56.847 | | X | | | | | | | | | X | X | X | | X | | | | | |
| 5 | 27.2 | 25.2 | -0.6 | 57.183 | X | | | | | | | | | | X | X | X | | X | | | | | |
| 6 | 28.6 | 26.2 | -1.8 | 56.801 | | X | | | | | | | | | X | X | X | | X | | | X | | |
| 6 | 28.3 | 25.9 | -1.2 | 56.901 | X | X | | | | | | | | | X | X | X | | X | | | | | |
| 7 | 29.0 | 26.2 | -0.9 | 56.783 | X | X | | | | | | | | | X | X | X | | X | | | X | | |
| 7 | 28.8 | 26.0 | -0.4 | 56.860 | | X | | | | | | | | | X | X | X | | X | | | X | | X |
| 8 | 29.3 | 26.1 | 0.5 | 56.839 | X | X | | | | | | | | | X | X | X | | X | | | X | X | |
| 8 | 29.2 | 26.0 | 0.7 | 56.868 | X | X | | | | | | | | X | X | X | X | | X | | | X | | |
| 9 | 29.5 | 25.9 | 2.0 | 56.910 | X | X | | | | | | | | X | X | X | X | | X | | | X | X | |
| 9 | 29.5 | 25.8 | 2.0 | 56.918 | X | X | | | | | | | | | X | X | X | | X | | | X | X | X |
| 10 | 29.7 | 25.7 | 3.5 | 56.990 | X | X | | | | | | | | X | X | X | X | | X | | | X | X | X |
| 10 | 29.7 | 25.6 | 3.6 | 57.002 | X | X | | | | | | | | X | X | X | X | | X | X | | X | X | |
| 11 | 30.0 | 25.5 | 4.8 | 57.038 | X | X | | X | | X | | | | X | X | X | X | | X | | | X | X | |
| 11 | 29.9 | 25.4 | 5.1 | 57.082 | X | X | | | | | | | | X | X | X | X | | X | X | | X | X | X |
| 12 | 30.2 | 25.3 | 6.3 | 57.115 | X | X | | X | X | X | | | | X | X | X | X | | X | | | X | X | |
| 12 | 30.2 | 25.3 | 6.3 | 57.122 | X | X | | X | | X | | | | X | X | X | X | | X | X | | X | X | |
| 13 | 30.4 | 25.1 | 7.9 | 57.219 | X | X | | X | X | X | | | | X | X | X | X | | X | | | X | X | X |
| 13 | 30.4 | 25.1 | 7.9 | 57.221 | X | X | | X | X | X | | | | X | X | X | X | | X | X | | X | X | |
| 14 | 30.5 | 24.8 | 9.6 | 57.326 | X | X | | X | X | X | | | | X | X | X | X | | X | X | | X | X | X |
| 14 | 30.5 | 24.7 | 9.6 | 57.339 | X | X | X | X | X | X | | | | X | X | X | X | | X | X | | X | X | |
| 15 | 30.6 | 24.5 | 11.3 | 57.450 | X | X | | X | X | X | | | | X | X | X | X | | X | X | X | X | X | X |
| 15 | 30.6 | 24.4 | 11.4 | 57.463 | X | X | X | X | X | X | | | | X | X | X | X | | X | X | | X | X | X |
| 16 | 30.7 | 24.1 | 13.2 | 57.596 | X | X | X | X | X | X | | | | X | X | X | X | | X | X | X | X | X | X |
| 16 | 30.7 | 24.0 | 13.2 | 57.607 | X | X | | X | X | X | | | X | X | X | X | X | | X | X | X | X | X | X |
| 17 | 30.8 | 23.7 | 15.0 | 57.748 | X | X | X | X | X | X | | | X | X | X | X | X | | X | X | X | X | X | X |
| 17 | 30.7 | 23.6 | 15.1 | 57.765 | X | X | X | X | X | X | X | | | X | X | X | X | | X | X | X | X | X | X |
| 18 | 30.8 | 23.2 | 17.0 | 57.920 | X | X | X | X | X | X | | X | X | X | X | X | X | | X | X | X | X | X | X |
| 18 | 30.8 | 23.2 | 17.0 | 57.921 | X | X | X | X | X | X | X | | X | X | X | X | X | | X | X | X | X | X | X |
| 19 | 30.8 | 22.8 | 19.0 | 58.092 | X | X | X | X | X | X | X | X | X | X | X | X | X | | X | X | X | X | X | X |
| 19 | 30.8 | 22.7 | 19.0 | 58.096 | X | X | X | X | X | X | X | | X | X | X | X | X | X | X | X | X | X | X | X |
| 20 | 30.8 | 22.3 | 21.0 | 58.269 | X | X | X | X | X | X | X | X | X | X | X | X | X | X | X | X | X | X | X | X |

# Chapter 29 Solutions

Solutions to this chapter (Two-Way Analysis of Variance) can be found on the *BPS4* companion Web site.